Student Quick Tips

Use this Student Quick Tips guide for a quick and easy start with McGraw-Hill Connect. You'll get valuable tips on registering, doing assignments, and accessing resources, as well as information about the support center hours.

Getting Started

TIP: To get started in Connect, you will need the following:

- Your instructor's Connect Web Address

    Sample of Connect Web Address:

    http://www.mcgrawhillconnect.com/class/instructorname_section_name

- Connect Access Code

TIP: If you do not have an access code or have not yet secured your tuition funds, you can click "Free Trial" during registration. This trial will provide temporary Connect access (typically three weeks) and will remind you to purchase online access before the end of your trial.

Registration and Sign In

1. Go to the Connect Web Address provided by your instructor
2. Click on **Register Now**
3. Enter your email address

TIP: If you already have a McGraw-Hill account, you will be asked for your password and will not be required to create a new account.

4. Enter a registration code or choose **Buy Online** to purchase access online

5. Follow the on-screen directions

TIP: Please choose your Security Question and Answer carefully. We will ask you for this information if you forget your password.

6. When registration is complete, click on **Go to Connect Now**

7. You are now ready to use **Connect**

Trouble Logging In?

- Ensure you are using the same email address you used during registration

- If you have forgotten your password, click on the "Forgot Password?" link at your Instructor's Connect Course Web Address

- When logged into Connect, you can update your account information (e.g. email address, password, and security question/answer) by clicking on the *"My Account"* link located at the top-right corner

Home (Assignments)

TIP: If you are unable to begin an assignment, verify the following:

- The assignment is available (start and due dates)

- That you have not exceeded the maximum number of attempts

- That you have not achieved a score of 100%

- If your assignment contains questions that require manual grading, you will not be able to begin your next attempt until your instructor has graded those questions

TIP: Based on the assignment policy settings established by your Instructor, you may encounter the following limitations when working on your assignment(s):

- Ability to Print Assignment

- Timed assignments – once you begin a "*timed assignment*," the timer will not stop by design

TIP: "*Save & Exit*" vs. "*Submit*" button

- If you are unable to complete your assignment in one sitting, utilize the "*Save & Exit*" button to save your work and complete it at a later time

- Once you have completed your assignment, utilize the "*Submit*" button in order for your assignment to be graded

Library

TIP: The *Library* section of your Connect account provides shortcuts to various resources.

- If you purchased ConnectPlus, you will see an *eBook* link, which can also be accessed from the section information widget of the *Home* tab

- *Recorded Lectures* can be accessed if your instructor is using *Tegrity Campus* to capture lectures. You may also access recorded lectures when taking an assignment by clicking on the projector icon in the navigation bar

- Many McGraw-Hill textbooks offer additional resources such as narrated slides and additional problems, which are accessible through the *Student Resources* link

Reports

TIP: Once you submit your assignment, you can view your available results in the *Reports* tab.

- If you see a dash (-) as your score, your instructor has either delayed or restricted your ability to see the assignment feedback

- Your instructor has the ability to limit the amount of information (e.g. questions, answers, scores) you can view for each submitted assignment

Need More Help?

CONTACT US ONLINE

Visit us at:

www.mcgrawhillconnect.com/support

Browse our support materials including tutorial videos and our searchable Connect knowledge base. If you cannot find an answer to your question, click on "Contact Us" button to send us an email.

GIVE US A CALL

Call us at:

1-800-331-5094

Our live support is available:

Mon-Thurs: 9 am – 12 pm ET
Friday: 9 am – 7 pm ET
Sunday: 7 pm – 12 pm ET

Reactions at Supports and Connections for a Two-Dimensional Structure

Support or Connection		Reaction	Number of Unknowns
Rollers	Rocker Frictionless surface	Force with known line of action	1
Short cable	Short link	Force with known line of action	1
Collar on frictionless rod	Frictionless pin in slot	90° Force with known line of action	1
Frictionless pin or hinge	Rough surface	or α Force of unknown direction	2
Fixed support		or α Force and couple	3

The first step in the solution of any problem concerning the equilibrium of a rigid body is to construct an appropriate free-body diagram of the body. As part of that process, it is necessary to show on the diagram the reactions through which the ground and other bodies oppose a possible motion of the body. The figures on this and the facing page summarize the possible reactions exerted on two- and three-dimensional bodies.

Reactions at Supports and Connections for a Three-Dimensional Structure

Ball / **Frictionless surface** — Force with known line of action (one unknown)	**Cable** — Force with known line of action (one unknown)

Roller on rough surface / Wheel on rail — Two force components

Rough surface / Ball and socket — Three force components

Universal joint — Three force components and one couple

Fixed support — Three force components and three couples

Hinge and bearing supporting radial load only — Two force components (and two couples; see page 191)

Pin and bracket / Hinge and bearing supporting axial thrust and radial load — Three force components (and two couples; see page 191)

Select Material From

VECTOR MECHANICS FOR ENGINEERS: STATICS

TENTH EDITION

FERDINAND P. BEER
Late of Lehigh University

E. RUSSELL JOHNSTON, JR.
Late of University of Connecticut

DAVID F. MAZUREK
U.S. Coast Guard Academy

Rensselaer Polytechnic Institute

 Learning Solutions

Boston   Burr Ridge, IL   Dubuque, IA   New York   San Francisco   St. Louis
Bangkok   Bogotá   Caracas   Lisbon   London   Madrid
Mexico City   Milan   New Delhi   Seoul   Singapore   Sydney   Taipei   Toronto

Select Material From
Vector Mechanics for Engineers: Statics, Tenth Edition
Rensselaer Polytechnic Institute

This book is a McGraw-Hill Learning Solutions textbook and contains select material from *Vector Mechanics for Engineers: Statics*, Tenth Edition by Ferdinand P. Beer, E. Russell Johnston, Jr. and David F. Mazurek. Copyright © 2013, 2010, 2007, 2004 by The McGraw-Hill Companies, Inc. Reprinted with permission of the publisher. Many custom published texts are modified versions or adaptations of our best-selling textbooks. Some adaptations are printed in black and white to keep prices at a minimum, while others are in color.

1 2 3 4 5 6 7 8 9 0 STA STA 14 13 12

ISBN-13: 978-0-07-777562-9
ISBN-10: 0-07-777562-7
Part of:
ISBN-13: 978-0-07-777563-6
ISBN-10: 0-07-777563-5

Learning Solutions Consultant: Jessica Watts
Learning Solutions Representative: Nikki Schmitt
Production Editor: Lori Kueter
Printer/Binder: Stromberg Allen
Cover Photo Credits: © 2012 JupiterImages Corporation

About the Authors

As publishers of the books by Ferd Beer and Russ Johnston, we are often asked how they happened to write their books together with one of them at Lehigh and the other at the University of Connecticut.

The answer to this question is simple. Russ Johnston's first teaching appointment was in the Department of Civil Engineering and Mechanics at Lehigh University. There he met Ferd Beer, who had joined that department two years earlier and was in charge of the courses in mechanics.

Ferd was delighted to discover that the young man who had been hired chiefly to teach graduate structural engineering courses was not only willing but eager to help him reorganize the mechanics courses. Both believed that these courses should be taught from a few basic principles and that the various concepts involved would be best understood and remembered by the students if they were presented to them in a graphic way. Together they wrote lecture notes in statics and dynamics, to which they later added problems they felt would appeal to future engineers, and soon they produced the manuscript of the first edition of *Mechanics for Engineers* that was published in June 1956.

The second edition of *Mechanics for Engineers* and the first edition of *Vector Mechanics for Engineers* found Russ Johnston at Worcester Polytechnic Institute and the next editions at the University of Connecticut. In the meantime, both Ferd and Russ assumed administrative responsibilities in their departments, and both were involved in research, consulting, and supervising graduate students—Ferd in the area of stochastic processes and random vibrations and Russ in the area of elastic stability and structural analysis and design. However, their interest in improving the teaching of the basic mechanics courses had not subsided, and they both taught sections of these courses as they kept revising their texts and began writing the manuscript of the first edition of their *Mechanics of Materials* text.

Their collaboration spanned more than half a century and many successful revisions of all of their textbooks, and Ferd's and Russ's contributions to engineering education have earned them a number of honors and awards. They were presented with the Western Electric Fund Award for excellence in the instruction of engineering students by their respective regional sections of the American Society for Engineering Education, and they both received the Distinguished Educator Award from the Mechanics Division of the same society. Starting in 2001, the New Mechanics Educator Award of the Mechanics Division has been named in honor of the Beer and Johnston author team.

Ferdinand P. Beer. Born in France and educated in France and Switzerland, Ferd received an M.S. degree from the Sorbonne and an Sc.D. degree in theoretical mechanics from the University of Geneva. He came to the United States after serving in the French army during the early part of World War II and taught for four years at Williams College in the Williams-MIT joint arts and engineering program. Following his service at Williams College, Ferd joined the faculty of Lehigh University where he taught for thirty-seven years. He held several positions, including University Distinguished Professor and chairman of the Department of Mechanical Engineering and Mechanics, and in 1995 Ferd was awarded an honorary Doctor of Engineering degree by Lehigh University.

E. Russell Johnston, Jr. Born in Philadelphia, Russ holds a B.S. degree in civil engineering from the University of Delaware and an Sc.D. degree in the field of structural engineering from the Massachusetts Institute of Technology. He taught at Lehigh University and Worcester Polytechnic Institute before joining the faculty of the University of Connecticut where he held the position of chairman of the Department of Civil Engineering and taught for twenty-six years. In 1991 Russ received the Outstanding Civil Engineer Award from the Connecticut Section of the American Society of Civil Engineers.

David F. Mazurek. David holds a B.S. degree in ocean engineering and an M.S. degree in civil engineering from the Florida Institute of Technology and a Ph.D. degree in civil engineering from the University of Connecticut. He was employed by the Electric Boat Division of General Dynamics Corporation and taught at Lafayette College prior to joining the U.S. Coast Guard Academy, where he has been since 1990. He has served on the American Railway Engineering & Maintenance-of-Way Association's Committee 15—Steel Structures since 1991. Professional interests include bridge engineering, structural forensics, and blast-resistant design. He is a registered Professional Engineer in Connecticut and Pennsylvania.

Brief Contents

Contents

1 Introduction   1

2 Statics of Particles   14

3 Rigid Bodies: Equivalent Systems of Forces 74

4 Equilibrium of Rigid Bodies 158

5 Distributed Forces: Centroids and Centers of Gravity 218

6   Analysis of Structures   282

8 Friction 410

Preface

OBJECTIVES

The main objective of a first course in mechanics should be to develop in the engineering student the ability to analyze any problem in a simple and logical manner and to apply to its solution a few, well-understood, basic principles. It is hoped that this text, designed for the first course in statics offered in the sophomore year, and the volume that follows, *Vector Mechanics for Engineers: Dynamics*, will help the instructor achieve this goal.†

GENERAL APPROACH

Vector analysis is introduced early in the text and is used in the presentation and discussion of the fundamental principles of mechanics. Vector methods are also used to solve many problems, particularly three-dimensional problems where these techniques result in a simpler and more concise solution. The emphasis in this text, however, remains on the correct understanding of the principles of mechanics and on their application to the solution of engineering problems, and vector analysis is presented chiefly as a convenient tool.‡

Practical Applications Are Introduced Early. One of the characteristics of the approach used in these volumes is that mechanics of *particles* is clearly separated from the mechanics of *rigid bodies*. This approach makes it possible to consider simple practical applications at an early stage and to postpone the introduction of the more difficult concepts. For example:

- In *Statics*, statics of particles is treated first (Chap. 2); after the rules of addition and subtraction of vectors are introduced, the principle of equilibrium of a particle is immediately applied to practical situations involving only concurrent forces. The statics of rigid bodies is considered in Chaps. 3 and 4. In Chap. 3, the vector and scalar products of two vectors are introduced and used to define the moment of a force about a point and about an axis. The presentation of these new concepts is followed by a thorough and rigorous discussion of equivalent systems of forces leading, in Chap. 4, to many practical applications involving the equilibrium of rigid bodies under general force systems.
- In *Dynamics*, the same division is observed. The basic concepts of force, mass, and acceleration, of work and energy, and

---

FORCES IN A PLANE

2.2 FORCE ON A PARTICLE. RESULTANT OF TWO FORCES

A force represents the action of one body on another and is generally characterized by its *point of application*, its *magnitude*, and its *direction*. Forces acting on a given particle, however, have the same point of application. Each force considered in this chapter will thus be completely defined by its magnitude and direction.

The magnitude of a force is characterized by a certain number of units. As indicated in Chap. 1, the SI units used by engineers to measure the magnitude of a force are the newton (N) and its multiple the kilonewton (kN), equal to 1000 N, while the U.S. customary units used for the same purpose are the pound (lb) and its multiple the kilopound (kip), equal to 1000 lb. The direction of a force is defined by the *line of action* and the *sense* of the force. The line of action is the infinite straight line along which the force acts; it is characterized by the angle it forms with some fixed axis (Fig. 2.1). The force itself is represented by a segment of

Fig. 2.1   (a)   (b)

---

†This text is available in a single volume, *Vector Mechanics for Engineers: Statics and Dynamics*, tenth edition.

‡In a parallel text, *Mechanics for Engineers: Statics*, fifth edition, the use of vector algebra is limited to the addition and subtraction of vectors.

of impulse and momentum are introduced and first applied to problems involving only particles. Thus, students can familiarize themselves with the three basic methods used in dynamics and learn their respective advantages before facing the difficulties associated with the motion of rigid bodies.

New Concepts Are Introduced in Simple Terms.

Since this text is designed for the first course in statics, new concepts are presented in simple terms and every step is explained in detail. On the other hand, by discussing the broader aspects of the problems considered, and by stressing methods of general applicability, a definite maturity of approach is achieved. For example, the concepts of partial constraints and statical indeterminacy are introduced early and are used throughout.

Fundamental Principles Are Placed in the Context of Simple Applications.

The fact that mechanics is essentially a *deductive* science based on a few fundamental principles is stressed. Derivations have been presented in their logical sequence and with all the rigor warranted at this level. However, the learning process being largely *inductive*, simple applications are considered first. For example:

- The statics of particles precedes the statics of rigid bodies, and problems involving internal forces are postponed until Chap. 6.
- In Chap. 4, equilibrium problems involving only coplanar forces are considered first and solved by ordinary algebra, while problems involving three-dimensional forces and requiring the full use of vector algebra are discussed in the second part of the chapter.

Free-Body Diagrams Are Used Both to Solve Equilibrium Problems and to Express the Equivalence of Force Systems.

Free-body diagrams are introduced early, and their importance is emphasized throughout the text. They are used not only to solve equilibrium problems but also to express the equivalence of two systems of forces or, more generally, of two systems of vectors. The advantage of this approach becomes apparent in the study of the dynamics of rigid bodies, where it is used to solve three-dimensional as well as two-dimensional problems. By placing the emphasis on "free-body-diagram equations" rather than on the standard algebraic equations of motion, a more intuitive and more complete understanding of the fundamental principles of dynamics can be achieved. This approach, which was first introduced in 1962 in the first edition of *Vector Mechanics for Engineers*, has now gained wide acceptance among mechanics teachers in this country. It is, therefore, used in preference to the method of dynamic equilibrium and to the equations of motion in the solution of all sample problems in this book.

A Four-Color Presentation Uses Color to Distinguish Vectors.

Color has been used, not only to enhance the quality of the illustrations, but also to help students distinguish among the various types of vectors they will encounter. While there was no intention to "color code" this text, the same color is used in any given chapter to represent vectors of the same type. Throughout *Statics*, for example, red

---

4.1 INTRODUCTION

We saw in the preceding chapter that the external forces acting on a rigid body can be reduced to a force-couple system at some arbitrary point O. When the force and the couple are both equal to zero, the external forces form a system equivalent to zero, and the rigid body is said to be in *equilibrium*.

The necessary and sufficient conditions for the equilibrium of a rigid body, therefore, can be obtained by setting $\mathbf{R}$ and $\mathbf{M}_O^R$ equal to zero in the relations (3.52) of Sec. 3.17:

$$\Sigma \mathbf{F} = 0 \qquad \Sigma \mathbf{M}_O = \Sigma(\mathbf{r} \times \mathbf{F}) = 0 \qquad (4.1)$$

Resolving each force and each moment into its rectangular components, we can express the necessary and sufficient conditions for the equilibrium of a rigid body with the following six scalar equations:

$$\Sigma F_x = 0 \qquad \Sigma F_y = 0 \qquad \Sigma F_z = 0 \qquad (4.2)$$
$$\Sigma M_x = 0 \qquad \Sigma M_y = 0 \qquad \Sigma M_z = 0 \qquad (4.3)$$

The equations obtained can be used to determine unknown forces applied to the rigid body or unknown reactions exerted on it by its supports. We note that Eqs. (4.2) express the fact that the components of the external forces in the x, y, and z directions are balanced; Eqs. (4.3) express the fact that the moments of the external forces about the x, y, and z axes are balanced. Therefore, for a rigid body in equilibrium, the system of the external forces will impart no translational or rotational motion to the body considered.

In order to write the equations of equilibrium for a rigid body, it is essential to first identify all of the forces acting on that body and then to draw the corresponding *free-body diagram*. In this chapter we first consider the equilibrium of *two-dimensional structures* subjected to forces contained in their planes and learn how to draw their free-body diagrams. In addition to the forces *applied* to a structure, the *reactions* exerted on the structure by its supports will be considered. A specific reaction will be associated with each type of support. You will learn how to determine whether the structure is properly supported, so that you can know in advance whether the equations of equilibrium can be solved for the unknown forces and reactions.

Later in the chapter, the equilibrium of three-dimensional structures will be considered, and the same kind of analysis will be given to these structures and their supports.

4.2 FREE-BODY DIAGRAM

In solving a problem concerning the equilibrium of a rigid body, it is essential to consider *all* of the forces acting on the body; it is equally important to exclude any force which is not directly applied to the body. Omitting a force or adding an extraneous one would destroy the conditions of equilibrium. Therefore, the first step in the solution of the problem should be to draw a *free-body diagram* of the rigid body under consideration. Free-body diagrams have already been used on many occasions in Chap. 2. However, in view of their importance to the solution of equilibrium problems, we summarize here the various steps which must be followed in drawing a free-body diagram.

Photo 4.1 A free-body diagram of the tractor shown would include all of the external forces acting on the tractor: the weight of the tractor, the forces exerted by the ground on the tires.

1. A clear decision should be made regarding the choice of the free body to be used. This body is then detached from the ground and is separated from all other bodies. The contour of the body thus isolated is sketched.

2. All external forces should be indicated on the free-body diagram. These forces represent the actions exerted *on* the free body *by* the ground and *by* the bodies which have been detached; they should be applied at the various points where the free body was supported by the ground or was connected to other bodies. The *weight* of the free body should also be included among the external forces, since it represents the attraction exerted by the earth on the various particles forming the free body. As will be seen in Chap. 5, the weight should be applied at the center of gravity of the body. When the free body is made of several parts, the forces the various parts exert on each other should *not* be included among the external forces. These forces are *internal forces* as far as the free body is concerned.

3. The magnitudes and directions of the *known external forces* should be clearly marked on the free-body diagram. When indicating the directions of these forces, it must be remembered that the forces shown on the free-body diagram must be those which are exerted *on*, and not *by*, the free body. Known external forces generally include the *weight* of the free body and *forces applied* for a given purpose.

4. *Unknown external forces* usually consist of the *reactions*, through which the ground and other bodies oppose a possible motion of the free body. The reactions constrain the free body to remain in the same position, and, for that reason, are sometimes called *constraining forces*. Reactions are exerted at the points where the free body is *supported by* or *connected to* other bodies and should be clearly indicated. Reactions are discussed in detail in Secs. 4.3 and 4.8.

5. The free-body diagram should also include dimensions, since these may be needed in the computation of moments of forces. Any other detail, however, should be omitted.

Photo 4.2 In Chap. 6, we will discuss how to determine the internal forces in structures made of several connected pieces, such as the forces in the members that support the bucket of the tractor of Photo 4.1.

is used exclusively to represent forces and couples, while position vectors are shown in blue and dimensions in black. This makes it easier for the students to identify the forces acting on a given particle or rigid body and to follow the discussion of sample problems and other examples given in the text.

A Careful Balance Between SI and U.S. Customary Units Is Consistently Maintained.

Because of the current trend in the American government and industry to adopt the international system of units (SI metric units), the SI units most frequently used in mechanics are introduced in Chap. 1 and are used throughout the text. Approximately half of the sample problems and 60 percent of the homework problems are stated in these units, while the remainder are in U.S. customary units. The authors believe that this approach will best serve the need of students, who, as engineers, will have to be conversant with both systems of units.

It also should be recognized that using both SI and U.S. customary units entails more than the use of conversion factors. Since the SI system of units is an absolute system based on the units of time, length, and mass, whereas the U.S. customary system is a gravitational system based on the units of time, length, and force, different approaches are required for the solution of many problems. For example, when SI units are used, a body is generally specified by its mass expressed in kilograms; in most problems of statics it will be necessary to determine the weight of the body in newtons, and an additional calculation will be required for this purpose. On the other hand, when U.S. customary units are used, a body is specified by its weight in pounds and, in dynamics problems, an additional calculation will be required to determine its mass in slugs (or lb · s²/ft). The authors, therefore, believe that problem assignments should include both systems of units.

The *Instructor's and Solutions Manual* provides six different lists of assignments so that an equal number of problems stated in SI units and in U.S. customary units can be selected. If so desired, two complete lists of assignments can also be selected with up to 75 percent of the problems stated in SI units.

Optional Sections Offer Advanced or Specialty Topics.

A large number of optional sections have been included. These sections are indicated by asterisks and thus are easily distinguished from those which form the core of the basic statics course. They may be omitted without prejudice to the understanding of the rest of the text.

Among the topics covered in these additional sections are the reduction of a system of forces to a wrench, applications to hydrostatics, shear and bending-moment diagrams for beams, equilibrium of cables, products of inertia and Mohr's circle, the determination of the principal axes and the mass moments of inertia of a body of arbitrary shape, and the method of virtual work. The sections on beams are especially useful when the course in statics is immediately followed by a course in mechanics of materials, while the sections on the inertia properties of three-dimensional bodies are primarily intended for students who will later study in dynamics the three-dimensional motion of rigid bodies.

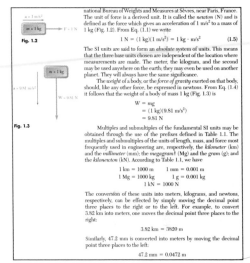

The material presented in the text and most of the problems require no previous mathematical knowledge beyond algebra, trigonometry, and elementary calculus; all the elements of vector algebra necessary to the understanding of the text are carefully presented in Chaps. 2 and 3. In general, a greater emphasis is placed on the correct understanding of the basic mathematical concepts involved than on the nimble manipulation of mathematical formulas. In this connection, it should be mentioned that the determination of the centroids of composite areas precedes the calculation of centroids by integration, thus making it possible to establish the concept of the moment of an area firmly before introducing the use of integration.

Guided Tour

Chapter Introduction. Each chapter begins with an introductory section setting the purpose and goals of the chapter and describing in simple terms the material to be covered and its application to the solution of engineering problems. New chapter outlines provide students with a preview of chapter topics.

Chapter Lessons. The body of the text is divided into units, each consisting of one or several theory sections, one or several sample problems, and a large number of problems to be assigned. Each unit corresponds to a well-defined topic and generally can be covered in one lesson. In a number of cases, however, the instructor will find it desirable to devote more than one lesson to a given topic. *The Instructor's and Solutions Manual* contains suggestions on the coverage of each lesson.

Sample Problems. The sample problems are set up in much the same form that students will use when solving the assigned problems. They thus serve the double purpose of amplifying the text and demonstrating the type of neat, orderly work that students should cultivate in their own solutions.

Solving Problems on Your Own. A section entitled *Solving Problems on Your Own* is included for each lesson, between the sample problems and the problems to be assigned. The purpose of these sections is to help students organize in their own minds the preceding theory of the text and the solution methods of the sample problems so that they can more successfully solve the homework problems. Also included in these sections are specific suggestions and strategies that will enable the students to more efficiently attack any assigned problems.

Homework Problem Sets. Most of the problems are of a practical nature and should appeal to engineering students. They are primarily designed, however, to illustrate the material presented in the text and to help students understand the principles of mechanics. The problems are grouped according to the portions of material they illustrate and

REVIEW AND SUMMARY

This chapter was devoted to the method of work and energy and to the method of impulse and momentum. In the first half of the chapter we studied the method of work and energy and its application to the analysis of the motion of particles.

Work of a force We first considered a force $\mathbf{F}$ acting on a particle A and defined the *work of* $\mathbf{F}$ *corresponding to the small displacement* $d\mathbf{r}$ [Sec. 13.2] as the quantity

$$dU = \mathbf{F} \cdot d\mathbf{r} \qquad (13.1)$$

or, recalling the definition of the scalar product of two vectors,

$$dU = F\,ds\,\cos\alpha \qquad (13.1')$$

where α is the angle between $\mathbf{F}$ and $d\mathbf{r}$ (Fig. 13.29). The work of $\mathbf{F}$ during a finite displacement from A_1 to A_2, denoted by $U_{1\to2}$, was obtained by integrating Eq. (13.1) along the path described by the particle:

$$U_{1\to2} = \int_{A_1}^{A_2} \mathbf{F} \cdot d\mathbf{r} \qquad (13.2)$$

For a force defined by its rectangular components, we wrote

$$U_{1\to2} = \int_{A_1}^{A_2} (F_x\,dx + F_y\,dy + F_z\,dz) \qquad (13.2'')$$

Fig. 13.29

are arranged in order of increasing difficulty. Problems requiring special attention are indicated by asterisks. Answers to 70 percent of the problems are given at the end of the book. Problems for which the answers are given are set in straight type in the text, while problems for which no answer is given are set in italic.

Chapter Review and Summary. Each chapter ends with a review and summary of the material covered in that chapter. Marginal notes are used to help students organize their review work, and cross-references have been included to help them find the portions of material requiring their special attention.

Review Problems. A set of review problems is included at the end of each chapter. These problems provide students further opportunity to apply the most important concepts introduced in the chapter.

REVIEW PROBLEMS

6.164 Using the method of joints, determine the force in each member of the truss shown. State whether each member is in tension or compression.

6.165 Using the method of joints, determine the force in each member of the roof truss shown. State whether each member is in tension or compression.

Fig. P6.164

Fig. P6.165

COMPUTER PROBLEMS

2.C1 Write a computer program that can be used to determine the magnitude and direction of the resultant of n coplanar forces applied at a point A. Use this program to solve Probs. 2.32, 2.33, 2.35, and 2.38.

Fig. P2.C1

2.C2 A load P is supported by two cables as shown. Write a computer program that can be used to determine the tension in each cable for any given value of P and for values of θ ranging from $\theta_1 = \beta - 90°$ to $\theta_2 = 90° - \alpha$, using given increments $\Delta\theta$. Use this program to determine for the following three sets of numerical values (a) the tension in each cable for values of θ ranging from θ_1 to θ_2, (b) the value of θ for which the tension in the two cables is as small as possible, (c) the corresponding value of the tension:

(1) $\alpha = 35°$, $\beta = 75°$, $P = 400$ lb, $\Delta\theta = 5°$
(2) $\alpha = 50°$, $\beta = 30°$, $P = 600$ lb, $\Delta\theta = 10°$
(3) $\alpha = 40°$, $\beta = 60°$, $P = 250$ lb, $\Delta\theta = 5°$

Fig. P2.C2

2.C3 An acrobat is walking on a tightrope of length $L = 20.1$ m attached to supports A and B at a distance of 20.0 m from each other. The combined weight of the acrobat and his balancing pole is 800 N, and the friction between his shoes and the rope is large enough to prevent him from slipping. Neglecting the weight of the rope and any elastic deformation, write a computer program to calculate the deflection y and the tension in portions AC and BC of the rope for values of x from 0.5 m to 10.0 m using 0.5-m increments. From the data obtained, determine (a) the maximum deflection of the rope, (b) the maximum tension in the rope, (c) the smallest values of the tension in portions AC and BC of the rope.

Computer Problems. Each chapter includes a set of problems designed to be solved with computational software. Many of these problems provide an introduction to the design process. For example, they may involve the determination of the motion of a particle under initial conditions, the kinematic or kinetic analysis of mechanisms in successive positions, or the numerical integration of various equations of motion. Developing the algorithm required to solve a given mechanics problem will benefit the students in two different ways: (1) It will help them gain a better understanding of the mechanics principles involved; (2) it will provide them with an opportunity to apply their computer skills to the solution of a meaningful engineering problem.

What Resources Support This Textbook?

Instructor's and Solutions Manual. *The Instructor's and Solutions Manual* that accompanies the tenth edition features typeset, one-per-page solutions to the end of chapter problems. This Manual also features a number of tables designed to assist instructors in creating a schedule of assignments for their course. The various topics covered in the text have been listed in Table I and a suggested number of periods to be spent on each topic has been indicated. Table II prepares a brief description of all groups of problems and a classification of the problems in each group according to the units used. Sample lesson schedules are shown in Tables III, IV, and V, together with various alternative lists of assigned homework problems.

McGraw-Hill Connect Engineering McGraw-Hill Connect Engineering is a web-based assignment and assessment platform that gives students the means to better connect with their coursework, their instructors, and the important concepts that they will need to know for success now and in the future. With Connect Engineering, instructors can deliver assignments, quizzes, and tests easily online. Students can practice important skills at their own pace and on their own schedule.

Connect Engineering for *Vector Mechanics for Engineers* is available at **www.mhhe.com/beerjohnston** and includes algorithmic problems from the text, Lecture PowerPoints, an image bank, and animations.

Hands-on Mechanics. Hands-on Mechanics is a website designed for instructors who are interested in incorporating three-dimensional, hands-on teaching aids into their lectures. Developed through a partnership between the McGraw-Hill Engineering Team and the Department of Civil and Mechanical Engineering at the United States Military Academy at West Point, this website not only provides detailed instructions for how to build 3-D teaching tools using materials found in any lab or local hardware store, but also provides a community where educators can share ideas, trade best practices, and submit their own original demonstrations for posting on the site. Visit **www.handsonmechanics.com**.

CourseSmart. This text is offered through CourseSmart for both instructors and students. CourseSmart is an online browser where students can purchase access to this and other McGraw-Hill textbooks in a digital format. Through their browser, students can access the complete text online at almost half the cost of a traditional text. Purchasing the eTextbook also allows students to take advantage of CourseSmart's web tools for learning, which include full text search, notes and highlighting, and e-mail tools for sharing notes among classmates. To learn more about CourseSmart options, contact your sales representative or visit **www.coursesmart.com**.

Acknowledgments

A special thanks go to Amy Mazurek who thoroughly checked the solutions and answers of all problems in this edition and then prepared the solutions for the accompanying *Instructor's and Solutions Manual*.

We are pleased to recognize Dennis Ormond of Fine Line Illustrations for the artful illustrations which contribute so much to the effectiveness of the text.

The authors thank the many companies that provided photographs for this edition.

The authors also thank the members of the staff at McGraw-Hill for their support and dedication during the preparation of this new edition. We particularly wish to acknowledge the contributions of Senior Sponsoring Editor Bill Stenquist, Developmental Editors Lora Neyens and Katie Neubauer, and Lead Project Manager Sheila Frank.

David F. Mazurek

The authors gratefully acknowledge the many helpful comments and suggestions offered by focus group attendees users of the previous editions of *Vector Mechanics for Engineers*.

George Adams
Northeastern University

William Altenhof
University of Windsor

Sean B. Anderson
Boston University

Manohar Arora
Colorado School of Mines

Gilbert Baladi
Michigan State University

Brock E. Barry
United States Military

Francois Barthelat
McGill University

Oscar Barton Jr.
U.S. Naval Academy

M. Asghar Bhatti
University of Iowa

Shaohong Cheng
University of Windsor

Philip Datseris
University of Rhode Island

Daniel Dickrell, III
University of Florida

Timothy A. Doughty
University of Portland

Howard Epstein
University of Conneticut

Asad Esmaeily
Kansas State University,
Civil Engineering
Department

David Fleming
Florida Institute of
Technology

Ali gordon
University of Central
Florida, Orlando

Jeff Hanson
Texas Tech University

David A. Jenkins
University of Florida

Shaofan Li
University of California,
Berkeley

Tom Mase
California Polytechnic
State University

Gregory Miller
University of Washington

William R. Murray
Cal Poly State University

Eric Musslman
University of Minnesota,
Duluth

Masoud Olia
Wentworth Institute of
Technology

Mark Olles
Renssalaer Polytechnic
Institute

Renee K. B. Petersen
Washington State
University

Carisa Ramming
Oklahoma State
University

Amir G Rezaei
California State Polytechnic University, Pomona

Martin Sadd
University of Rhode
Island

Stefan Seelecke
North Carolina State
University

Yixin Shao
McGill University

Muhammad Sharif
The University of
Alabama

Anthony Sinclair
University of Toronto

Lizhi Sun
University of California,
Irvine

Jeffrey Thomas
Northwestern University

Robert J. Witt
University of Wisconsin,
Madison

Jiashi Yang
University of Nebraska

Xiangwa Zeng
Case Western Reserve
University

Connect. Learn. Succeed.

McGraw-Hill Higher Education's mission is to help prepare students for the world that awaits. McGraw-Hill provides textbooks, eBooks and other digital instructional content, as well as experiential learning and assignment/assessment platforms, that connect instructors and students to valuable course content—and connect instructors and students to each other.

With the highest quality tools and content, students can engage with their coursework when, where, and however they learn best, enabling greater learning and deeper comprehension.

In turn, students can learn to their full potential and, thus, succeed academically now and in the real world.

Connect:
Instructor Resources
- McGraw-Hill Connect®
- Simulations
- McGraw-Hill Create™
- McGraw-Hill Tegrity®
- Learning Solutions
- Instructor Solutions Manual
- PowerPoint® Lecture Outlines
- Clicker Questions
- Electronic Images from the Text
- EzTest Test Bank

Learn:
Course Content
- Textbooks/Readers
- eBooks
- PowerPoint Presentations
- Enhanced Cartridges
- In-class Simulations
- Lecture Aids
- Custom Publishing

Succeed:
Student Resources
- Online Homework
- Simulations
- Questions
- eBook

Connect
Learn
Succeed™

Learn more at www.mhhe.com

Mcgraw-Hill Tegrity®

Tegrity is a service that makes class time available all the time by automatically capturing every lecture in a searchable format for students to review when they study and complete assignments. With a simple one-click start-and-stop process, you capture all computer screens and corresponding audio. Students replay any part of any class with easy-to-use browser-based viewing on a PC or Mac. Educators know that the more students can see, hear, and experience class resources, the better they learn. With Tegrity, students quickly recall key moments by using Tegrity's unique search feature. This search helps students efficiently find what they need, when they need it across an entire semester of class recordings. Help turn all your students' study time into learning moments immediately supported by your lecture.

To learn more about Tegrity watch a 2-minute Flash demo at http://tegritycampus.mhhe.com.

List of Symbols

a	Constant; radius; distance
$\mathbf{A}, \mathbf{B}, \mathbf{C}, \ldots$	Reactions at supports and connections
$A, B, C, \ldots$	Points
A	Area
b	Width; distance
c	Constant
C	Centroid
d	Distance
e	Base of natural logarithms
$\mathbf{F}$	Force; friction force
g	Acceleration of gravity
G	Center of gravity; constant of gravitation
h	Height; sag of cable
$\mathbf{i}, \mathbf{j}, \mathbf{k}$	Unit vectors along coordinate axes
$I, I_x, \ldots$	Moments of inertia
$\bar{I}$	Centroidal moment of inertia
$I_{xy}, \ldots$	Products of inertia
J	Polar moment of inertia
k	Spring constant
k_x, k_y, k_O	Radii of gyration
$\bar{k}$	Centroidal radius of gyration
l	Length
L	Length; span
m	Mass
$\mathbf{M}$	Couple; moment
$\mathbf{M}_O$	Moment about point O
$\mathbf{M}_O^R$	Moment resultant about point O
M	Magnitude of couple or moment; mass of earth
M_{OL}	Moment about axis OL
$\mathbf{N}$	Normal component of reaction
O	Origin of coordinates
p	Pressure
$\mathbf{P}$	Force; vector
$\mathbf{Q}$	Force; vector
$\mathbf{r}$	Position vector
r	Radius; distance; polar coordinate
$\mathbf{R}$	Resultant force; resultant vector; reaction
R	Radius of earth
$\mathbf{s}$	Position vector
s	Length of arc; length of cable
$\mathbf{S}$	Force; vector
t	Thickness
$\mathbf{T}$	Force
T	Tension
U	Work

$\mathbf{V}$	Vector product; shearing force
V	Volume; potential energy; shear
w	Load per unit length
$\mathbf{W}, W$	Weight; load
x, y, z	Rectangular coordinates; distances
$\bar{x}, \bar{y}, \bar{z}$	Rectangular coordinates of centroid or center of gravity
α, β, γ	Angles
γ	Specific weight
δ	Elongation
$\delta\mathbf{r}$	Virtual displacement
δU	Virtual work
$\boldsymbol{\lambda}$	Unit vector along a line
η	Efficiency
θ	Angular coordinate; angle; polar coordinate
μ	Coefficient of friction
ρ	Density
ϕ	Angle of friction; angle

In the latter part of the seventeenth century, Sir Isaac Newton stated the fundamental principles of mechanics, which are the foundation of much of today's engineering.

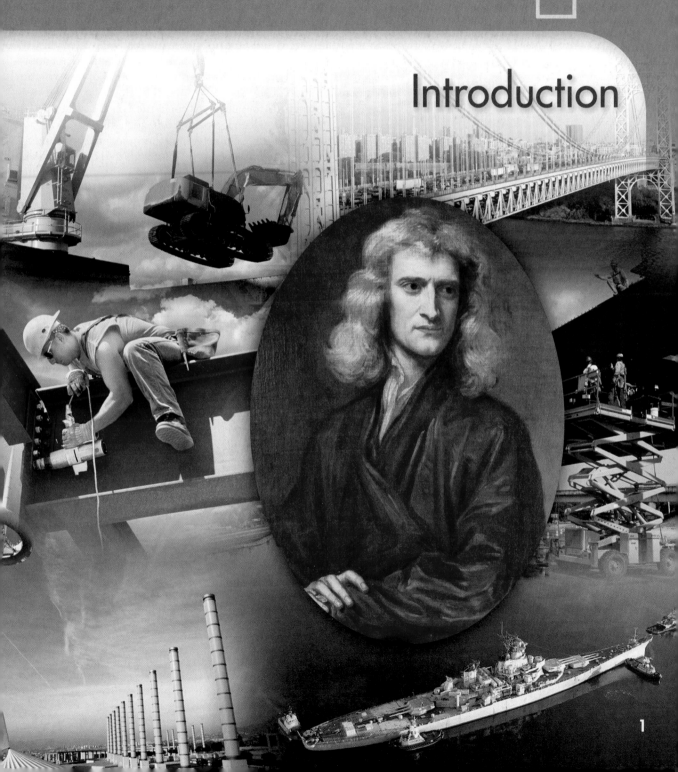

Introduction

1.1 WHAT IS MECHANICS?

Mechanics can be defined as that science which describes and predicts the conditions of rest or motion of bodies under the action of forces. It is divided into three parts: mechanics of *rigid bodies*, mechanics of *deformable bodies*, and mechanics of *fluids*.

The mechanics of rigid bodies is subdivided into *statics* and *dynamics*, the former dealing with bodies at rest, the latter with bodies in motion. In this part of the study of mechanics, bodies are assumed to be perfectly rigid. Actual structures and machines, however, are never absolutely rigid and deform under the loads to which they are subjected. But these deformations are usually small and do not appreciably affect the conditions of equilibrium or motion of the structure under consideration. They are important, though, as far as the resistance of the structure to failure is concerned and are studied in mechanics of materials, which is a part of the mechanics of deformable bodies. The third division of mechanics, the mechanics of fluids, is subdivided into the study of *incompressible fluids* and of *compressible fluids*. An important subdivision of the study of incompressible fluids is *hydraulics*, which deals with problems involving water.

Mechanics is a physical science, since it deals with the study of physical phenomena. However, some associate mechanics with mathematics, while many consider it as an engineering subject. Both these views are justified in part. Mechanics is the foundation of most engineering sciences and is an indispensable prerequisite to their study. However, it does not have the *empiricism* found in some engineering sciences, i.e., it does not rely on experience or observation alone; by its rigor and the emphasis it places on deductive reasoning it resembles mathematics. But, again, it is not an *abstract* or even a *pure* science; mechanics is an *applied* science. The purpose of mechanics is to explain and predict physical phenomena and thus to lay the foundations for engineering applications.

1.2 FUNDAMENTAL CONCEPTS AND PRINCIPLES

Although the study of mechanics goes back to the time of Aristotle (384–322 B.C.) and Archimedes (287–212 B.C.), one has to wait until Newton (1642–1727) to find a satisfactory formulation of its fundamental principles. These principles were later expressed in a modified form by d'Alembert, Lagrange, and Hamilton. Their validity remained unchallenged, however, until Einstein formulated his *theory of relativity* (1905). While its limitations have now been recognized, *newtonian mechanics* still remains the basis of today's engineering sciences.

The basic concepts used in mechanics are *space, time, mass,* and *force.* These concepts cannot be truly defined; they should be accepted on the basis of our intuition and experience and used as a mental frame of reference for our study of mechanics.

The concept of *space* is associated with the notion of the position of a point *P*. The position of *P* can be defined by three lengths measured from a certain reference point, or *origin*, in three given directions. These lengths are known as the *coordinates* of *P*.

To define an event, it is not sufficient to indicate its position in space. The *time* of the event should also be given.

The concept of *mass* is used to characterize and compare bodies on the basis of certain fundamental mechanical experiments. Two bodies of the same mass, for example, will be attracted by the earth in the same manner; they will also offer the same resistance to a change in translational motion.

A *force* represents the action of one body on another. It can be exerted by actual contact or at a distance, as in the case of gravitational forces and magnetic forces. A force is characterized by its *point of application,* its *magnitude,* and its *direction;* a force is represented by a *vector* (Sec. 2.3).

In newtonian mechanics, space, time, and mass are absolute concepts, independent of each other. (This is not true in *relativistic mechanics,* where the time of an event depends upon its position, and where the mass of a body varies with its velocity.) On the other hand, the concept of force is not independent of the other three. Indeed, one of the fundamental principles of newtonian mechanics listed below indicates that the resultant force acting on a body is related to the mass of the body and to the manner in which its velocity varies with time.

You will study the conditions of rest or motion of particles and rigid bodies in terms of the four basic concepts we have introduced. By *particle* we mean a very small amount of matter which may be assumed to occupy a single point in space. A *rigid body* is a combination of a large number of particles occupying fixed positions with respect to each other. The study of the mechanics of particles is obviously a prerequisite to that of rigid bodies. Besides, the results obtained for a particle can be used directly in a large number of problems dealing with the conditions of rest or motion of actual bodies.

The study of elementary mechanics rests on six fundamental principles based on experimental evidence.

The Parallelogram Law for the Addition of Forces.   This states that two forces acting on a particle may be replaced by a single force, called their *resultant,* obtained by drawing the diagonal of the parallelogram which has sides equal to the given forces (Sec. 2.2).

The Principle of Transmissibility.   This states that the conditions of equilibrium or of motion of a rigid body will remain unchanged if a force acting at a given point of the rigid body is replaced by a force of the same magnitude and same direction, but acting at a different point, provided that the two forces have the same line of action (Sec. 3.3).

Newton's Three Fundamental Laws.   Formulated by Sir Isaac Newton in the latter part of the seventeenth century, these laws can be stated as follows:

FIRST LAW.   If the resultant force acting on a particle is zero, the particle will remain at rest (if originally at rest) or will move with constant speed in a straight line (if originally in motion) (Sec. 2.10).

SECOND LAW.   If the resultant force acting on a particle is not zero, the particle will have an acceleration proportional to the magnitude of the resultant and in the direction of this resultant force.

As you will see in Sec. 12.2, this law can be stated as

$$\mathbf{F} = m\mathbf{a} \tag{1.1}$$

where $\mathbf{F}$, m, and $\mathbf{a}$ represent, respectively, the resultant force acting on the particle, the mass of the particle, and the acceleration of the particle, expressed in a consistent system of units.

THIRD LAW.   The forces of action and reaction between bodies in contact have the same magnitude, same line of action, and opposite sense (Sec. 6.1).

Newton's Law of Gravitation.   This states that two particles of mass M and m are mutually attracted with equal and opposite forces $\mathbf{F}$ and $-\mathbf{F}$ (Fig. 1.1) of magnitude F given by the formula

$$F = G\frac{Mm}{r^2} \tag{1.2}$$

Fig. 1.1

where r = distance between the two particles
G = universal constant called the *constant of gravitation*

Newton's law of gravitation introduces the idea of an action exerted at a distance and extends the range of application of Newton's third law: the action $\mathbf{F}$ and the reaction $-\mathbf{F}$ in Fig. 1.1 are equal and opposite, and they have the same line of action.

A particular case of great importance is that of the attraction of the earth on a particle located on its surface. The force $\mathbf{F}$ exerted by the earth on the particle is then defined as the *weight* $\mathbf{W}$ of the particle. Taking M equal to the mass of the earth, m equal to the mass of the particle, and r equal to the radius R of the earth, and introducing the constant

$$g = \frac{GM}{R^2} \tag{1.3}$$

the magnitude W of the weight of a particle of mass m may be expressed as†

$$W = mg \tag{1.4}$$

The value of R in formula (1.3) depends upon the elevation of the point considered; it also depends upon its latitude, since the earth is not truly spherical. The value of g therefore varies with the position of the point considered. As long as the point actually remains on the surface of the earth, it is sufficiently accurate in most engineering computations to assume that g equals 9.81 m/s^2 or 32.2 ft/s^2.

Photo 1.1   When in earth orbit, people and objects are said to be *weightless* even though the gravitational force acting is approximately 90% of that experienced on the surface of the earth. This apparent contradiction will be resolved in Chapter 12 when we apply Newton's second law to the motion of particles.

†A more accurate definition of the weight $\mathbf{W}$ should take into account the rotation of the earth.

The principles we have just listed will be introduced in the course of our study of mechanics as they are needed. The study of the statics of particles carried out in Chap. 2 will be based on the parallelogram law of addition and on Newton's first law alone. The principle of transmissibility will be introduced in Chap. 3 as we begin the study of the statics of rigid bodies, and Newton's third law in Chap. 6 as we analyze the forces exerted on each other by the various members forming a structure. In the study of dynamics, Newton's second law and Newton's law of gravitation will be introduced. It will then be shown that Newton's first law is a particular case of Newton's second law (Sec. 12.2) and that the principle of transmissibility could be derived from the other principles and thus eliminated (Sec. 16.5). In the meantime, however, Newton's first and third laws, the parallelogram law of addition, and the principle of transmissibility will provide us with the necessary and sufficient foundation for the entire study of the statics of particles, rigid bodies, and systems of rigid bodies.

As noted earlier, the six fundamental principles listed above are based on experimental evidence. Except for Newton's first law and the principle of transmissibility, they are independent principles which cannot be derived mathematically from each other or from any other elementary physical principle. On these principles rests most of the intricate structure of newtonian mechanics. For more than two centuries a tremendous number of problems dealing with the conditions of rest and motion of rigid bodies, deformable bodies, and fluids have been solved by applying these fundamental principles. Many of the solutions obtained could be checked experimentally, thus providing a further verification of the principles from which they were derived. It is only in the twentieth century that Newton's mechanics was found at fault, in the study of the motion of atoms and in the study of the motion of certain planets, where it must be supplemented by the theory of relativity. But on the human or engineering scale, where velocities are small compared with the speed of light, Newton's mechanics has yet to be disproved.

1.3 SYSTEMS OF UNITS

With the four fundamental concepts introduced in the preceding section are associated the so-called *kinetic units*, i.e., the units of *length, time, mass,* and *force*. These units cannot be chosen independently if Eq. (1.1) is to be satisfied. Three of the units may be defined arbitrarily; they are then referred to as *basic units*. The fourth unit, however, must be chosen in accordance with Eq. (1.1) and is referred to as a *derived unit*. Kinetic units selected in this way are said to form a *consistent system of units*.

International System of Units (SI Units†). In this system, which will be in universal use after the United States has completed its conversion to SI units, the base units are the units of length, mass, and time, and they are called, respectively, the *meter* (m), the *kilogram* (kg), and the *second* (s). All three are arbitrarily defined. The second,

†SI stands for *Système International d'Unités* (French).

which was originally chosen to represent 1/86 400 of the mean solar day, is now defined as the duration of 9 192 631 770 cycles of the radiation corresponding to the transition between two levels of the fundamental state of the cesium-133 atom. The meter, originally defined as one ten-millionth of the distance from the equator to either pole, is now defined as 1 650 763.73 wavelengths of the orange-red light corresponding to a certain transition in an atom of krypton-86. The kilogram, which is approximately equal to the mass of 0.001 m³ of water, is defined as the mass of a platinum-iridium standard kept at the International Bureau of Weights and Measures at Sèvres, near Paris, France. The unit of force is a derived unit. It is called the *newton* (N) and is defined as the force which gives an acceleration of 1 m/s² to a mass of 1 kg (Fig. 1.2). From Eq. (1.1) we write

$$1 \text{ N} = (1 \text{ kg})(1 \text{ m/s}^2) = 1 \text{ kg} \cdot \text{m/s}^2 \tag{1.5}$$

The SI units are said to form an *absolute* system of units. This means that the three base units chosen are independent of the location where measurements are made. The meter, the kilogram, and the second may be used anywhere on the earth; they may even be used on another planet. They will always have the same significance.

The *weight* of a body, or the *force of gravity* exerted on that body, should, like any other force, be expressed in newtons. From Eq. (1.4) it follows that the weight of a body of mass 1 kg (Fig. 1.3) is

Fig. 1.2

Fig. 1.3

$$W = mg$$
$$= (1 \text{ kg})(9.81 \text{ m/s}^2)$$
$$= 9.81 \text{ N}$$

Multiples and submultiples of the fundamental SI units may be obtained through the use of the prefixes defined in Table 1.1. The multiples and submultiples of the units of length, mass, and force most frequently used in engineering are, respectively, the *kilometer* (km) and the *millimeter* (mm); the *megagram*† (Mg) and the *gram* (g); and the *kilonewton* (kN). According to Table 1.1, we have

$$1 \text{ km} = 1000 \text{ m} \qquad 1 \text{ mm} = 0.001 \text{ m}$$
$$1 \text{ Mg} = 1000 \text{ kg} \qquad 1 \text{ g} = 0.001 \text{ kg}$$
$$1 \text{ kN} = 1000 \text{ N}$$

The conversion of these units into meters, kilograms, and newtons, respectively, can be effected by simply moving the decimal point three places to the right or to the left. For example, to convert 3.82 km into meters, one moves the decimal point three places to the right:

$$3.82 \text{ km} = 3820 \text{ m}$$

Similarly, 47.2 mm is converted into meters by moving the decimal point three places to the left:

$$47.2 \text{ mm} = 0.0472 \text{ m}$$

---

†Also known as a *metric ton*.

TABLE 1.1   SI Prefixes

Multiplication Factor	Prefix†	Symbol
$1\ 000\ 000\ 000\ 000 = 10^{12}$	tera	T
$1\ 000\ 000\ 000 = 10^{9}$	giga	G
$1\ 000\ 000 = 10^{6}$	mega	M
$1\ 000 = 10^{3}$	kilo	k
$100 = 10^{2}$	hecto‡	h
$10 = 10^{1}$	deka‡	da
$0.1 = 10^{-1}$	deci‡	d
$0.01 = 10^{-2}$	centi‡	c
$0.001 = 10^{-3}$	milli	m
$0.000\ 001 = 10^{-6}$	micro	μ
$0.000\ 000\ 001 = 10^{-9}$	nano	n
$0.000\ 000\ 000\ 001 = 10^{-12}$	pico	p
$0.000\ 000\ 000\ 000\ 001 = 10^{-15}$	femto	f
$0.000\ 000\ 000\ 000\ 000\ 001 = 10^{-18}$	atto	a

†The first syllable of every prefix is accented so that the prefix will retain its identity. Thus, the preferred pronunciation of kilometer places the accent on the first syllable, not the second.

‡The use of these prefixes should be avoided, except for the measurement of areas and volumes and for the nontechnical use of centimeter, as for body and clothing measurements.

Using scientific notation, one may also write

$$3.82 \text{ km} = 3.82 \times 10^{3} \text{ m}$$
$$47.2 \text{ mm} = 47.2 \times 10^{-3} \text{ m}$$

The multiples of the unit of time are the *minute* (min) and the *hour* (h). Since 1 min = 60 s and 1 h = 60 min = 3600 s, these multiples cannot be converted as readily as the others.

By using the appropriate multiple or submultiple of a given unit, one can avoid writing very large or very small numbers. For example, one usually writes 427.2 km rather than 427 200 m, and 2.16 mm rather than 0.002 16 m.†

Units of Area and Volume.   The unit of area is the *square meter* (m^2), which represents the area of a square of side 1 m; the unit of volume is the *cubic meter* (m^3), equal to the volume of a cube of side 1 m. In order to avoid exceedingly small or large numerical values in the computation of areas and volumes, one uses systems of subunits obtained by respectively squaring and cubing not only the millimeter but also two intermediate submultiples of the meter, namely, the *decimeter* (dm) and the *centimeter* (cm). Since, by definition,

$$1 \text{ dm} = 0.1 \text{ m} = 10^{-1} \text{ m}$$
$$1 \text{ cm} = 0.01 \text{ m} = 10^{-2} \text{ m}$$
$$1 \text{ mm} = 0.001 \text{ m} = 10^{-3} \text{ m}$$

†It should be noted that when more than four digits are used on either side of the decimal point to express a quantity in SI units—as in 427 200 m or 0.002 16 m—spaces, never commas, should be used to separate the digits into groups of three. This is to avoid confusion with the comma used in place of a decimal point, which is the convention in many countries.

the submultiples of the unit of area are

$$1 \, dm^2 = (1 \, dm)^2 = (10^{-1} \, m)^2 = 10^{-2} \, m^2$$
$$1 \, cm^2 = (1 \, cm)^2 = (10^{-2} \, m)^2 = 10^{-4} \, m^2$$
$$1 \, mm^2 = (1 \, mm)^2 = (10^{-3} \, m)^2 = 10^{-6} \, m^2$$

and the submultiples of the unit of volume are

$$1 \, dm^3 = (1 \, dm)^3 = (10^{-1} \, m)^3 = 10^{-3} \, m^3$$
$$1 \, cm^3 = (1 \, cm)^3 = (10^{-2} \, m)^3 = 10^{-6} \, m^3$$
$$1 \, mm^3 = (1 \, mm)^3 = (10^{-3} \, m)^3 = 10^{-9} \, m^3$$

It should be noted that when the volume of a liquid is being measured, the cubic decimeter (dm^3) is usually referred to as a *liter* (L).

Other derived SI units used to measure the moment of a force, the work of a force, etc., are shown in Table 1.2. While these units will be introduced in later chapters as they are needed, we should note an important rule at this time: When a derived unit is obtained by dividing a base unit by another base unit, a prefix may be used in the numerator of the derived unit but not in its denominator. For example, the constant k of a spring which stretches 20 mm under a load of 100 N will be expressed as

$$k = \frac{100 \, N}{20 \, mm} = \frac{100 \, N}{0.020 \, m} = 5000 \, N/m \qquad or \qquad k = 5 \, kN/m$$

but never as $k = 5 \, N/mm$.

TABLE 1.2 Principal SI Units Used in Mechanics

Quantity	Unit	Symbol	Formula
Acceleration	Meter per second squared	. . .	m/s^2
Angle	Radian	rad	†
Angular acceleration	Radian per second squared	. . .	rad/s^2
Angular velocity	Radian per second	. . .	rad/s
Area	Square meter	. . .	m^2
Density	Kilogram per cubic meter	. . .	kg/m^3
Energy	Joule	J	$N \cdot m$
Force	Newton	N	$kg \cdot m/s^2$
Frequency	Hertz	Hz	s^{-1}
Impulse	Newton-second	. . .	$kg \cdot m/s$
Length	Meter	m	‡
Mass	Kilogram	kg	‡
Moment of a force	Newton-meter	. . .	$N \cdot m$
Power	Watt	W	J/s
Pressure	Pascal	Pa	N/m^2
Stress	Pascal	Pa	N/m^2
Time	Second	s	‡
Velocity	Meter per second	. . .	m/s
Volume			
Solids	Cubic meter	. . .	m^3
Liquids	Liter	L	$10^{-3} m^3$
Work	Joule	J	$N \cdot m$

†Supplementary unit (1 revolution $= 2\pi$ rad $= 360°$).
‡Base unit.

U.S. Customary Units. Most practicing American engineers still commonly use a system in which the base units are the units of length, force, and time. These units are, respectively, the *foot* (ft), the *pound* (lb), and the *second* (s). The second is the same as the corresponding SI unit. The foot is defined as 0.3048 m. The pound is defined as the *weight* of a platinum standard, called the *standard pound,* which is kept at the National Institute of Standards and Technology outside Washington, the mass of which is 0.453 592 43 kg. Since the weight of a body depends upon the earth's gravitational attraction, which varies with location, it is specified that the standard pound should be placed at sea level and at a latitude of 45° to properly define a force of 1 lb. Clearly the U.S. customary units do not form an absolute system of units. Because of their dependence upon the gravitational attraction of the earth, they form a *gravitational* system of units.

While the standard pound also serves as the unit of mass in commercial transactions in the United States, it cannot be so used in engineering computations, since such a unit would not be consistent with the base units defined in the preceding paragraph. Indeed, when acted upon by a force of 1 lb, that is, when subjected to the force of gravity, the standard pound receives the acceleration of gravity, $g = 32.2$ ft/s^2 (Fig. 1.4), not the unit acceleration required by Eq. (1.1). The unit of mass consistent with the foot, the pound, and the second is the mass which receives an acceleration of 1 ft/s^2 when a force of 1 lb is applied to it (Fig. 1.5). This unit, sometimes called a *slug,* can be derived from the equation $F = ma$ after substituting 1 lb and 1 ft/s^2 for F and a, respectively. We write

$$F = ma \qquad 1 \text{ lb} = (1 \text{ slug})(1 \text{ ft/s}^2)$$

and obtain

$$1 \text{ slug} = \frac{1 \text{ lb}}{1 \text{ ft/s}^2} = 1 \text{ lb} \cdot \text{s}^2/\text{ft} \qquad (1.6)$$

Fig. 1.4

Fig. 1.5

Comparing Figs. 1.4 and 1.5, we conclude that the slug is a mass 32.2 times larger than the mass of the standard pound.

The fact that in the U.S. customary system of units bodies are characterized by their weight in pounds rather than by their mass in slugs will be a convenience in the study of statics, where one constantly deals with weights and other forces and only seldom with masses. However, in the study of dynamics, where forces, masses, and accelerations are involved, the mass m of a body will be expressed in slugs when its weight W is given in pounds. Recalling Eq. (1.4), we write

$$m = \frac{W}{g} \qquad (1.7)$$

where g is the acceleration of gravity ($g = 32.2$ ft/s^2).

Other U.S. customary units frequently encountered in engineering problems are the *mile* (mi), equal to 5280 ft; the *inch* (in.), equal to $\frac{1}{12}$ ft; and the *kilopound* (kip), equal to a force of 1000 lb. The *ton* is often used to represent a mass of 2000 lb but, like the pound, must be converted into slugs in engineering computations.

The conversion into feet, pounds, and seconds of quantities expressed in other U.S. customary units is generally more involved and requires greater attention than the corresponding operation in SI units. If, for example, the magnitude of a velocity is given as $v = 30$ mi/h, we convert it to ft/s as follows. First we write

$$v = 30 \, \frac{\text{mi}}{\text{h}}$$

Since we want to get rid of the unit miles and introduce instead the unit feet, we should multiply the right-hand member of the equation by an expression containing miles in the denominator and feet in the numerator. But, since we do not want to change the value of the right-hand member, the expression used should have a value equal to unity. The quotient (5280 ft)/(1 mi) is such an expression. Operating in a similar way to transform the unit hour into seconds, we write

$$v = \left(30 \, \frac{\text{mi}}{\text{h}} \right) \left(\frac{5280 \, \text{ft}}{1 \, \text{mi}} \right) \left(\frac{1 \, \text{h}}{3600 \, \text{s}} \right)$$

Carrying out the numerical computations and canceling out units which appear in both the numerator and the denominator, we obtain

$$v = 44 \, \frac{\text{ft}}{\text{s}} = 44 \text{ ft/s}$$

1.4 CONVERSION FROM ONE SYSTEM OF UNITS TO ANOTHER

There are many instances when an engineer wishes to convert into SI units a numerical result obtained in U.S. customary units or vice versa. Because the unit of time is the same in both systems, only two kinetic base units need be converted. Thus, since all other kinetic units can be derived from these base units, only two conversion factors need be remembered.

Units of Length.   By definition the U.S. customary unit of length is

$$1 \text{ ft} = 0.3048 \text{ m} \tag{1.8}$$

It follows that

$$1 \text{ mi} = 5280 \text{ ft} = 5280(0.3048 \text{ m}) = 1609 \text{ m}$$

or

$$1 \text{ mi} = 1.609 \text{ km} \tag{1.9}$$

Also

$$1 \text{ in.} = \tfrac{1}{12} \text{ ft} = \tfrac{1}{12}(0.3048 \text{ m}) = 0.0254 \text{ m}$$

or

$$1 \text{ in.} = 25.4 \text{ mm} \tag{1.10}$$

Units of Force.   Recalling that the U.S. customary unit of force (pound) is defined as the weight of the standard pound (of mass 0.4536 kg) at sea level and at a latitude of 45° (where $g = 9.807$ m/s²) and using Eq. (1.4), we write

$$W = mg$$
$$1 \text{ lb} = (0.4536 \text{ kg})(9.807 \text{ m/s}^2) = 4.448 \text{ kg} \cdot \text{m/s}^2$$

or, recalling Eq. (1.5),

$$1 \text{ lb} = 4.448 \text{ N} \tag{1.11}$$

Units of Mass.   The U.S. customary unit of mass (slug) is a derived unit. Thus, using Eqs. (1.6), (1.8), and (1.11), we write

$$1 \text{ slug} = 1 \text{ lb} \cdot \text{s}^2/\text{ft} = \frac{1 \text{ lb}}{1 \text{ ft/s}^2} = \frac{4.448 \text{ N}}{0.3048 \text{ m/s}^2} = 14.59 \text{ N} \cdot \text{s}^2/\text{m}$$

and, recalling Eq. (1.5),

$$1 \text{ slug} = 1 \text{ lb} \cdot \text{s}^2/\text{ft} = 14.59 \text{ kg} \tag{1.12}$$

Although it cannot be used as a consistent unit of mass, we recall that the mass of the standard pound is, by definition,

$$1 \text{ pound mass} = 0.4536 \text{ kg} \tag{1.13}$$

This constant may be used to determine the *mass* in SI units (kilograms) of a body which has been characterized by its *weight* in U.S. customary units (pounds).

To convert a derived U.S. customary unit into SI units, one simply multiplies or divides by the appropriate conversion factors. For example, to convert the moment of a force which was found to be $M = 47 \text{ lb} \cdot \text{in.}$ into SI units, we use formulas (1.10) and (1.11) and write

$$M = 47 \text{ lb} \cdot \text{in.} = 47(4.448 \text{ N})(25.4 \text{ mm})$$
$$= 5310 \text{ N} \cdot \text{mm} = 5.31 \text{ N} \cdot \text{m}$$

The conversion factors given in this section may also be used to convert a numerical result obtained in SI units into U.S. customary units. For example, if the moment of a force was found to be $M = 40 \text{ N} \cdot \text{m}$, we write, following the procedure used in the last paragraph of Sec. 1.3,

$$M = 40 \text{ N} \cdot \text{m} = (40 \text{ N} \cdot \text{m})\left(\frac{1 \text{ lb}}{4.448 \text{ N}}\right)\left(\frac{1 \text{ ft}}{0.3048 \text{ m}}\right)$$

Carrying out the numerical computations and canceling out units which appear in both the numerator and the denominator, we obtain

$$M = 29.5 \text{ lb} \cdot \text{ft}$$

The U.S. customary units most frequently used in mechanics are listed in Table 1.3 with their SI equivalents.

1.5 METHOD OF PROBLEM SOLUTION

You should approach a problem in mechanics as you would approach an actual engineering situation. By drawing on your own experience and intuition, you will find it easier to understand and formulate the problem. Once the problem has been clearly stated, however, there is

TABLE 1.3 U.S. Customary Units and Their SI Equivalents

Quantity	U.S. Customary Unit	SI Equivalent
Acceleration	ft/s^2	0.3048 m/s^2
	in./s^2	0.0254 m/s^2
Area	ft^2	0.0929 m^2
	in^2	645.2 mm^2
Energy	ft · lb	1.356 J
Force	kip	4.448 kN
	lb	4.448 N
	oz	0.2780 N
Impulse	lb · s	4.448 N · s
Length	ft	0.3048 m
	in.	25.40 mm
	mi	1.609 km
Mass	oz mass	28.35 g
	lb mass	0.4536 kg
	slug	14.59 kg
	ton	907.2 kg
Moment of a force	lb · ft	1.356 N · m
	lb · in.	0.1130 N · m
Moment of inertia		
Of an area	in^4	0.4162×10^6 mm^4
Of a mass	lb · ft · s^2	1.356 kg · m^2
Momentum	lb · s	4.448 kg · m/s
Power	ft · lb/s	1.356 W
	hp	745.7 W
Pressure or stress	lb/ft^2	47.88 Pa
	lb/in^2 (psi)	6.895 kPa
Velocity	ft/s	0.3048 m/s
	in./s	0.0254 m/s
	mi/h (mph)	0.4470 m/s
	mi/h (mph)	1.609 km/h
Volume	ft^3	0.02832 m^3
	in^3	16.39 cm^3
Liquids	gal	3.785 L
	qt	0.9464 L
Work	ft · lb	1.356 J

no place in its solution for your particular fancy. *The solution must be based on the six fundamental principles stated in Sec. 1.2 or on theorems derived from them.* Every step taken must be justified on that basis. Strict rules must be followed, which lead to the solution in an almost automatic fashion, leaving no room for your intuition or "feeling." After an answer has been obtained, it should be checked. Here again, you may call upon your common sense and personal experience. If not completely satisfied with the result obtained, you should carefully check your formulation of the problem, the validity of the methods used for its solution, and the accuracy of your computations.

The *statement* of a problem should be clear and precise. It should contain the given data and indicate what information is required. A neat drawing showing all quantities involved should be included. Separate diagrams should be drawn for all bodies involved, indicating clearly the forces acting on each body. These diagrams are known as *free-body diagrams* and are described in detail in Secs. 2.11 and 4.2.

The *fundamental principles* of mechanics listed in Sec. 1.2 *will be used to write equations* expressing the conditions of rest or motion of the bodies considered. Each equation should be clearly related to one of the free-body diagrams. You will then proceed to solve the problem, observing strictly the usual rules of algebra and recording neatly the various steps taken.

After the answer has been obtained, it should be *carefully checked*. Mistakes in *reasoning* can often be detected by checking the units. For example, to determine the moment of a force of 50 N about a point 0.60 m from its line of action, we would have written (Sec. 3.12)

$$M = Fd = (50 \text{ N})(0.60 \text{ m}) = 30 \text{ N} \cdot \text{m}$$

The unit $N \cdot m$ obtained by multiplying newtons by meters is the correct unit for the moment of a force; if another unit had been obtained, we would have known that some mistake had been made.

Errors in *computation* will usually be found by substituting the numerical values obtained into an equation which has not yet been used and verifying that the equation is satisfied. The importance of correct computations in engineering cannot be overemphasized.

1.6 NUMERICAL ACCURACY

The accuracy of the solution of a problem depends upon two items: (1) the accuracy of the given data and (2) the accuracy of the computations performed.

The solution cannot be more accurate than the less accurate of these two items. For example, if the loading of a bridge is known to be 75,000 lb with a possible error of 100 lb either way, the relative error which measures the degree of accuracy of the data is

$$\frac{100 \text{ lb}}{75,000 \text{ lb}} = 0.0013 = 0.13 \text{ percent}$$

In computing the reaction at one of the bridge supports, it would then be meaningless to record it as 14,322 lb. The accuracy of the solution cannot be greater than 0.13 percent, no matter how accurate the computations are, and the possible error in the answer may be as large as (0.13/100)(14,322 lb) ≈ 20 lb. The answer should be properly recorded as 14,320 ± 20 lb.

In engineering problems, the data are seldom known with an accuracy greater than 0.2 percent. It is therefore seldom justified to write the answers to such problems with an accuracy greater than 0.2 percent. A practical rule is to use 4 figures to record numbers beginning with a "1" and 3 figures in all other cases. Unless otherwise indicated, the data given in a problem should be assumed known with a comparable degree of accuracy. A force of 40 lb, for example, should be read 40.0 lb, and a force of 15 lb should be read 15.00 lb.

Pocket electronic calculators are widely used by practicing engineers and engineering students. The speed and accuracy of these calculators facilitate the numerical computations in the solution of many problems. However, students should not record more significant figures than can be justified merely because they are easily obtained. As noted above, an accuracy greater than 0.2 percent is seldom necessary or meaningful in the solution of practical engineering problems.

Many engineering problems can be solved by considering the equilibrium of a "particle." In the case of this excavator, which is being loaded onto a ship, a relation between the tensions in the various cables involved can be obtained by considering the equilibrium of the hook to which the cables are attached.

Statics of Particles

Chapter 2 Statics of Particles

2.1   INTRODUCTION

In this chapter you will study the effect of forces acting on particles. First you will learn how to replace two or more forces acting on a given particle by a single force having the same effect as the original forces. This single equivalent force is the *resultant* of the original forces acting on the particle. Later the relations which exist among the various forces acting on a particle in a state of *equilibrium* will be derived and used to determine some of the forces acting on the particle.

The use of the word "particle" does not imply that our study will be limited to that of small corpuscles. What it means is that the size and shape of the bodies under consideration will not significantly affect the solution of the problems treated in this chapter and that all the forces acting on a given body will be assumed to be applied at the same point. Since such an assumption is verified in many practical applications, you will be able to solve a number of engineering problems in this chapter.

The first part of the chapter is devoted to the study of forces contained in a single plane, and the second part to the analysis of forces in three-dimensional space.

FORCES IN A PLANE

2.2   FORCE ON A PARTICLE. RESULTANT OF TWO FORCES

A force represents the action of one body on another and is generally characterized by its *point of application,* its *magnitude,* and its *direction.* Forces acting on a given particle, however, have the same point of application. Each force considered in this chapter will thus be completely defined by its magnitude and direction.

The magnitude of a force is characterized by a certain number of units. As indicated in Chap. 1, the SI units used by engineers to measure the magnitude of a force are the newton (N) and its multiple the kilonewton (kN), equal to 1000 N, while the U.S. customary units used for the same purpose are the pound (lb) and its multiple the kilopound (kip), equal to 1000 lb. The direction of a force is defined by the *line of action* and the *sense* of the force. The line of action is the infinite straight line along which the force acts; it is characterized by the angle it forms with some fixed axis (Fig. 2.1). The force itself is represented by a segment of

Fig. 2.1   (a)   (b)

that line; through the use of an appropriate scale, the length of this segment may be chosen to represent the magnitude of the force. Finally, the sense of the force should be indicated by an arrowhead. It is important in defining a force to indicate its sense. Two forces having the same magnitude and the same line of action but different sense, such as the forces shown in Fig. 2.1*a* and *b*, will have directly opposite effects on a particle.

Experimental evidence shows that two forces **P** and **Q** acting on a particle *A* (Fig. 2.2*a*) can be replaced by a single force **R** which has the same effect on the particle (Fig. 2.2*c*). This force is called the *resultant* of the forces **P** and **Q** and can be obtained, as shown in Fig. 2.2*b*, by constructing a parallelogram, using **P** and **Q** as two adjacent sides of the parallelogram. *The diagonal that passes through A represents the resultant.* This method for finding the resultant is known as the *parallelogram law* for the addition of two forces. This law is based on experimental evidence; it cannot be proved or derived mathematically.

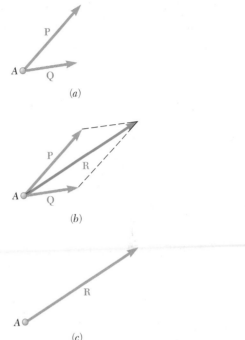

Fig. 2.2

2.3 VECTORS

It appears from the above that forces do not obey the rules of addition defined in ordinary arithmetic or algebra. For example, two forces acting at a right angle to each other, one of 4 lb and the other of 3 lb, add up to a force of 5 lb, *not* to a force of 7 lb. Forces are not the only quantities which follow the parallelogram law of addition. As you will see later, *displacements, velocities, accelerations,* and *momenta* are other examples of physical quantities possessing magnitude and direction that are added according to the parallelogram law. All these quantities can be represented mathematically by *vectors*, while those physical quantities which have magnitude but not direction, such as *volume, mass,* or *energy,* are represented by plain numbers or *scalars.*

Vectors are defined as *mathematical expressions possessing magnitude and direction, which add according to the parallelogram law.* Vectors are represented by arrows in the illustrations and will be distinguished from scalar quantities in this text through the use of boldface type (**P**). In longhand writing, a vector may be denoted by drawing a short arrow above the letter used to represent it ($\vec{P}$) or by underlining the letter (*P*). The last method may be preferred since underlining can also be used on a typewriter or computer. The magnitude of a vector defines the length of the arrow used to represent the vector. In this text, italic type will be used to denote the magnitude of a vector. Thus, the magnitude of the vector **P** will be denoted by *P*.

A vector used to represent a force acting on a given particle has a well-defined point of application, namely, the particle itself. Such a vector is said to be a *fixed,* or *bound,* vector and cannot be moved without modifying the conditions of the problem. Other physical quantities, however, such as couples (see Chap. 3), are represented by vectors which may be freely moved in space; these

Fig. 2.4

vectors are called *free* vectors. Still other physical quantities, such as forces acting on a rigid body (see Chap. 3), are represented by vectors which can be moved, or slid, along their lines of action; they are known as *sliding* vectors.†

Two vectors which have the same magnitude and the same direction are said to be *equal*, whether or not they also have the same point of application (Fig. 2.4); equal vectors may be denoted by the same letter.

The *negative vector* of a given vector **P** is defined as a vector having the same magnitude as **P** and a direction opposite to that of **P** (Fig. 2.5); the negative of the vector **P** is denoted by −**P**. The vectors **P** and −**P** are commonly referred to as *equal and opposite* vectors. Clearly, we have

$$\mathbf{P} + (-\mathbf{P}) = 0$$

Fig. 2.5

2.4 ADDITION OF VECTORS

We saw in the preceding section that, by definition, vectors add according to the parallelogram law. Thus, the sum of two vectors **P** and **Q** is obtained by attaching the two vectors to the same point A and constructing a parallelogram, using **P** and **Q** as two sides of the parallelogram (Fig. 2.6). The diagonal that passes through A represents the sum of the vectors **P** and **Q**, and this sum is denoted by **P** + **Q**. The fact that the sign + is used to denote both vector and scalar addition should not cause any confusion if vector and scalar quantities are always carefully distinguished. Thus, we should note that the magnitude of the vector **P** + **Q** is *not*, in general, equal to the sum $P + Q$ of the magnitudes of the vectors **P** and **Q**.

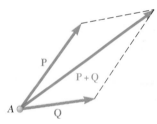

Fig. 2.6

Since the parallelogram constructed on the vectors **P** and **Q** does not depend upon the order in which **P** and **Q** are selected, we conclude that the addition of two vectors is *commutative*, and we write

$$\mathbf{P} + \mathbf{Q} = \mathbf{Q} + \mathbf{P} \tag{2.1}$$

†Some expressions have magnitude and direction, but do not add according to the parallelogram law. While these expressions may be represented by arrows, they *cannot* be considered as vectors.

A group of such expressions is the finite rotations of a rigid body. Place a closed book on a table in front of you, so that it lies in the usual fashion, with its front cover up and its binding to the left. Now rotate it through 180° about an axis parallel to the binding (Fig. 2.3*a*); this rotation may be represented by an arrow of length equal to 180 units and oriented as shown. Picking up the book as it lies in its new position, rotate

(*a*)   (*b*)

Fig. 2.3 Finite rotations of a rigid body

From the parallelogram law, we can derive an alternative method for determining the sum of two vectors. This method, known as the *triangle rule*, is derived as follows. Consider Fig. 2.6, where the sum of the vectors **P** and **Q** has been determined by the parallelogram law. Since the side of the parallelogram opposite **Q** is equal to **Q** in magnitude and direction, we could draw only half of the parallelogram (Fig. 2.7*a*). The sum of the two vectors can thus be found by *arranging **P** and **Q** in tip-to-tail fashion and then connecting the tail of **P** with the tip of **Q**. In Fig. 2.7*b*, the other half of the parallelogram is considered, and the same result is obtained. This confirms the fact that vector addition is commutative.

The *subtraction* of a vector is defined as the addition of the corresponding negative vector. Thus, the vector **P** − **Q** representing the difference between the vectors **P** and **Q** is obtained by adding to **P** the negative vector −**Q** (Fig. 2.8). We write

$$\mathbf{P} - \mathbf{Q} = \mathbf{P} + (-\mathbf{Q}) \tag{2.2}$$

Here again we should observe that, while the same sign is used to denote both vector and scalar subtraction, confusion will be avoided if care is taken to distinguish between vector and scalar quantities.

We will now consider the *sum of three or more vectors*. The sum of three vectors **P**, **Q**, and **S** will, *by definition*, be obtained by first adding the vectors **P** and **Q** and then adding the vector **S** to the vector **P** + **Q**. We thus write

$$\mathbf{P} + \mathbf{Q} + \mathbf{S} = (\mathbf{P} + \mathbf{Q}) + \mathbf{S} \tag{2.3}$$

Similarly, the sum of four vectors will be obtained by adding the fourth vector to the sum of the first three. It follows that the sum of any number of vectors can be obtained by applying repeatedly the parallelogram law to successive pairs of vectors until all the given vectors are replaced by a single vector.

Fig. 2.7

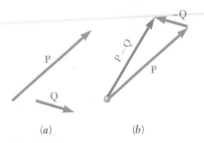

Fig. 2.8

---

it now through 180° about a horizontal axis perpendicular to the binding (Fig. 2.3*b*); this second rotation may be represented by an arrow 180 units long and oriented as shown. But the book could have been placed in this final position through a single 180° rotation about a vertical axis (Fig. 2.3*c*). We conclude that the sum of the two 180° rotations represented by arrows directed respectively along the *z* and *x* axes is a 180° rotation represented by an arrow directed along the *y* axis (Fig. 2.3*d*). Clearly, the finite rotations of a rigid body *do not* obey the parallelogram law of addition; therefore, they *cannot* be represented by vectors.

Fig. 2.9

If the given vectors are *coplanar*, i.e., if they are contained in the same plane, their sum can be easily obtained graphically. For this case, the repeated application of the triangle rule is preferred to the application of the parallelogram law. In Fig. 2.9 the sum of three vectors **P**, **Q**, and **S** was obtained in that manner. The triangle rule was first applied to obtain the sum **P** + **Q** of the vectors **P** and **Q**; it was applied again to obtain the sum of the vectors **P** + **Q** and **S**. The determination of the vector **P** + **Q**, however, could have been omitted and the sum of the three vectors could have been obtained directly, as shown in Fig. 2.10, by *arranging the given vectors in tip-to-tail fashion and connecting the tail of the first vector with the tip of the last one*. This is known as the *polygon rule* for the addition of vectors.

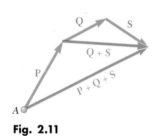

Fig. 2.10

We observe that the result obtained would have been unchanged if, as shown in Fig. 2.11, the vectors **Q** and **S** had been replaced by their sum **Q** + **S**. We may thus write

$$\mathbf{P} + \mathbf{Q} + \mathbf{S} = (\mathbf{P} + \mathbf{Q}) + \mathbf{S} = \mathbf{P} + (\mathbf{Q} + \mathbf{S}) \tag{2.4}$$

which expresses the fact that vector addition is *associative*. Recalling that vector addition has also been shown, in the case of two vectors, to be commutative, we write

$$\begin{aligned}\mathbf{P} + \mathbf{Q} + \mathbf{S} &= (\mathbf{P} + \mathbf{Q}) + \mathbf{S} = \mathbf{S} + (\mathbf{P} + \mathbf{Q}) \\ &= \mathbf{S} + (\mathbf{Q} + \mathbf{P}) = \mathbf{S} + \mathbf{Q} + \mathbf{P}\end{aligned} \tag{2.5}$$

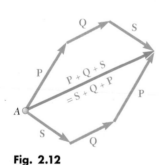

Fig. 2.11

This expression, as well as others which may be obtained in the same way, shows that the order in which several vectors are added together is immaterial (Fig. 2.12).

Product of a Scalar and a Vector. Since it is convenient to denote the sum **P** + **P** by 2**P**, the sum **P** + **P** + **P** by 3**P**, and, in general, the sum of *n* equal vectors **P** by the product *n***P**, we will define the product *n***P** of a positive integer *n* and a vector **P** as a vector having the same direction as **P** and the magnitude *nP*. Extending this definition to include all scalars, and recalling the definition of a negative vector given in Sec. 2.3, we define the product *k***P** of a scalar *k* and a vector **P** as a vector having the same direction as **P** (if *k* is positive), or a direction opposite to that of **P** (if *k* is negative), and a magnitude equal to the product of *P* and of the absolute value of *k* (Fig. 2.13).

Fig. 2.12

2.5 RESULTANT OF SEVERAL CONCURRENT FORCES

Consider a particle *A* acted upon by several coplanar forces, i.e., by several forces contained in the same plane (Fig. 2.14*a*). Since the forces considered here all pass through *A*, they are also said to be *concurrent*. The vectors representing the forces acting on *A* may be added by the polygon rule (Fig. 2.14*b*). Since the use of the polygon rule is equivalent to the repeated application of the parallelogram law, the vector **R** thus obtained represents the resultant of the given concurrent forces, i.e., the single force which has the same effect on

Fig. 2.13

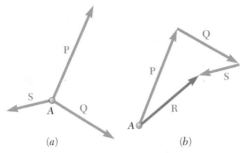

Fig. 2.14

the particle A as the given forces. As indicated in the previous section, the order in which the vectors **P**, **Q**, and **S** representing the given forces are added together is immaterial.

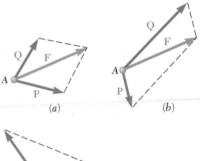

(a)   (b)

2.6 RESOLUTION OF A FORCE INTO COMPONENTS

We have seen that two or more forces acting on a particle may be replaced by a single force which has the same effect on the particle. Conversely, a single force **F** acting on a particle may be replaced by two or more forces which, together, have the same effect on the particle. These forces are called the *components* of the original force **F**, and the process of substituting them for **F** is called *resolving the force* **F** *into components*.

Clearly, for each force **F** there exist an infinite number of possible sets of components. Sets of *two components* **P** *and* **Q** are the most important as far as practical applications are concerned. But, even then, the number of ways in which a given force **F** may be resolved into two components is unlimited (Fig. 2.15). Two cases are of particular interest:

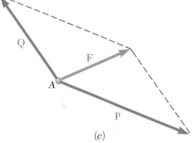

(c)

Fig. 2.15

1. *One of the Two Components,* **P**, *Is Known.* The second component, **Q**, is obtained by applying the triangle rule and joining the tip of **P** to the tip of F (Fig. 2.16); the magnitude and direction of **Q** are determined graphically or by trigonometry. Once **Q** has been determined, both components **P** and **Q** should be applied at A.

Fig. 2.16

2. *The Line of Action of Each Component Is Known.* The magnitude and sense of the components are obtained by applying the parallelogram law and drawing lines, through the tip of **F**, parallel to the given lines of action (Fig. 2.17). This process leads to two well-defined components, **P** and **Q**, which can be determined graphically or computed trigonometrically by applying the law of sines.

Many other cases can be encountered; for example, the direction of one component may be known, while the magnitude of the other component is to be as small as possible (see Sample Prob. 2.2). In all cases the appropriate triangle or parallelogram which satisfies the given conditions is drawn.

Fig. 2.17

SAMPLE PROBLEM 2.1

The two forces **P** and **Q** act on a bolt *A*. Determine their resultant.

SOLUTION

Graphical Solution. A parallelogram with sides equal to **P** and **Q** is drawn to scale. The magnitude and direction of the resultant are measured and found to be

$$R = 98 \text{ N} \qquad \alpha = 35° \qquad \mathbf{R} = 98 \text{ N} \angle 35° \quad \blacktriangleleft$$

The triangle rule may also be used. Forces **P** and **Q** are drawn in tip-to-tail fashion. Again the magnitude and direction of the resultant are measured.

$$R = 98 \text{ N} \qquad \alpha = 35° \qquad \mathbf{R} = 98 \text{ N} \angle 35° \quad \blacktriangleleft$$

Trigonometric Solution. The triangle rule is again used; two sides and the included angle are known. We apply the law of cosines.

$$R^2 = P^2 + Q^2 - 2PQ \cos B$$
$$R^2 = (40 \text{ N})^2 + (60 \text{ N})^2 - 2(40 \text{ N})(60 \text{ N}) \cos 155°$$
$$R = 97.73 \text{ N}$$

Now, applying the law of sines, we write

$$\frac{\sin A}{Q} = \frac{\sin B}{R} \qquad \frac{\sin A}{60 \text{ N}} = \frac{\sin 155°}{97.73 \text{ N}} \tag{1}$$

Solving Eq. (1) for sin *A*, we have

$$\sin A = \frac{(60 \text{ N}) \sin 155°}{97.73 \text{ N}}$$

Using a calculator, we first compute the quotient, then its arc sine, and obtain

$$A = 15.04° \qquad \alpha = 20° + A = 35.04°$$

We use 3 significant figures to record the answer (cf. Sec. 1.6):

$$\mathbf{R} = 97.7 \text{ N} \angle 35.0° \quad \blacktriangleleft$$

Alternative Trigonometric Solution. We construct the right triangle *BCD* and compute

$$CD = (60 \text{ N}) \sin 25° = 25.36 \text{ N}$$
$$BD = (60 \text{ N}) \cos 25° = 54.38 \text{ N}$$

Then, using triangle *ACD*, we obtain

$$\tan A = \frac{25.36 \text{ N}}{94.38 \text{ N}} \qquad A = 15.04°$$

$$R = \frac{25.36}{\sin A} \qquad R = 97.73 \text{ N}$$

Again, $\qquad \alpha = 20° + A = 35.04° \qquad \mathbf{R} = 97.7 \text{ N} \angle 35.0° \quad \blacktriangleleft$

SAMPLE PROBLEM 2.2

A barge is pulled by two tugboats. If the resultant of the forces exerted by the tugboats is a 5000-lb force directed along the axis of the barge, determine (*a*) the tension in each of the ropes knowing that $\alpha = 45°$, (*b*) the value of α for which the tension in rope 2 is minimum.

SOLUTION

a. Tension for $\alpha = 45°$. *Graphical Solution.* The parallelogram law is used; the diagonal (resultant) is known to be equal to 5000 lb and to be directed to the right. The sides are drawn parallel to the ropes. If the drawing is done to scale, we measure

$$T_1 = 3700 \text{ lb} \qquad T_2 = 2600 \text{ lb} \quad \blacktriangleleft$$

Trigonometric Solution. The triangle rule can be used. We note that the triangle shown represents half of the parallelogram shown above. Using the law of sines, we write

$$\frac{T_1}{\sin 45°} = \frac{T_2}{\sin 30°} = \frac{5000 \text{ lb}}{\sin 105°}$$

With a calculator, we first compute and store the value of the last quotient. Multiplying this value successively by sin 45° and sin 30°, we obtain

$$T_1 = 3660 \text{ lb} \qquad T_2 = 2590 \text{ lb} \quad \blacktriangleleft$$

b. Value of α for Minimum T_2. To determine the value of α for which the tension in rope 2 is minimum, the triangle rule is again used. In the sketch shown, line *1-1'* is the known direction of $\mathbf{T}_1$. Several possible directions of $\mathbf{T}_2$ are shown by the lines *2-2'*. We note that the minimum value of T_2 occurs when $\mathbf{T}_1$ and $\mathbf{T}_2$ are perpendicular. The minimum value of T_2 is

$$T_2 = (5000 \text{ lb}) \sin 30° = 2500 \text{ lb}$$

Corresponding values of T_1 and α are

$$T_1 = (5000 \text{ lb}) \cos 30° = 4330 \text{ lb}$$
$$\alpha = 90° - 30° \qquad\qquad \alpha = 60° \quad \blacktriangleleft$$

SOLVING PROBLEMS ON YOUR OWN

The preceding sections were devoted to the *parallelogram law* for the addition of vectors and to its applications.

Two sample problems were presented. In Sample Prob. 2.1, the parallelogram law was used to determine the resultant of two forces of known magnitude and direction. In Sample Prob. 2.2, it was used to resolve a given force into two components of known direction.

You will now be asked to solve problems on your own. Some may resemble one of the sample problems; others may not. What all problems and sample problems in this section have in common is that they can be solved by the direct application of the parallelogram law.

Your solution of a given problem should consist of the following steps:

1. Identify which of the forces are the applied forces and which is the resultant. It is often helpful to write the vector equation which shows how the forces are related. For example, in Sample Prob. 2.1 we would have

$$\mathbf{R} = \mathbf{P} + \mathbf{Q}$$

You may want to keep that relation in mind as you formulate the next part of your solution.

2. Draw a parallelogram with the applied forces as two adjacent sides and the resultant as the included diagonal (Fig. 2.2). Alternatively, you can *use the triangle rule,* with the applied forces drawn in tip-to-tail fashion and the resultant extending from the tail of the first vector to the tip of the second (Fig. 2.7).

3. Indicate all dimensions. Using one of the triangles of the parallelogram, or the triangle constructed according to the triangle rule, indicate all dimensions—whether sides or angles—and determine the unknown dimensions either graphically or by trigonometry. If you use trigonometry, remember that the law of cosines should be applied first if two sides and the included angle are known [Sample Prob. 2.1], and the law of sines should be applied first if one side and all angles are known [Sample Prob. 2.2].

If you have had prior exposure to mechanics, you might be tempted to ignore the solution techniques of this lesson in favor of resolving the forces into rectangular components. While this latter method is important and will be considered in the next section, use of the parallelogram law simplifies the solution of many problems and should be mastered at this time.

2.1 Two forces are applied at point B of beam AB. Determine graphically the magnitude and direction of their resultant using (*a*) the parallelogram law, (*b*) the triangle rule.

Fig. P2.1

2.2 The cable stays AB and AD help support pole AC. Knowing that the tension is 120 lb in AB and 40 lb in AD, determine graphically the magnitude and direction of the resultant of the forces exerted by the stays at A using (*a*) the parallelogram law, (*b*) the triangle rule.

Fig. P2.2

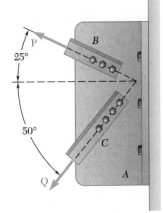

Fig. P2.3 and P2.4

2.3 Two structural members B and C are bolted to bracket A. Knowing that both members are in tension and that $P = 10$ kN and $Q = 15$ kN, determine graphically the magnitude and direction of the resultant force exerted on the bracket using (*a*) the parallelogram law, (*b*) the triangle rule.

2.4 Two structural members B and C are bolted to bracket A. Knowing that both members are in tension and that $P = 6$ kips and $Q = 4$ kips, determine graphically the magnitude and direction of the resultant force exerted on the bracket using (*a*) the parallelogram law, (*b*) the triangle rule.

2.5 A stake is being pulled out of the ground by means of two ropes as shown. Knowing that $\alpha = 30°$, determine by trigonometry (*a*) the magnitude of the force **P** so that the resultant force exerted on the stake is vertical, (*b*) the corresponding magnitude of the resultant.

†Answers to all problems set in straight type (such as **2.1**) are given at the end of the book. Answers to problems with a number set in italic type (such as **2.3**) are not given.

Fig. P2.5

25

1600 N

Fig. P2.6 and P2.7

Fig. P2.8 and P2.9

Fig. P2.11, P2.12, and P2.13

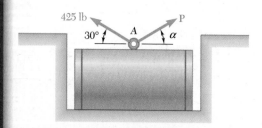

2.6 A trolley that moves along a horizontal beam is acted upon by two forces as shown. (a) Knowing that $\alpha = 25°$, determine by trigonometry the magnitude of the force **P** so that the resultant force exerted on the trolley is vertical. (b) What is the corresponding magnitude of the resultant?

2.7 A trolley that moves along a horizontal beam is acted upon by two forces as shown. Determine by trigonometry the magnitude and direction of the force **P** so that the resultant is a vertical force of 2500 N.

2.8 A telephone cable is clamped at A to the pole AB. Knowing that the tension in the left-hand portion of the cable is $T_1 = 800$ lb, determine by trigonometry (a) the required tension T_2 in the right-hand portion if the resultant **R** of the forces exerted by the cable at A is to be vertical, (b) the corresponding magnitude of **R**.

2.9 A telephone cable is clamped at A to the pole AB. Knowing that the tension in the right-hand portion of the cable is $T_2 = 1000$ lb, determine by trigonometry (a) the required tension T_1 in the left-hand portion if the resultant **R** of the forces exerted by the cable at A is to be vertical, (b) the corresponding magnitude of **R**.

2.10 Two forces are applied as shown to a hook support. Knowing that the magnitude of **P** is 35 N, determine by trigonometry (a) the required angle α if the resultant **R** of the two forces applied to the support is to be horizontal, (b) the corresponding magnitude of **R**.

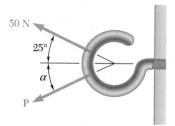

Fig. P2.10

2.11 A steel tank is to be positioned in an excavation. Knowing that $\alpha = 20°$, determine by trigonometry (a) the required magnitude of the force **P** if the resultant **R** of the two forces applied at A is to be vertical, (b) the corresponding magnitude of **R**.

2.12 A steel tank is to be positioned in an excavation. Knowing that the magnitude of **P** is 500 lb, determine by trigonometry (a) the required angle α if the resultant **R** of the two forces applied at A is to be vertical, (b) the corresponding magnitude of **R**.

2.13 A steel tank is to be positioned in an excavation. Determine by trigonometry (a) the magnitude and direction of the smallest force **P** for which the resultant **R** of the two forces applied at A is vertical, (b) the corresponding magnitude of **R**.

2.14 For the hook support of Prob. 2.10, determine by trigonometry (a) the magnitude and direction of the smallest force **P** for which the resultant **R** of the two forces applied to the support is horizontal, (b) the corresponding magnitude of **R**.

2.15 Solve Prob. 2.2 by trigonometry.

2.16 Solve Prob. 2.4 by trigonometry.

2.17 For the stake of Prob. 2.5, knowing that the tension in one rope is 120 N, determine by trigonometry the magnitude and direction of the force **P** so that the resultant is a vertical force of 160 N.

2.18 For the hook support of Prob. 2.10, knowing that $P = 75$ N and $\alpha = 50°$, determine by trigonometry the magnitude and direction of the resultant of the two forces applied to the support.

2.19 Two forces **P** and **Q** are applied to the lid of a storage bin as shown. Knowing that $P = 48$ N and $Q = 60$ N, determine by trigonometry the magnitude and direction of the resultant of the two forces.

2.20 Two forces **P** and **Q** are applied to the lid of a storage bin as shown. Knowing that $P = 60$ N and $Q = 48$ N, determine by trigonometry the magnitude and direction of the resultant of the two forces.

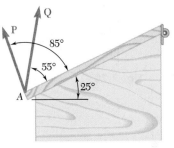

Fig. P2.19 and *P2.20*

2.7 RECTANGULAR COMPONENTS OF A FORCE. UNIT VECTORS†

In many problems it will be found desirable to resolve a force into two components which are perpendicular to each other. In Fig. 2.18, the force **F** has been resolved into a component $\mathbf{F}_x$ along the x axis and a component $\mathbf{F}_y$ along the y axis. The parallelogram drawn to obtain the two components is a *rectangle*, and $\mathbf{F}_x$ and $\mathbf{F}_y$ are called *rectangular components.*

Fig. 2.18

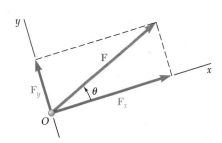

Fig. 2.19

The x and y axes are usually chosen horizontal and vertical, respectively, as in Fig. 2.18; they may, however, be chosen in any two perpendicular directions, as shown in Fig. 2.19. In determining the rectangular components of a force, the student should think of the construction lines shown in Figs. 2.18 and 2.19 as being *parallel* to the x and y axes, rather than *perpendicular* to these axes. This practice will help avoid mistakes in determining *oblique* components as in Sec. 2.6.

---

†The properties established in Secs. 2.7 and 2.8 may be readily extended to the rectangular components of any vector quantity.

Fig. 2.20

Fig. 2.21

(a)

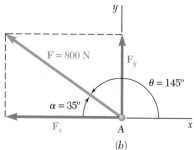

(b)

Fig. 2.22

Two vectors of unit magnitude, directed respectively along the positive x and y axes, will be introduced at this point. These vectors are called *unit vectors* and are denoted by $\mathbf{i}$ and $\mathbf{j}$, respectively (Fig. 2.20). Recalling the definition of the product of a scalar and a vector given in Sec. 2.4, we note that the rectangular components $\mathbf{F}_x$ and $\mathbf{F}_y$ of a force $\mathbf{F}$ may be obtained by multiplying respectively the unit vectors $\mathbf{i}$ and $\mathbf{j}$ by appropriate scalars (Fig. 2.21). We write

$$\mathbf{F}_x = F_x\mathbf{i} \qquad \mathbf{F}_y = F_y\mathbf{j} \tag{2.6}$$

and

$$\mathbf{F} = F_x\mathbf{i} + F_y\mathbf{j} \tag{2.7}$$

While the scalars F_x and F_y may be positive or negative, depending upon the sense of $\mathbf{F}_x$ and of $\mathbf{F}_y$, their absolute values are respectively equal to the magnitudes of the component forces $\mathbf{F}_x$ and $\mathbf{F}_y$. The scalars F_x and F_y are called the *scalar components* of the force $\mathbf{F}$, while the actual component forces $\mathbf{F}_x$ and $\mathbf{F}_y$ should be referred to as the *vector components* of $\mathbf{F}$. However, when there exists no possibility of confusion, the vector as well as the scalar components of $\mathbf{F}$ may be referred to simply as the *components* of $\mathbf{F}$. We note that the scalar component F_x is positive when the vector component $\mathbf{F}_x$ has the same sense as the unit vector $\mathbf{i}$ (i.e., the same sense as the positive x axis) and is negative when $\mathbf{F}_x$ has the opposite sense. A similar conclusion may be drawn regarding the sign of the scalar component F_y.

Denoting by F the magnitude of the force $\mathbf{F}$ and by θ the angle between $\mathbf{F}$ and the x axis, measured counterclockwise from the positive x axis (Fig. 2.21), we may express the scalar components of $\mathbf{F}$ as follows:

$$F_x = F \cos \theta \qquad F_y = F \sin \theta \tag{2.8}$$

We note that the relations obtained hold for any value of the angle θ from 0° to 360° and that they define the signs as well as the absolute values of the scalar components F_x and F_y.

EXAMPLE 1. A force of 800 N is exerted on a bolt A as shown in Fig. 2.22a. Determine the horizontal and vertical components of the force.

In order to obtain the correct sign for the scalar components F_x and F_y, the value $180° - 35° = 145°$ should be substituted for θ in Eqs. (2.8). However, it will be found more practical to determine by inspection the signs of F_x and F_y (Fig. 2.22b) and to use the trigonometric functions of the angle $\alpha = 35°$. We write, therefore,

$$F_x = -F \cos \alpha = -(800 \text{ N}) \cos 35° = -655 \text{ N}$$
$$F_y = +F \sin \alpha = +(800 \text{ N}) \sin 35° = +459 \text{ N}$$

The vector components of $\mathbf{F}$ are thus

$$\mathbf{F}_x = -(655 \text{ N})\mathbf{i} \qquad \mathbf{F}_y = +(459 \text{ N})\mathbf{j}$$

and we may write $\mathbf{F}$ in the form

$$\mathbf{F} = -(655 \text{ N})\mathbf{i} + (459 \text{ N})\mathbf{j} \quad \blacksquare$$

EXAMPLE 2.   A man pulls with a force of 300 N on a rope attached to a building, as shown in Fig. 2.23a. What are the horizontal and vertical components of the force exerted by the rope at point A?

It is seen from Fig. 2.23b that

$$F_x = +(300 \text{ N}) \cos \alpha \qquad F_y = -(300 \text{ N}) \sin \alpha$$

Observing that $AB = 10$ m, we find from Fig. 2.23a

$$\cos \alpha = \frac{8 \text{ m}}{AB} = \frac{8 \text{ m}}{10 \text{ m}} = \frac{4}{5} \qquad \sin \alpha = \frac{6 \text{ m}}{AB} = \frac{6 \text{ m}}{10 \text{ m}} = \frac{3}{5}$$

We thus obtain

$$F_x = +(300 \text{ N})\tfrac{4}{5} = +240 \text{ N} \qquad F_y = -(300 \text{ N})\tfrac{3}{5} = -180 \text{ N}$$

and write

$$\mathbf{F} = (240 \text{ N})\mathbf{i} - (180 \text{ N})\mathbf{j} \quad \blacksquare$$

When a force $\mathbf{F}$ is defined by its rectangular components F_x and F_y (see Fig. 2.21), the angle θ defining its direction can be obtained by writing

$$\tan \theta = \frac{F_y}{F_x} \tag{2.9}$$

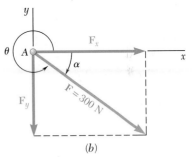

(a)

(b)

Fig. 2.23

The magnitude F of the force can be obtained by applying the Pythagorean theorem and writing

$$F = \sqrt{F_x^2 + F_y^2} \tag{2.10}$$

or by solving for F one of the Eqs. (2.8).

EXAMPLE 3.   A force $\mathbf{F} = (700 \text{ lb})\mathbf{i} + (1500 \text{ lb})\mathbf{j}$ is applied to a bolt A. Determine the magnitude of the force and the angle θ it forms with the horizontal.

First we draw a diagram showing the two rectangular components of the force and the angle θ (Fig. 2.24). From Eq. (2.9), we write

$$\tan \theta = \frac{F_y}{F_x} = \frac{1500 \text{ lb}}{700 \text{ lb}}$$

Using a calculator,† we enter 1500 lb and divide by 700 lb; computing the arc tangent of the quotient, we obtain $\theta = 65.0°$. Solving the second of Eqs. (2.8) for F, we have

$$F = \frac{F_y}{\sin \theta} = \frac{1500 \text{ lb}}{\sin 65.0°} = 1655 \text{ lb}$$

The last calculation is facilitated if the value of F_y is stored when originally entered; it may then be recalled to be divided by $\sin \theta$. ■

Fig. 2.24

†It is assumed that the calculator used has keys for the computation of trigonometric and inverse trigonometric functions. Some calculators also have keys for the direct conversion of rectangular coordinates into polar coordinates, and vice versa. Such calculators eliminate the need for the computation of trigonometric functions in Examples 1, 2, and 3 and in problems of the same type.

(a)

(b)

(c)

(d)

Fig. 2.25

2.8 ADDITION OF FORCES BY SUMMING X AND Y COMPONENTS

It was seen in Sec. 2.2 that forces should be added according to the parallelogram law. From this law, two other methods, more readily applicable to the *graphical* solution of problems, were derived in Secs. 2.4 and 2.5: the triangle rule for the addition of two forces and the polygon rule for the addition of three or more forces. It was also seen that the force triangle used to define the resultant of two forces could be used to obtain a *trigonometric* solution.

When three or more forces are to be added, no practical trigonometric solution can be obtained from the force polygon which defines the resultant of the forces. In this case, an *analytic* solution of the problem can be obtained by resolving each force into two rectangular components. Consider, for instance, three forces **P**, **Q**, and **S** acting on a particle A (Fig. 2.25a). Their resultant **R** is defined by the relation

$$\mathbf{R} = \mathbf{P} + \mathbf{Q} + \mathbf{S} \tag{2.11}$$

Resolving each force into its rectangular components, we write

$$R_x\mathbf{i} + R_y\mathbf{j} = P_x\mathbf{i} + P_y\mathbf{j} + Q_x\mathbf{i} + Q_y\mathbf{j} + S_x\mathbf{i} + S_y\mathbf{j}$$
$$= (P_x + Q_x + S_x)\mathbf{i} + (P_y + Q_y + S_y)\mathbf{j}$$

from which it follows that

$$R_x = P_x + Q_x + S_x \qquad R_y = P_y + Q_y + S_y \tag{2.12}$$

or, for short,

$$R_x = \Sigma F_x \qquad R_y = \Sigma F_y \tag{2.13}$$

We thus conclude that *the scalar components R_x and R_y of the resultant **R** of several forces acting on a particle are obtained by adding algebraically the corresponding scalar components of the given forces.*[†]

In practice, the determination of the resultant **R** is carried out in three steps as illustrated in Fig. 2.25. First the given forces shown in Fig. 2.25a are resolved into their x and y components (Fig. 2.25b). Adding these components, we obtain the x and y components of **R** (Fig. 2.25c). Finally, the resultant $\mathbf{R} = R_x\mathbf{i} + R_y\mathbf{j}$ is determined by applying the parallelogram law (Fig. 2.25d). The procedure just described will be carried out most efficiently if the computations are arranged in a table. While it is the only practical analytic method for adding three or more forces, it is also often preferred to the trigonometric solution in the case of the addition of two forces.

[†]Clearly, this result also applies to the addition of other vector quantities, such as velocities, accelerations, or momenta.

SAMPLE PROBLEM 2.3

Four forces act on bolt A as shown. Determine the resultant of the forces on the bolt.

SOLUTION

The x and y components of each force are determined by trigonometry as shown and are entered in the table below. According to the convention adopted in Sec. 2.7, the scalar number representing a force component is positive if the force component has the same sense as the corresponding coordinate axis. Thus, x components acting to the right and y components acting upward are represented by positive numbers.

Force	Magnitude, N	x Component, N	y Component, N
F_1	150	+129.9	+75.0
F_2	80	−27.4	+75.2
F_3	110	0	−110.0
F_4	100	+96.6	−25.9
		$R_x = +199.1$	$R_y = +14.3$

Thus, the resultant $\mathbf{R}$ of the four forces is

$$\mathbf{R} = R_x\mathbf{i} + R_y\mathbf{j} \qquad \mathbf{R} = (199.1 \text{ N})\mathbf{i} + (14.3 \text{ N})\mathbf{j} \ \blacktriangleleft$$

The magnitude and direction of the resultant may now be determined. From the triangle shown, we have

$$\tan \alpha = \frac{R_y}{R_x} = \frac{14.3 \text{ N}}{199.1 \text{ N}} \qquad \alpha = 4.1°$$

$$R = \frac{14.3 \text{ N}}{\sin \alpha} = 199.6 \text{ N} \qquad \mathbf{R} = 199.6 \text{ N} \measuredangle 4.1° \ \blacktriangleleft$$

With a calculator, the last computation may be facilitated if the value of R_y is stored when originally entered; it may then be recalled to be divided by $\sin \alpha$. (Also see the footnote on p. 29.)

SOLVING PROBLEMS ON YOUR OWN

You saw in the preceding lesson that the resultant of two forces may be determined either graphically or from the trigonometry of an oblique triangle.

A. When three or more forces are involved, the determination of their resultant **R** is best carried out by first resolving each force into *rectangular components*. Two cases may be encountered, depending upon the way in which each of the given forces is defined:

Case 1. The force F is defined by its magnitude F and the angle α it forms with the x axis. The x and y components of the force can be obtained by multiplying F by $\cos \alpha$ and $\sin \alpha$, respectively [Example 1].

Case 2. The force F is defined by its magnitude F and the coordinates of two points A and B on its line of action (Fig. 2.23). The angle α that **F** forms with the x axis may first be determined by trigonometry. However, the components of **F** may also be obtained directly from proportions among the various dimensions involved, without actually determining α [Example 2].

B. Rectangular components of the resultant. The components R_x and R_y of the resultant can be obtained by adding algebraically the corresponding components of the given forces [Sample Prob. 2.3].

You can express the resultant in *vectorial form* using the unit vectors **i** and **j**, which are directed along the x and y axes, respectively:

$$\mathbf{R} = R_x\mathbf{i} + R_y\mathbf{j}$$

Alternatively, you can determine the *magnitude and direction* of the resultant by solving the right triangle of sides R_x and R_y for R and for the angle that **R** forms with the x axis.

PROBLEMS

2.21 and 2.22   Determine the x and y components of each of the forces shown.

Fig. P2.21

Fig. P2.22

2.23 and 2.24   Determine the x and y components of each of the forces shown.

Fig. P2.23

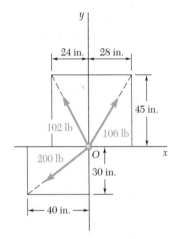

Fig. P2.24

2.25   The hydraulic cylinder BD exerts on member ABC a force $\mathbf{P}$ directed along line BD. Knowing that $\mathbf{P}$ must have a 750-N component perpendicular to member ABC, determine (*a*) the magnitude of the force $\mathbf{P}$, (*b*) its component parallel to ABC.

Fig. P2.25

2.26 Cable *AC* exerts on beam *AB* a force **P** directed along line *AC*. Knowing that **P** must have a 350-lb vertical component, determine (*a*) the magnitude of the force **P**, (*b*) its horizontal component.

Fig. P2.26

2.27 Member *BC* exerts on member *AC* a force **P** directed along line *BC*. Knowing that **P** must have a 325-N horizontal component, determine (*a*) the magnitude of the force **P**, (*b*) its vertical component.

2.28 Member *BD* exerts on member *ABC* a force **P** directed along line *BD*. Knowing that **P** must have a 240-lb vertical component, determine (*a*) the magnitude of the force **P**, (*b*) its horizontal component.

Fig. P2.27

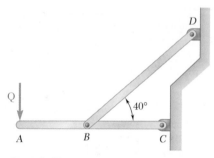

Fig. P2.28

2.29 The guy wire *BD* exerts on the telephone pole *AC* a force **P** directed along *BD*. Knowing that **P** must have a 720-N component perpendicular to the pole *AC*, determine (*a*) the magnitude of the force **P**, (*b*) its component along line *AC*.

2.30 The hydraulic cylinder *BC* exerts on member *AB* a force **P** directed along line *BC*. Knowing that **P** must have a 600-N component perpendicular to member *AB*, determine (*a*) the magnitude of the force **P**, (*b*) its component along line *AB*.

2.31 Determine the resultant of the three forces of Prob. 2.23.

2.32 Determine the resultant of the three forces of Prob. 2.21.

2.33 Determine the resultant of the three forces of Prob. 2.22.

2.34 Determine the resultant of the three forces of Prob. 2.24.

Fig. P2.29

Fig. P2.30

2.35 Knowing that $\alpha = 35°$, determine the resultant of the three forces shown.

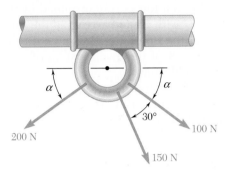

Fig. P2.35

2.36 Knowing that the tension in rope AC is 365 N, determine the resultant of the three forces exerted at point C of post BC.

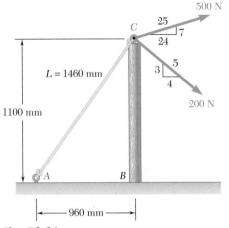

Fig. P2.36

2.37 Knowing that $\alpha = 40°$, determine the resultant of the three forces shown.

2.38 Knowing that $\alpha = 75°$, determine the resultant of the three forces shown.

2.39 For the collar of Prob. 2.35, determine (a) the required value of α if the resultant of the three forces shown is to be vertical, (b) the corresponding magnitude of the resultant.

2.40 For the post of Prob. 2.36, determine (a) the required tension in rope AC if the resultant of the three forces exerted at point C is to be horizontal, (b) the corresponding magnitude of the resultant.

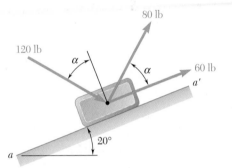

Fig. P2.37 and P2.38

2.41 A hoist trolley is subjected to the three forces shown. Knowing that $\alpha = 40°$, determine (a) the required magnitude of the force **P** if the resultant of the three forces is to be vertical, (b) the corresponding magnitude of the resultant.

2.42 A hoist trolley is subjected to the three forces shown. Knowing that $P = 250$ lb, determine (a) the required value of α if the resultant of the three forces is to be vertical, (b) the corresponding magnitude of the resultant.

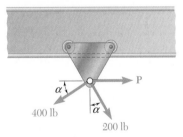

Fig. P2.41 and P2.42

2.9 EQUILIBRIUM OF A PARTICLE

In the preceding sections, we discussed the methods for determining the resultant of several forces acting on a particle. Although it has not occurred in any of the problems considered so far, it is quite possible for the resultant to be zero. In such a case, the net effect of the given forces is zero, and the particle is said to be in equilibrium. We thus have the following definition: *When the resultant of all the forces acting on a particle is zero, the particle is in equilibrium.*

A particle which is acted upon by two forces will be in equilibrium if the two forces have the same magnitude and the same line of action but opposite sense. The resultant of the two forces is then zero. Such a case is shown in Fig. 2.26.

Fig. 2.26

Another case of equilibrium of a particle is represented in Fig. 2.27, where four forces are shown acting on A. In Fig. 2.28, the resultant of the given forces is determined by the polygon rule. Starting from point O with $\mathbf{F}_1$ and arranging the forces in tip-to-tail fashion, we find that the tip of $\mathbf{F}_4$ coincides with the starting point O. Thus the resultant $\mathbf{R}$ of the given system of forces is zero, and the particle is in equilibrium.

The closed polygon drawn in Fig. 2.28 provides a *graphical* expression of the equilibrium of A. To express *algebraically* the conditions for the equilibrium of a particle, we write

$$\mathbf{R} = \Sigma\mathbf{F} = 0 \tag{2.14}$$

Fig. 2.27

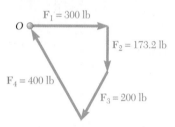

Resolving each force $\mathbf{F}$ into rectangular components, we have

$$\Sigma(F_x\mathbf{i} + F_y\mathbf{j}) = 0 \qquad \text{or} \qquad (\Sigma F_x)\mathbf{i} + (\Sigma F_y)\mathbf{j} = 0$$

We conclude that the necessary and sufficient conditions for the equilibrium of a particle are

$$\Sigma F_x = 0 \qquad \Sigma F_y = 0 \tag{2.15}$$

Fig. 2.28

Returning to the particle shown in Fig. 2.27, we check that the equilibrium conditions are satisfied. We write

$$\begin{aligned}
\Sigma F_x &= 300 \text{ lb} - (200 \text{ lb}) \sin 30° - (400 \text{ lb}) \sin 30° \\
&= 300 \text{ lb} - 100 \text{ lb} - 200 \text{ lb} = 0 \\
\Sigma F_y &= -173.2 \text{ lb} - (200 \text{ lb}) \cos 30° + (400 \text{ lb}) \cos 30° \\
&= -173.2 \text{ lb} - 173.2 \text{ lb} + 346.4 \text{ lb} = 0
\end{aligned}$$

2.10   NEWTON'S FIRST LAW OF MOTION

In the latter part of the seventeenth century, Sir Isaac Newton formulated three fundamental laws upon which the science of mechanics is based. The first of these laws can be stated as follows:

If the resultant force acting on a particle is zero, the particle will remain at rest (if originally at rest) or will move with constant speed in a straight line (if originally in motion).

From this law and from the definition of equilibrium given in Sec. 2.9, it is seen that a particle in equilibrium either is at rest or is moving in a straight line with constant speed. In the following section, various problems concerning the equilibrium of a particle will be considered.

2.11   PROBLEMS INVOLVING THE EQUILIBRIUM OF A PARTICLE. FREE-BODY DIAGRAMS

In practice, a problem in engineering mechanics is derived from an actual physical situation. A sketch showing the physical conditions of the problem is known as a *space diagram*.

The methods of analysis discussed in the preceding sections apply to a system of forces acting on a particle. A large number of problems involving actual structures, however, can be reduced to problems concerning the equilibrium of a particle. This is done by choosing a significant particle and drawing a separate diagram showing this particle and all the forces acting on it. Such a diagram is called a *free-body diagram.*

As an example, consider the 75-kg crate shown in the space diagram of Fig. 2.29a. This crate was lying between two buildings, and it is now being lifted onto a truck, which will remove it. The crate is supported by a vertical cable, which is joined at A to two ropes which pass over pulleys attached to the buildings at B and C. It is desired to determine the tension in each of the ropes AB and AC.

In order to solve this problem, a free-body diagram showing a particle in equilibrium must be drawn. Since we are interested in the rope tensions, the free-body diagram should include at least one of these tensions or, if possible, both tensions. Point A is seen to be a good free body for this problem. The free-body diagram of point A is shown in Fig. 2.29b. It shows point A and the forces exerted on A by the vertical cable and the two ropes. The force exerted by the cable is directed downward, and its magnitude is equal to the weight W of the crate. Recalling Eq. (1.4), we write

$$W = mg = (75 \text{ kg})(9.81 \text{ m/s}^2) = 736 \text{ N}$$

and indicate this value in the free-body diagram. The forces exerted by the two ropes are not known. Since they are respectively equal in magnitude to the tensions in rope AB and rope AC, we denote them by $\mathbf{T}_{AB}$ and $\mathbf{T}_{AC}$ and draw them away from A in the directions shown in the space diagram. No other detail is included in the free-body diagram.

Since point A is in equilibrium, the three forces acting on it must form a closed triangle when drawn in tip-to-tail fashion. This *force triangle* has been drawn in Fig. 2.29c. The values T_{AB} and T_{AC} of the tension in the ropes may be found graphically if the triangle is drawn to scale, or they may be found by trigonometry. If the latter method of solution is chosen, we use the law of sines and write

$$\frac{T_{AB}}{\sin 60°} = \frac{T_{AC}}{\sin 40°} = \frac{736 \text{ N}}{\sin 80°}$$
$$T_{AB} = 647 \text{ N} \qquad T_{AC} = 480 \text{ N}$$

When a particle is in *equilibrium under three forces,* the problem can be solved by drawing a force triangle. When a particle is in *equilibrium under more than three forces,* the problem can be solved graphically by drawing a force polygon. If an analytic solution is desired, the *equations of equilibrium* given in Sec. 2.9 should be solved:

$$\Sigma F_x = 0 \qquad \Sigma F_y = 0 \qquad (2.15)$$

These equations can be solved for no more than *two unknowns;* similarly, the force triangle used in the case of equilibrium under three forces can be solved for two unknowns.

The more common types of problems are those in which the two unknowns represent (1) the two components (or the magnitude and direction) of a single force, (2) the magnitudes of two forces, each of known direction. Problems involving the determination of the maximum or minimum value of the magnitude of a force are also encountered (see Probs. 2.57 through 2.62).

(a) Space diagram

(b) Free-body diagram   (c) Force triangle

Fig. 2.29

Photo 2.1 As illustrated in the above example, it is possible to determine the tensions in the cables supporting the shaft shown by treating the hook as a particle and then applying the equations of equilibrium to the forces acting on the hook.

SAMPLE PROBLEM 2.4

In a ship-unloading operation, a 3500-lb automobile is supported by a cable. A rope is tied to the cable at A and pulled in order to center the automobile over its intended position. The angle between the cable and the vertical is 2°, while the angle between the rope and the horizontal is 30°. What is the tension in the rope?

SOLUTION

Free-Body Diagram. Point A is chosen as a free body, and the complete free-body diagram is drawn. T_{AB} is the tension in the cable AB, and T_{AC} is the tension in the rope.

Equilibrium Condition. Since only three forces act on the free body, we draw a force triangle to express that it is in equilibrium. Using the law of sines, we write

$$\frac{T_{AB}}{\sin 120°} = \frac{T_{AC}}{\sin 2°} = \frac{3500 \text{ lb}}{\sin 58°}$$

With a calculator, we first compute and store the value of the last quotient. Multiplying this value successively by $\sin 120°$ and $\sin 2°$, we obtain

$$T_{AB} = 3570 \text{ lb} \qquad T_{AC} = 144 \text{ lb} \quad \blacktriangleleft$$

SAMPLE PROBLEM 2.5

Determine the magnitude and direction of the smallest force $\mathbf{F}$ which will maintain the package shown in equilibrium. Note that the force exerted by the rollers on the package is perpendicular to the incline.

SOLUTION

Free-Body Diagram. We choose the package as a free body, assuming that it can be treated as a particle. We draw the corresponding free-body diagram.

Equilibrium Condition. Since only three forces act on the free body, we draw a force triangle to express that it is in equilibrium. Line 1-$1'$ represents the known direction of $\mathbf{P}$. In order to obtain the minimum value of the force $\mathbf{F}$, we choose the direction of $\mathbf{F}$ perpendicular to that of $\mathbf{P}$. From the geometry of the triangle obtained, we find

$$F = (294 \text{ N}) \sin 15° = 76.1 \text{ N} \qquad \alpha = 15°$$
$$\mathbf{F} = 76.1 \text{ N} \;\measuredangle 15° \quad \blacktriangleleft$$

SAMPLE PROBLEM 2.6

As part of the design of a new sailboat, it is desired to determine the drag force which may be expected at a given speed. To do so, a model of the proposed hull is placed in a test channel and three cables are used to keep its bow on the centerline of the channel. Dynamometer readings indicate that for a given speed, the tension is 40 lb in cable AB and 60 lb in cable AE. Determine the drag force exerted on the hull and the tension in cable AC.

SOLUTION

Determination of the Angles. First, the angles α and β defining the direction of cables AB and AC are determined. We write

$$\tan \alpha = \frac{7 \text{ ft}}{4 \text{ ft}} = 1.75 \qquad \tan \beta = \frac{1.5 \text{ ft}}{4 \text{ ft}} = 0.375$$
$$\alpha = 60.26° \qquad\qquad \beta = 20.56°$$

Free-Body Diagram. Choosing the hull as a free body, we draw the free-body diagram shown. It includes the forces exerted by the three cables on the hull, as well as the drag force $\mathbf{F}_D$ exerted by the flow.

Equilibrium Condition. We express that the hull is in equilibrium by writing that the resultant of all forces is zero:

$$\mathbf{R} = \mathbf{T}_{AB} + \mathbf{T}_{AC} + \mathbf{T}_{AE} + \mathbf{F}_D = 0 \qquad (1)$$

Since more than three forces are involved, we resolve the forces into x and y components:

$$\mathbf{T}_{AB} = -(40 \text{ lb}) \sin 60.26°\mathbf{i} + (40 \text{ lb}) \cos 60.26°\mathbf{j}$$
$$= -(34.73 \text{ lb})\mathbf{i} + (19.84 \text{ lb})\mathbf{j}$$
$$\mathbf{T}_{AC} = T_{AC} \sin 20.56°\mathbf{i} + T_{AC} \cos 20.56°\mathbf{j}$$
$$= 0.3512T_{AC}\mathbf{i} + 0.9363T_{AC}\mathbf{j}$$
$$\mathbf{T}_{AE} = -(60 \text{ lb})\mathbf{j}$$
$$\mathbf{F}_D = F_D\mathbf{i}$$

Substituting the expressions obtained into Eq. (1) and factoring the unit vectors $\mathbf{i}$ and $\mathbf{j}$, we have

$$(-34.73 \text{ lb} + 0.3512T_{AC} + F_D)\mathbf{i} + (19.84 \text{ lb} + 0.9363T_{AC} - 60 \text{ lb})\mathbf{j} = 0$$

This equation will be satisfied if, and only if, the coefficients of $\mathbf{i}$ and $\mathbf{j}$ are equal to zero. We thus obtain the following two equilibrium equations, which express, respectively, that the sum of the x components and the sum of the y components of the given forces must be zero.

$$(\Sigma F_x = 0:) \qquad -34.73 \text{ lb} + 0.3512T_{AC} + F_D = 0 \qquad (2)$$
$$(\Sigma F_y = 0:) \qquad 19.84 \text{ lb} + 0.9363T_{AC} - 60 \text{ lb} = 0 \qquad (3)$$

From Eq. (3) we find $\qquad\qquad\qquad\qquad\qquad T_{AC} = +42.9 \text{ lb}$ ◄
and, substituting this value into Eq. (2), $\qquad\qquad\qquad F_D = +19.66 \text{ lb}$ ◄

In drawing the free-body diagram, we assumed a sense for each unknown force. A positive sign in the answer indicates that the assumed sense is correct. The complete force polygon may be drawn to check the results.

SOLVING PROBLEMS
ON YOUR OWN

When a particle is in *equilibrium*, the resultant of the forces acting on the particle must be zero. Expressing this fact in the case of a particle under *coplanar forces* will provide you with two relations among these forces. As you saw in the preceding sample problems, these relations may be used to determine two unknowns—such as the magnitude and direction of one force or the magnitudes of two forces.

Drawing a free-body diagram is the first step in the solution of a problem involving the equilibrium of a particle. This diagram shows the particle and all the forces acting on it. Indicate in your free-body diagram the magnitudes of known forces, as well as any angle or dimensions that define the direction of a force. Any unknown magnitude or angle should be denoted by an appropriate symbol. Nothing else should be included in the free-body diagram.

Drawing a clear and accurate free-body diagram is a must in the solution of any equilibrium problem. Skipping this step might save you pencil and paper, but is very likely to lead you to a wrong solution.

Case 1. If only three forces are involved in the free-body diagram, the rest of the solution is best carried out by drawing these forces in tip-to-tail fashion to form a *force triangle*. This triangle can be solved graphically or by trigonometry for no more than two unknowns [Sample Probs. 2.4 and 2.5].

Case 2. If more than three forces are involved, it is to your advantage to use an *analytic solution*. You select x and y axes and resolve each of the forces shown in the free-body diagram into x and y components. Expressing that the sum of the x components and the sum of the y components of all the forces are both zero, you will obtain two equations which you can solve for no more than two unknowns [Sample Prob. 2.6].

It is strongly recommended that when using an analytic solution the equations of equilibrium be written in the same form as Eqs. (2) and (3) of Sample Prob. 2.6. The practice adopted by some students of initially placing the unknowns on the left side of the equation and the known quantities on the right side may lead to confusion in assigning the appropriate sign to each term.

We have noted that regardless of the method used to solve a two-dimensional equilibrium problem we can determine at most two unknowns. If a two-dimensional problem involves more than two unknowns, one or more additional relations must be obtained from the information contained in the statement of the problem.

PROBLEMS

FREE BODY PRACTICE PROBLEMS

2.F1 Two cables are tied together at C and loaded as shown. Draw the free-body diagram needed to determine the tension in AC and BC.

2.F2 A chairlift has been stopped in the position shown. Knowing that each chair weighs 250 N and that the skier in chair E weighs 765 N, draw the free-body diagrams needed to determine the weight of the skier in chair F.

Fig. P2.F1

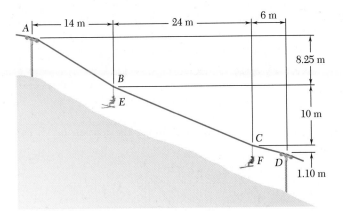

Fig. P2.F2

2.F3 Two cables are tied together at A and loaded as shown. Draw the free-body diagram needed to determine the tension in each cable.

2.F4 The 60-lb collar A can slide on a frictionless vertical rod and is connected as shown to a 65-lb counterweight C. Draw the free-body diagram needed to determine the value of h for which the system is in equilibrium.

Fig. P2.F3

Fig. P2.F4

END-OF-SECTION PROBLEMS

2.43 and 2.44 Two cables are tied together at C and are loaded as shown. Determine the tension (a) in cable AC, (b) in cable BC.

Fig. P2.43

Fig. P2.44

2.45 Knowing that $\alpha = 20°$, determine the tension (a) in cable AC, (b) in rope BC.

Fig. P2.45

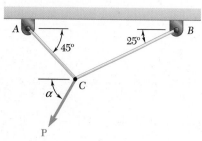

Fig. P2.46

2.46 Knowing that $\alpha = 55°$ and that boom AC exerts on pin C a force directed along line AC, determine (a) the magnitude of that force, (b) the tension in cable BC.

2.47 Two cables are tied together at C and loaded as shown. Determine the tension (a) in cable AC, (b) in cable BC.

Fig. P2.47

2.48 Two cables are tied together at C and are loaded as shown. Knowing that $\mathbf{P} = 500$ N and $\alpha = 60°$, determine the tension (a) in cable AC, (b) in cable BC.

Fig. P2.48

2.49 Two forces of magnitude $T_A = 8$ kips and $T_B = 15$ kips are applied as shown to a welded connection. Knowing that the connection is in equilibrium, determine the magnitudes of the forces T_C and T_D.

2.50 Two forces of magnitude $T_A = 6$ kips and $T_C = 9$ kips are applied as shown to a welded connection. Knowing that the connection is in equilibrium, determine the magnitudes of the forces T_B and T_D.

2.51 Two cables are tied together at C and loaded as shown. Knowing that $P = 360$ N, determine the tension (a) in cable AC, (b) in cable BC.

2.52 Two cables are tied together at C and loaded as shown. Determine the range of values of P for which both cables remain taut.

2.53 A sailor is being rescued using a boatswain's chair that is suspended from a pulley that can roll freely on the support cable ACB and is pulled at a constant speed by cable CD. Knowing that $\alpha = 30°$ and $\beta = 10°$ and that the combined weight of the boatswain's chair and the sailor is 900 N, determine the tension (a) in the support cable ACB, (b) in the traction cable CD.

Fig. P2.49 and P2.50

Fig. P2.51 and P2.52

Fig. P2.53 and P2.54

2.54 A sailor is being rescued using a boatswain's chair that is suspended from a pulley that can roll freely on the support cable ACB and is pulled at a constant speed by cable CD. Knowing that $\alpha = 25°$ and $\beta = 15°$ and that the tension in cable CD is 80 N, determine (a) the combined weight of the boatswain's chair and the sailor, (b) the tension in the support cable ACB.

2.55 Two forces $\mathbf{P}$ and $\mathbf{Q}$ are applied as shown to an aircraft connection. Knowing that the connection is in equilibrium and that $P = 500$ lb and $Q = 650$ lb, determine the magnitudes of the forces exerted on the rods A and B.

2.56 Two forces $\mathbf{P}$ and $\mathbf{Q}$ are applied as shown to an aircraft connection. Knowing that the connection is in equilibrium and that the magnitudes of the forces exerted on rods A and B are $F_A = 750$ lb and $F_B = 400$ lb, determine the magnitudes of $\mathbf{P}$ and $\mathbf{Q}$.

Fig. P2.55 and P2.56

Fig. P2.57 and P2.58

Fig. P2.62

2.57 Two cables tied together at C are loaded as shown. Knowing that the maximum allowable tension in each cable is 800 N, determine (a) the magnitude of the largest force **P** that can be applied at C, (b) the corresponding value of α.

2.58 Two cables tied together at C are loaded as shown. Knowing that the maximum allowable tension is 1200 N in cable AC and 600 N in cable BC, determine (a) the magnitude of the largest force **P** that can be applied at C, (b) the corresponding value of α.

2.59 For the situation described in Fig. P2.45, determine (a) the value of α for which the tension in rope BC is as small as possible, (b) the corresponding value of the tension.

2.60 For the structure and loading of Prob. 2.46, determine (a) the value of α for which the tension in cable BC is as small as possible, (b) the corresponding value of the tension.

2.61 For the cables of Prob. 2.48, it is known that the maximum allowable tension is 600 N in cable AC and 750 N in cable BC. Determine (a) the maximum force **P** that can be applied at C, (b) the corresponding value of α.

2.62 A movable bin and its contents have a combined weight of 2.8 kN. Determine the shortest chain sling ACB that can be used to lift the loaded bin if the tension in the chain is not to exceed 5 kN.

2.63 Collar A is connected as shown to a 50-lb load and can slide on a frictionless horizontal rod. Determine the magnitude of the force **P** required to maintain the equilibrium of the collar when (a) $x = 4.5$ in., (b) $x = 15$ in.

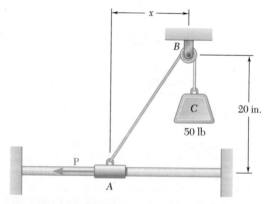

Fig. P2.63 and P2.64

2.64 Collar A is connected as shown to a 50-lb load and can slide on a frictionless horizontal rod. Determine the distance x for which the collar is in equilibrium when $P = 48$ lb.

2.65 Three forces are applied to a bracket as shown. The directions of the two 150-N forces may vary, but the angle between these forces is always 50°. Determine the range of values of α for which the magnitude of the resultant of the forces acting at A is less than 600 N.

Fig. P2.65

2.66 A 200-kg crate is to be supported by the rope-and-pulley arrangement shown. Determine the magnitude and direction of the force **P** that must be exerted on the free end of the rope to maintain equilibrium. (*Hint:* The tension in the rope is the same on each side of a simple pulley. This can be proved by the methods of Chap. 4.)

Fig. P2.66

2.67 A 600-lb crate is supported by several rope-and-pulley arrangements as shown. Determine for each arrangement the tension in the rope. (See the hint for Prob. 2.66.)

(a) (b) (c) (d) (e)

Fig. P2.67

2.68 Solve parts *b* and *d* of Prob. 2.67, assuming that the free end of the rope is attached to the crate.

2.69 A load **Q** is applied to the pulley *C*, which can roll on the cable *ACB*. The pulley is held in the position shown by a second cable *CAD*, which passes over the pulley *A* and supports a load **P**. Knowing that *P* = 750 N, determine (*a*) the tension in cable *ACB*, (*b*) the magnitude of load **Q**.

2.70 An 1800-N load **Q** is applied to the pulley *C*, which can roll on the cable *ACB*. The pulley is held in the position shown by a second cable *CAD*, which passes over the pulley *A* and supports a load **P**. Determine (*a*) the tension in cable *ACB*, (*b*) the magnitude of load **P**.

Fig. P2.69 and P2.70

(a)

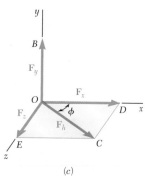

(b)

(c)

Fig. 2.30

2.12 RECTANGULAR COMPONENTS OF A FORCE IN SPACE

The problems considered in the first part of this chapter involved only two dimensions; they could be formulated and solved in a single plane. In this section and in the remaining sections of the chapter, we will discuss problems involving the three dimensions of space.

Consider a force **F** acting at the origin O of the system of rectangular coordinates x, y, z. To define the direction of **F**, we draw the vertical plane $OBAC$ containing **F** (Fig. 2.30a). This plane passes through the vertical y axis; its orientation is defined by the angle ϕ it forms with the xy plane. The direction of **F** within the plane is defined by the angle θ_y that **F** forms with the y axis. The force **F** may be resolved into a vertical component $\mathbf{F}_y$ and a horizontal component $\mathbf{F}_h$; this operation, shown in Fig. 2.30b, is carried out in plane $OBAC$ according to the rules developed in the first part of the chapter. The corresponding scalar components are

$$F_y = F \cos \theta_y \qquad F_h = F \sin \theta_y \qquad (2.16)$$

But $\mathbf{F}_h$ may be resolved into two rectangular components $\mathbf{F}_x$ and $\mathbf{F}_z$ along the x and z axes, respectively. This operation, shown in Fig. 2.30c, is carried out in the xz plane. We obtain the following expressions for the corresponding scalar components:

$$F_x = F_h \cos \phi = F \sin \theta_y \cos \phi$$
$$F_z = F_h \sin \phi = F \sin \theta_y \sin \phi \qquad (2.17)$$

The given force **F** has thus been resolved into three rectangular vector components $\mathbf{F}_x$, $\mathbf{F}_y$, $\mathbf{F}_z$, which are directed along the three coordinate axes.

Applying the Pythagorean theorem to the triangles OAB and OCD of Fig. 2.30, we write

$$F^2 = (OA)^2 = (OB)^2 + (BA)^2 = F_y^2 + F_h^2$$
$$F_h^2 = (OC)^2 = (OD)^2 + (DC)^2 = F_x^2 + F_z^2$$

Eliminating F_h^2 from these two equations and solving for F, we obtain the following relation between the magnitude of **F** and its rectangular scalar components:

$$F = \sqrt{F_x^2 + F_y^2 + F_z^2} \qquad (2.18)$$

The relationship existing between the force **F** and its three components $\mathbf{F}_x$, $\mathbf{F}_y$, $\mathbf{F}_z$ is more easily visualized if a "box" having $\mathbf{F}_x$, $\mathbf{F}_y$, $\mathbf{F}_z$ for edges is drawn as shown in Fig. 2.31. The force **F** is then represented by the diagonal OA of this box. Figure 2.31b shows the right triangle OAB used to derive the first of the formulas (2.16): $F_y = F \cos \theta_y$. In Fig. 2.31a and c, two other right triangles have also been drawn: OAD and OAE. These triangles are seen to occupy in the box positions comparable with that of triangle OAB. Denoting by θ_x and θ_z, respectively, the angles that **F** forms

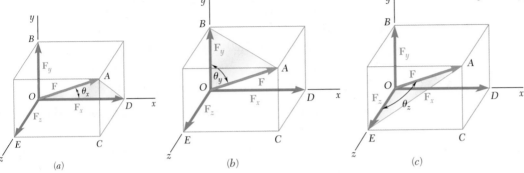

Fig. 2.31

with the x and z axes, we can derive two formulas similar to $F_y = F \cos \theta_y$. We thus write

$$F_x = F \cos \theta_x \qquad F_y = F \cos \theta_y \qquad F_z = F \cos \theta_z \qquad (2.19)$$

The three angles θ_x, θ_y, θ_z define the direction of the force **F**; they are more commonly used for this purpose than the angles θ_y and ϕ introduced at the beginning of this section. The cosines of θ_x, θ_y, θ_z are known as the *direction cosines* of the force **F**.

Introducing the unit vectors **i**, **j**, and **k**, directed respectively along the x, y, and z axes (Fig. 2.32), we can express **F** in the form

$$\mathbf{F} = F_x\mathbf{i} + F_y\mathbf{j} + F_z\mathbf{k} \qquad (2.20)$$

where the scalar components F_x, F_y, F_z are defined by the relations (2.19).

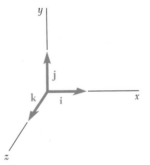

Fig. 2.32

EXAMPLE 1. A force of 500 N forms angles of 60°, 45°, and 120°, respectively, with the x, y, and z axes. Find the components F_x, F_y, and F_z of the force.

Substituting $F = 500$ N, $\theta_x = 60°$, $\theta_y = 45°$, $\theta_z = 120°$ into formulas (2.19), we write

$$F_x = (500 \text{ N}) \cos 60° = +250 \text{ N}$$
$$F_y = (500 \text{ N}) \cos 45° = +354 \text{ N}$$
$$F_z = (500 \text{ N}) \cos 120° = -250 \text{ N}$$

Carrying into Eq. (2.20) the values obtained for the scalar components of **F**, we have

$$\mathbf{F} = (250 \text{ N})\mathbf{i} + (354 \text{ N})\mathbf{j} - (250 \text{ N})\mathbf{k}$$

As in the case of two-dimensional problems, a plus sign indicates that the component has the same sense as the corresponding axis, and a minus sign indicates that it has the opposite sense. ■

The angle a force **F** forms with an axis should be measured from the positive side of the axis and will always be between 0 and 180°. An angle θ_x smaller than 90° (acute) indicates that **F** (assumed attached to O) is on the same side of the yz plane as the positive x axis; cos θ_x and F_x will then be positive. An angle θ_x larger than 90° (obtuse) indicates

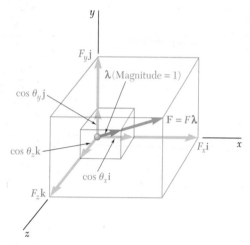

Fig. 2.33

that **F** is on the other side of the yz plane; $\cos \theta_x$ and F_x will then be negative. In Example 1 the angles θ_x and θ_y are acute, while θ_z is obtuse; consequently, F_x and F_y are positive, while F_z is negative.

Substituting into (2.20) the expressions obtained for F_x, F_y, F_z in (2.19), we write

$$\mathbf{F} = F(\cos \theta_x \mathbf{i} + \cos \theta_y \mathbf{j} + \cos \theta_z \mathbf{k}) \tag{2.21}$$

which shows that the force **F** can be expressed as the product of the scalar F and the vector

$$\boldsymbol{\lambda} = \cos \theta_x \mathbf{i} + \cos \theta_y \mathbf{j} + \cos \theta_z \mathbf{k} \tag{2.22}$$

Clearly, the vector $\boldsymbol{\lambda}$ is a vector whose magnitude is equal to 1 and whose direction is the same as that of **F** (Fig. 2.33). The vector $\boldsymbol{\lambda}$ is referred to as the *unit vector* along the line of action of **F**. It follows from (2.22) that the components of the unit vector $\boldsymbol{\lambda}$ are respectively equal to the direction cosines of the line of action of **F**:

$$\lambda_x = \cos \theta_x \qquad \lambda_y = \cos \theta_y \qquad \lambda_z = \cos \theta_z \tag{2.23}$$

We should observe that the values of the three angles θ_x, θ_y, θ_z are not independent. Recalling that the sum of the squares of the components of a vector is equal to the square of its magnitude, we write

$$\lambda_x^2 + \lambda_y^2 + \lambda_z^2 = 1$$

or, substituting for λ_x, λ_y, λ_z from (2.23),

$$\cos^2 \theta_x + \cos^2 \theta_y + \cos^2 \theta_z = 1 \tag{2.24}$$

In Example 1, for instance, once the values $\theta_x = 60°$ and $\theta_y = 45°$ have been selected, the value of θ_z *must* be equal to $60°$ or $120°$ in order to satisfy identity (2.24).

When the components F_x, F_y, F_z of a force **F** are given, the magnitude F of the force is obtained from (2.18).† The relations (2.19) can then be solved for the direction cosines,

$$\cos \theta_x = \frac{F_x}{F} \qquad \cos \theta_y = \frac{F_y}{F} \qquad \cos \theta_z = \frac{F_z}{F} \tag{2.25}$$

and the angles θ_x, θ_y, θ_z characterizing the direction of **F** can be found.

EXAMPLE 2. A force **F** has the components $F_x = 20$ lb, $F_y = -30$ lb, $F_z = 60$ lb. Determine its magnitude F and the angles θ_x, θ_y, θ_z it forms with the coordinate axes.

From formula (2.18) we obtain†

$$F = \sqrt{F_x^2 + F_y^2 + F_z^2}$$
$$= \sqrt{(20 \text{ lb})^2 + (-30 \text{ lb})^2 + (60 \text{ lb})^2}$$
$$= \sqrt{4900} \text{ lb} = 70 \text{ lb}$$

---

†With a calculator programmed to convert rectangular coordinates into polar coordinates, the following procedure will be found more expeditious for computing F: First determine F_h from its two rectangular components F_x and F_z (Fig. 2.30c), then determine F from its two rectangular components F_h and F_y (Fig. 2.30b). The actual order in which the three components F_x, F_y, F_z are entered is immaterial.

Substituting the values of the components and magnitude of $\mathbf{F}$ into Eqs. (2.25), we write

$$\cos \theta_x = \frac{F_x}{F} = \frac{20 \text{ lb}}{70 \text{ lb}} \qquad \cos \theta_y = \frac{F_y}{F} = \frac{-30 \text{ lb}}{70 \text{ lb}} \qquad \cos \theta_z = \frac{F_z}{F} = \frac{60 \text{ lb}}{70 \text{ lb}}$$

Calculating successively each quotient and its arc cosine, we obtain

$$\theta_x = 73.4° \qquad \theta_y = 115.4° \qquad \theta_z = 31.0°$$

These computations can be carried out easily with a calculator. ∎

2.13 FORCE DEFINED BY ITS MAGNITUDE AND TWO POINTS ON ITS LINE OF ACTION

In many applications, the direction of a force $\mathbf{F}$ is defined by the coordinates of two points, $M(x_1, y_1, z_1)$ and $N(x_2, y_2, z_2)$, located on its line of action (Fig. 2.34). Consider the vector $\overrightarrow{MN}$ joining M and N

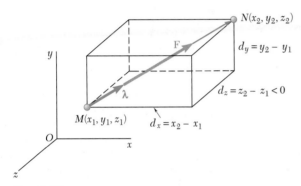

Fig. 2.34

and of the same sense as $\mathbf{F}$. Denoting its scalar components by d_x, d_y, d_z, respectively, we write

$$\overrightarrow{MN} = d_x\mathbf{i} + d_y\mathbf{j} + d_z\mathbf{k} \tag{2.26}$$

The unit vector $\boldsymbol{\lambda}$ along the line of action of $\mathbf{F}$ (i.e., along the line MN) may be obtained by dividing the vector $\overrightarrow{MN}$ by its magnitude MN. Substituting for $\overrightarrow{MN}$ from (2.26) and observing that MN is equal to the distance d from M to N, we write

$$\boldsymbol{\lambda} = \frac{\overrightarrow{MN}}{MN} = \frac{1}{d}(d_x\mathbf{i} + d_y\mathbf{j} + d_z\mathbf{k}) \tag{2.27}$$

Recalling that $\mathbf{F}$ is equal to the product of F and λ, we have

$$\mathbf{F} = F\boldsymbol{\lambda} = \frac{F}{d}(d_x\mathbf{i} + d_y\mathbf{j} + d_z\mathbf{k}) \tag{2.28}$$

from which it follows that the scalar components of $\mathbf{F}$ are, respectively,

$$F_x = \frac{Fd_x}{d} \qquad F_y = \frac{Fd_y}{d} \qquad F_z = \frac{Fd_z}{d} \tag{2.29}$$

The relations (2.29) considerably simplify the determination of the components of a force $\mathbf{F}$ of given magnitude F when the line of action of $\mathbf{F}$ is defined by two points M and N. Subtracting the coordinates of M from those of N, we first determine the components of the vector $\overrightarrow{MN}$ and the distance d from M to N:

$$d_x = x_2 - x_1 \qquad d_y = y_2 - y_1 \qquad d_z = z_2 - z_1$$
$$d = \sqrt{d_x^2 + d_y^2 + d_z^2}$$

Substituting for F and for d_x, d_y, d_z, and d into the relations (2.29), we obtain the components F_x, F_y, F_z of the force.

The angles θ_x, θ_y, θ_z that $\mathbf{F}$ forms with the coordinate axes can then be obtained from Eqs. (2.25). Comparing Eqs. (2.22) and (2.27), we can also write

$$\cos \theta_x = \frac{d_x}{d} \qquad \cos \theta_y = \frac{d_y}{d} \qquad \cos \theta_z = \frac{d_z}{d} \qquad (2.30)$$

and determine the angles θ_x, θ_y, θ_z directly from the components and magnitude of the vector $\overrightarrow{MN}$.

2.14 ADDITION OF CONCURRENT FORCES IN SPACE

The resultant $\mathbf{R}$ of two or more forces in space will be determined by summing their rectangular components. Graphical or trigonometric methods are generally not practical in the case of forces in space.

The method followed here is similar to that used in Sec. 2.8 with coplanar forces. Setting

$$\mathbf{R} = \Sigma \mathbf{F}$$

we resolve each force into its rectangular components and write

$$R_x \mathbf{i} + R_y \mathbf{j} + R_z \mathbf{k} = \Sigma(F_x \mathbf{i} + F_y \mathbf{j} + F_z \mathbf{k})$$
$$= (\Sigma F_x)\mathbf{i} + (\Sigma F_y)\mathbf{j} + (\Sigma F_z)\mathbf{k}$$

from which it follows that

$$R_x = \Sigma F_x \qquad R_y = \Sigma F_y \qquad R_z = \Sigma F_z \qquad (2.31)$$

The magnitude of the resultant and the angles θ_x, θ_y, θ_z that the resultant forms with the coordinate axes are obtained using the method discussed in Sec. 2.12. We write

$$R = \sqrt{R_x^2 + R_y^2 + R_z^2} \qquad (2.32)$$

$$\cos \theta_x = \frac{R_x}{R} \qquad \cos \theta_y = \frac{R_y}{R} \qquad \cos \theta_z = \frac{R_z}{R} \qquad (2.33)$$

SAMPLE PROBLEM 2.7

A tower guy wire is anchored by means of a bolt at A. The tension in the wire is 2500 N. Determine (a) the components F_x, F_y, F_z of the force acting on the bolt, (b) the angles θ_x, θ_y, θ_z defining the direction of the force.

SOLUTION

a. Components of the Force.   The line of action of the force acting on the bolt passes through A and B, and the force is directed from A to B. The components of the vector $\overrightarrow{AB}$, which has the same direction as the force, are

$$d_x = -40 \text{ m} \qquad d_y = +80 \text{ m} \qquad d_z = +30 \text{ m}$$

The total distance from A to B is

$$AB = d = \sqrt{d_x^2 + d_y^2 + d_z^2} = 94.3 \text{ m}$$

Denoting by $\mathbf{i}$, $\mathbf{j}$, $\mathbf{k}$ the unit vectors along the coordinate axes, we have

$$\overrightarrow{AB} = -(40 \text{ m})\mathbf{i} + (80 \text{ m})\mathbf{j} + (30 \text{ m})\mathbf{k}$$

Introducing the unit vector $\boldsymbol{\lambda} = \overrightarrow{AB}/AB$, we write

$$\mathbf{F} = F\boldsymbol{\lambda} = F\frac{\overrightarrow{AB}}{AB} = \frac{2500 \text{ N}}{94.3 \text{ m}}\overrightarrow{AB}$$

Substituting the expression found for $\overrightarrow{AB}$, we obtain

$$\mathbf{F} = \frac{2500 \text{ N}}{94.3 \text{ m}}[-(40 \text{ m})\mathbf{i} + (80 \text{ m})\mathbf{j} + (30 \text{ m})\mathbf{k}]$$

$$\mathbf{F} = -(1060 \text{ N})\mathbf{i} + (2120 \text{ N})\mathbf{j} + (795 \text{ N})\mathbf{k}$$

The components of $\mathbf{F}$, therefore, are

$$F_x = -1060 \text{ N} \qquad F_y = +2120 \text{ N} \qquad F_z = +795 \text{ N} \blacktriangleleft$$

b. Direction of the Force.   Using Eqs. (2.25), we write

$$\cos \theta_x = \frac{F_x}{F} = \frac{-1060 \text{ N}}{2500 \text{ N}} \qquad \cos \theta_y = \frac{F_y}{F} = \frac{+2120 \text{ N}}{2500 \text{ N}}$$

$$\cos \theta_z = \frac{F_z}{F} = \frac{+795 \text{ N}}{2500 \text{ N}}$$

Calculating successively each quotient and its arc cosine, we obtain

$$\theta_x = 115.1° \qquad \theta_y = 32.0° \qquad \theta_z = 71.5° \blacktriangleleft$$

(*Note.* This result could have been obtained by using the components and magnitude of the vector $\overrightarrow{AB}$ rather than those of the force $\mathbf{F}$.)

27 ft

8 ft

D

B

11 ft

16 ft

C

A

A wall section of precast concrete is temporarily held by the cables shown. Knowing that the tension is 840 lb in cable AB and 1200 lb in cable AC, determine the magnitude and direction of the resultant of the forces exerted by cables AB and AC on stake A.

SOLUTION

Components of the Forces. The force exerted by each cable on stake A will be resolved into x, y, and z components. We first determine the components and magnitude of the vectors $\overrightarrow{AB}$ and $\overrightarrow{AC}$, measuring them from A toward the wall section. Denoting by $\mathbf{i}$, $\mathbf{j}$, $\mathbf{k}$ the unit vectors along the coordinate axes, we write

$$\overrightarrow{AB} = -(16\text{ ft})\mathbf{i} + (8\text{ ft})\mathbf{j} + (11\text{ ft})\mathbf{k} \qquad AB = 21\text{ ft}$$
$$\overrightarrow{AC} = -(16\text{ ft})\mathbf{i} + (8\text{ ft})\mathbf{j} - (16\text{ ft})\mathbf{k} \qquad AC = 24\text{ ft}$$

Denoting by $\boldsymbol{\lambda}_{AB}$ the unit vector along AB, we have

$$\mathbf{T}_{AB} = T_{AB}\boldsymbol{\lambda}_{AB} = T_{AB}\frac{\overrightarrow{AB}}{AB} = \frac{840\text{ lb}}{21\text{ ft}}\overrightarrow{AB}$$

C

y

B

8 ft

$\mathbf{T}_{AC} = (1200\text{ lb})\,\boldsymbol{\lambda}_{AC}$

$\boldsymbol{\lambda}_{AC}$

$\boldsymbol{\lambda}_{AB}$

16 ft

$\mathbf{T}_{AB} = (840\text{ lb})\,\boldsymbol{\lambda}_{AB}$

k   i

A

11 ft

z

16 ft

x

Substituting the expression found for $\overrightarrow{AB}$, we obtain

$$\mathbf{T}_{AB} = \frac{840\text{ lb}}{21\text{ ft}}[-(16\text{ ft})\mathbf{i} + (8\text{ ft})\mathbf{j} + (11\text{ ft})\mathbf{k}]$$
$$\mathbf{T}_{AB} = -(640\text{ lb})\mathbf{i} + (320\text{ lb})\mathbf{j} + (440\text{ lb})\mathbf{k}$$

Denoting by $\boldsymbol{\lambda}_{AC}$ the unit vector along AC, we obtain in a similar way

$$\mathbf{T}_{AC} = T_{AC}\boldsymbol{\lambda}_{AC} = T_{AC}\frac{\overrightarrow{AC}}{AC} = \frac{1200\text{ lb}}{24\text{ ft}}\overrightarrow{AC}$$
$$\mathbf{T}_{AC} = -(800\text{ lb})\mathbf{i} + (400\text{ lb})\mathbf{j} - (800\text{ lb})\mathbf{k}$$

Resultant of the Forces. The resultant $\mathbf{R}$ of the forces exerted by the two cables is

$$\mathbf{R} = \mathbf{T}_{AB} + \mathbf{T}_{AC} = -(1440\text{ lb})\mathbf{i} + (720\text{ lb})\mathbf{j} - (360\text{ lb})\mathbf{k}$$

The magnitude and direction of the resultant are now determined:

$$R = \sqrt{R_x^2 + R_y^2 + R_z^2} = \sqrt{(-1440)^2 + (720)^2 + (-360)^2}$$

$$R = 1650\text{ lb} \quad \blacktriangleleft$$

From Eqs. (2.33) we obtain

$$\cos\theta_x = \frac{R_x}{R} = \frac{-1440\text{ lb}}{1650\text{ lb}} \qquad \cos\theta_y = \frac{R_y}{R} = \frac{+720\text{ lb}}{1650\text{ lb}}$$

$$\cos\theta_z = \frac{R_z}{R} = \frac{-360\text{ lb}}{1650\text{ lb}}$$

Calculating successively each quotient and its arc cosine, we have

$$\theta_x = 150.8° \qquad \theta_y = 64.1° \qquad \theta_z = 102.6° \quad \blacktriangleleft$$

SOLVING PROBLEMS
ON YOUR OWN

In this lesson we saw that *forces in space* may be defined by their magnitude and direction or by the three rectangular components F_x, F_y, and F_z.

A. When a force is defined by its magnitude and direction, its rectangular components F_x, F_y, and F_z may be found as follows:

Case 1. If the direction of the force **F** is defined by the angles θ_y and ϕ shown in Fig. 2.30, projections of **F** through these angles or their complements will yield the components of **F** [Eqs. (2.17)]. Note that the x and z components of **F** are found by first projecting **F** onto the horizontal plane; the projection $\mathbf{F}_h$ obtained in this way is then resolved into the components $\mathbf{F}_x$ and $\mathbf{F}_z$ (Fig. 2.30c).

Case 2. If the direction of the force **F** is defined by the angles θ_x, θ_y, θ_z that **F** forms with the coordinate axes, each component can be obtained by multiplying the magnitude F of the force by the cosine of the corresponding angle [Example 1]:

$$F_x = F \cos \theta_x \qquad F_y = F \cos \theta_y \qquad F_z = F \cos \theta_z$$

Case 3. If the drection of the force **F** is defined by two points M and N located on its line of action (Fig. 2.34), you will first express the vector $\overrightarrow{MN}$ drawn from M to N in terms of its components d_x, d_y, d_z and the unit vectors **i**, **j**, **k**:

$$\overrightarrow{MN} = d_x\mathbf{i} + d_y\mathbf{j} + d_z\mathbf{k}$$

Next, you will determine the unit vector $\boldsymbol{\lambda}$ along the line of action of **F** by dividing the vector $\overrightarrow{MN}$ by its magnitude MN. Multiplying $\boldsymbol{\lambda}$ by the magnitude of **F**, you will obtain the desired expression for **F** in terms of its rectangular components [Sample Prob. 2.7]:

$$\mathbf{F} = F\boldsymbol{\lambda} = \frac{F}{d}(d_x\mathbf{i} + d_y\mathbf{j} + d_z\mathbf{k})$$

It is advantageous to use a consistent and meaningful system of notation when determining the rectangular components of a force. The method used in this text is illustrated in Sample Prob. 2.8 where, for example, the force $\mathbf{T}_{AB}$ acts from stake A toward point B. Note that the subscripts have been ordered to agree with the direction of the force. It is recommended that you adopt the same notation, as it will help you identify point 1 (the first subscript) and point 2 (the second subscript).

When forming the vector defining the line of action of a force, you may think of its scalar components as the number of steps you must take in each coordinate direction to go from point 1 to point 2. It is essential that you always remember to assign the correct sign to each of the components.

(continued)

B. When a force is defined by its rectangular components F_x, F_y, F_z, you can obtain its magnitude F by writing

$$F = \sqrt{F_x^2 + F_y^2 + F_z^2}$$

You can determine the direction cosines of the line of action of **F** by dividing the components of the force by F:

$$\cos \theta_x = \frac{F_x}{F} \quad \cos \theta_y = \frac{F_y}{F} \quad \cos \theta_z = \frac{F_z}{F}$$

From the direction cosines you can obtain the angles θ_x, θ_y, θ_z that **F** forms with the coordinate axes [Example 2].

C. To determine the resultant R of two or more forces in three-dimensional space, first determine the rectangular components of each force by one of the procedures described above. Adding these components will yield the components R_x, R_y, R_z of the resultant. The magnitude and direction of the resultant may then be obtained as indicated above for a force **F** [Sample Prob. 2.8].

PROBLEMS

2.71 Determine (*a*) the *x*, *y*, and *z* components of the 900-N force, (*b*) the angles θ_x, θ_y, and θ_z that the force forms with the coordinate axes.

2.72 Determine (*a*) the *x*, *y*, and *z* components of the 750-N force, (*b*) the angles θ_x, θ_y, and θ_z that the force forms with the coordinate axes.

2.73 A gun is aimed at a point *A* located 35° east of north. Knowing that the barrel of the gun forms an angle of 40° with the horizontal and that the maximum recoil force is 400 N, determine (*a*) the *x*, *y*, and *z* components of that force, (*b*) the values of the angles θ_x, θ_y, and θ_z defining the direction of the recoil force. (Assume that the *x*, *y*, and *z* axes are directed, respectively, east, up, and south.)

2.74 Solve Prob. 2.73, assuming that point *A* is located 15° north of west and that the barrel of the gun forms an angle of 25° with the horizontal.

2.75 Cable *AB* is 65 ft long, and the tension in that cable is 3900 lb. Determine (*a*) the *x*, *y*, and *z* components of the force exerted by the cable on the anchor *B*, (*b*) the angles θ_x, θ_y, and θ_z defining the direction of that force.

2.76 Cable *AC* is 70 ft long, and the tension in that cable is 5250 lb. Determine (*a*) the *x*, *y*, and *z* components of the force exerted by the cable on the anchor *C*, (*b*) the angles θ_x, θ_y, and θ_z defining the direction of that force.

2.77 The end of the coaxial cable *AE* is attached to the pole *AB*, which is strengthened by the guy wires *AC* and *AD*. Knowing that the tension in wire *AC* is 120 lb, determine (*a*) the components of the force exerted by this wire on the pole, (*b*) the angles θ_x, θ_y, and θ_z that the force forms with the coordinate axes.

2.78 The end of the coaxial cable *AE* is attached to the pole *AB*, which is strengthened by the guy wires *AC* and *AD*. Knowing that the tension in wire *AD* is 85 lb, determine (*a*) the components of the force exerted by this wire on the pole, (*b*) the angles θ_x, θ_y, and θ_z that the force forms with the coordinate axes.

2.79 Determine the magnitude and direction of the force $\mathbf{F} = (690 \text{ lb})\mathbf{i} + (300 \text{ lb})\mathbf{j} - (580 \text{ lb})\mathbf{k}$.

2.80 Determine the magnitude and direction of the force $\mathbf{F} = (650 \text{ N})\mathbf{i} - (320 \text{ N})\mathbf{j} + (760 \text{ N})\mathbf{k}$.

2.81 A force acts at the origin of a coordinate system in a direction defined by the angles $\theta_x = 75°$ and $\theta_z = 130°$. Knowing that the *y* component of the force is +300 lb, determine (*a*) the angle θ_y, (*b*) the other components and the magnitude of the force.

Fig. P2.71 and P2.72

Fig. P2.75 and P2.76

Fig. P2.77 and P2.78

2.82 A force acts at the origin of a coordinate system in a direction defined by the angles $\theta_y = 55°$ and $\theta_z = 45°$. Knowing that the x component of the force is -500 N, determine (a) the angle θ_x, (b) the other components and the magnitude of the force.

2.83 A force **F** of magnitude 230 N acts at the origin of a coordinate system. Knowing that $\theta_x = 32.5°$, $F_y = -60$ N, and $F_z > 0$, determine (a) the components F_x and F_z, (b) the angles θ_y and θ_z.

2.84 A force **F** of magnitude 210 N acts at the origin of a coordinate system. Knowing that $F_x = 80$ N, $\theta_z = 151.2°$, and $F_y < 0$, determine (a) the components F_y and F_z, (b) the angles θ_x and θ_y.

2.85 In order to move a wrecked truck, two cables are attached at A and pulled by winches B and C as shown. Knowing that the tension in cable AB is 2 kips, determine the components of the force exerted at A by the cable.

2.86 In order to move a wrecked truck, two cables are attached at A and pulled by winches B and C as shown. Knowing that the tension in cable AC is 1.5 kips, determine the components of the force exerted at A by the cable.

2.87 Knowing that the tension in cable AB is 1425 N, determine the components of the force exerted on the plate at B.

Fig. P2.85 and P2.86

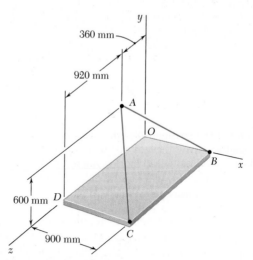

Fig. P2.87 and P2.88

2.88 Knowing that the tension in cable AC is 2130 N, determine the components of the force exerted on the plate at C.

2.89 A frame ABC is supported in part by cable DBE that passes through a frictionless ring at B. Knowing that the tension in the cable is 385 N, determine the components of the force exerted by the cable on the support at D.

2.90 For the frame and cable of Prob. 2.89, determine the components of the force exerted by the cable on the support at E.

Fig. P2.89

2.91 Find the magnitude and direction of the resultant of the two forces shown knowing that $P = 600$ N and $Q = 450$ N.

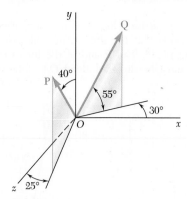

Fig. P2.91 and P2.92

2.92 Find the magnitude and direction of the resultant of the two forces shown knowing that $P = 450$ N and $Q = 600$ N.

2.93 Knowing that the tension is 425 lb in cable AB and 510 lb in cable AC, determine the magnitude and direction of the resultant of the forces exerted at A by the two cables.

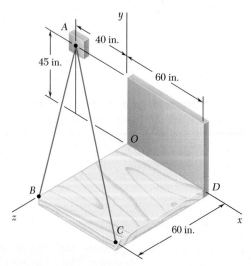

Fig. P2.93 and P2.94

2.94 Knowing that the tension is 510 lb in cable AB and 425 lb in cable AC, determine the magnitude and direction of the resultant of the forces exerted at A by the two cables.

2.95 For the frame of Prob. 2.89, determine the magnitude and direction of the resultant of the forces exerted by the cable at B knowing that the tension in the cable is 385 N.

2.96 For the cables of Prob. 2.87, knowing that the tension is 1425 N in cable AB and 2130 N in cable AC, determine the magnitude and direction of the resultant of the forces exerted at A by the two cables.

2.97 The boom OA carries a load **P** and is supported by two cables as shown. Knowing that the tension in cable AB is 183 lb and that the resultant of the load **P** and of the forces exerted at A by the two cables must be directed along OA, determine the tension in cable AC.

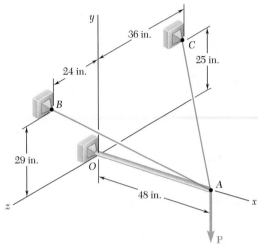

Fig. P2.97

2.98 For the boom and loading of Prob. 2.97, determine the magnitude of the load **P**.

2.15 EQUILIBRIUM OF A PARTICLE IN SPACE

According to the definition given in Sec. 2.9, a particle A is in equilibrium if the resultant of all the forces acting on A is zero. The components R_x, R_y, R_z of the resultant are given by the relations (2.31); expressing that the components of the resultant are zero, we write

$$\Sigma F_x = 0 \qquad \Sigma F_y = 0 \qquad \Sigma F_z = 0 \qquad (2.34)$$

Equations (2.34) represent the necessary and sufficient conditions for the equilibrium of a particle in space. They can be used to solve problems dealing with the equilibrium of a particle involving no more than three unknowns.

To solve such problems, you first should draw a free-body diagram showing the particle in equilibrium and *all* the forces acting on it. You can then write the equations of equilibrium (2.34) and solve them for three unknowns. In the more common types of problems, these unknowns will represent (1) the three components of a single force or (2) the magnitude of three forces, each of known direction.

Photo 2.2 While the tension in the *four* cables supporting the car cannot be found using the *three* equations of (2.34), a relation between the tensions can be obtained by considering the equilibrium of the hook.

SAMPLE PROBLEM 2.9

A 200-kg cylinder is hung by means of two cables AB and AC, which are attached to the top of a vertical wall. A horizontal force $\mathbf{P}$ perpendicular to the wall holds the cylinder in the position shown. Determine the magnitude of $\mathbf{P}$ and the tension in each cable.

SOLUTION

Free-Body Diagram. Point A is chosen as a free body; this point is subjected to four forces, three of which are of unknown magnitude.

Introducing the unit vectors $\mathbf{i}$, $\mathbf{j}$, $\mathbf{k}$, we resolve each force into rectangular components.

$$\mathbf{P} = P\mathbf{i}$$
$$\mathbf{W} = -mg\mathbf{j} = -(200 \text{ kg})(9.81 \text{ m/s}^2)\mathbf{j} = -(1962 \text{ N})\mathbf{j} \tag{1}$$

In the case of $\mathbf{T}_{AB}$ and $\mathbf{T}_{AC}$, it is necessary first to determine the components and magnitudes of the vectors $\overrightarrow{AB}$ and $\overrightarrow{AC}$. Denoting by $\boldsymbol{\lambda}_{AB}$ the unit vector along AB, we write

$$\overrightarrow{AB} = -(1.2 \text{ m})\mathbf{i} + (10 \text{ m})\mathbf{j} + (8 \text{ m})\mathbf{k} \qquad AB = 12.862 \text{ m}$$

$$\boldsymbol{\lambda}_{AB} = \frac{\overrightarrow{AB}}{12.862 \text{ m}} = -0.09330\mathbf{i} + 0.7775\mathbf{j} + 0.6220\mathbf{k}$$

$$\mathbf{T}_{AB} = T_{AB}\boldsymbol{\lambda}_{AB} = -0.09330T_{AB}\mathbf{i} + 0.7775T_{AB}\mathbf{j} + 0.6220T_{AB}\mathbf{k} \tag{2}$$

Denoting by $\boldsymbol{\lambda}_{AC}$ the unit vector along AC, we write in a similar way

$$\overrightarrow{AC} = -(1.2 \text{ m})\mathbf{i} + (10 \text{ m})\mathbf{j} - (10 \text{ m})\mathbf{k} \qquad AC = 14.193 \text{ m}$$

$$\boldsymbol{\lambda}_{AC} = \frac{\overrightarrow{AC}}{14.193 \text{ m}} = -0.08455\mathbf{i} + 0.7046\mathbf{j} - 0.7046\mathbf{k}$$

$$\mathbf{T}_{AC} = T_{AC}\boldsymbol{\lambda}_{AC} = -0.08455T_{AC}\mathbf{i} + 0.7046T_{AC}\mathbf{j} - 0.7046T_{AC}\mathbf{k} \tag{3}$$

Equilibrium Condition. Since A is in equilibrium, we must have

$$\Sigma\mathbf{F} = 0: \qquad \mathbf{T}_{AB} + \mathbf{T}_{AC} + \mathbf{P} + \mathbf{W} = 0$$

or, substituting from (1), (2), (3) for the forces and factoring $\mathbf{i}$, $\mathbf{j}$, $\mathbf{k}$,

$$(-0.09330T_{AB} - 0.08455T_{AC} + P)\mathbf{i}$$
$$+ (0.7775T_{AB} + 0.7046T_{AC} - 1962 \text{ N})\mathbf{j}$$
$$+ (0.6220T_{AB} - 0.7046T_{AC})\mathbf{k} = 0$$

Setting the coefficients of $\mathbf{i}$, $\mathbf{j}$, $\mathbf{k}$ equal to zero, we write three scalar equations, which express that the sums of the x, y, and z components of the forces are respectively equal to zero.

$$(\Sigma F_x = 0:) \qquad -0.09330T_{AB} - 0.08455T_{AC} + P = 0$$
$$(\Sigma F_y = 0:) \qquad +0.7775T_{AB} + 0.7046T_{AC} - 1962 \text{ N} = 0$$
$$(\Sigma F_z = 0:) \qquad +0.6220T_{AB} - 0.7046T_{AC} = 0$$

Solving these equations, we obtain

$$P = 235 \text{ N} \qquad T_{AB} = 1402 \text{ N} \qquad T_{AC} = 1238 \text{ N} \quad \blacktriangleleft$$

SOLVING PROBLEMS
ON YOUR OWN

W e saw earlier that when a particle is in *equilibrium*, the resultant of the forces acting on the particle must be zero. Expressing this fact in the case of the equilibrium of a *particle in three-dimensional space* will provide you with three relations among the forces acting on the particle. These relations may be used to determine three unknowns—usually the magnitudes of three forces.

Your solution will consist of the following steps:

1. Draw a free-body diagram of the particle. This diagram shows the particle and all the forces acting on it. Indicate on the diagram the magnitudes of known forces, as well as any angles or dimensions that define the direction of a force. Any unknown magnitude or angle should be denoted by an appropriate symbol. Nothing else should be included in your free-body diagram.

2. Resolve each of the forces into rectangular components. Following the method used in the preceding lesson, you will determine for each force $\mathbf{F}$ the unit vector $\boldsymbol{\lambda}$ defining the direction of that force and express $\mathbf{F}$ as the product of its magnitude F and the unit vector $\boldsymbol{\lambda}$. You will obtain an expression of the form

$$\mathbf{F} = F\boldsymbol{\lambda} = \frac{F}{d}\,(d_x\mathbf{i} + d_y\mathbf{j} + d_z\mathbf{k})$$

where d, d_x, d_y, and d_z are dimensions obtained from the free-body diagram of the particle. If a force is known in magnitude as well as in direction, then F is known and the expression obtained for $\mathbf{F}$ is well defined; otherwise F is one of the three unknowns that should be determined.

3. Set the resultant, or sum, of the forces exerted on the particle equal to zero. You will obtain a vectorial equation consisting of terms containing the unit vectors $\mathbf{i}$, $\mathbf{j}$, or $\mathbf{k}$. You will group the terms containing the same unit vector and factor that vector. For the vectorial equation to be satisfied, the coefficient of each of the unit vectors must be set equal to zero. This will yield three scalar equations that you can solve for no more than three unknowns [Sample Prob. 2.9].

PROBLEMS

FREE BODY PRACTICE PROBLEMS

2.F5 A 36-lb triangular plate is supported by three cables as shown. Draw the free-body diagram needed to determine the tension in each wire.

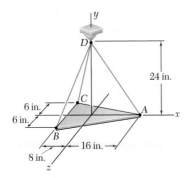

Fig. P2.F5

2.F6 A 70-kg cylinder is supported by two cables AC and BC, which are attached to the top of vertical posts. A horizontal force **P**, perpendicular to the plane containing the posts, holds the cylinder in the position shown. Draw the free-body diagram needed to determine the magnitude of **P** and the force in each cable.

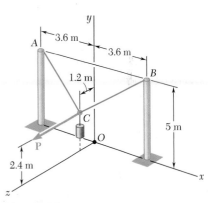

Fig. P2.F6

2.F7 Three cables are connected at point D, which is located 18 in. below the T-shaped pipe support ABC. The cables support a 180-lb cylinder as shown. Draw the free-body diagram needed to determine the tension in each cable.

2.F8 A 100-kg container is suspended from ring A, to which cables AC and AE are attached. A force P is applied to end F of a third cable that passes over a pulley at B and through ring A and then is attached to a support at D. Draw the free-body diagram needed to determine the magnitude of P. (*Hint:* The tension is the same in all portions of cable $FBAD$.)

Fig. P2.F7

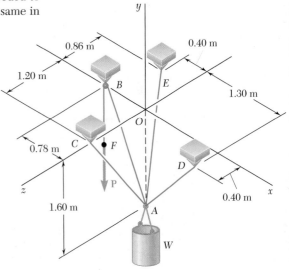

Fig. P2.F8

61

END-OF-SECTION PROBLEMS

2.99 A container is supported by three cables that are attached to a ceiling as shown. Determine the weight W of the container, knowing that the tension in cable AB is 6 kN.

Fig. P2.99 and P2.100

2.100 A container is supported by three cables that are attached to a ceiling as shown. Determine the weight W of the container, knowing that the tension in cable AD is 4.3 kN.

2.101 Three cables are used to tether a balloon as shown. Determine the vertical force **P** exerted by the balloon at A knowing that the tension in cable AD is 481 N.

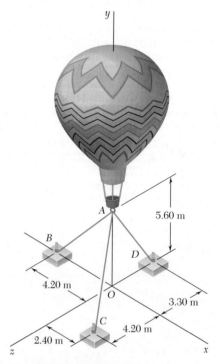

Fig. P2.101 and P2.102

2.102 Three cables are used to tether a balloon as shown. Knowing that the balloon exerts an 800-N vertical force at A, determine the tension in each cable.

2.103 A crate is supported by three cables as shown. Determine the weight of the crate knowing that the tension in cable AB is 750 lb.

2.104 A crate is supported by three cables as shown. Determine the weight of the crate knowing that the tension in cable AD is 616 lb.

2.105 A crate is supported by three cables as shown. Determine the weight of the crate knowing that the tension in cable AC is 544 lb.

2.106 A 1600-lb crate is supported by three cables as shown. Determine the tension in each cable.

2.107 Three cables are connected at A, where the forces **P** and **Q** are applied as shown. Knowing that $Q = 0$, find the value of P for which the tension in cable AD is 305 N.

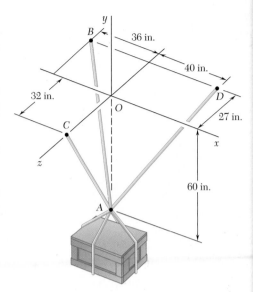

Fig. P2.103, P2.104, *P2.105*, and P2.106

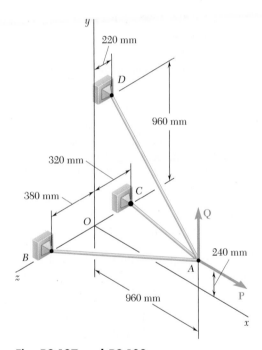

Fig. P2.107 and P2.108

2.108 Three cables are connected at A, where the forces **P** and **Q** are applied as shown. Knowing that $P = 1200$ N, determine the values of Q for which cable AD is taut.

2.109 A rectangular plate is supported by three cables as shown. Knowing that the tension in cable AC is 60 N, determine the weight of the plate.

2.110 A rectangular plate is supported by three cables as shown. Knowing that the tension in cable AD is 520 N, determine the weight of the plate.

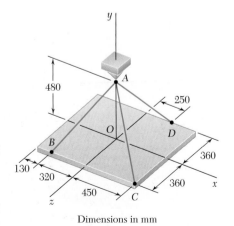

Dimensions in mm

Fig. P2.109 and P2.110

2.111 A transmission tower is held by three guy wires attached to a pin at A and anchored by bolts at B, C, and D. If the tension in wire AB is 630 lb, determine the vertical force **P** exerted by the tower on the pin at A.

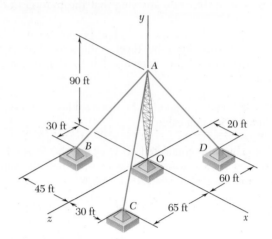

Fig. P2.111 and P2.112

2.112 A transmission tower is held by three guy wires attached to a pin at A and anchored by bolts at B, C, and D. If the tension in wire AC is 920 lb, determine the vertical force **P** exerted by the tower on the pin at A.

2.113 In trying to move across a slippery icy surface, a 180-lb man uses two ropes AB and AC. Knowing that the force exerted on the man by the icy surface is perpendicular to that surface, determine the tension in each rope.

2.114 Solve Prob. 2.113, assuming that a friend is helping the man at A by pulling on him with a force $\mathbf{P} = -(60\ \text{lb})\mathbf{k}$.

2.115 For the rectangular plate of Probs. 2.109 and 2.110, determine the tension in each of the three cables knowing that the weight of the plate is 792 N.

2.116 For the cable system of Probs. 2.107 and 2.108, determine the tension in each cable knowing that $P = 2880$ N and $Q = 0$.

2.117 For the cable system of Probs. 2.107 and 2.108, determine the tension in each cable knowing that $P = 2880$ N and $Q = 576$ N.

2.118 For the cable system of Probs. 2.107 and 2.108, determine the tension in each cable knowing that $P = 2880$ N and $Q = -576$ N (**Q** is directed downward).

2.119 For the transmission tower of Probs. 2.111 and 2.112, determine the tension in each guy wire knowing that the tower exerts on the pin at A an upward vertical force of 2100 lb.

2.120 A horizontal circular plate weighing 60 lb is suspended as shown from three wires that are attached to a support at D and form 30° angles with the vertical. Determine the tension in each wire.

Fig. P2.113

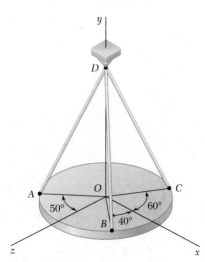

Fig. P2.120

2.121 Cable *BAC* passes through a frictionless ring *A* and is attached to fixed supports at *B* and *C*, while cables *AD* and *AE* are both tied to the ring and are attached, respectively, to supports at *D* and *E*. Knowing that a 200-lb vertical load **P** is applied to ring *A*, determine the tension in each of the three cables.

2.122 Knowing that the tension in cable *AE* of Prob. 2.121 is 75 lb, determine (*a*) the magnitude of the load **P**, (*b*) the tension in cables *BAC* and *AD*.

2.123 A container of weight *W* is suspended from ring *A*. Cable *BAC* passes through the ring and is attached to fixed supports at *B* and *C*. Two forces **P** = *P***i** and **Q** = *Q***k** are applied to the ring to maintain the container in the position shown. Knowing that *W* = 376 N, determine *P* and *Q*. (*Hint*: The tension is the same in both portions of cable *BAC*.)

Fig. P2.121

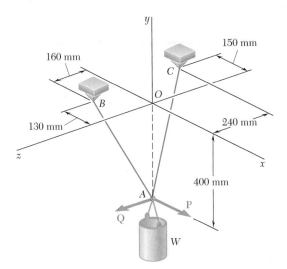

Fig. P2.123

2.124 For the system of Prob. 2.123, determine *W* and *Q* knowing that *P* = 164 N.

2.125 Collars *A* and *B* are connected by a 525-mm-long wire and can slide freely on frictionless rods. If a force **P** = (341 N)**j** is applied to collar *A*, determine (*a*) the tension in the wire when *y* = 155 mm, (*b*) the magnitude of the force **Q** required to maintain the equilibrium of the system.

2.126 Solve Prob. 2.125 assuming that *y* = 275 mm.

Fig. P2.125

REVIEW AND SUMMARY

In this chapter we have studied the effect of forces on particles, i.e., on bodies of such shape and size that all forces acting on them may be assumed applied at the same point.

Resultant of two forces

Fig. 2.35

Forces are *vector quantities;* they are characterized by a *point of application,* a *magnitude,* and a *direction,* and they add according to the *parallelogram law* (Fig. 2.35). The magnitude and direction of the resultant **R** of two forces **P** and **Q** can be determined either graphically or by trigonometry, using successively the law of cosines and the law of sines [Sample Prob. 2.1].

Components of a force

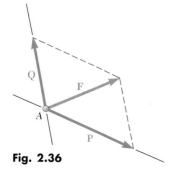

Fig. 2.36

Any given force acting on a particle can be resolved into two or more *components,* i.e., it can be replaced by two or more forces which have the same effect on the particle. A force **F** can be resolved into two components **P** and **Q** by drawing a parallelogram which has **F** for its diagonal; the components **P** and **Q** are then represented by the two adjacent sides of the parallelogram (Fig. 2.36) and can be determined either graphically or by trigonometry [Sec. 2.6].

A force **F** is said to have been resolved into two *rectangular components* if its components F_x and F_y are perpendicular to each other and are directed along the coordinate axes (Fig. 2.37). Introducing the *unit vectors* **i** and **j** along the x and y axes, respectively, we write [Sec. 2.7]

Rectangular components
Unit vectors

Fig. 2.37

$$\mathbf{F}_x = F_x\mathbf{i} \qquad \mathbf{F}_y = F_y\mathbf{j} \qquad (2.6)$$

and

$$\mathbf{F} = F_x\mathbf{i} + F_y\mathbf{j} \qquad (2.7)$$

where F_x and F_y are the *scalar components* of **F**. These components, which can be positive or negative, are defined by the relations

$$F_x = F \cos \theta \qquad F_y = F \sin \theta \qquad (2.8)$$

When the rectangular components F_x and F_y of a force **F** are given, the angle θ defining the direction of the force can be obtained by writing

$$\tan \theta = \frac{F_y}{F_x} \qquad (2.9)$$

The magnitude F of the force can then be obtained by solving one of the equations (2.8) for F or by applying the Pythagorean theorem and writing

$$F = \sqrt{F_x^2 + F_y^2} \qquad (2.10)$$

When *three or more coplanar forces* act on a particle, the rectangular components of their resultant **R** can be obtained by adding algebraically the corresponding components of the given forces [Sec. 2.8]. We have

$$R_x = \Sigma F_x \qquad R_y = \Sigma F_y \qquad (2.13)$$

The magnitude and direction of **R** can then be determined from relations similar to Eqs. (2.9) and (2.10) [Sample Prob. 2.3].

A force **F** in *three-dimensional space* can be resolved into rectangular components F_x, F_y, and F_z [Sec. 2.12]. Denoting by θ_x, θ_y, and θ_z, respectively, the angles that **F** forms with the x, y, and z axes (Fig. 2.38), we have

$$F_x = F \cos \theta_x \qquad F_y = F \cos \theta_y \qquad F_z = F \cos \theta_z \qquad (2.19)$$

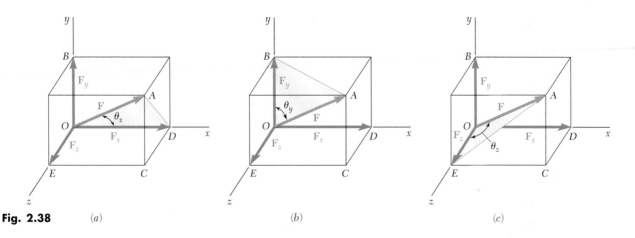

Fig. 2.38   (a)   (b)   (c)

The cosines of θ_x, θ_y, θ_z are known as the *direction cosines* of the force **F**. Introducing the unit vectors **i**, **j**, **k** along the coordinate axes, we write

$$\mathbf{F} = F_x\mathbf{i} + F_y\mathbf{j} + F_z\mathbf{k} \qquad (2.20)$$

or

$$\mathbf{F} = F(\cos \theta_x\mathbf{i} + \cos \theta_y\mathbf{j} + \cos \theta_z\mathbf{k}) \qquad (2.21)$$

which shows (Fig. 2.39) that **F** is the product of its magnitude F and the unit vector

$$\boldsymbol{\lambda} = \cos \theta_x\mathbf{i} + \cos \theta_y\mathbf{j} + \cos \theta_z\mathbf{k}$$

Since the magnitude of $\boldsymbol{\lambda}$ is equal to unity, we must have

$$\cos^2 \theta_x + \cos^2 \theta_y + \cos^2 \theta_z = 1 \qquad (2.24)$$

When the rectangular components F_x, F_y, F_z of a force **F** are given, the magnitude F of the force is found by writing

$$F = \sqrt{F_x^2 + F_y^2 + F_z^2} \qquad (2.18)$$

and the direction cosines of **F** are obtained from Eqs. (2.19). We have

$$\cos \theta_x = \frac{F_x}{F} \qquad \cos \theta_y = \frac{F_y}{F} \qquad \cos \theta_z = \frac{F_z}{F} \qquad (2.25)$$

Fig. 2.39

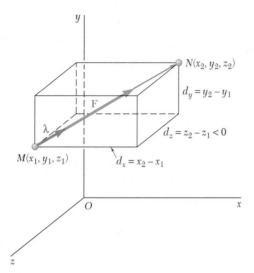

Fig. 2.40

When a force $\mathbf{F}$ is defined in three-dimensional space by its magnitude F and two points M and N on its line of action [Sec. 2.13], its rectangular components can be obtained as follows. We first express the vector $\overrightarrow{MN}$ joining points M and N in terms of its components d_x, d_y, and d_z (Fig. 2.40); we write

$$\overrightarrow{MN} = d_x\mathbf{i} + d_y\mathbf{j} + d_z\mathbf{k} \qquad (2.26)$$

We next determine the unit vector $\boldsymbol{\lambda}$ along the line of action of $\mathbf{F}$ by dividing $\overrightarrow{MN}$ by its magnitude $MN = d$:

$$\boldsymbol{\lambda} = \frac{\overrightarrow{MN}}{MN} = \frac{1}{d}(d_x\mathbf{i} + d_y\mathbf{j} + d_z\mathbf{k}) \qquad (2.27)$$

Recalling that $\mathbf{F}$ is equal to the product of F and $\boldsymbol{\lambda}$, we have

$$\mathbf{F} = F\boldsymbol{\lambda} = \frac{F}{d}(d_x\mathbf{i} + d_y\mathbf{j} + d_z\mathbf{k}) \qquad (2.28)$$

from which it follows [Sample Probs. 2.7 and 2.8] that the scalar components of $\mathbf{F}$ are, respectively,

$$F_x = \frac{Fd_x}{d} \qquad F_y = \frac{Fd_y}{d} \qquad F_z = \frac{Fd_z}{d} \qquad (2.29)$$

Resultant of forces in space

When *two or more forces* act on a particle in *three-dimensional space*, the rectangular components of their resultant $\mathbf{R}$ can be obtained by adding algebraically the corresponding components of the given forces [Sec. 2.14]. We have

$$R_x = \Sigma F_x \qquad R_y = \Sigma F_y \qquad R_z = \Sigma F_z \qquad (2.31)$$

The magnitude and direction of $\mathbf{R}$ can then be determined from relations similar to Eqs. (2.18) and (2.25) [Sample Prob. 2.8].

Equilibrium of a particle

A particle is said to be in *equilibrium* when the resultant of all the forces acting on it is zero [Sec. 2.9]. The particle will then remain at rest (if originally at rest) or move with constant speed in a straight line (if originally in motion) [Sec. 2.10].

Free-body diagram

To solve a problem involving a particle in equilibrium, one first should draw a *free-body diagram* of the particle showing all the forces acting on it [Sec. 2.11]. If *only three coplanar forces* act on the particle, a *force triangle* may be drawn to express that the particle is in equilibrium. Using graphical methods of trigonometry, this triangle can be solved for no more than two unknowns [Sample Prob. 2.4]. If *more than three coplanar forces* are involved, the equations of equilibrium

$$\Sigma F_x = 0 \qquad \Sigma F_y = 0 \qquad (2.15)$$

should be used. These equations can be solved for no more than two unknowns [Sample Prob. 2.6].

Equilibrium in space

When a particle is in *equilibrium in three-dimensional space* [Sec. 2.15], the three equations of equilibrium

$$\Sigma F_x = 0 \qquad \Sigma F_y = 0 \qquad \Sigma F_z = 0 \qquad (2.34)$$

should be used. These equations can be solved for no more than three unknowns [Sample Prob. 2.9].

REVIEW PROBLEMS

2.127 Two structural members A and B are bolted to a bracket as shown. Knowing that both members are in compression and that the force is 15 kN in member A and 10 kN in member B, determine by trigonometry the magnitude and direction of the resultant of the forces applied to the bracket by members A and B.

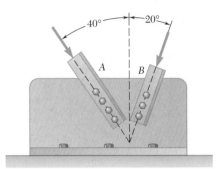

Fig. P2.127

2.128 Member BD exerts on member ABC a force **P** directed along line BD. Knowing that **P** must have a 300-lb horizontal component, determine (a) the magnitude of the force **P**, (b) its vertical component.

Fig. P2.128

2.129 Determine (a) the required tension in cable AC, knowing that the resultant of the three forces exerted at point C of boom BC must be directed along BC, (b) the corresponding magnitude of the resultant.

Fig. P2.129

2.130 Two cables are tied together at C and are loaded as shown. Determine the tension (a) in cable AC, (b) in cable BC.

Fig. P2.130

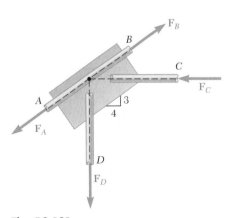

2.131 A welded connection is in equilibrium under the action of the four forces shown. Knowing that $F_A = 8$ kN and $F_B = 16$ kN, determine the magnitudes of the other two forces.

Fig. P2.131

69

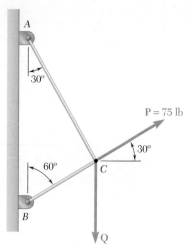

Fig. P2.132

2.132 Two cables tied together at C are loaded as shown. Determine the range of values of Q for which the tension will not exceed 60 lb in either cable.

2.133 A horizontal circular plate is suspended as shown from three wires that are attached to a support at D and form 30° angles with the vertical. Knowing that the x component of the force exerted by wire AD on the plate is 110.3 N, determine (a) the tension in wire AD, (b) the angles θ_x, θ_y, and θ_z that the force exerted at A forms with the coordinate axes.

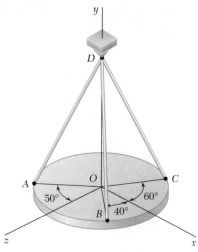

Fig. P2.133

2.134 A force acts at the origin of a coordinate system in a direction defined by the angles $\theta_y = 55°$ and $\theta_z = 45°$. Knowing that the x component of the force is -500 lb, determine (a) the angle θ_x, (b) the other components and the magnitude of the force.

2.135 Find the magnitude and direction of the resultant of the two forces shown knowing that $P = 300$ N and $Q = 400$ N.

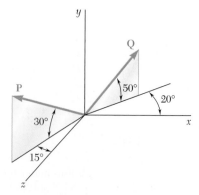

Fig. P2.135

2.136 Three cables are used to tether a balloon as shown. Determine the vertical force **P** exerted by the balloon at A knowing that the tension in cable AC is 444 N.

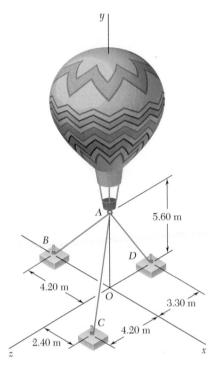

Fig. P2.136

2.137 Collars A and B are connected by a 25-in.-long wire and can slide freely on frictionless rods. If a 60-lb force **Q** is applied to collar B as shown, determine (a) the tension in the wire when x = 9 in., (b) the corresponding magnitude of the force **P** required to maintain the equilibrium of the system.

2.138 Collars A and B are connected by a 25-in.-long wire and can slide freely on frictionless rods. Determine the distances x and z for which the equilibrium of the system is maintained when P = 120 lb and Q = 60 lb.

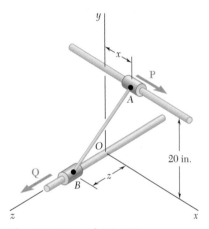

Fig. P2.137 and P2.138

COMPUTER PROBLEMS

2.C1 Write a computer program that can be used to determine the magnitude and direction of the resultant of n coplanar forces applied at a point A. Use this program to solve Probs. 2.32, 2.33, 2.35, and 2.38.

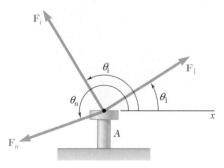

Fig. P2.C1

2.C2 A load $\mathbf{P}$ is supported by two cables as shown. Write a computer program that can be used to determine the tension in each cable for any given value of P and for values of θ ranging from $\theta_1 = \beta - 90°$ to $\theta_2 = 90° - \alpha$, using given increments $\Delta\theta$. Use this program to determine for the following three sets of numerical values (a) the tension in each cable for values of θ ranging from θ_1 to θ_2, (b) the value of θ for which the tension in the two cables is as small as possible, (c) the corresponding value of the tension:

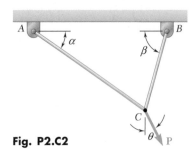

Fig. P2.C2

(1) $\alpha = 35°$, $\beta = 75°$, $P = 400$ lb, $\Delta\theta = 5°$
(2) $\alpha = 50°$, $\beta = 30°$, $P = 600$ lb, $\Delta\theta = 10°$
(3) $\alpha = 40°$, $\beta = 60°$, $P = 250$ lb, $\Delta\theta = 5°$

2.C3 An acrobat is walking on a tightrope of length $L = 20.1$ m attached to supports A and B at a distance of 20.0 m from each other. The combined weight of the acrobat and his balancing pole is 800 N, and the friction between his shoes and the rope is large enough to prevent him from slipping. Neglecting the weight of the rope and any elastic deformation, write a computer program to calculate the deflection y and the tension in portions AC and BC of the rope for values of x from 0.5 m to 10.0 m using 0.5-m increments. From the data obtained, determine (a) the maximum deflection of the rope, (b) the maximum tension in the rope, (c) the smallest values of the tension in portions AC and BC of the rope.

Fig. P2.C3

2.C4 Write a computer program that can be used to determine the magnitude and direction of the resultant of n forces $\mathbf{F}_i$, where $i = 1, 2, \ldots, n$, that are applied at point A_0 of coordinates x_0, y_0, and z_0, knowing that the line of action of $\mathbf{F}_i$ passes through point A_i of coordinates x_i, y_i, and z_i. Use this program to solve Probs. 2.93, 2.94, and 2.95.

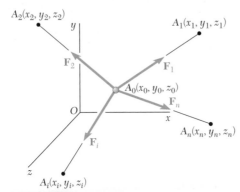

Fig. P2.C4

2.C5 Three cables are attached at points A_1, A_2, and A_3, respectively, and are connected at point A_0, to which a given load $\mathbf{P}$ is applied as shown. Write a computer program that can be used to determine the tension in each of the cables. Use this program to solve Probs. 2.102, 2.106, 2.107, and 2.115.

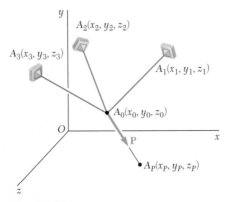

Fig. P2.C5

The battleship USS *New Jersey* is maneuvered by four tugboats at Bremerton Naval Shipyard. It will be shown in this chapter that the forces exerted on the ship by the tugboats could be replaced by an equivalent force exerted by a single, more powerful, tugboat.

CHAPTER

3

Rigid Bodies:
Equivalent Systems of Forces

3.1   INTRODUCTION

In the preceding chapter it was assumed that each of the bodies considered could be treated as a single particle. Such a view, however, is not always possible, and a body, in general, should be treated as a combination of a large number of particles. The size of the body will have to be taken into consideration, as well as the fact that forces will act on different particles and thus will have different points of application.

Most of the bodies considered in elementary mechanics are assumed to be *rigid*, a *rigid body* being defined as one which does not deform. Actual structures and machines, however, are never absolutely rigid and deform under the loads to which they are subjected. But these deformations are usually small and do not appreciably affect the conditions of equilibrium or motion of the structure under consideration. They are important, though, as far as the resistance of the structure to failure is concerned and are considered in the study of mechanics of materials.

In this chapter you will study the effect of forces exerted on a rigid body, and you will learn how to replace a given system of forces by a simpler equivalent system. This analysis will rest on the fundamental assumption that the effect of a given force on a rigid body remains unchanged if that force is moved along its line of action (*principle of transmissibility*). It follows that forces acting on a rigid body can be represented by *sliding vectors*, as indicated earlier in Sec. 2.3.

Two important concepts associated with the effect of a force on a rigid body are the *moment of a force about a point* (Sec. 3.6) and the *moment of a force about an axis* (Sec. 3.11). Since the determination of these quantities involves the computation of vector products and scalar products of two vectors, the fundamentals of vector algebra will be introduced in this chapter and applied to the solution of problems involving forces acting on rigid bodies.

Another concept introduced in this chapter is that of a *couple*, i.e., the combination of two forces which have the same magnitude, parallel lines of action, and opposite sense (Sec. 3.12). As you will see, any system of forces acting on a rigid body can be replaced by an equivalent system consisting of one force acting at a given point and one couple. This basic system is called a *force-couple system*. In the case of concurrent, coplanar, or parallel forces, the equivalent force-couple system can be further reduced to a single force, called the *resultant* of the system, or to a single couple, called the *resultant couple* of the system.

3.2   EXTERNAL AND INTERNAL FORCES

Forces acting on rigid bodies can be separated into two groups: (1) *external forces* and (2) *internal forces*.

1. The *external forces* represent the action of other bodies on the rigid body under consideration. They are entirely responsible for the external behavior of the rigid body. They will either cause it to move or ensure that it remains at rest. We shall be concerned only with external forces in this chapter and in Chaps. 4 and 5.

2. The *internal forces* are the forces which hold together the particles forming the rigid body. If the rigid body is structurally composed of several parts, the forces holding the component parts together are also defined as internal forces. Internal forces will be considered in Chaps. 6 and 7.

As an example of external forces, let us consider the forces acting on a disabled truck that three people are pulling forward by means of a rope attached to the front bumper (Fig. 3.1). The external forces acting on the truck are shown in a *free-body diagram* (Fig. 3.2). Let us first consider the *weight* of the truck. Although it embodies the effect of the earth's pull on each of the particles forming the truck, the weight can be represented by the single force **W**. The *point of application* of this force, i.e., the point at which the force acts, is defined as the *center of gravity* of the truck. It will be seen in Chap. 5 how centers of gravity can be determined. The weight **W** tends to make the truck move vertically downward. In fact, it would actually cause the truck to move downward, i.e., to fall, if it were not for the presence of the ground. The ground opposes the downward motion of the truck by means of the reactions $\mathbf{R}_1$ and $\mathbf{R}_2$. These forces are exerted *by* the ground *on* the truck and must therefore be included among the external forces acting on the truck.

Fig. 3.1

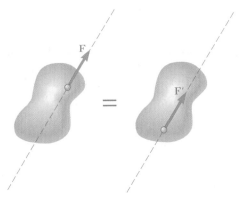

Fig. 3.2

The people pulling on the rope exert the force **F**. The point of application of **F** is on the front bumper. The force **F** tends to make the truck move forward in a straight line and does actually make it move, since no external force opposes this motion. (Rolling resistance has been neglected here for simplicity.) This forward motion of the truck, during which each straight line keeps its original orientation (the floor of the truck remains horizontal, and the walls remain vertical), is known as a *translation*. Other forces might cause the truck to move differently. For example, the force exerted by a jack placed under the front axle would cause the truck to pivot about its rear axle. Such a motion is a *rotation*. It can be concluded, therefore, that each of the *external forces* acting on a *rigid body* can, if unopposed, impart to the rigid body a motion of translation or rotation, or both.

3.3 PRINCIPLE OF TRANSMISSIBILITY. EQUIVALENT FORCES

The *principle of transmissibility* states that the conditions of equilibrium or motion of a rigid body will remain unchanged if a force **F** acting at a given point of the rigid body is replaced by a force **F′** of the same magnitude and same direction, but acting at a different point, *provided that the two forces have the same line of action* (Fig. 3.3). The two forces **F** and **F′** have the same effect on the rigid body and are said to be *equivalent*. This principle, which states that the action of a force may be *transmitted* along its line of action, is based on experimental evidence. It *cannot* be derived from the properties established so far in this text and must therefore be accepted as an experimental law. However, as you will see in Sec. 16.5, the principle of transmissibility can be derived from the study of the dynamics of rigid bodies, but this study requires the introduction of Newton's

Fig. 3.3

second and third laws and of a number of other concepts as well. Therefore, our study of the statics of rigid bodies will be based on the three principles introduced so far, i.e., the parallelogram law of addition, Newton's first law, and the principle of transmissibility.

It was indicated in Chap. 2 that the forces acting on a particle could be represented by vectors. These vectors had a well-defined point of application, namely, the particle itself, and were therefore fixed, or bound, vectors. In the case of forces acting on a rigid body, however, the point of application of the force does not matter, as long as the line of action remains unchanged. Thus, forces acting on a rigid body must be represented by a different kind of vector, known as a *sliding vector*, since forces may be allowed to slide along their lines of action. We should note that all the properties which will be derived in the following sections for the forces acting on a rigid body will be valid more generally for any system of sliding vectors. In order to keep our presentation more intuitive, however, we will carry it out in terms of physical forces rather than in terms of mathematical sliding vectors.

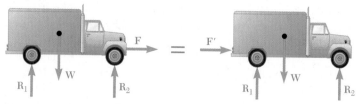

Fig. 3.4

Returning to the example of the truck, we first observe that the line of action of the force **F** is a horizontal line passing through both the front and the rear bumpers of the truck (Fig. 3.4). Using the principle of transmissibility, we can therefore replace **F** by an *equivalent force* **F′** acting on the rear bumper. In other words, the conditions of motion are unaffected, and all the other external forces acting on the truck (**W**, $\mathbf{R}_1$, $\mathbf{R}_2$) remain unchanged if the people push on the rear bumper instead of pulling on the front bumper.

The principle of transmissibility and the concept of equivalent forces have limitations, however. Consider, for example, a short bar AB acted upon by equal and opposite axial forces $\mathbf{P}_1$ and $\mathbf{P}_2$, as shown in Fig. 3.5a. According to the principle of transmissibility, the force $\mathbf{P}_2$ can be replaced by a force $\mathbf{P}_2'$ having the same magnitude, the same direction, and the same line of action but acting at A instead of B (Fig. 3.5b). The forces $\mathbf{P}_1$ and $\mathbf{P}_2'$ acting on the same particle

Fig. 3.5

can be added according to the rules of Chap. 2, and, as these forces are equal and opposite, their sum is equal to zero. Thus, in terms of the external behavior of the bar, the original system of forces shown in Fig. 3.5a is equivalent to no force at all (Fig. 3.5c).

Consider now the two equal and opposite forces P_1 and P_2 acting on the bar AB as shown in Fig. 3.5d. The force P_2 can be replaced by a force P_2' having the same magnitude, the same direction, and the same line of action but acting at B instead of at A (Fig. 3.5e). The forces P_1 and P_2' can then be added, and their sum is again zero (Fig. 3.5f). From the point of view of the mechanics of rigid bodies, the systems shown in Fig. 3.5a and d are thus equivalent. But the *internal forces* and *deformations* produced by the two systems are clearly different. The bar of Fig. 3.5a is in *tension* and, if not absolutely rigid, will increase in length slightly; the bar of Fig. 3.5d is in *compression* and, if not absolutely rigid, will decrease in length slightly. Thus, while the principle of transmissibility may be used freely to determine the conditions of motion or equilibrium of rigid bodies and to compute the external forces acting on these bodies, it should be avoided, or at least used with care, in determining internal forces and deformations.

3.4   VECTOR PRODUCT OF TWO VECTORS

In order to gain a better understanding of the effect of a force on a rigid body, a new concept, the concept of *a moment of a force about a point*, will be introduced at this time. This concept will be more clearly understood, and applied more effectively, if we first add to the mathematical tools at our disposal the *vector product* of two vectors.

The vector product of two vectors P and Q is defined as the vector V which satisfies the following conditions.

1. The line of action of V is perpendicular to the plane containing P and Q (Fig. 3.6a).
2. The magnitude of V is the product of the magnitudes of P and Q and of the sine of the angle θ formed by P and Q (the measure of which will always be 180° or less); we thus have

$$V = PQ \sin \theta \qquad (3.1)$$

3. The direction of V is obtained from the *right-hand rule*. Close your right hand and hold it so that your fingers are curled in the same sense as the rotation through θ which brings the vector P in line with the vector Q; your thumb will then indicate the direction of the vector V (Fig. 3.6b). Note that if P and Q do not have a common point of application, they should first be redrawn from the same point. The three vectors P, Q, and V—taken in that order—are said to form a *right-handed triad.*†

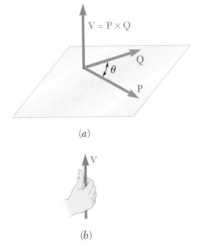

(a)

(b)

Fig. 3.6

---

†We should note that the x, y, and z axes used in Chap. 2 form a right-handed system of orthogonal axes and that the unit vectors i, j, k defined in Sec. 2.12 form a right-handed orthogonal triad.

As stated above, the vector **V** satisfying these three conditions (which define it uniquely) is referred to as the vector product of **P** and **Q**; it is represented by the mathematical expression

$$\mathbf{V} = \mathbf{P} \times \mathbf{Q} \tag{3.2}$$

Because of the notation used, the vector product of two vectors **P** and **Q** is also referred to as the *cross product* of **P** and **Q**.

It follows from Eq. (3.1) that, when two vectors **P** and **Q** have either the same direction or opposite directions, their vector product is zero. In the general case when the angle θ formed by the two vectors is neither 0° nor 180°, Eq. (3.1) can be given a simple geometric interpretation: The magnitude V of the vector product of **P** and **Q** is equal to the area of the parallelogram which has **P** and **Q** for sides (Fig. 3.7). The vector product **P** × **Q** will therefore remain unchanged if we replace **Q** by a vector **Q**′ which is coplanar with **P** and **Q** and such that the line joining the tips of **Q** and **Q**′ is parallel to **P**. We write

$$\mathbf{V} = \mathbf{P} \times \mathbf{Q} = \mathbf{P} \times \mathbf{Q}' \tag{3.3}$$

From the third condition used to define the vector product **V** of **P** and **Q**, namely, the condition stating that **P**, **Q**, and **V** must form a right-handed triad, it follows that vector products *are not commutative*, i.e., **Q** × **P** is not equal to **P** × **Q**. Indeed, we can easily check that **Q** × **P** is represented by the vector −**V**, which is equal and opposite to **V**. We thus write

$$\mathbf{Q} \times \mathbf{P} = -(\mathbf{P} \times \mathbf{Q}) \tag{3.4}$$

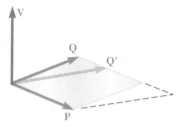

Fig. 3.7

EXAMPLE Let us compute the vector product **V** = **P** × **Q** where the vector **P** is of magnitude 6 and lies in the zx plane at an angle of 30° with the x axis, and where the vector **Q** is of magnitude 4 and lies along the x axis (Fig. 3.8).

It follows immediately from the definition of the vector product that the vector **V** must lie along the y axis, have the magnitude

$$V = PQ \sin \theta = (6)(4) \sin 30° = 12$$

and be directed upward. ∎

Fig. 3.8

We saw that the commutative property does not apply to vector products. We may wonder whether the *distributive* property holds, i.e., whether the relation

$$\mathbf{P} \times (\mathbf{Q}_1 + \mathbf{Q}_2) = \mathbf{P} \times \mathbf{Q}_1 + \mathbf{P} \times \mathbf{Q}_2 \tag{3.5}$$

is valid. The answer is *yes*. Many readers are probably willing to accept without formal proof an answer which they intuitively feel is correct. However, since the entire structure of both vector algebra and statics depends upon the relation (3.5), we should take time out to derive it.

We can, without any loss of generality, assume that **P** is directed along the y axis (Fig. 3.9a). Denoting by **Q** the sum of **Q**$_1$ and **Q**$_2$, we drop perpendiculars from the tips of **Q**, **Q**$_1$, and **Q**$_2$ onto the zx plane, defining in this way the vectors **Q**′, **Q**$_1'$, and **Q**$_2'$. These vectors will be referred to, respectively, as the *projections* of **Q**, **Q**$_1$, and **Q**$_2$ on the zx plane. Recalling the property expressed by Eq. (3.3), we

note that the left-hand member of Eq. (3.5) can be replaced by
$\mathbf{P} \times \mathbf{Q}'$ and that, similarly, the vector products $\mathbf{P} \times \mathbf{Q}_1$ and $\mathbf{P} \times \mathbf{Q}_2$
can respectively be replaced by $\mathbf{P} \times \mathbf{Q}_1'$ and $\mathbf{P} \times \mathbf{Q}_2'$. Thus, the
relation to be proved can be written in the form

$$\mathbf{P} \times \mathbf{Q}' = \mathbf{P} \times \mathbf{Q}_1' + \mathbf{P} \times \mathbf{Q}_2' \qquad (3.5')$$

We now observe that $\mathbf{P} \times \mathbf{Q}'$ can be obtained from $\mathbf{Q}'$ by
multiplying this vector by the scalar P and rotating it counterclockwise through 90° in the zx plane (Fig. 3.9b); the other two vector

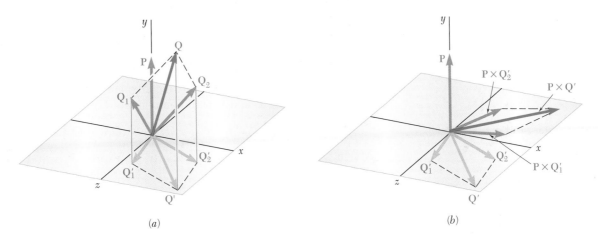

(a)   (b)

Fig. 3.9

products in (3.5′) can be obtained in the same manner from $\mathbf{Q}_1'$ and
$\mathbf{Q}_2'$, respectively. Now, since the projection of a parallelogram onto
an arbitrary plane is a parallelogram, the projection $\mathbf{Q}'$ of the sum
$\mathbf{Q}$ of $\mathbf{Q}_1$ and $\mathbf{Q}_2$ must be the sum of the projections $\mathbf{Q}_1'$ and $\mathbf{Q}_2'$ of
$\mathbf{Q}_1$ and $\mathbf{Q}_2$ on the same plane (Fig. 3.9a). This relation between the
vectors $\mathbf{Q}'$, $\mathbf{Q}_1'$, and $\mathbf{Q}_2'$ will still hold after the three vectors have
been multiplied by the scalar P and rotated through 90° (Fig. 3.9b).
Thus, the relation (3.5′) has been proved, and we can now be sure
that the distributive property holds for vector products.

A third property, the associative property, does not apply to
vector products; we have in general

$$(\mathbf{P} \times \mathbf{Q}) \times \mathbf{S} \neq \mathbf{P} \times (\mathbf{Q} \times \mathbf{S}) \qquad (3.6)$$

3.5 VECTOR PRODUCTS EXPRESSED IN TERMS OF RECTANGULAR COMPONENTS

Let us now determine the vector product of any two of the unit
vectors $\mathbf{i}$, $\mathbf{j}$, and $\mathbf{k}$, which were defined in Chap. 2. Consider first the
product $\mathbf{i} \times \mathbf{j}$ (Fig. 3.10a). Since both vectors have a magnitude
equal to 1 and since they are at a right angle to each other, their
vector product will also be a unit vector. This unit vector must be $\mathbf{k}$,
since the vectors $\mathbf{i}$, $\mathbf{j}$, and $\mathbf{k}$ are mutually perpendicular and form a
right-handed triad. On the other hand, it follows from the right-hand
rule given on page 79 that the product $\mathbf{j} \times \mathbf{i}$ will be equal to $-\mathbf{k}$
(Fig. 3.10b). Finally, it should be observed that the vector product

(a)

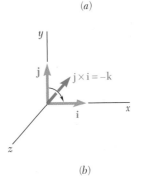

(b)

Fig. 3.10

of a unit vector with itself, such as $\mathbf{i} \times \mathbf{i}$, is equal to zero, since both vectors have the same direction. The vector products of the various possible pairs of unit vectors are

$$
\begin{array}{lll}
\mathbf{i} \times \mathbf{i} = 0 & \mathbf{j} \times \mathbf{i} = -\mathbf{k} & \mathbf{k} \times \mathbf{i} = \mathbf{j} \\
\mathbf{i} \times \mathbf{j} = \mathbf{k} & \mathbf{j} \times \mathbf{j} = 0 & \mathbf{k} \times \mathbf{j} = -\mathbf{i} \\
\mathbf{i} \times \mathbf{k} = -\mathbf{j} & \mathbf{j} \times \mathbf{k} = \mathbf{i} & \mathbf{k} \times \mathbf{k} = 0
\end{array} \tag{3.7}
$$

Fig. 3.11

By arranging in a circle and in counterclockwise order the three letters representing the unit vectors (Fig. 3.11), we can simplify the determination of the sign of the vector product of two unit vectors: The product of two unit vectors will be positive if they follow each other in counterclockwise order and will be negative if they follow each other in clockwise order.

We can now easily express the vector product $\mathbf{V}$ of two given vectors $\mathbf{P}$ and $\mathbf{Q}$ in terms of the rectangular components of these vectors. Resolving $\mathbf{P}$ and $\mathbf{Q}$ into components, we first write

$$
\mathbf{V} = \mathbf{P} \times \mathbf{Q} = (P_x\mathbf{i} + P_y\mathbf{j} + P_z\mathbf{k}) \times (Q_x\mathbf{i} + Q_y\mathbf{j} + Q_z\mathbf{k})
$$

Making use of the distributive property, we express $\mathbf{V}$ as the sum of vector products, such as $P_x\mathbf{i} \times Q_y\mathbf{j}$. Observing that each of the expressions obtained is equal to the vector product of two unit vectors, such as $\mathbf{i} \times \mathbf{j}$, multiplied by the product of two scalars, such as P_xQ_y, and recalling the identities (3.7), we obtain, after factoring out $\mathbf{i}$, $\mathbf{j}$, and $\mathbf{k}$,

$$
\mathbf{V} = (P_yQ_z - P_zQ_y)\mathbf{i} + (P_zQ_x - P_xQ_z)\mathbf{j} + (P_xQ_y - P_yQ_x)\mathbf{k} \tag{3.8}
$$

The rectangular components of the vector product $\mathbf{V}$ are thus found to be

$$
\begin{aligned}
V_x &= P_yQ_z - P_zQ_y \\
V_y &= P_zQ_x - P_xQ_z \\
V_z &= P_xQ_y - P_yQ_x
\end{aligned} \tag{3.9}
$$

Returning to Eq. (3.8), we observe that its right-hand member represents the expansion of a determinant. The vector product $\mathbf{V}$ can thus be expressed in the following form, which is more easily memorized:[†]

$$
\mathbf{V} = \begin{vmatrix} \mathbf{i} & \mathbf{j} & \mathbf{k} \\ P_x & P_y & P_z \\ Q_x & Q_y & Q_z \end{vmatrix} \tag{3.10}
$$

[†]Any determinant consisting of three rows and three columns can be evaluated by repeating the first and second columns and forming products along each diagonal line. The sum of the products obtained along the red lines is then subtracted from the sum of the products obtained along the black lines.

3.6 MOMENT OF A FORCE ABOUT A POINT

Let us now consider a force **F** acting on a rigid body (Fig. 3.12*a*). As we know, the force **F** is represented by a vector which defines its magnitude and direction. However, the effect of the force on the rigid body depends also upon its point of application *A*. The position of *A* can be conveniently defined by the vector **r** which joins the fixed reference point *O* with *A*; this vector is known as the *position vector* of *A*.† The position vector **r** and the force **F** define the plane shown in Fig. 3.12*a*.

We will define the *moment of* **F** *about O* as the vector product of **r** and **F**:

$$\mathbf{M}_O = \mathbf{r} \times \mathbf{F} \tag{3.11}$$

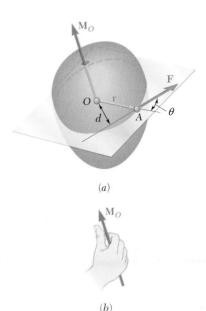

(a)

(b)

Fig. 3.12

According to the definition of the vector product given in Sec. 3.4, the moment $\mathbf{M}_O$ must be perpendicular to the plane containing *O* and the force **F**. The sense of $\mathbf{M}_O$ is defined by the sense of the rotation which will bring the vector **r** in line with the vector **F**; this rotation will be observed as *counterclockwise* by an observer located at the tip of $\mathbf{M}_O$. Another way of defining the sense of $\mathbf{M}_O$ is furnished by a variation of the right-hand rule: Close your right hand and hold it so that your fingers are curled in the sense of the rotation that **F** would impart to the rigid body about a fixed axis directed along the line of action of $\mathbf{M}_O$; your thumb will indicate the sense of the moment $\mathbf{M}_O$ (Fig. 3.12*b*).

Finally, denoting by *θ* the angle between the lines of action of the position vector **r** and the force **F**, we find that the magnitude of the moment of **F** about *O* is

$$M_O = rF \sin \theta = Fd \tag{3.12}$$

where *d* represents the perpendicular distance from *O* to the line of action of **F**. Since the tendency of a force **F** to make a rigid body rotate about a fixed axis perpendicular to the force depends upon the distance of **F** from that axis as well as upon the magnitude of **F**, we note that *the magnitude of* $\mathbf{M}_O$ *measures the tendency of the force* **F** *to make the rigid body rotate about a fixed axis directed along* $\mathbf{M}_O$.

In the SI system of units, where a force is expressed in newtons (N) and a distance in meters (m), the moment of a force is expressed in newton-meters (N · m). In the U.S. customary system of units, where a force is expressed in pounds and a distance in feet or inches, the moment of a force is expressed in lb · ft or lb · in.

We can observe that although the moment $\mathbf{M}_O$ of a force about a point depends upon the magnitude, the line of action, and the sense of the force, it does *not* depend upon the actual position of the point of application of the force along its line of action. Conversely, the moment $\mathbf{M}_O$ of a force **F** does not characterize the position of the point of application of **F**.

---

†We can easily verify that position vectors obey the law of vector addition and, thus, are truly vectors. Consider, for example, the position vectors **r** and **r′** of *A* with respect to two reference points *O* and *O′* and the position vector **s** of *O* with respect to *O′* (Fig. 3.40*a*, Sec. 3.16). We verify that the position vector $\mathbf{r'} = \overrightarrow{O'A}$ can be obtained from the position vectors $\mathbf{s} = \overrightarrow{O'O}$ and $\mathbf{r} = \overrightarrow{OA}$ by applying the triangle rule for the addition of vectors.

However, as it will be seen presently, the moment $\mathbf{M}_O$ of a force $\mathbf{F}$ of given magnitude and direction *completely defines the line of action of* $\mathbf{F}$. Indeed, the line of action of $\mathbf{F}$ must lie in a plane through O perpendicular to the moment $\mathbf{M}_O$; its distance d from O must be equal to the quotient M_O/F of the magnitudes of $\mathbf{M}_O$ and $\mathbf{F}$; and the sense of $\mathbf{M}_O$ determines whether the line of action of $\mathbf{F}$ is to be drawn on one side or the other of the point O.

We recall from Sec. 3.3 that the principle of transmissibility states that two forces $\mathbf{F}$ and $\mathbf{F}'$ are equivalent (i.e., have the same effect on a rigid body) if they have the same magnitude, same direction, and same line of action. This principle can now be restated as follows: *Two forces* $\mathbf{F}$ *and* $\mathbf{F}'$ *are equivalent if, and only if, they are equal* (i.e., have the same magnitude and same direction) *and have equal moments about a given point* O. The necessary and sufficient conditions for two forces $\mathbf{F}$ and $\mathbf{F}'$ to be equivalent are thus

$$\mathbf{F} = \mathbf{F}' \qquad \text{and} \qquad \mathbf{M}_O = \mathbf{M}'_O \tag{3.13}$$

We should observe that it follows from this statement that if the relations (3.13) hold for a given point O, they will hold for any other point.

Problems Involving Only Two Dimensions. Many applications deal with two-dimensional structures, i.e., structures which have length and breadth but only negligible depth and which are subjected to forces contained in the plane of the structure. Two-dimensional structures and the forces acting on them can be readily represented on a sheet of paper or on a blackboard. Their analysis is therefore considerably simpler than that of three-dimensional structures and forces.

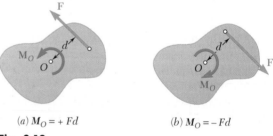

(a) $M_O = + Fd$ (b) $M_O = - Fd$

Fig. 3.13

Consider, for example, a rigid slab acted upon by a force $\mathbf{F}$ (Fig. 3.13). The moment of $\mathbf{F}$ about a point O chosen in the plane of the figure is represented by a vector $\mathbf{M}_O$ perpendicular to that plane and of magnitude Fd. In the case of Fig. 3.13a the vector $\mathbf{M}_O$ points *out of* the paper, while in the case of Fig. 3.13b it points *into* the paper. As we look at the figure, we observe in the first case that $\mathbf{F}$ tends to rotate the slab counterclockwise and in the second case that it tends to rotate the slab clockwise. Therefore, it is natural to refer to the sense of the moment of $\mathbf{F}$ about O in Fig. 3.13a as counterclockwise $\curvearrowleft$, and in Fig. 3.13b as clockwise $\curvearrowright$.

Since the moment of a force $\mathbf{F}$ acting in the plane of the figure must be perpendicular to that plane, we need only specify the *magnitude* and the *sense* of the moment of $\mathbf{F}$ about O. This can be done by assigning to the magnitude M_O of the moment a positive or negative sign according to whether the vector $\mathbf{M}_O$ points out of or into the paper.

3.7   VARIGNON'S THEOREM

The distributive property of vector products can be used to determine the moment of the resultant of several *concurrent forces*. If several forces $\mathbf{F}_1$, $\mathbf{F}_2$, ... are applied at the same point A (Fig. 3.14), and if we denote by $\mathbf{r}$ the position vector of A, it follows immediately from Eq. (3.5) of Sec. 3.4 that

$$\mathbf{r} \times (\mathbf{F}_1 + \mathbf{F}_2 + \cdots) = \mathbf{r} \times \mathbf{F}_1 + \mathbf{r} \times \mathbf{F}_2 + \cdots \quad (3.14)$$

In words, *the moment about a given point O of the resultant of several concurrent forces is equal to the sum of the moments of the various forces about the same point O*. This property, which was originally established by the French mathematician Varignon (1654–1722) long before the introduction of vector algebra, is known as *Varignon's theorem*.

The relation (3.14) makes it possible to replace the direct determination of the moment of a force $\mathbf{F}$ by the determination of the moments of two or more component forces. As you will see in the next section, $\mathbf{F}$ will generally be resolved into components parallel to the coordinate axes. However, it may be more expeditious in some instances to resolve $\mathbf{F}$ into components which are not parallel to the coordinate axes (see Sample Prob. 3.3).

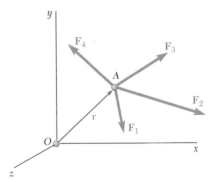

Fig. 3.14

3.8   RECTANGULAR COMPONENTS OF THE MOMENT OF A FORCE

In general, the determination of the moment of a force in space will be considerably simplified if the force and the position vector of its point of application are resolved into rectangular x, y, and z components. Consider, for example, the moment $\mathbf{M}_O$ about O of a force $\mathbf{F}$ whose components are F_x, F_y, and F_z and which is applied at a point A of coordinates x, y, and z (Fig. 3.15). Observing that the components of the position vector $\mathbf{r}$ are respectively equal to the coordinates x, y, and z of the point A, we write

$$\mathbf{r} = x\mathbf{i} + y\mathbf{j} + z\mathbf{k} \quad (3.15)$$
$$\mathbf{F} = F_x\mathbf{i} + F_y\mathbf{j} + F_z\mathbf{k} \quad (3.16)$$

Substituting for $\mathbf{r}$ and $\mathbf{F}$ from (3.15) and (3.16) into

$$\mathbf{M}_O = \mathbf{r} \times \mathbf{F} \quad (3.11)$$

and recalling the results obtained in Sec. 3.5, we write the moment $\mathbf{M}_O$ of $\mathbf{F}$ about O in the form

$$\mathbf{M}_O = M_x\mathbf{i} + M_y\mathbf{j} + M_z\mathbf{k} \quad (3.17)$$

where the components M_x, M_y, and M_z are defined by the relations

$$\begin{aligned}
M_x &= yF_z - zF_y \\
M_y &= zF_x - xF_z \\
M_z &= xF_y - yF_x
\end{aligned} \quad (3.18)$$

Fig. 3.15

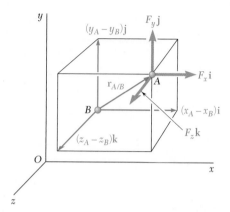

Fig. 3.16

As you will see in Sec. 3.11, the scalar components M_x, M_y, and M_z of the moment $\mathbf{M}_O$ measure the tendency of the force $\mathbf{F}$ to impart to a rigid body a motion of rotation about the x, y, and z axes, respectively. Substituting from (3.18) into (3.17), we can also write $\mathbf{M}_O$ in the form of the determinant

$$\mathbf{M}_O = \begin{vmatrix} \mathbf{i} & \mathbf{j} & \mathbf{k} \\ x & y & z \\ F_x & F_y & F_z \end{vmatrix} \tag{3.19}$$

To compute the moment $\mathbf{M}_B$ about an arbitrary point B of a force $\mathbf{F}$ applied at A (Fig. 3.16), we must replace the position vector $\mathbf{r}$ in Eq. (3.11) by a vector drawn from B to A. This vector is the *position vector of A relative to B* and will be denoted by $\mathbf{r}_{A/B}$. Observing that $\mathbf{r}_{A/B}$ can be obtained by subtracting $\mathbf{r}_B$ from $\mathbf{r}_A$, we write

$$\mathbf{M}_B = \mathbf{r}_{A/B} \times \mathbf{F} = (\mathbf{r}_A - \mathbf{r}_B) \times \mathbf{F} \tag{3.20}$$

or, using the determinant form,

$$\mathbf{M}_B = \begin{vmatrix} \mathbf{i} & \mathbf{j} & \mathbf{k} \\ x_{A/B} & y_{A/B} & z_{A/B} \\ F_x & F_y & F_z \end{vmatrix} \tag{3.21}$$

where $x_{A/B}$, $y_{A/B}$, and $z_{A/B}$ denote the components of the vector $\mathbf{r}_{A/B}$:

$$x_{A/B} = x_A - x_B \qquad y_{A/B} = y_A - y_B \qquad z_{A/B} = z_A - z_B$$

In the case of *problems involving only two dimensions*, the force $\mathbf{F}$ can be assumed to lie in the xy plane (Fig. 3.17). Setting $z = 0$ and $F_z = 0$ in Eq. (3.19), we obtain

$$\mathbf{M}_O = (xF_y - yF_x)\mathbf{k}$$

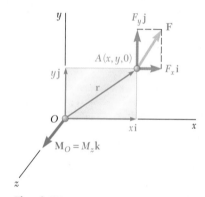

Fig. 3.17

We verify that the moment of $\mathbf{F}$ about O is perpendicular to the plane of the figure and that it is completely defined by the scalar

$$M_O = M_z = xF_y - yF_x \tag{3.22}$$

As noted earlier, a positive value for M_O indicates that the vector $\mathbf{M}_O$ points out of the paper (the force $\mathbf{F}$ tends to rotate the body counterclockwise about O), and a negative value indicates that the vector $\mathbf{M}_O$ points into the paper (the force $\mathbf{F}$ tends to rotate the body clockwise about O).

To compute the moment about $B(x_B, y_B)$ of a force lying in the xy plane and applied at $A(x_A, y_A)$ (Fig. 3.18), we set $z_{A/B} = 0$ and $F_z = 0$ in the relations (3.21) and note that the vector $\mathbf{M}_B$ is perpendicular to the xy plane and is defined in magnitude and sense by the scalar

$$M_B = (x_A - x_B)F_y - (y_A - y_B)F_x \tag{3.23}$$

Fig. 3.18

SAMPLE PROBLEM 3.1

A 100-lb vertical force is applied to the end of a lever which is attached to a shaft at O. Determine (a) the moment of the 100-lb force about O; (b) the horizontal force applied at A which creates the same moment about O; (c) the smallest force applied at A which creates the same moment about O; (d) how far from the shaft a 240-lb vertical force must act to create the same moment about O; (e) whether any one of the forces obtained in parts b, c, and d is equivalent to the original force.

SOLUTION

a. Moment about O. The perpendicular distance from O to the line of action of the 100-lb force is

$$d = (24 \text{ in.}) \cos 60° = 12 \text{ in.}$$

The magnitude of the moment about O of the 100-lb force is

$$M_O = Fd = (100 \text{ lb})(12 \text{ in.}) = 1200 \text{ lb} \cdot \text{in.}$$

Since the force tends to rotate the lever clockwise about O, the moment will be represented by a vector $\mathbf{M}_O$ perpendicular to the plane of the figure and pointing *into* the paper. We express this fact by writing

$$\mathbf{M}_O = 1200 \text{ lb} \cdot \text{in.} \ \downarrow \quad \blacktriangleleft$$

b. Horizontal Force. In this case, we have

$$d = (24 \text{ in.}) \sin 60° = 20.8 \text{ in.}$$

Since the moment about O must be 1200 lb · in., we write

$$M_O = Fd$$
$$1200 \text{ lb} \cdot \text{in.} = F(20.8 \text{ in.})$$
$$F = 57.7 \text{ lb} \qquad \mathbf{F} = 57.7 \text{ lb} \rightarrow \quad \blacktriangleleft$$

c. Smallest Force. Since $M_O = Fd$, the smallest value of F occurs when d is maximum. We choose the force perpendicular to OA and note that $d = 24$ in.; thus

$$M_O = Fd$$
$$1200 \text{ lb} \cdot \text{in.} = F(24 \text{ in.})$$
$$F = 50 \text{ lb} \qquad \mathbf{F} = 50 \text{ lb} \ \diagdown 30° \quad \blacktriangleleft$$

d. 240-lb Vertical Force. In this case $M_O = Fd$ yields

$$1200 \text{ lb} \cdot \text{in.} = (240 \text{ lb})d \qquad d = 5 \text{ in.}$$

but
$$OB \cos 60° = d \qquad\qquad OB = 10 \text{ in.} \quad \blacktriangleleft$$

e. None of the forces considered in parts b, c, and d is equivalent to the original 100-lb force. Although they have the same moment about O, they have different x and y components. In other words, although each force tends to rotate the shaft in the same manner, each causes the lever to pull on the shaft in a different way.

SAMPLE PROBLEM 3.2

A force of 800 N acts on a bracket as shown. Determine the moment of the force about B.

SOLUTION

The moment $\mathbf{M}_B$ of the force $\mathbf{F}$ about B is obtained by forming the vector product

$$\mathbf{M}_B = \mathbf{r}_{A/B} \times \mathbf{F}$$

where $\mathbf{r}_{A/B}$ is the vector drawn from B to A. Resolving $\mathbf{r}_{A/B}$ and $\mathbf{F}$ into rectangular components, we have

$$\mathbf{r}_{A/B} = -(0.2 \text{ m})\mathbf{i} + (0.16 \text{ m})\mathbf{j}$$
$$\mathbf{F} = (800 \text{ N}) \cos 60°\mathbf{i} + (800 \text{ N}) \sin 60°\mathbf{j}$$
$$= (400 \text{ N})\mathbf{i} + (693 \text{ N})\mathbf{j}$$

Recalling the relations (3.7) for the cross products of unit vectors (Sec. 3.5), we obtain

$$\mathbf{M}_B = \mathbf{r}_{A/B} \times \mathbf{F} = [-(0.2 \text{ m})\mathbf{i} + (0.16 \text{ m})\mathbf{j}] \times [(400 \text{ N})\mathbf{i} + (693 \text{ N})\mathbf{j}]$$
$$= -(138.6 \text{ N} \cdot \text{m})\mathbf{k} - (64.0 \text{ N} \cdot \text{m})\mathbf{k}$$
$$= -(202.6 \text{ N} \cdot \text{m})\mathbf{k} \qquad \mathbf{M}_B = 203 \text{ N} \cdot \text{m} \; \downarrow \quad \blacktriangleleft$$

The moment $\mathbf{M}_B$ is a vector perpendicular to the plane of the figure and pointing *into* the paper.

SAMPLE PROBLEM 3.3

A 30-lb force acts on the end of the 3-ft lever as shown. Determine the moment of the force about O.

SOLUTION

The force is replaced by two components, one component $\mathbf{P}$ in the direction of OA and one component $\mathbf{Q}$ perpendicular to OA. Since O is on the line of action of $\mathbf{P}$, the moment of $\mathbf{P}$ about O is zero and the moment of the 30-lb force reduces to the moment of $\mathbf{Q}$, which is clockwise and, thus, is represented by a negative scalar.

$$Q = (30 \text{ lb}) \sin 20° = 10.26 \text{ lb}$$
$$M_O = -Q(3 \text{ ft}) = -(10.26 \text{ lb})(3 \text{ ft}) = -30.8 \text{ lb} \cdot \text{ft}$$

Since the value obtained for the scalar M_O is negative, the moment $\mathbf{M}_O$ points *into* the paper. We write

$$\mathbf{M}_O = 30.8 \text{ lb} \cdot \text{ft} \; \downarrow \quad \blacktriangleleft$$

80 mm · 300 mm
240 mm
80 mm
240 mm

D
B
A
C

SAMPLE PROBLEM 3.4

A rectangular plate is supported by brackets at A and B and by a wire CD. Knowing that the tension in the wire is 200 N, determine the moment about A of the force exerted by the wire on point C.

SOLUTION

The moment $\mathbf{M}_A$ about A of the force $\mathbf{F}$ exerted by the wire on point C is obtained by forming the vector product

$$\mathbf{M}_A = \mathbf{r}_{C/A} \times \mathbf{F} \qquad (1)$$

where $\mathbf{r}_{C/A}$ is the vector drawn from A to C,

$$\mathbf{r}_{C/A} = \overrightarrow{AC} = (0.3 \text{ m})\mathbf{i} + (0.08 \text{ m})\mathbf{k} \qquad (2)$$

and $\mathbf{F}$ is the 200-N force directed along CD. Introducing the unit vector $\boldsymbol{\lambda} = \overrightarrow{CD}/CD$, we write

$$\mathbf{F} = F\boldsymbol{\lambda} = (200 \text{ N}) \frac{\overrightarrow{CD}}{CD} \qquad (3)$$

Resolving the vector $\overrightarrow{CD}$ into rectangular components, we have

$$\overrightarrow{CD} = -(0.3 \text{ m})\mathbf{i} + (0.24 \text{ m})\mathbf{j} - (0.32 \text{ m})\mathbf{k} \qquad CD = 0.50 \text{ m}$$

Substituting into (3), we obtain

$$\mathbf{F} = \frac{200 \text{ N}}{0.50 \text{ m}} [-(0.3 \text{ m})\mathbf{i} + (0.24 \text{ m})\mathbf{j} - (0.32 \text{ m})\mathbf{k}]$$
$$= -(120 \text{ N})\mathbf{i} + (96 \text{ N})\mathbf{j} - (128 \text{ N})\mathbf{k} \qquad (4)$$

Substituting for $\mathbf{r}_{C/A}$ and $\mathbf{F}$ from (2) and (4) into (1) and recalling the relations (3.7) of Sec. 3.5, we obtain

$$\mathbf{M}_A = \mathbf{r}_{C/A} \times \mathbf{F} = (0.3\mathbf{i} + 0.08\mathbf{k}) \times (-120\mathbf{i} + 96\mathbf{j} - 128\mathbf{k})$$
$$= (0.3)(96)\mathbf{k} + (0.3)(-128)(-\mathbf{j}) + (0.08)(-120)\mathbf{j} + (0.08)(96)(-\mathbf{i})$$
$$\mathbf{M}_A = -(7.68 \text{ N} \cdot \text{m})\mathbf{i} + (28.8 \text{ N} \cdot \text{m})\mathbf{j} + (28.8 \text{ N} \cdot \text{m})\mathbf{k} \qquad \blacktriangleleft$$

Alternative Solution. As indicated in Sec. 3.8, the moment $\mathbf{M}_A$ can be expressed in the form of a determinant:

$$\mathbf{M}_A = \begin{vmatrix} \mathbf{i} & \mathbf{j} & \mathbf{k} \\ x_C - x_A & y_C - y_A & z_C - z_A \\ F_x & F_y & F_z \end{vmatrix} = \begin{vmatrix} \mathbf{i} & \mathbf{j} & \mathbf{k} \\ 0.3 & 0 & 0.08 \\ -120 & 96 & -128 \end{vmatrix}$$

$$\mathbf{M}_A = -(7.68 \text{ N} \cdot \text{m})\mathbf{i} + (28.8 \text{ N} \cdot \text{m})\mathbf{j} + (28.8 \text{ N} \cdot \text{m})\mathbf{k} \qquad \blacktriangleleft$$

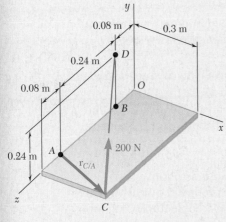

y
0.08 m · 0.3 m
0.24 m
D
0.08 m
O
B
x
0.24 m
A
$\mathbf{r}_{C/A}$
200 N
z
C

D
$(28.8 \text{ N·m})\mathbf{j}$
$-(7.68 \text{ N·m})\mathbf{i}$
A
$F = (200 \text{ N})\boldsymbol{\lambda}$
$(28.8 \text{ N·m})\mathbf{k}$
C

SOLVING PROBLEMS
ON YOUR OWN

In this lesson we introduced the *vector product* or *cross product* of two vectors. In the following problems, you may want to use the vector product to compute the *moment of a force about a point* and also to determine the *perpendicular distance* from a point to a line.

We defined the moment of the force $\mathbf{F}$ about the point O of a rigid body as

$$\mathbf{M}_O = \mathbf{r} \times \mathbf{F} \tag{3.11}$$

where $\mathbf{r}$ is the position vector *from O to any point* on the line of action of $\mathbf{F}$. Since the vector product is not commutative, it is absolutely necessary when computing such a product that you place the vectors in the proper order and that each vector have the correct sense. The moment $\mathbf{M}_O$ is important because its magnitude is a measure of the tendency of the force $\mathbf{F}$ to cause the rigid body to rotate about an axis directed along $\mathbf{M}_O$.

1. Computing the moment $\mathbf{M}_O$ of a force in two dimensions. You can use one of the following procedures:

   a. Use Eq. (3.12), $M_O = Fd$, which expresses the magnitude of the moment as the product of the magnitude of $\mathbf{F}$ and the *perpendicular distance d* from O to the line of action of $\mathbf{F}$ [Sample Prob. 3.1].

   b. Express $\mathbf{r}$ and $\mathbf{F}$ in component form and formally evaluate the vector product $\mathbf{M}_O = \mathbf{r} \times \mathbf{F}$ [Sample Prob. 3.2].

   c. Resolve $\mathbf{F}$ into components respectively parallel and perpendicular to the position vector $\mathbf{r}$. Only the perpendicular component contributes to the moment of $\mathbf{F}$ [Sample Prob. 3.3].

   d. Use Eq. (3.22), $M_O = M_z = xF_y - yF_x$. When applying this method, the simplest approach is to treat the scalar components of $\mathbf{r}$ and $\mathbf{F}$ as positive and then to assign, by observation, the proper sign to the moment produced by each force component. For example, applying this method to solve Sample Prob. 3.2, we observe that both force components tend to produce a clockwise rotation about B. Therefore, the moment of each force about B should be represented by a negative scalar. We then have for the total moment

$$M_B = -(0.16 \text{ m})(400 \text{ N}) - (0.20 \text{ m})(693 \text{ N}) = -202.6 \text{ N} \cdot \text{m}$$

2. Computing the moment $\mathbf{M}_O$ of a force F in three dimensions. Following the method of Sample Prob. 3.4, the first step in the process is to select the most convenient (simplest) position vector $\mathbf{r}$. You should next express $\mathbf{F}$ in terms of its rectangular components. The final step is to evaluate the vector product $\mathbf{r} \times \mathbf{F}$ to determine the moment. In most three-dimensional problems you will find it easiest to calculate the vector product using a determinant.

3. Determining the perpendicular distance d from a point A to a given line. First assume that a force $\mathbf{F}$ of known magnitude F lies along the given line. Next determine its moment about A by forming the vector product $\mathbf{M}_A = \mathbf{r} \times \mathbf{F}$, and calculate this product as indicated above. Then compute its magnitude M_A. Finally, substitute the values of F and M_A into the equation $M_A = Fd$ and solve for d.

PROBLEMS

3.1 A 20-lb force is applied to the control rod AB as shown. Knowing that the length of the rod is 9 in. and that $\alpha = 25°$, determine the moment of the force about point B by resolving the force into horizontal and vertical components.

3.2 A 20-lb force is applied to the control rod AB as shown. Knowing that the length of the rod is 9 in. and that $\alpha = 25°$, determine the moment of the force about point B by resolving the force into components along AB and in a direction perpendicular to AB.

3.3 A 20-lb force is applied to the control rod AB as shown. Knowing that the length of the rod is 9 in. and that the moment of the force about B is 120 lb · in. clockwise, determine the value of α.

Fig. P3.1, P3.2, and P3.3

3.4 A crate of mass 80 kg is held in the position shown. Determine (a) the moment produced by the weight $\mathbf{W}$ of the crate about E, (b) the smallest force applied at B that creates a moment of equal magnitude and opposite sense about E.

3.5 A crate of mass 80 kg is held in the position shown. Determine (a) the moment produced by the weight $\mathbf{W}$ of the crate about E, (b) the smallest force applied at A that creates a moment of equal magnitude and opposite sense about E, (c) the magnitude, sense, and point of application on the bottom of the crate of the smallest vertical force that creates a moment of equal magnitude and opposite sense about E.

3.6 A 300-N force $\mathbf{P}$ is applied at point A of the bell crank shown. (a) Compute the moment of the force $\mathbf{P}$ about O by resolving it into horizontal and vertical components. (b) Using the result of part a, determine the perpendicular distance from O to the line of action of $\mathbf{P}$.

Fig. P3.4 and P3.5

Fig. P3.6 and P3.7

3.7 A 400-N force $\mathbf{P}$ is applied at point A of the bell crank shown. (a) Compute the moment of the force $\mathbf{P}$ about O by resolving it into components along line OA and in a direction perpendicular to that line. (b) Determine the magnitude and direction of the smallest force $\mathbf{Q}$ applied at B that has the same moment as $\mathbf{P}$ about O.

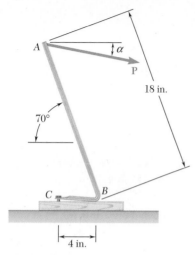

Fig. P3.8

3.8 It is known that a vertical force of 200 lb is required to remove the nail at C from the board. As the nail first starts moving, determine (a) the moment about B of the force exerted on the nail, (b) the magnitude of the force $\mathbf{P}$ that creates the same moment about B if $\alpha = 10°$, (c) the smallest force $\mathbf{P}$ that creates the same moment about B.

3.9 and 3.10 It is known that the connecting rod AB exerts on the crank BC a 500-lb force directed down and to the left along the centerline of AB. Determine the moment of the force about C.

Fig. P3.9   **Fig. P3.10**

3.11 A winch puller AB is used to straighten a fence post. Knowing that the tension in cable BC is 1040 N and length d is 1.90 m, determine the moment about D of the force exerted by the cable at C by resolving that force into horizontal and vertical components applied (a) at point C, (b) at point E.

3.12 It is known that a force with a moment of 960 N · m about D is required to straighten the fence post CD. If $d = 2.80$ m, determine the tension that must be developed in the cable of winch puller AB to create the required moment about point D.

3.13 It is known that a force with a moment of 960 N · m about D is required to straighten the fence post CD. If the capacity of winch puller AB is 2400 N, determine the minimum value of distance d to create the specified moment about point D.

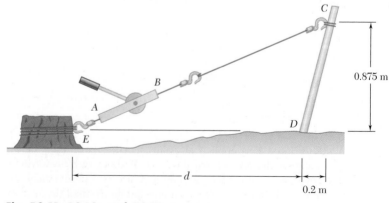

Fig. P3.11, P3.12, and P3.13

3.14 A mechanic uses a piece of pipe *AB* as a lever when tightening an alternator belt. When he pushes down at *A*, a force of 485 N is exerted on the alternator at *B*. Determine the moment of that force about bolt *C* if its line of action passes through *O*.

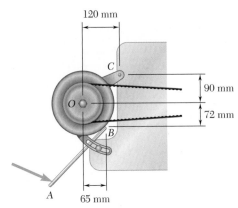

Fig. P3.14

3.15 Form the vector products **B** × **C** and **B'** × **C,** where *B* = *B'*, and use the results obtained to prove the identity

$$\sin \alpha \cos \beta = \tfrac{1}{2} \sin (\alpha + \beta) + \tfrac{1}{2} \sin (\alpha - \beta).$$

3.16 The vectors **P** and **Q** are two adjacent sides of a parallelogram. Determine the area of the parallelogram when (*a*) **P** = −7**i** + 3**j** − 3**k** and **Q** = 2**i** + 2**j** + 5**k**, (*b*) **P** = 6**i** − 5**j** − 2**k** and **Q** = −2**i** + 5**j** − **k**.

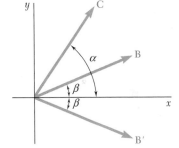

Fig. P3.15

3.17 A plane contains the vectors **A** and **B**. Determine the unit vector normal to the plane when **A** and **B** are equal to, respectively, (*a*) **i** + 2**j** − 5**k** and 4**i** − 7**j** − 5**k**, (*b*) 3**i** − 3**j** + 2**k** and −2**i** + 6**j** − 4**k**.

3.18 A line passes through the points (20 m, 16 m) and (−1 m, −4 m). Determine the perpendicular distance *d* from the line to the origin *O* of the system of coordinates.

3.19 Determine the moment about the origin *O* of the force **F** = 4**i** − 3**j** + 5**k** that acts at a point *A*. Assume that the position vector of *A* is (*a*) **r** = 2**i** + 3**j** − 4**k**, (*b*) **r** = −8**i** + 6**j** − 10**k**, (*c*) **r** = 8**i** − 6**j** + 5**k**.

3.20 Determine the moment about the origin *O* of the force **F** = 2**i** + 3**j** − 4**k** that acts at a point *A*. Assume that the position vector of *A* is (*a*) **r** = 3**i** − 6**j** + 5**k**, (*b*) **r** = **i** − 4**j** − 2**k**, (*c*) **r** = 4**i** + 6**j** − 8**k**.

3.21 The wire *AE* is stretched between the corners *A* and *E* of a bent plate. Knowing that the tension in the wire is 435 N, determine the moment about *O* of the force exerted by the wire (*a*) on corner *A*, (*b*) on corner *E*.

Fig. P3.21

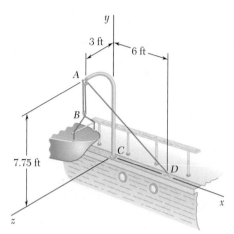

Fig. P3.22

3.22 A small boat hangs from two davits, one of which is shown in the figure. The tension in line $ABAD$ is 82 lb. Determine the moment about C of the resultant force $\mathbf{R}_A$ exerted on the davit at A.

3.23 A 6-ft-long fishing rod AB is securely anchored in the sand of a beach. After a fish takes the bait, the resulting force in the line is 6 lb. Determine the moment about A of the force exerted by the line at B.

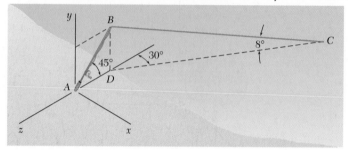

Fig. P3.23

3.24 A precast concrete wall section is temporarily held by two cables as shown. Knowing that the tension in cable BD is 900 N, determine the moment about point O of the force exerted by the cable at B.

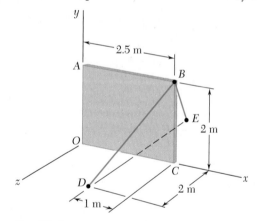

Fig. P3.24

3.25 A 200-N force is applied as shown to the bracket ABC. Determine the moment of the force about A.

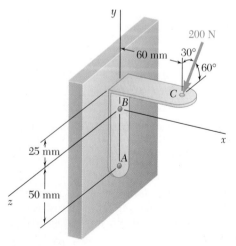

Fig. P3.25

3.26 The 6-m boom AB has a fixed end A. A steel cable is stretched from the free end B of the boom to a point C located on the vertical wall. If the tension in the cable is 2.5 kN, determine the moment about A of the force exerted by the cable at B.

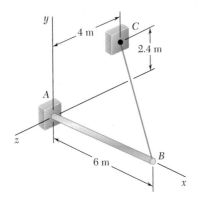

Fig. P3.26

3.27 In Prob. 3.21, determine the perpendicular distance from point O to wire AE.

3.28 In Prob. 3.21, determine the perpendicular distance from point B to wire AE.

3.29 In Prob. 3.22, determine the perpendicular distance from point C to portion AD of the line $ABAD$.

3.30 In Prob. 3.23, determine the perpendicular distance from point A to a line drawn through points B and C.

3.31 In Prob. 3.23, determine the perpendicular distance from point D to a line drawn through points B and C.

3.32 In Prob. 3.24, determine the perpendicular distance from point O to cable BD.

3.33 In Prob. 3.24, determine the perpendicular distance from point C to cable BD.

3.34 Determine the value of a that minimizes the perpendicular distance from point C to a section of pipeline that passes through points A and B.

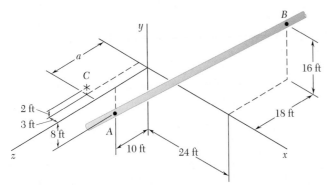

Fig. P3.34

3.9 SCALAR PRODUCT OF TWO VECTORS

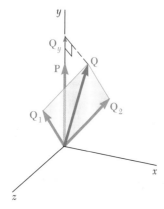

Fig. 3.19

The *scalar product* of two vectors $\mathbf{P}$ and $\mathbf{Q}$ is defined as the product of the magnitudes of $\mathbf{P}$ and $\mathbf{Q}$ and of the cosine of the angle θ formed by $\mathbf{P}$ and $\mathbf{Q}$ (Fig. 3.19). The scalar product of $\mathbf{P}$ and $\mathbf{Q}$ is denoted by $\mathbf{P} \cdot \mathbf{Q}$. We write therefore

$$\mathbf{P} \cdot \mathbf{Q} = PQ \cos \theta \tag{3.24}$$

Note that the expression just defined is not a vector but a *scalar*, which explains the name *scalar product*; because of the notation used, $\mathbf{P} \cdot \mathbf{Q}$ is also referred to as the *dot product* of the vectors $\mathbf{P}$ and $\mathbf{Q}$.

It follows from its very definition that the scalar product of two vectors is *commutative*, i.e., that

$$\mathbf{P} \cdot \mathbf{Q} = \mathbf{Q} \cdot \mathbf{P} \tag{3.25}$$

To prove that the scalar product is also *distributive*, we must prove the relation

$$\mathbf{P} \cdot (\mathbf{Q}_1 + \mathbf{Q}_2) = \mathbf{P} \cdot \mathbf{Q}_1 + \mathbf{P} \cdot \mathbf{Q}_2 \tag{3.26}$$

We can, without any loss of generality, assume that $\mathbf{P}$ is directed along the y axis (Fig. 3.20). Denoting by $\mathbf{Q}$ the sum of $\mathbf{Q}_1$ and $\mathbf{Q}_2$ and by θ_y the angle $\mathbf{Q}$ forms with the y axis, we express the left-hand member of (3.26) as follows:

$$\mathbf{P} \cdot (\mathbf{Q}_1 + \mathbf{Q}_2) = \mathbf{P} \cdot \mathbf{Q} = PQ \cos \theta_y = PQ_y \tag{3.27}$$

where Q_y is the y component of $\mathbf{Q}$. We can, in a similar way, express the right-hand member of (3.26) as

$$\mathbf{P} \cdot \mathbf{Q}_1 + \mathbf{P} \cdot \mathbf{Q}_2 = P(Q_1)_y + P(Q_2)_y \tag{3.28}$$

Fig. 3.20

Since $\mathbf{Q}$ is the sum of $\mathbf{Q}_1$ and $\mathbf{Q}_2$, its y component must be equal to the sum of the y components of $\mathbf{Q}_1$ and $\mathbf{Q}_2$. Thus, the expressions obtained in (3.27) and (3.28) are equal, and the relation (3.26) has been proved.

As far as the third property—the associative property—is concerned, we note that this property cannot apply to scalar products. Indeed, $(\mathbf{P} \cdot \mathbf{Q}) \cdot \mathbf{S}$ has no meaning, since $\mathbf{P} \cdot \mathbf{Q}$ is not a vector but a scalar.

The scalar product of two vectors $\mathbf{P}$ and $\mathbf{Q}$ can be expressed in terms of their rectangular components. Resolving $\mathbf{P}$ and $\mathbf{Q}$ into components, we first write

$$\mathbf{P} \cdot \mathbf{Q} = (P_x\mathbf{i} + P_y\mathbf{j} + P_z\mathbf{k}) \cdot (Q_x\mathbf{i} + Q_y\mathbf{j} + Q_z\mathbf{k})$$

Making use of the distributive property, we express $\mathbf{P} \cdot \mathbf{Q}$ as the sum of scalar products, such as $P_x\mathbf{i} \cdot Q_x\mathbf{i}$ and $P_x\mathbf{i} \cdot Q_y\mathbf{j}$. However, from the definition of the scalar product it follows that the scalar products of the unit vectors are either zero or one.

$$\begin{array}{lll} \mathbf{i} \cdot \mathbf{i} = 1 & \mathbf{j} \cdot \mathbf{j} = 1 & \mathbf{k} \cdot \mathbf{k} = 1 \\ \mathbf{i} \cdot \mathbf{j} = 0 & \mathbf{j} \cdot \mathbf{k} = 0 & \mathbf{k} \cdot \mathbf{i} = 0 \end{array} \qquad (3.29)$$

Thus, the expression obtained for $\mathbf{P} \cdot \mathbf{Q}$ reduces to

$$\mathbf{P} \cdot \mathbf{Q} = P_x Q_x + P_y Q_y + P_z Q_z \qquad (3.30)$$

In the particular case when $\mathbf{P}$ and $\mathbf{Q}$ are equal, we note that

$$\mathbf{P} \cdot \mathbf{P} = P_x^2 + P_y^2 + P_z^2 = P^2 \qquad (3.31)$$

Applications

1. *Angle formed by two given vectors.* Let two vectors be given in terms of their components:

$$\mathbf{P} = P_x \mathbf{i} + P_y \mathbf{j} + P_z \mathbf{k}$$
$$\mathbf{Q} = Q_x \mathbf{i} + Q_y \mathbf{j} + Q_z \mathbf{k}$$

To determine the angle formed by the two vectors, we equate the expressions obtained in (3.24) and (3.30) for their scalar product and write

$$PQ \cos \theta = P_x Q_x + P_y Q_y + P_z Q_z$$

Solving for $\cos \theta$, we have

$$\cos \theta = \frac{P_x Q_x + P_y Q_y + P_z Q_z}{PQ} \qquad (3.32)$$

2. *Projection of a vector on a given axis.* Consider a vector $\mathbf{P}$ forming an angle θ with an axis, or directed line, OL (Fig. 3.21). The *projection of* $\mathbf{P}$ *on the axis* OL is defined as the scalar

$$P_{OL} = P \cos \theta \qquad (3.33)$$

We note that the projection P_{OL} is equal in absolute value to the length of the segment OA; it will be positive if OA has the same sense as the axis OL, that is, if θ is acute, and negative otherwise. If $\mathbf{P}$ and OL are at a right angle, the projection of $\mathbf{P}$ on OL is zero.

Consider now a vector $\mathbf{Q}$ directed along OL and of the same sense as OL (Fig. 3.22). The scalar product of $\mathbf{P}$ and $\mathbf{Q}$ can be expressed as

$$\mathbf{P} \cdot \mathbf{Q} = PQ \cos \theta = P_{OL} Q \qquad (3.34)$$

Fig. 3.21

Fig. 3.22

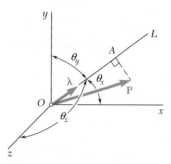

Fig. 3.23

from which it follows that

$$P_{OL} = \frac{\mathbf{P} \cdot \mathbf{Q}}{Q} = \frac{P_x Q_x + P_y Q_y + P_z Q_z}{Q} \qquad (3.35)$$

In the particular case when the vector selected along OL is the unit vector $\boldsymbol{\lambda}$ (Fig. 3.23), we write

$$P_{OL} = \mathbf{P} \cdot \boldsymbol{\lambda} \qquad (3.36)$$

Resolving $\mathbf{P}$ and $\boldsymbol{\lambda}$ into rectangular components and recalling from Sec. 2.12 that the components of $\boldsymbol{\lambda}$ along the coordinate axes are respectively equal to the direction cosines of OL, we express the projection of $\mathbf{P}$ on OL as

$$P_{OL} = P_x \cos \theta_x + P_y \cos \theta_y + P_z \cos \theta_z \qquad (3.37)$$

where θ_x, θ_y, and θ_z denote the angles that the axis OL forms with the coordinate axes.

3.10 MIXED TRIPLE PRODUCT OF THREE VECTORS

We define the *mixed triple product* of the three vectors $\mathbf{S}$, $\mathbf{P}$, and $\mathbf{Q}$ as the scalar expression

$$\mathbf{S} \cdot (\mathbf{P} \times \mathbf{Q}) \qquad (3.38)$$

obtained by forming the scalar product of $\mathbf{S}$ with the vector product of $\mathbf{P}$ and $\mathbf{Q}$.†

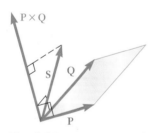

Fig. 3.24

A simple geometrical interpretation can be given for the mixed triple product of $\mathbf{S}$, $\mathbf{P}$, and $\mathbf{Q}$ (Fig. 3.24). We first recall from Sec. 3.4 that the vector $\mathbf{P} \times \mathbf{Q}$ is perpendicular to the plane containing $\mathbf{P}$ and $\mathbf{Q}$ and that its magnitude is equal to the area of the parallelogram which has $\mathbf{P}$ and $\mathbf{Q}$ for sides. On the other hand, Eq. (3.34) indicates that the scalar product of $\mathbf{S}$ and $\mathbf{P} \times \mathbf{Q}$ can be obtained by multiplying the magnitude of $\mathbf{P} \times \mathbf{Q}$ (i.e., the area of the parallelogram defined by $\mathbf{P}$ and $\mathbf{Q}$) by the projection of $\mathbf{S}$ on the vector $\mathbf{P} \times \mathbf{Q}$ (i.e., by the projection of $\mathbf{S}$ on the normal to the plane containing the parallelogram). The mixed triple product is thus equal, in absolute value, to the volume of the parallelepiped having the vectors $\mathbf{S}$, $\mathbf{P}$, and $\mathbf{Q}$ for sides (Fig. 3.25). We note that the sign of the mixed triple product will be positive if $\mathbf{S}$, $\mathbf{P}$, and $\mathbf{Q}$ form a right-handed triad and negative if they form a left-handed triad [that is, $\mathbf{S} \cdot (\mathbf{P} \times \mathbf{Q})$ will be negative if the rotation which brings $\mathbf{P}$ into line with $\mathbf{Q}$ is observed as clockwise from the

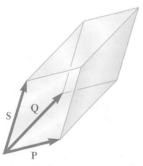

Fig. 3.25

†Another kind of triple product will be introduced later (Chap. 15): the *vector triple product* $\mathbf{S} \times (\mathbf{P} \times \mathbf{Q})$.

tip of **S**]. The mixed triple product will be zero if **S**, **P**, and **Q** are coplanar.

Since the parallelepiped defined in the preceding paragraph is independent of the order in which the three vectors are taken, the six mixed triple products which can be formed with **S**, **P**, and **Q** will all have the same absolute value, although not the same sign. It is easily shown that

$$\mathbf{S} \cdot (\mathbf{P} \times \mathbf{Q}) = \mathbf{P} \cdot (\mathbf{Q} \times \mathbf{S}) = \mathbf{Q} \cdot (\mathbf{S} \times \mathbf{P})$$
$$= -\mathbf{S} \cdot (\mathbf{Q} \times \mathbf{P}) = -\mathbf{P} \cdot (\mathbf{S} \times \mathbf{Q}) = -\mathbf{Q} \cdot (\mathbf{P} \times \mathbf{S})$$
$$(3.39)$$

Arranging in a circle and in counterclockwise order the letters representing the three vectors (Fig. 3.26), we observe that the sign of the mixed triple product remains unchanged if the vectors are permuted in such a way that they are still read in counterclockwise order. Such a permutation is said to be a *circular permutation*. It also follows from Eq. (3.39) and from the commutative property of scalar products that the mixed triple product of **S**, **P**, and **Q** can be defined equally well as $\mathbf{S} \cdot (\mathbf{P} \times \mathbf{Q})$ or $(\mathbf{S} \times \mathbf{P}) \cdot \mathbf{Q}$.

Fig. 3.26

The mixed triple product of the vectors **S**, **P**, and **Q** can be expressed in terms of the rectangular components of these vectors. Denoting **P** × **Q** by **V** and using formula (3.30) to express the scalar product of **S** and **V**, we write

$$\mathbf{S} \cdot (\mathbf{P} \times \mathbf{Q}) = \mathbf{S} \cdot \mathbf{V} = S_x V_x + S_y V_y + S_z V_z$$

Substituting from the relations (3.9) for the components of **V**, we obtain

$$\mathbf{S} \cdot (\mathbf{P} \times \mathbf{Q}) = S_x(P_y Q_z - P_z Q_y) + S_y(P_z Q_x - P_x Q_z)$$
$$+ S_z(P_x Q_y - P_y Q_x) \quad (3.40)$$

This expression can be written in a more compact form if we observe that it represents the expansion of a determinant:

$$\mathbf{S} \cdot (\mathbf{P} \times \mathbf{Q}) = \begin{vmatrix} S_x & S_y & S_z \\ P_x & P_y & P_z \\ Q_x & Q_y & Q_z \end{vmatrix} \quad (3.41)$$

By applying the rules governing the permutation of rows in a determinant, we could easily verify the relations (3.39) which were derived earlier from geometrical considerations.

3.11 MOMENT OF A FORCE ABOUT A GIVEN AXIS

Now that we have further increased our knowledge of vector algebra, we can introduce a new concept, the concept of *moment of a force about an axis*. Consider again a force **F** acting on a rigid body and the moment $\mathbf{M}_O$ of that force about O (Fig. 3.27). Let OL be

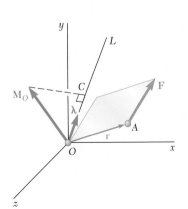

Fig. 3.27

an axis through O; *we define the moment M_{OL} of* **F** *about OL as the projection OC of the moment* **M_O** *onto the axis OL.* Denoting by **λ** the unit vector along OL and recalling from Secs. 3.9 and 3.6, respectively, the expressions (3.36) and (3.11) obtained for the projection of a vector on a given axis and for the moment $\mathbf{M}_O$ of a force **F**, we write

$$M_{OL} = \boldsymbol{\lambda} \cdot \mathbf{M}_O = \boldsymbol{\lambda} \cdot (\mathbf{r} \times \mathbf{F}) \tag{3.42}$$

which shows that the moment M_{OL} of **F** about the axis OL is the scalar obtained by forming the mixed triple product of **λ**, **r**, and **F**. Expressing M_{OL} in the form of a determinant, we write

$$M_{OL} = \begin{vmatrix} \lambda_x & \lambda_y & \lambda_z \\ x & y & z \\ F_x & F_y & F_z \end{vmatrix} \tag{3.43}$$

where λx, λy, λz = direction cosines of axis OL
x, y, z = coordinates of point of application of **F**
F_x, F_y, F_z = components of force **F**

The physical significance of the moment M_{OL} of a force **F** about a fixed axis OL becomes more apparent if we resolve **F** into two rectangular components $\mathbf{F}_1$ and $\mathbf{F}_2$, with $\mathbf{F}_1$ parallel to OL and $\mathbf{F}_2$ lying in a plane P perpendicular to OL (Fig. 3.28). Resolving **r** similarly into two components $\mathbf{r}_1$ and $\mathbf{r}_2$ and substituting for **F** and **r** into (3.42), we write

$$\begin{aligned} M_{OL} &= \boldsymbol{\lambda} \cdot [(\mathbf{r}_1 + \mathbf{r}_2) \times (\mathbf{F}_1 + \mathbf{F}_2)] \\ &= \boldsymbol{\lambda} \cdot (\mathbf{r}_1 \times \mathbf{F}_1) + \boldsymbol{\lambda} \cdot (\mathbf{r}_1 \times \mathbf{F}_2) + \boldsymbol{\lambda} \cdot (\mathbf{r}_2 \times \mathbf{F}_1) + \boldsymbol{\lambda} \cdot (\mathbf{r}_2 \times \mathbf{F}_2) \end{aligned}$$

Noting that all of the mixed triple products except the last one are equal to zero, since they involve vectors which are coplanar when drawn from a common origin (Sec. 3.10), we have

$$M_{OL} = \boldsymbol{\lambda} \cdot (\mathbf{r}_2 \times \mathbf{F}_2) \tag{3.44}$$

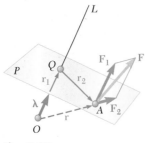

Fig. 3.28

The vector product $\mathbf{r}_2 \times \mathbf{F}_2$ is perpendicular to the plane P and represents the moment of the component $\mathbf{F}_2$ of **F** about the point Q where OL intersects P. Therefore, the scalar M_{OL}, which will be positive if $\mathbf{r}_2 \times \mathbf{F}_2$ and OL have the same sense and negative otherwise, measures the tendency of $\mathbf{F}_2$ to make the rigid body rotate about the fixed axis OL. Since the other component $\mathbf{F}_1$ of **F** does not tend to make the body rotate about OL, we conclude that *the moment M_{OL} of* **F** *about OL measures the tendency of the force* **F** *to impart to the rigid body a motion of rotation about the fixed axis OL.*

It follows from the definition of the moment of a force about an axis that the moment of **F** about a coordinate axis is equal to the component of $\mathbf{M}_O$ along that axis. Substituting successively each of the unit vectors **i**, **j**, and **k** for **λ** in (3.42), we observe that the expressions thus obtained for the *moments of* **F** *about the coordinate axes* are respectively equal to the expressions obtained in Sec. 3.8 for the components of the moment $\mathbf{M}_O$ of **F** about O:

$$\begin{aligned}
M_x &= yF_z - zF_y \\
M_y &= zF_x - xF_z \\
M_z &= xF_y - yF_x
\end{aligned} \tag{3.18}$$

We observe that just as the components F_x, F_y, and F_z of a force **F** acting on a rigid body measure, respectively, the tendency of **F** to move the rigid body in the x, y, and z directions, the moments M_x, M_y, and M_z of **F** about the coordinate axes measure the tendency of **F** to impart to the rigid body a motion of rotation about the x, y, and z axes, respectively.

More generally, the moment of a force **F** applied at A about an axis which does not pass through the origin is obtained by choosing an arbitrary point B on the axis (Fig. 3.29) and determining the projection on the axis BL of the moment $\mathbf{M}_B$ of **F** about B. We write

$$M_{BL} = \boldsymbol{\lambda} \cdot \mathbf{M}_B = \boldsymbol{\lambda} \cdot (\mathbf{r}_{A/B} \times \mathbf{F}) \tag{3.45}$$

where $\mathbf{r}_{A/B} = \mathbf{r}_A - \mathbf{r}_B$ represents the vector drawn from B to A. Expressing M_{BL} in the form of a determinant, we have

$$M_{BL} = \begin{vmatrix} \lambda_x & \lambda_y & \lambda_z \\ x_{A/B} & y_{A/B} & z_{A/B} \\ F_x & F_y & F_z \end{vmatrix} \tag{3.46}$$

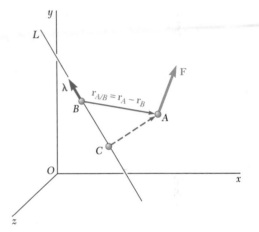

Fig. 3.29

where $\lambda_x, \lambda_y, \lambda_z$ = direction cosines of axis BL
$x_{A/B} = x_A - x_B \qquad y_{A/B} = y_A - y_B \qquad z_{A/B} = z_A - z_B$
F_x, F_y, F_z = components of force **F**

It should be noted that the result obtained is independent of the choice of the point B on the given axis. Indeed, denoting by M_{CL} the result obtained with a different point C, we have

$$\begin{aligned}
M_{CL} &= \boldsymbol{\lambda} \cdot [(\mathbf{r}_A - \mathbf{r}_C) \times \mathbf{F}] \\
&= \boldsymbol{\lambda} \cdot [(\mathbf{r}_A - \mathbf{r}_B) \times \mathbf{F}] + \boldsymbol{\lambda} \cdot [(\mathbf{r}_B - \mathbf{r}_C) \times \mathbf{F}]
\end{aligned}$$

But, since the vectors **λ** and $\mathbf{r}_B - \mathbf{r}_C$ lie in the same line, the volume of the parallelepiped having the vectors **λ**, $\mathbf{r}_B - \mathbf{r}_C$, and **F** for sides is zero, as is the mixed triple product of these three vectors (Sec. 3.10). The expression obtained for M_{CL} thus reduces to its first term, which is the expression used earlier to define M_{BL}. In addition, it follows from Sec. 3.6 that, when computing the moment of **F** about the given axis, A can be any point on the line of action of **F**.

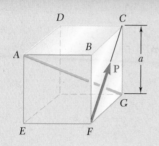

SAMPLE PROBLEM 3.5

A cube of side a is acted upon by a force $\mathbf{P}$ as shown. Determine the moment of $\mathbf{P}$ (*a*) about A, (*b*) about the edge AB, (*c*) about the diagonal AG of the cube, (*d*). Using the result of part *c*, determine the perpendicular distance between AG and FC.

SOLUTION

a. Moment about A. Choosing x, y, and z axes as shown, we resolve into rectangular components the force $\mathbf{P}$ and the vector $\mathbf{r}_{F/A} = \overrightarrow{AF}$ drawn from A to the point of application F of $\mathbf{P}$.

$$\mathbf{r}_{F/A} = a\mathbf{i} - a\mathbf{j} = a(\mathbf{i} - \mathbf{j})$$
$$\mathbf{P} = (P/\sqrt{2})\mathbf{j} - (P/\sqrt{2})\mathbf{k} = (P/\sqrt{2})(\mathbf{j} - \mathbf{k})$$

The moment of $\mathbf{P}$ about A is

$$\mathbf{M}_A = \mathbf{r}_{F/A} \times \mathbf{P} = a(\mathbf{i} - \mathbf{j}) \times (P/\sqrt{2})(\mathbf{j} - \mathbf{k})$$
$$\mathbf{M}_A = (aP/\sqrt{2})(\mathbf{i} + \mathbf{j} + \mathbf{k}) \blacktriangleleft$$

b. Moment about AB. Projecting $\mathbf{M}_A$ on AB, we write

$$M_{AB} = \mathbf{i} \cdot \mathbf{M}_A = \mathbf{i} \cdot (aP/\sqrt{2})(\mathbf{i} + \mathbf{j} + \mathbf{k})$$
$$M_{AB} = aP/\sqrt{2} \blacktriangleleft$$

We verify that, since AB is parallel to the x axis, M_{AB} is also the x component of the moment $\mathbf{M}_A$.

c. Moment about Diagonal AG. The moment of $\mathbf{P}$ about AG is obtained by projecting $\mathbf{M}_A$ on AG. Denoting by $\boldsymbol{\lambda}$ the unit vector along AG, we have

$$\boldsymbol{\lambda} = \frac{\overrightarrow{AG}}{AG} = \frac{a\mathbf{i} - a\mathbf{j} - a\mathbf{k}}{a\sqrt{3}} = (1/\sqrt{3})(\mathbf{i} - \mathbf{j} - \mathbf{k})$$
$$M_{AG} = \boldsymbol{\lambda} \cdot \mathbf{M}_A = (1/\sqrt{3})(\mathbf{i} - \mathbf{j} - \mathbf{k}) \cdot (aP/\sqrt{2})(\mathbf{i} + \mathbf{j} + \mathbf{k})$$
$$M_{AG} = (aP/\sqrt{6})(1 - 1 - 1) \quad M_{AG} = -aP/\sqrt{6} \blacktriangleleft$$

Alternative Method. The moment of $\mathbf{P}$ about AG can also be expressed in the form of a determinant:

$$M_{AG} = \begin{vmatrix} \lambda_x & \lambda_y & \lambda_z \\ x_{F/A} & y_{F/A} & z_{F/A} \\ F_x & F_y & F_z \end{vmatrix} = \begin{vmatrix} 1/\sqrt{3} & -1/\sqrt{3} & -1/\sqrt{3} \\ a & -a & 0 \\ 0 & P/\sqrt{2} & -P/\sqrt{2} \end{vmatrix} = -aP/\sqrt{6}$$

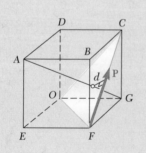

d. Perpendicular Distance between AG and FC. We first observe that $\mathbf{P}$ is perpendicular to the diagonal AG. This can be checked by forming the scalar product $\mathbf{P} \cdot \boldsymbol{\lambda}$ and verifying that it is zero:

$$\mathbf{P} \cdot \boldsymbol{\lambda} = (P/\sqrt{2})(\mathbf{j} - \mathbf{k}) \cdot (1/\sqrt{3})(\mathbf{i} - \mathbf{j} - \mathbf{k}) = (P\sqrt{6})(0 - 1 + 1) = 0$$

The moment M_{AG} can then be expressed as $-Pd$, where d is the perpendicular distance from AG to FC. (The negative sign is used since the rotation imparted to the cube by $\mathbf{P}$ appears as clockwise to an observer at G.) Recalling the value found for M_{AG} in part *c*,

$$M_{AG} = -Pd = -aP/\sqrt{6} \qquad d = a/\sqrt{6} \blacktriangleleft$$

SOLVING PROBLEMS ON YOUR OWN

In the problems for this lesson you will apply the *scalar product* or *dot product* of two vectors to determine the *angle formed by two given vectors* and the *projection of a force on a given axis*. You will also use the *mixed triple product* of three vectors to find the *moment of a force about a given axis* and the *perpendicular distance between two lines*.

1. Calculating the angle formed by two given vectors. First express the vectors in terms of their components and determine the magnitudes of the two vectors. The cosine of the desired angle is then obtained by dividing the scalar product of the two vectors by the product of their magnitudes [Eq. (3.32)].

2. Computing the projection of a vector P on a given axis OL. In general, begin by expressing $\mathbf{P}$ and the unit vector $\boldsymbol{\lambda}$, that defines the direction of the axis, in component form. Take care that $\boldsymbol{\lambda}$ has the correct sense (that is, $\boldsymbol{\lambda}$ is directed from O to L). The required projection is then equal to the scalar product $\mathbf{P} \cdot \boldsymbol{\lambda}$. However, if you know the angle θ formed by $\mathbf{P}$ and $\boldsymbol{\lambda}$, the projection is also given by $P \cos \theta$.

3. Determining the moment M_{OL} of a force about a given axis OL. We defined M_{OL} as

$$M_{OL} = \boldsymbol{\lambda} \cdot \mathbf{M}_O = \boldsymbol{\lambda} \cdot (\mathbf{r} \times \mathbf{F}) \tag{3.42}$$

where $\boldsymbol{\lambda}$ is the unit vector along OL and $\mathbf{r}$ is a position vector *from any point* on the line OL *to any point* on the line of action of $\mathbf{F}$. As was the case for the moment of a force about a point, choosing the most convenient position vector will simplify your calculations. Also, recall the warning of the previous lesson: The vectors $\mathbf{r}$ and $\mathbf{F}$ must have the correct sense, and they must be placed in the proper order. The procedure you should follow when computing the moment of a force about an axis is illustrated in part *c* of Sample Prob. 3.5. The two essential steps in this procedure are to first express $\boldsymbol{\lambda}$, $\mathbf{r}$, and $\mathbf{F}$ in terms of their rectangular components and to then evaluate the mixed triple product $\boldsymbol{\lambda} \cdot (\mathbf{r} \times \mathbf{F})$ to determine the moment about the axis. In most three-dimensional problems the most convenient way to compute the mixed triple product is by using a determinant.

As noted in the text, when $\boldsymbol{\lambda}$ is directed along one of the coordinate axes, M_{OL} is equal to the scalar component of $\mathbf{M}_O$ along that axis.

(continued)

4. Determining the perpendicular distance between two lines. You should remember that it is the perpendicular component $\mathbf{F}_2$ of the force $\mathbf{F}$ that tends to make a body rotate about a given axis OL (Fig. 3.28). It then follows that

$$M_{OL} = F_2 d$$

where M_{OL} is the moment of $\mathbf{F}$ about axis OL and d is the perpendicular distance between OL and the line of action of $\mathbf{F}$. This last equation gives us a simple technique for determining d. First assume that a force $\mathbf{F}$ of known magnitude F lies along one of the given lines and that the unit vector $\boldsymbol{\lambda}$ lies along the other line. Next compute the moment M_{OL} of the force $\mathbf{F}$ about the second line using the method discussed above. The magnitude of the parallel component, F_1, of $\mathbf{F}$ is obtained using the scalar product:

$$F_1 = \mathbf{F} \cdot \boldsymbol{\lambda}$$

The value of F_2 is then determined from

$$F_2 = \sqrt{F^2 - F_1^2}$$

Finally, substitute the values of M_{OL} and F_2 into the equation $M_{OL} = F_2 d$ and solve for d.

You should now realize that the calculation of the perpendicular distance in part d of Sample Prob. 3.5 was simplified by $\mathbf{P}$ being perpendicular to the diagonal AG. In general, the two given lines will not be perpendicular, so that the technique just outlined will have to be used when determining the perpendicular distance between them.

PROBLEMS

3.35 Given the vectors **P** = 3**i** − **j** + 2**k**, **Q** = 4**i** + 5**j** − 3**k**, and **S** = −2**i** + 3**j** − **k**, compute the scalar products **P** · **Q**, **P** · **S**, and **Q** · **S**.

3.36 Form the scalar product **B** · **C** and use the result obtained to prove the identity

$$\cos(\alpha - \beta) = \cos\alpha\cos\beta + \sin\alpha\sin\beta$$

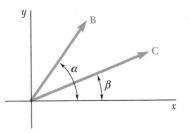

Fig. P3.36

3.37 Consider the volleyball net shown. Determine the angle formed by guy wires *AB* and *AC*.

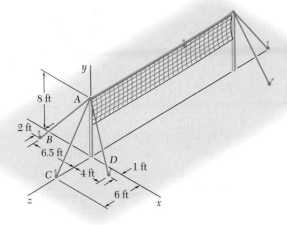

Fig. P3.37 and P3.38

3.38 Consider the volleyball net shown. Determine the angle formed by guy wires *AC* and *AD*.

3.39 Three cables are used to support a container as shown. Determine the angle formed by cables *AB* and *AD*.

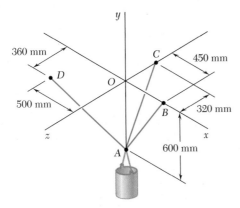

Fig. P3.39 and *P3.40*

3.40 Three cables are used to support a container as shown. Determine the angle formed by cables *AC* and *AD*.

105

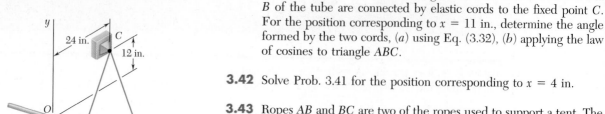

Fig. P3.41

3.41 The 20-in. tube AB can slide along a horizontal rod. The ends A and B of the tube are connected by elastic cords to the fixed point C. For the position corresponding to $x = 11$ in., determine the angle formed by the two cords, (*a*) using Eq. (3.32), (*b*) applying the law of cosines to triangle ABC.

3.42 Solve Prob. 3.41 for the position corresponding to $x = 4$ in.

3.43 Ropes AB and BC are two of the ropes used to support a tent. The two ropes are attached to a stake at B. If the tension in rope AB is 540 N, determine (*a*) the angle between rope AB and the stake, (*b*) the projection on the stake of the force exerted by rope AB at point B.

Fig. P3.43 and *P3.44*

3.44 Ropes AB and BC are two of the ropes used to support a tent. The two ropes are attached to a stake at B. If the tension in rope BC is 490 N, determine (*a*) the angle between rope BC and the stake, (*b*) the projection on the stake of the force exerted by rope BC at point B.

3.45 Given the vectors $\mathbf{P} = 4\mathbf{i} - 2\mathbf{j} + 3\mathbf{k}$, $\mathbf{Q} = 2\mathbf{i} + 4\mathbf{j} - 5\mathbf{k}$, and $\mathbf{S} = S_x\mathbf{i} - \mathbf{j} + 2\mathbf{k}$, determine the value of S_x for which the three vectors are coplanar.

3.46 Determine the volume of the parallelepiped of Fig. 3.25 when (*a*) $\mathbf{P} = 4\mathbf{i} - 3\mathbf{j} + 2\mathbf{k}$, $\mathbf{Q} = -2\mathbf{i} - 5\mathbf{j} + \mathbf{k}$, and $\mathbf{S} = 7\mathbf{i} + \mathbf{j} - \mathbf{k}$, (*b*) $\mathbf{P} = 5\mathbf{i} - \mathbf{j} + 6\mathbf{k}$, $\mathbf{Q} = 2\mathbf{i} + 3\mathbf{j} + \mathbf{k}$, and $\mathbf{S} = -3\mathbf{i} - 2\mathbf{j} + 4\mathbf{k}$.

3.47 Knowing that the tension in cable AB is 570 N, determine the moment about each of the coordinate axes of the force exerted on the plate at B.

3.48 Knowing that the tension in cable AC is 1065 N, determine the moment about each of the coordinate axes of the force exerted on the plate at C.

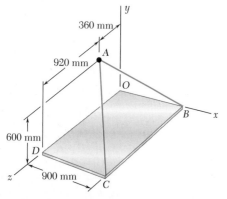

Fig. P3.47 and P3.48

3.49 A small boat hangs from two davits, one of which is shown in the figure. It is known that the moment about the z axis of the resultant force $\mathbf{R}_A$ exerted on the davit at A must not exceed 279 lb · ft in absolute value. Determine the largest allowable tension in line ABAD when x = 6 ft.

Fig. P3.49

3.50 For the davit of Prob. 3.49, determine the largest allowable distance x when the tension in line ABAD is 60 lb.

3.51 A farmer uses cables and winch pullers B and E to plumb one side of a small barn. If it is known that the sum of the moments about the x axis of the forces exerted by the cables on the barn at points A and D is equal to 4728 lb · ft, determine the magnitude of $\mathbf{T}_{DE}$ when $T_{AB} = 255$ lb.

3.52 Solve Prob. 3.51 when the tension in cable AB is 306 lb.

3.53 A single force $\mathbf{P}$ acts at C in a direction perpendicular to the handle BC of the crank shown. Knowing that $M_x = +20$ N · m and $M_y = -8.75$ N · m, and $M_z = -30$ N · m, determine the magnitude of $\mathbf{P}$ and the values of ϕ and θ.

Fig. P3.51

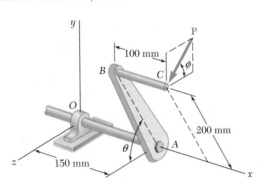

Fig. P3.53 and P3.54

3.54 A single force $\mathbf{P}$ acts at C in a direction perpendicular to the handle BC of the crank shown. Determine the moment M_x of $\mathbf{P}$ about the x axis when $\theta = 65°$, knowing that $M_y = -15$ N · m and $M_z = -36$ N · m.

3.55 The triangular plate ABC is supported by ball-and-socket joints at B and D and is held in the position shown by cables AE and CF. If the force exerted by cable AE at A is 55 N, determine the moment of that force about the line joining points D and B.

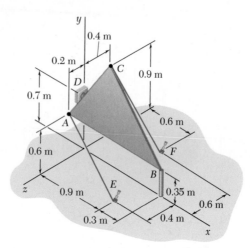

Fig. P3.55 and P3.56

3.56 The triangular plate ABC is supported by ball-and-socket joints at B and D and is held in the position shown by cables AE and CF. If the force exerted by cable CF at C is 33 N, determine the moment of that force about the line joining points D and B.

3.57 The 23-in. vertical rod CD is welded to the midpoint C of the 50-in. rod AB. Determine the moment about AB of the 235-lb force $\mathbf{P}$.

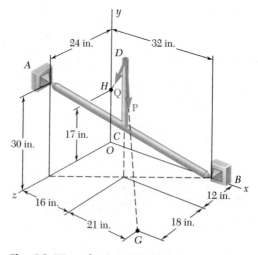

Fig. P3.57 and P3.58

3.58 The 23-in. vertical rod CD is welded to the midpoint C of the 50-in. rod AB. Determine the moment about AB of the 174-lb force $\mathbf{Q}$.

3.59 The frame *ACD* is hinged at *A* and *D* and is supported by a cable that passes through a ring at *B* and is attached to hooks at *G* and *H*. Knowing that the tension in the cable is 450 N, determine the moment about the diagonal *AD* of the force exerted on the frame by portion *BH* of the cable.

3.60 In Prob. 3.59, determine the moment about the diagonal *AD* of the force exerted on the frame by portion *BG* of the cable.

3.61 A regular tetrahedron has six edges of length *a*. A force **P** is directed as shown along edge *BC*. Determine the moment of **P** about edge *OA*.

Fig. P3.59

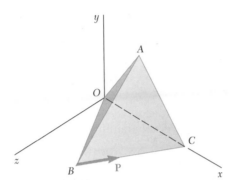

Fig. P3.61 and *P3.62*

3.62 A regular tetrahedron has six edges of length *a*. (*a*) Show that two opposite edges, such as *OA* and *BC*, are perpendicular to each other. (*b*) Use this property and the result obtained in Prob. 3.61 to determine the perpendicular distance between edges *OA* and *BC*.

3.63 Two forces $\mathbf{F}_1$ and $\mathbf{F}_2$ in space have the same magnitude *F*. Prove that the moment of $\mathbf{F}_1$ about the line of action of $\mathbf{F}_2$ is equal to the moment of $\mathbf{F}_2$ about the line of action of $\mathbf{F}_1$.

***3.64** In Prob. 3.55, determine the perpendicular distance between cable *AE* and the line joining points *D* and *B*.

***3.65** In Prob. 3.56, determine the perpendicular distance between cable *CF* and the line joining points *D* and *B*.

***3.66** In Prob. 3.57, determine the perpendicular distance between rod *AB* and the line of action of **P**.

***3.67** In Prob. 3.58, determine the perpendicular distance between rod *AB* and the line of action of **Q**.

***3.68** In Prob. 3.59, determine the perpendicular distance between portion *BH* of the cable and the diagonal *AD*.

***3.69** In Prob. 3.60, determine the perpendicular distance between portion *BG* of the cable and the diagonal *AD*.

Fig. 3.30

Fig. 3.31

Fig. 3.32

Photo 3.1 The parallel upward and downward forces of equal magnitude exerted on the arms of the lug nut wrench are an example of a couple.

3.12 MOMENT OF A COUPLE

*Two forces **F** and −**F** having the same magnitude, parallel lines of action, and opposite sense are said to form a couple* (Fig. 3.30). Clearly, the sum of the components of the two forces in any direction is zero. The sum of the moments of the two forces about a given point, however, is not zero. While the two forces will not translate the body on which they act, they will tend to make it rotate.

Denoting by $\mathbf{r}_A$ and $\mathbf{r}_B$, respectively, the position vectors of the points of application of **F** and −**F** (Fig. 3.31), we find that the sum of the moments of the two forces about O is

$$\mathbf{r}_A \times \mathbf{F} + \mathbf{r}_B \times (-\mathbf{F}) = (\mathbf{r}_A - \mathbf{r}_B) \times \mathbf{F}$$

Setting $\mathbf{r}_A - \mathbf{r}_B = \mathbf{r}$, where $\mathbf{r}$ is the vector joining the points of application of the two forces, we conclude that the sum of the moments of **F** and −**F** about O is represented by the vector

$$\mathbf{M} = \mathbf{r} \times \mathbf{F} \qquad (3.47)$$

The vector **M** is called the *moment of the couple;* it is a vector perpendicular to the plane containing the two forces, and its magnitude is

$$M = rF \sin \theta = Fd \qquad (3.48)$$

where d is the perpendicular distance between the lines of action of **F** and −**F**. The sense of **M** is defined by the right-hand rule.

Since the vector $\mathbf{r}$ in (3.47) is independent of the choice of the origin O of the coordinate axes, we note that the same result would have been obtained if the moments of **F** and −**F** had been computed about a different point O'. Thus, the moment **M** of a couple is a *free vector* (Sec. 2.3) which can be applied at any point (Fig. 3.32).

From the definition of the moment of a couple, it also follows that two couples, one consisting of the forces $\mathbf{F}_1$ and $-\mathbf{F}_1$, the other of the forces $\mathbf{F}_2$ and $-\mathbf{F}_2$ (Fig. 3.33), will have equal moments if

$$F_1 d_1 = F_2 d_2 \qquad (3.49)$$

and if the two couples lie in parallel planes (or in the same plane) and have the same sense.

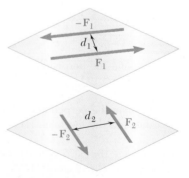

Fig. 3.33

3.13 EQUIVALENT COUPLES

Figure 3.34 shows three couples which act successively on the same rectangular box. As seen in the preceding section, the only motion a couple can impart to a rigid body is a rotation. Since each of the three couples shown has the same moment **M** (same direction and same magnitude $M = 120$ lb · in.), we can expect the three couples to have the same effect on the box.

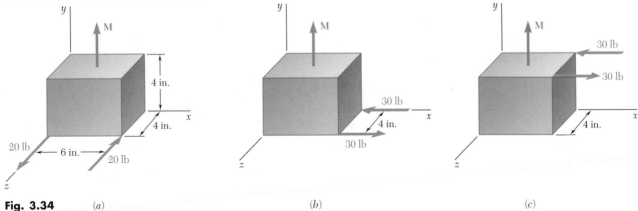

Fig. 3.34   (a)   (b)   (c)

As reasonable as this conclusion appears, we should not accept it hastily. While intuitive feeling is of great help in the study of mechanics, it should not be accepted as a substitute for logical reasoning. Before stating that two systems (or groups) of forces have the same effect on a rigid body, we should prove that fact on the basis of the experimental evidence introduced so far. This evidence consists of the parallelogram law for the addition of two forces (Sec. 2.2) and the principle of transmissibility (Sec. 3.3). Therefore, we will state that *two systems of forces are equivalent* (i.e., they have the same effect on a rigid body) *if we can transform one of them into the other by means of one or several of the following operations*: (1) replacing two forces acting on the same particle by their resultant; (2) resolving a force into two components; (3) canceling two equal and opposite forces acting on the same particle; (4) attaching to the same particle two equal and opposite forces; (5) moving a force along its line of action. Each of these operations is easily justified on the basis of the parallelogram law or the principle of transmissibility.

Let us now prove that *two couples having the same moment* **M** *are equivalent*. First consider two couples contained in the same plane, and assume that this plane coincides with the plane of the figure (Fig. 3.35). The first couple consists of the forces **F**$_1$ and $-$**F**$_1$ of magnitude F_1, which are located at a distance d_1 from each other (Fig. 3.35a), and the second couple consists of the forces **F**$_2$ and $-$**F**$_2$ of magnitude F_2, which are located at a distance d_2 from each other (Fig. 3.35d). Since the two couples have the same moment **M**, which is perpendicular to the plane of the figure, they must have the same sense (assumed here to be counterclockwise), and the relation

$$F_1d_1 = F_2d_2 \qquad (3.49)$$

must be satisfied. To prove that they are equivalent, we shall show that the first couple can be transformed into the second by means of the operations listed above.

Fig. 3.35

(a)

(b)

(c)

(d)

Fig. 3.36

Denoting by A, B, C, and D the points of intersection of the lines of action of the two couples, we first slide the forces $\mathbf{F}_1$ and $-\mathbf{F}_1$ until they are attached, respectively, at A and B, as shown in Fig. 3.35b. The force $\mathbf{F}_1$ is then resolved into a component $\mathbf{P}$ along line AB and a component $\mathbf{Q}$ along AC (Fig. 3.35c); similarly, the force $-\mathbf{F}_1$ is resolved into $-\mathbf{P}$ along AB and $-\mathbf{Q}$ along BD. The forces $\mathbf{P}$ and $-\mathbf{P}$ have the same magnitude, the same line of action, and opposite sense; they can be moved along their common line of action until they are applied at the same point and may then be canceled. Thus the couple formed by $\mathbf{F}_1$ and $-\mathbf{F}_1$ reduces to a couple consisting of $\mathbf{Q}$ and $-\mathbf{Q}$.

We will now show that the forces $\mathbf{Q}$ and $-\mathbf{Q}$ are respectively equal to the forces $-\mathbf{F}_2$ and $\mathbf{F}_2$. The moment of the couple formed by $\mathbf{Q}$ and $-\mathbf{Q}$ can be obtained by computing the moment of $\mathbf{Q}$ about B; similarly, the moment of the couple formed by $\mathbf{F}_1$ and $-\mathbf{F}_1$ is the moment of $\mathbf{F}_1$ about B. But, by Varignon's theorem, the moment of $\mathbf{F}_1$ is equal to the sum of the moments of its components $\mathbf{P}$ and $\mathbf{Q}$. Since the moment of $\mathbf{P}$ about B is zero, the moment of the couple formed by $\mathbf{Q}$ and $-\mathbf{Q}$ must be equal to the moment of the couple formed by $\mathbf{F}_1$ and $-\mathbf{F}_1$. Recalling (3.49), we write

$$Qd_2 = F_1d_1 = F_2d_2 \quad \text{and} \quad Q = F_2$$

Thus the forces $\mathbf{Q}$ and $-\mathbf{Q}$ are respectively equal to the forces $-\mathbf{F}_2$ and $\mathbf{F}_2$, and the couple of Fig. 3.35a is equivalent to the couple of Fig. 3.35d.

Next consider two couples contained in parallel planes P_1 and P_2; we will prove that they are equivalent if they have the same moment. In view of the foregoing, we can assume that the couples consist of forces of the same magnitude F acting along parallel lines (Fig. 3.36a and d). We propose to show that the couple contained in plane P_1 can be transformed into the couple contained in plane P_2 by means of the standard operations listed above.

Let us consider the two planes defined respectively by the lines of action of $\mathbf{F}_1$ and $-\mathbf{F}_2$ and by those of $-\mathbf{F}_1$ and $\mathbf{F}_2$ (Fig. 3.36b). At a point on their line of intersection we attach two forces $\mathbf{F}_3$ and $-\mathbf{F}_3$, respectively equal to $\mathbf{F}_1$ and $-\mathbf{F}_1$. The couple formed by $\mathbf{F}_1$ and $-\mathbf{F}_3$ can be replaced by a couple consisting of $\mathbf{F}_3$ and $-\mathbf{F}_2$ (Fig. 3.36c), since both couples clearly have the same moment and are contained in the same plane. Similarly, the couple formed by $-\mathbf{F}_1$ and $\mathbf{F}_3$ can be replaced by a couple consisting of $-\mathbf{F}_3$ and $\mathbf{F}_2$. Canceling the two equal and opposite forces $\mathbf{F}_3$ and $-\mathbf{F}_3$, we obtain the desired couple in plane P_2 (Fig. 3.36d). Thus, we conclude that two couples having the same moment **M** are equivalent, whether they are contained in the same plane or in parallel planes.

The property we have just established is very important for the correct understanding of the mechanics of rigid bodies. It indicates that when a couple acts on a rigid body, it does not matter where the two forces forming the couple act or what magnitude and direction they have. The only thing which counts is the *moment* of the couple (magnitude and direction). Couples with the same moment will have the same effect on the rigid body.

3.14 ADDITION OF COUPLES

Consider two intersecting planes P_1 and P_2 and two couples acting respectively in P_1 and P_2. We can, without any loss of generality, assume that the couple in P_1 consists of two forces $\mathbf{F}_1$ and $-\mathbf{F}_1$ perpendicular to the line of intersection of the two planes and acting respectively at A and B (Fig. 3.37a). Similarly, we assume that the couple in P_2 consists of two forces $\mathbf{F}_2$ and $-\mathbf{F}_2$ perpendicular to AB and acting respectively at A and B. It is clear that the resultant $\mathbf{R}$ of $\mathbf{F}_1$ and $\mathbf{F}_2$ and the resultant $-\mathbf{R}$ of $-\mathbf{F}_1$ and $-\mathbf{F}_2$ form a couple. Denoting by $\mathbf{r}$ the vector joining B to A and recalling the definition of the moment of a couple (Sec. 3.12), we express the moment $\mathbf{M}$ of the resulting couple as follows:

$$\mathbf{M} = \mathbf{r} \times \mathbf{R} = \mathbf{r} \times (\mathbf{F}_1 + \mathbf{F}_2)$$

and, by Varignon's theorem,

$$\mathbf{M} = \mathbf{r} \times \mathbf{F}_1 + \mathbf{r} \times \mathbf{F}_2$$

But the first term in the expression obtained represents the moment $\mathbf{M}_1$ of the couple in P_1, and the second term represents the moment $\mathbf{M}_2$ of the couple in P_2. We have

$$\mathbf{M} = \mathbf{M}_1 + \mathbf{M}_2 \tag{3.50}$$

and we conclude that the sum of two couples of moments $\mathbf{M}_1$ and $\mathbf{M}_2$ is a couple of moment $\mathbf{M}$ equal to the vector sum of $\mathbf{M}_1$ and $\mathbf{M}_2$ (Fig. 3.37b).

3.15 COUPLES CAN BE REPRESENTED BY VECTORS

As we saw in Sec. 3.13, couples which have the same moment, whether they act in the same plane or in parallel planes, are equivalent. There is therefore no need to draw the actual forces forming a given couple in order to define its effect on a rigid body (Fig. 3.38a). It is sufficient to draw an arrow equal in magnitude and direction to the moment $\mathbf{M}$ of the couple (Fig. 3.38b). On the other hand, we saw in Sec. 3.14 that the sum of two couples is itself a couple and that the moment $\mathbf{M}$ of the resultant couple can be obtained by forming the vector sum of the moments $\mathbf{M}_1$ and $\mathbf{M}_2$ of the given couples. Thus, couples obey the law of addition of vectors, and the arrow used in Fig. 3.38b to represent the couple defined in Fig. 3.38a can truly be considered a vector.

(a)

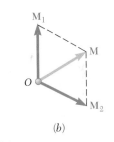

(b)

Fig. 3.37

The vector representing a couple is called a *couple vector*. Note that, in Fig. 3.38, a red arrow is used to distinguish the couple vector, *which represents the couple itself*, from the *moment* of the couple, which was represented by a green arrow in earlier figures. Also note that the symbol ↱ is added to this red arrow to avoid any confusion with vectors representing forces. A couple vector, like the moment of a couple, is a free vector. Its point of application, therefore, can be chosen at the origin of the system of coordinates, if so desired (Fig. 3.38c). Furthermore, the couple vector $\mathbf{M}$ can be resolved into component vectors $\mathbf{M}_x$, $\mathbf{M}_y$, and $\mathbf{M}_z$, which are directed along the coordinate axes (Fig. 3.38d). These component vectors represent couples acting, respectively, in the yz, zx, and xy planes.

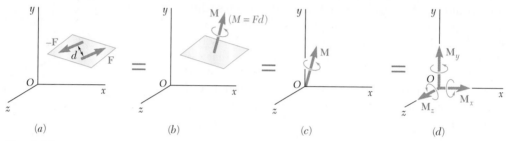

(a)   (b)   (c)   (d)

Fig. 3.38

3.16 RESOLUTION OF A GIVEN FORCE INTO A FORCE AT O AND A COUPLE

Consider a force $\mathbf{F}$ acting on a rigid body at a point A defined by the position vector $\mathbf{r}$ (Fig. 3.39a). Suppose that for some reason we would rather have the force act at point O. While we can move $\mathbf{F}$ along its line of action (principle of transmissibility), we cannot move it to a point O which does not lie on the original line of action without modifying the action of $\mathbf{F}$ on the rigid body.

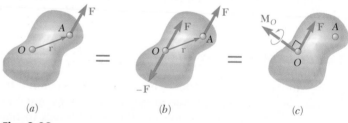

(a)   (b)   (c)

Fig. 3.39

We can, however, attach two forces at point O, one equal to $\mathbf{F}$ and the other equal to $-\mathbf{F}$, without modifying the action of the original force on the rigid body (Fig. 3.39b). As a result of this transformation, a force $\mathbf{F}$ is now applied at O; the other two forces form a couple of moment $\mathbf{M}_O = \mathbf{r} \times \mathbf{F}$. Thus, *any force $\mathbf{F}$ acting on a rigid body can be moved to an arbitrary point O provided that a couple is added whose moment is equal to the moment of $\mathbf{F}$ about O.* The couple tends to impart to the rigid body the same rotational motion about O that the force $\mathbf{F}$ tended to produce before it was transferred to O. The couple is represented by a couple vector $\mathbf{M}_O$ perpendicular to the plane containing $\mathbf{r}$ and $\mathbf{F}$. Since $\mathbf{M}_O$ is a free vector, it may be applied anywhere; for convenience, however, the couple vector is usually attached at O, together with $\mathbf{F}$, and the combination obtained is referred to as a *force-couple system* (Fig. 3.39c).

If the force $\mathbf{F}$ had been moved from A to a different point O' (Fig. 3.40a and c), the moment $\mathbf{M}_{O'} = \mathbf{r}' \times \mathbf{F}$ of $\mathbf{F}$ about O' should have been computed, and a new force-couple system, consisting of $\mathbf{F}$ and of the couple vector $\mathbf{M}_{O'}$, would have been attached at O'. The relation existing between the moments of $\mathbf{F}$ about O and O' is obtained by writing

$$\mathbf{M}_{O'} = \mathbf{r}' \times \mathbf{F} = (\mathbf{r} + \mathbf{s}) \times \mathbf{F} = \mathbf{r} \times \mathbf{F} + \mathbf{s} \times \mathbf{F}$$

$$\mathbf{M}_{O'} = \mathbf{M}_O + \mathbf{s} \times \mathbf{F} \tag{3.51}$$

where $\mathbf{s}$ is the vector joining O' to O. Thus, the moment $\mathbf{M}_{O'}$ of $\mathbf{F}$ about O' is obtained by adding to the moment $\mathbf{M}_O$ of $\mathbf{F}$ about O the vector product $\mathbf{s} \times \mathbf{F}$ representing the moment about O' of the force $\mathbf{F}$ applied at O.

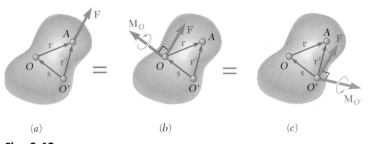

(a)   (b)   (c)

Fig. 3.40

This result could also have been established by observing that, in order to transfer to O' the force-couple system attached at O (Fig. 3.40b and c), the couple vector $\mathbf{M}_O$ can be freely moved to O'; to move the force $\mathbf{F}$ from O to O', however, it is necessary to add to $\mathbf{F}$ a couple vector whose moment is equal to the moment about O' of the force $\mathbf{F}$ applied at O. Thus, the couple vector $\mathbf{M}_{O'}$ must be the sum of $\mathbf{M}_O$ and the vector $\mathbf{s} \times \mathbf{F}$.

As noted above, the force-couple system obtained by transferring a force $\mathbf{F}$ from a point A to a point O consists of $\mathbf{F}$ and a couple vector $\mathbf{M}_O$ perpendicular to $\mathbf{F}$. Conversely, any force-couple system consisting of a force $\mathbf{F}$ and a couple vector $\mathbf{M}_O$ which are *mutually perpendicular* can be replaced by a single equivalent force. This is done by moving the force $\mathbf{F}$ in the plane perpendicular to $\mathbf{M}_O$ until its moment about O is equal to the moment of the couple to be eliminated.

Photo 3.2 The force exerted by each hand on the wrench could be replaced with an equivalent force-couple system acting on the nut.

Determine the components of the single couple equivalent to the two couples shown.

SOLUTION

Our computations will be simplified if we attach two equal and opposite 20-lb forces at A. This enables us to replace the original 20-lb-force couple by two new 20-lb-force couples, one of which lies in the zx plane and the other in a plane parallel to the xy plane. The three couples shown in the adjoining sketch can be represented by three couple vectors $\mathbf{M}_x$, $\mathbf{M}_y$, and $\mathbf{M}_z$ directed along the coordinate axes. The corresponding moments are

$$M_x = -(30 \text{ lb})(18 \text{ in.}) = -540 \text{ lb} \cdot \text{in.}$$
$$M_y = +(20 \text{ lb})(12 \text{ in.}) = +240 \text{ lb} \cdot \text{in.}$$
$$M_z = +(20 \text{ lb})(9 \text{ in.}) = +180 \text{ lb} \cdot \text{in.}$$

These three moments represent the components of the single couple $\mathbf{M}$ equivalent to the two given couples. We write

$$\mathbf{M} = -(540 \text{ lb} \cdot \text{in.})\mathbf{i} + (240 \text{ lb} \cdot \text{in.})\mathbf{j} + (180 \text{ lb} \cdot \text{in.})\mathbf{k} \quad \blacktriangleleft$$

Alternative Solution. The components of the equivalent single couple $\mathbf{M}$ can also be obtained by computing the sum of the moments of the four given forces about an arbitrary point. Selecting point D, we write

$$\mathbf{M} = \mathbf{M}_D = (18 \text{ in.})\mathbf{j} \times (-30 \text{ lb})\mathbf{k} + [(9 \text{ in.})\mathbf{j} - (12 \text{ in.})\mathbf{k}] \times (-20 \text{ lb})\mathbf{i}$$

and, after computing the various cross products,

$$\mathbf{M} = -(540 \text{ lb} \cdot \text{in.})\mathbf{i} + (240 \text{ lb} \cdot \text{in.})\mathbf{j} + (180 \text{ lb} \cdot \text{in.})\mathbf{k} \quad \blacktriangleleft$$

SAMPLE PROBLEM 3.7

Replace the couple and force shown by an equivalent single force applied to the lever. Determine the distance from the shaft to the point of application of this equivalent force.

SOLUTION

First the given force and couple are replaced by an equivalent force-couple system at O. We move the force $\mathbf{F} = -(400\text{ N})\mathbf{j}$ to O and at the same time add a couple of moment $\mathbf{M}_O$ equal to the moment about O of the force in its original position.

$$\mathbf{M}_O = \overrightarrow{OB} \times \mathbf{F} = [(0.150\,\text{m})\mathbf{i} + (0.260\,\text{m})\mathbf{j}] \times (-400\,\text{N})\mathbf{j}$$
$$= -(60\text{ N} \cdot \text{m})\mathbf{k}$$

This couple is added to the couple of moment $-(24\text{ N} \cdot \text{m})\mathbf{k}$ formed by the two 200-N forces, and a couple of moment $-(84\text{ N} \cdot \text{m})\mathbf{k}$ is obtained. This last couple can be eliminated by applying $\mathbf{F}$ at a point C chosen in such a way that

$$-(84\text{N} \cdot \text{m})\mathbf{k} = \overrightarrow{OC} \times \mathbf{F}$$
$$= [(OC) \cos 60°\mathbf{i} + (OC) \sin 60°\mathbf{j}] \times (-400\text{N})\mathbf{j}$$
$$= -(OC)\cos 60°(400\text{N})\mathbf{k}$$

We conclude that

$$(OC) \cos 60° = 0.210 \text{ m} = 210 \text{ mm} \qquad OC = 420 \text{ mm} \blacktriangleleft$$

Alternative Solution. Since the effect of a couple does not depend on its location, the couple of moment $-(24\text{ N} \cdot \text{m})\mathbf{k}$ can be moved to B; we thus obtain a force-couple system at B. The couple can now be eliminated by applying $\mathbf{F}$ at a point C chosen in such a way that

$$-(24\text{N} \cdot \text{m})\mathbf{k} = \overrightarrow{BC} \times \mathbf{F}$$
$$= -(BC) \cos 60°(400\text{N})\mathbf{k}$$

We conclude that

$$(BC) \cos 60° = 0.060 \text{ m} = 60 \text{ mm} \qquad BC = 120 \text{ mm}$$
$$OC = OB + BC = 300 \text{ mm} + 120 \text{ mm} \qquad OC = 420 \text{ mm} \blacktriangleleft$$

SOLVING PROBLEMS
ON YOUR OWN

In this lesson we discussed the properties of *couples*. To solve the problems which follow, you will need to remember that the net effect of a couple is to produce a moment **M**. Since this moment is independent of the point about which it is computed, **M** is a *free vector* and thus remains unchanged as it is moved from point to point. Also, two couples are *equivalent* (that is, they have the same effect on a given rigid body) if they produce the same moment.

When determining the moment of a couple, all previous techniques for computing moments apply. Also, since the moment of a couple is a free vector, it should be computed relative to the most convenient point.

Because the only effect of a couple is to produce a moment, it is possible to represent a couple with a vector, the *couple vector,* which is equal to the moment of the couple. The couple vector is a free vector and will be represented by a special symbol, ↻, to distinguish it from force vectors.

In solving the problems in this lesson, you will be called upon to perform the following operations:

1. Adding two or more couples. This results in a new couple, the moment of which is obtained by adding vectorially the moments of the given couples [Sample Prob. 3.6].

2. Replacing a force with an equivalent force-couple system at a specified point. As explained in Sec. 3.16, the force of the force-couple system is equal to the original force, while the required couple vector is equal to the moment of the original force about the given point. In addition, it is important to observe that the force and the couple vector are perpendicular to each other. Conversely, it follows that a force-couple system can be reduced to a single force only if the force and couple vector are mutually perpendicular (see the next paragraph).

3. Replacing a force-couple system (with F perpendicular to M) with a single equivalent force. Note that the requirement that **F** and **M** be mutually perpendicular will be satisfied in all two-dimensional problems. The single equivalent force is equal to **F** and is applied in such a way that its moment about the original point of application is equal to **M** [Sample Prob. 3.7].

3.70 A plate in the shape of a parallelogram is acted upon by two couples. Determine (a) the moment of the couple formed by the two 21-lb forces, (b) the perpendicular distance between the 12-lb forces if the resultant of the two couples is zero, (c) the value of α if the resultant couple is 72 lb · in. clockwise and d is 42 in.

Fig. P3.70

3.71 Four 1-in.-diameter pegs are attached to a board as shown. Two strings are passed around the pegs and pulled with the forces indicated. (a) Determine the resultant couple acting on the board. (b) If only one string is used, around which pegs should it pass and in what directions should it be pulled to create the same couple with the minimum tension in the string? (c) What is the value of that minimum tension?

Fig. P3.71 and P3.72

3.72 Four pegs of the same diameter are attached to a board as shown. Two strings are passed around the pegs and pulled with the forces indicated. Determine the diameter of the pegs knowing that the resultant couple applied to the board is 485 lb · in. counterclockwise.

3.73 A piece of plywood in which several holes are being drilled successively has been secured to a workbench by means of two nails. Knowing that the drill exerts a 12-N · m couple on the piece of plywood, determine the magnitude of the resulting forces applied to the nails if they are located (a) at A and B, (b) at B and C, (c) at A and C.

Fig. P3.73

119

Fig. P3.74

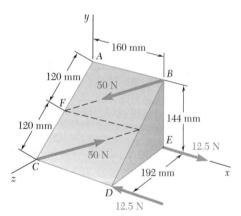

Fig. P3.76

3.74 Two parallel 40-N forces are applied to a lever as shown. Determine the moment of the couple formed by the two forces (*a*) by resolving each force into horizontal and vertical components and adding the moments of the two resulting couples, (*b*) by using the perpendicular distance between the two forces, (*c*) by summing the moments of the two forces about point *A*.

3.75 The two shafts of a speed-reducer unit are subjected to couples of magnitude $M_1 = 15$ lb · ft and $M_2 = 3$ lb · ft, respectively. Replace the two couples with a single equivalent couple, specifying its magnitude and the direction of its axis.

Fig. P3.75

3.76 Replace the two couples shown with a single equivalent couple, specifying its magnitude and the direction of its axis.

3.77 Solve Prob. 3.76, assuming that two 10-N vertical forces have been added, one acting upward at *C* and the other downward at *B*.

3.78 If $P = 0$, replace the two remaining couples with a single equivalent couple, specifying its magnitude and the direction of its axis.

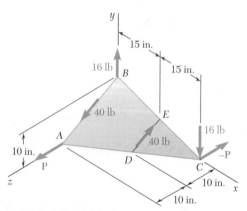

Fig. P3.78 and P3.79

3.79 If $P = 20$ lb, replace the three couples with a single equivalent couple, specifying its magnitude and the direction of its axis.

3.80 In a manufacturing operation, three holes are drilled simultane-ously in a workpiece. If the holes are perpendicular to the surfaces of the workpiece, replace the couples applied to the drills with a single equivalent couple, specifying its magnitude and the direction of its axis.

3.81 A 260-lb force is applied at A to the rolled-steel section shown. Replace that force with an equivalent force-couple system at the center C of the section.

Fig. P3.81

3.82 A 30-lb vertical force **P** is applied at A to the bracket shown, which is held by screws at B and C. (a) Replace **P** with an equivalent force-couple system at B. (b) Find the two horizontal forces at B and C that are equivalent to the couple obtained in part a.

3.83 The force **P** has a magnitude of 250 N and is applied at the end C of a 500-mm rod AC attached to a bracket at A and B. Assuming $\alpha = 30°$ and $\beta = 60°$, replace **P** with (a) an equivalent force-couple system at B, (b) an equivalent system formed by two parallel forces applied at A and B.

3.84 Solve Prob. 3.83, assuming $\alpha = \beta = 25°$.

3.85 The 80-N horizontal force **P** acts on a bell crank as shown. (a) Replace **P** with an equivalent force-couple system at B. (b) Find the two vertical forces at C and D that are equivalent to the couple found in part a.

Fig. P3.85

3.86 A dirigible is tethered by a cable attached to its cabin at B. If the tension in the cable is 1040 N, replace the force exerted by the cable at B with an equivalent system formed by two parallel forces applied at A and C.

Fig. P3.80

Fig. P3.82

Fig. P3.83

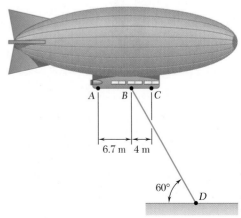

Fig. P3.86

3.87 Three control rods attached to a lever *ABC* exert on it the forces shown. (*a*) Replace the three forces with an equivalent force-couple system at *B*. (*b*) Determine the single force that is equivalent to the force-couple system obtained in part *a*, and specify its point of application on the lever.

Fig. P3.87

Fig. P3.88

3.88 A hexagonal plate is acted upon by the force **P** and the couple shown. Determine the magnitude and the direction of the smallest force **P** for which this system can be replaced with a single force at *E*.

3.89 A force and couple act as shown on a square plate of side *a* = 25 in. Knowing that *P* = 60 lb, *Q* = 40 lb, and *α* = 50°, replace the given force and couple with a single force applied at a point located (*a*) on line *AB*, (*b*) on line *AC*. In each case determine the distance from *A* to the point of application of the force.

Fig. P3.89 and P3.90

3.90 The force and couple shown are to be replaced by an equivalent single force. Knowing that *P* = 2*Q*, determine the required value of *α* if the line of action of the single equivalent force is to pass through (*a*) point *A*, (*b*) point *C*.

3.91 The shearing forces exerted on the cross section of a steel channel can be represented by a 900-N vertical force and two 250-N horizontal forces as shown. Replace this force and couple with a single force **F** applied at point *C*, and determine the distance *x* from *C* to line *BD*. (Point *C* is defined as the *shear center* of the section.)

Fig. P3.91

3.92 A force and a couple are applied as shown to the end of a cantilever beam. (*a*) Replace this system with a single force **F** applied at point *C*, and determine the distance *d* from *C* to a line drawn through points *D* and *E*. (*b*) Solve part *a* if the directions of the two 360-N forces are reversed.

3.93 An antenna is guyed by three cables as shown. Knowing that the tension in cable *AB* is 288 lb, replace the force exerted at *A* by cable *AB* with an equivalent force-couple system at the center *O* of the base of the antenna.

Fig. P3.92

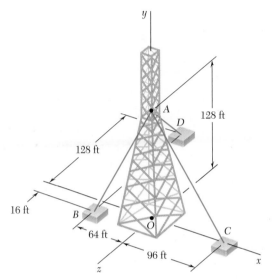

Fig. P3.93 and P3.94

3.94 An antenna is guyed by three cables as shown. Knowing that the tension in cable *AD* is 270 lb, replace the force exerted at *A* by cable *AD* with an equivalent force-couple system at the center *O* of the base of the antenna.

3.95 A 110-N force acting in a vertical plane parallel to the *yz* plane is applied to the 220-mm-long horizontal handle *AB* of a socket wrench. Replace the force with an equivalent force-couple system at the origin *O* of the coordinate system.

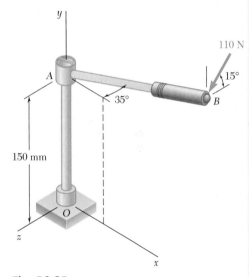

Fig. P3.95

3.96 An eccentric, compressive 1220-N force **P** is applied to the end of a cantilever beam. Replace **P** with an equivalent force-couple system at *G*.

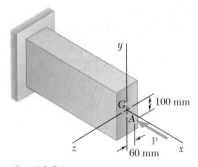

Fig. P3.96

3.97 To keep a door closed, a wooden stick is wedged between the floor and the doorknob. The stick exerts at B a 175-N force directed along line AB. Replace that force with an equivalent force-couple system at C.

3.98 A 46-lb force $\mathbf{F}$ and a 2120-lb · in. couple $\mathbf{M}$ are applied to corner A of the block shown. Replace the given force-couple system with an equivalent force-couple system at corner H.

Fig. P3.97

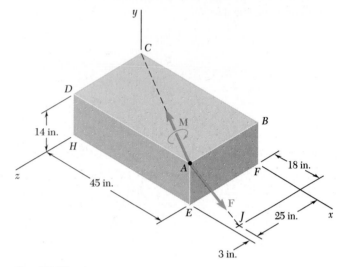

Fig. P3.98

3.99 A 77-N force $\mathbf{F}_1$ and a 31-N · m couple $\mathbf{M}_1$ are applied to corner E of the bent plate shown. If $\mathbf{F}_1$ and $\mathbf{M}_1$ are to be replaced with an equivalent force-couple system $(\mathbf{F}_2, \mathbf{M}_2)$ at corner B and if $(M_2)_z = 0$, determine (a) the distance d, (b) $\mathbf{F}_2$ and $\mathbf{M}_2$.

Fig. P3.99

3.100 A 2.6-kip force is applied at point D of the cast-iron post shown. Replace that force with an equivalent force-couple system at the center A of the base section.

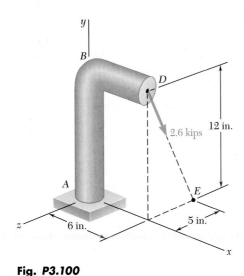

Fig. P3.100

3.17 REDUCTION OF A SYSTEM OF FORCES TO ONE FORCE AND ONE COUPLE

Consider a system of forces $\mathbf{F}_1$, $\mathbf{F}_2$, $\mathbf{F}_3$, . . . , acting on a rigid body at the points A_1, A_2, A_3, . . . , *defined by the position vectors* $\boldsymbol{r}_1$, $\boldsymbol{r}_2$, $\boldsymbol{r}_3$, *etc.* (Fig. 3.41a). As seen in the preceding section, $\mathbf{F}_1$ can be moved from A_1 to a given point O if a couple of moment $\mathbf{M}_1$ equal to the moment $\mathbf{r}_1 \times \mathbf{F}_1$ of $\mathbf{F}_1$ about O is added to the original system of forces. Repeating this procedure with $\mathbf{F}_2$, $\mathbf{F}_3$, . . . , we obtain the system shown in Fig. 3.41b, which consists of the original forces, now acting at O, and the added couple vectors. Since the forces are now concurrent, they can be added vectorially and replaced by their resultant $\mathbf{R}$. Similarly, the couple vectors $\mathbf{M}_1$, $\mathbf{M}_2$, $\mathbf{M}_3$, . . . , can be added vectorially and replaced by a single couple vector $\mathbf{M}_O^R$. Any system of forces, however complex, can thus be reduced to an *equivalent force-couple system acting at a given point O* (Fig. 3.41c). We

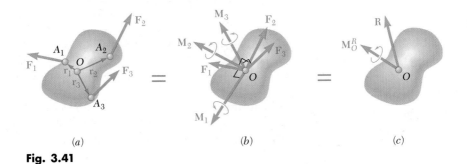

(a) (b) (c)

Fig. 3.41

should note that while each of the couple vectors $\mathbf{M}_1$, $\mathbf{M}_2$, $\mathbf{M}_3$, . . . , in Fig. 3.41*b* is perpendicular to its corresponding force, the resultant force $\mathbf{R}$ and the resultant couple vector $\mathbf{M}_O^R$ in Fig. 3.41*c* will not, in general, be perpendicular to each other.

The equivalent force-couple system is defined by the equations

$$\mathbf{R} = \Sigma\mathbf{F} \qquad \mathbf{M}_O^R = \Sigma\mathbf{M}_O = \Sigma(\mathbf{r} \times \mathbf{F}) \qquad (3.52)$$

which express that the force $\mathbf{R}$ is obtained by adding all the forces of the system, while the moment of the resultant couple vector $\mathbf{M}_O^R$, called the *moment resultant* of the system, is obtained by adding the moments about O of all the forces of the system.

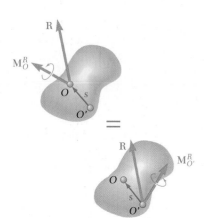

Fig. 3.42

Once a given system of forces has been reduced to a force and a couple at a point O, it can easily be reduced to a force and a couple at another point O'. While the resultant force $\mathbf{R}$ will remain unchanged, the new moment resultant $\mathbf{M}_{O'}^R$ will be equal to the sum of $\mathbf{M}_O^R$ and the moment about O' of the force $\mathbf{R}$ attached at O (Fig. 3.42). We have

$$\mathbf{M}_{O'}^R = \mathbf{M}_O^R + \mathbf{s} \times \mathbf{R} \qquad (3.53)$$

In practice, the reduction of a given system of forces to a single force $\mathbf{R}$ at O and a couple vector $\mathbf{M}_O^R$ will be carried out in terms of components. Resolving each position vector $\mathbf{r}$ and each force $\mathbf{F}$ of the system into rectangular components, we write

$$\mathbf{r} = x\mathbf{i} + y\mathbf{j} + z\mathbf{k} \qquad (3.54)$$
$$\mathbf{F} = F_x\mathbf{i} + F_y\mathbf{j} + F_z\mathbf{k} \qquad (3.55)$$

Substituting for $\mathbf{r}$ and $\mathbf{F}$ in (3.52) and factoring out the unit vectors $\mathbf{i}$, $\mathbf{j}$, $\mathbf{k}$, we obtain $\mathbf{R}$ and $\mathbf{M}_O^R$ in the form

$$\mathbf{R} = R_x\mathbf{i} + R_y\mathbf{j} + R_z\mathbf{k} \qquad \mathbf{M}_O^R = M_x^R\mathbf{i} + M_y^R\mathbf{j} + M_z^R\mathbf{k} \qquad (3.56)$$

The components R_x, R_y, R_z represent, respectively, the sums of the x, y, and z components of the given forces and measure the tendency of the system to impart to the rigid body a motion of translation in the x, y, or z direction. Similarly, the components M_x^R, M_y^R, M_z^R represent, respectively, the sum of the moments of the given forces about the x, y, and z axes and measure the tendency of the system to impart to the rigid body a motion of rotation about the x, y, or z axis.

If the magnitude and direction of the force $\mathbf{R}$ are desired, they can be obtained from the components R_x, R_y, R_z by means of the relations (2.18) and (2.19) of Sec. 2.12; similar computations will yield the magnitude and direction of the couple vector $\mathbf{M}_O^R$.

3.18 EQUIVALENT SYSTEMS OF FORCES

We saw in the preceding section that any system of forces acting on a rigid body can be reduced to a force-couple system at a given point O. This equivalent force-couple system characterizes completely the effect of the given force system on the rigid body. *Two systems of forces are equivalent, therefore, if they can be reduced to the same force-couple system at a given point O.* Recalling that the force-couple system at O is defined by the relations (3.52), we state that *two systems of forces, $\mathbf{F}_1$, $\mathbf{F}_2$, $\mathbf{F}_3$, . . . , and $\mathbf{F}'_1$, $\mathbf{F}'_2$, $\mathbf{F}'_3$, . . . , which act on the same rigid body are equivalent if, and only if, the sums of the forces and the sums of the moments about a given point O of the forces of the two systems are, respectively, equal.* Expressed mathematically, the necessary and sufficient conditions for the two systems of forces to be equivalent are

$$\Sigma\mathbf{F} = \Sigma\mathbf{F}' \quad \text{and} \quad \Sigma\mathbf{M}_O = \Sigma\mathbf{M}'_O \tag{3.57}$$

Photo 3.3 The forces exerted by the children upon the wagon can be replaced with an equivalent force-couple system when analyzing the motion of the wagon.

Note that to prove that two systems of forces are equivalent, the second of the relations (3.57) must be established with respect to *only one point O*. It will hold, however, with respect to *any* point if the two systems are equivalent.

Resolving the forces and moments in (3.57) into their rectangular components, we can express the necessary and sufficient conditions for the equivalence of two systems of forces acting on a rigid body as follows:

$$\begin{array}{ccc} \Sigma F_x = \Sigma F'_x & \Sigma F_y = \Sigma F'_y & \Sigma F_z = \Sigma F'_z \\ \Sigma M_x = \Sigma M'_x & \Sigma M_y = \Sigma M'_y & \Sigma M_z = \Sigma M'_z \end{array} \tag{3.58}$$

These equations have a simple physical significance. They express that two systems of forces are equivalent if they tend to impart to the rigid body (1) the same translation in the x, y, and z directions, respectively, and (2) the same rotation about the x, y, and z axes, respectively.

3.19 EQUIPOLLENT SYSTEMS OF VECTORS

In general, when two systems of vectors satisfy Eqs. (3.57) or (3.58), i.e., when their resultants and their moment resultants about an arbitrary point O are respectively equal, the two systems are said to be *equipollent*. The result established in the preceding section can thus be restated as follows: *If two systems of forces acting on a rigid body are equipollent, they are also equivalent.*

It is important to note that this statement does not apply to *any* system of vectors. Consider, for example, a system of forces acting on a set of independent particles which do *not* form a rigid body. A different system of forces acting on the same particles may happen to be equipollent to the first one; i.e., it may have the same resultant and the same moment resultant. Yet, since different forces will now act on the various particles, their effects on these particles will be different; the two systems of forces, while equipollent, are *not* equivalent.

3.20 FURTHER REDUCTION OF A SYSTEM OF FORCES

We saw in Sec. 3.17 that any given system of forces acting on a rigid body can be reduced to an equivalent force-couple system at O consisting of a force $\mathbf{R}$ equal to the sum of the forces of the system and a couple vector $\mathbf{M}_O^R$ of moment equal to the moment resultant of the system.

When $\mathbf{R} = 0$, the force-couple system reduces to the couple vector $\mathbf{M}_O^R$. The given system of forces can then be reduced to a single couple, called the *resultant couple* of the system.

Let us now investigate the conditions under which a given system of forces can be reduced to a single force. It follows from Sec. 3.16 that the force-couple system at O can be replaced by a single force $\mathbf{R}$ acting along a new line of action if $\mathbf{R}$ and $\mathbf{M}_O^R$ are mutually perpendicular. The systems of forces which can be reduced to a single force, or *resultant*, are therefore the systems for which the force $\mathbf{R}$ and the couple vector $\mathbf{M}_O^R$ are mutually perpendicular. While this condition *is generally not satisfied* by systems of forces in space, it *will be satisfied* by systems consisting of (1) concurrent forces, (2) coplanar forces, or (3) parallel forces. These three cases will be discussed separately.

1. *Concurrent forces* are applied at the same point and can therefore be added directly to obtain their resultant $\mathbf{R}$. Thus, they always reduce to a single force. Concurrent forces were discussed in detail in Chap. 2.

2. *Coplanar forces* act in the same plane, which may be assumed to be the plane of the figure (Fig. 3.43a). The sum $\mathbf{R}$ of the forces of the system will also lie in the plane of the figure, while the moment of each force about O, and thus the moment resultant $\mathbf{M}_O^R$, will be perpendicular to that plane. The force-couple system at O consists, therefore, of a force $\mathbf{R}$ and a couple vector $\mathbf{M}_O^R$ which are mutually perpendicular (Fig. 3.43b).† They can be reduced to a single force $\mathbf{R}$ by moving $\mathbf{R}$ in the plane of the figure until its moment about O becomes equal to $\mathbf{M}_O^R$. The distance from O to the line of action of $\mathbf{R}$ is $d = M_O^R/R$ (Fig. 3.43c).

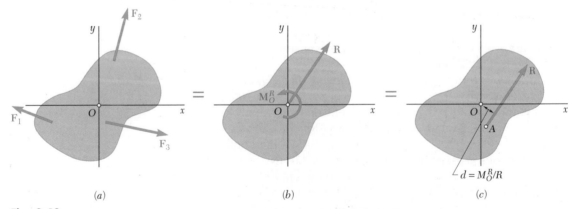

(a)   (b)   (c)

Fig. 3.43

†Since the couple vector $\mathbf{M}_O^R$ is perpendicular to the plane of the figure, it has been represented by the symbol ↺. A counterclockwise couple ↺ represents a vector pointing out of the paper, and a clockwise couple ↻ represents a vector pointing into the paper.

As noted in Sec. 3.17, the reduction of a system of forces is considerably simplified if the forces are resolved into rectangular components. The force-couple system at O is then characterized by the components (Fig. 3.44a)

$$R_x = \Sigma F_x \qquad R_y = \Sigma F_y \qquad M_z^R = M_O^R = \Sigma M_O \qquad (3.59)$$

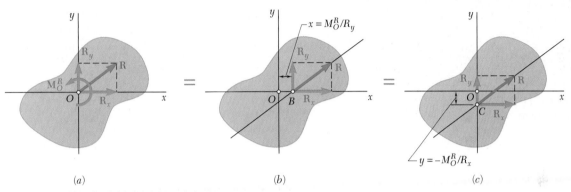

(a)   (b)   (c)

Fig. 3.44

To reduce the system to a single force $\mathbf{R}$, we express that the moment of $\mathbf{R}$ about O must be equal to $\mathbf{M}_O^R$. Denoting by x and y the coordinates of the point of application of the resultant and recalling formula (3.22) of Sec. 3.8, we write

$$x R_y - y R_x = M_O^R$$

which represents the equation of the line of action of $\mathbf{R}$. We can also determine directly the x and y intercepts of the line of action of the resultant by noting that $\mathbf{M}_O^R$ must be equal to the moment about O of the y component of $\mathbf{R}$ when $\mathbf{R}$ is attached at B (Fig. 3.44b) and to the moment of its x component when $\mathbf{R}$ is attached at C (Fig. 3.44c).

3. *Parallel forces* have parallel lines of action and may or may not have the same sense. Assuming here that the forces are parallel to the y axis (Fig. 3.45a), we note that their sum $\mathbf{R}$ will also be parallel to the y axis. On the other hand, since the moment of a given force must be perpendicular to that force, the moment about O of each force of the system, and thus the moment resultant $\mathbf{M}_O^R$, will lie in the zx plane. The force-couple system at O consists,

(a)   (b)   (c)

Fig. 3.45

Photo 3.4 The parallel wind forces acting on the highway signs can be reduced to a single equivalent force. Determining this force can simplify the calculation of the forces acting on the supports of the frame to which the signs are attached.

therefore, of a force **R** and a couple vector $\mathbf{M}_O^R$ which are mutually perpendicular (Fig. 3.45*b*). They can be reduced to a single force **R** (Fig. 3.45*c*) or, if **R** = 0, to a single couple of moment $\mathbf{M}_O^R$.

In practice, the force-couple system at O will be characterized by the components

$$R_y = \Sigma F_y \qquad M_x^R = \Sigma M_x \qquad M_z^R = \Sigma M_z \qquad (3.60)$$

The reduction of the system to a single force can be carried out by moving **R** to a new point of application $A(x, 0, z)$ chosen so that the moment of **R** about O is equal to $\mathbf{M}_O^R$. We write

$$\mathbf{r} \times \mathbf{R} = \mathbf{M}_O^R$$
$$(x\mathbf{i} + z\mathbf{k}) \times R_y\mathbf{j} = M_x^R\mathbf{i} + M_z^R\mathbf{k}$$

By computing the vector products and equating the coefficients of the corresponding unit vectors in both members of the equation, we obtain two scalar equations which define the coordinates of A:

$$-zR_y = M_x^R \qquad xR_y = M_z^R$$

These equations express that the moments of **R** about the x and z axes must, respectively, be equal to M_x^R and M_z^R.

*3.21 REDUCTION OF A SYSTEM OF FORCES TO A WRENCH

In the general case of a system of forces in space, the equivalent force-couple system at O consists of a force **R** and a couple vector $\mathbf{M}_O^R$ which are not perpendicular, and neither of which is zero (Fig. 3.46*a*). Thus, the system of forces *cannot* be reduced to a single force or to a single couple. The couple vector, however, can be replaced by two other couple vectors obtained by resolving $\mathbf{M}_O^R$ into a component $\mathbf{M}_1$ along **R** and a component $\mathbf{M}_2$ in a plane perpendicular to **R** (Fig. 3.46*b*). The couple vector $\mathbf{M}_2$ and the force **R** can then be replaced by a single force **R** acting along a new line of action. The original system of forces thus reduces to **R** and to the couple vector $\mathbf{M}_1$ (Fig. 3.46*c*), i.e., to **R** and a couple acting in the plane perpendicular to **R**. This particular force-couple system is called a *wrench* because the resulting combination of push and twist is the same as that which would be caused by an actual wrench. The line of action of **R** is known as the *axis of the wrench*, and the ratio $p = M_1/R$ is called the *pitch*

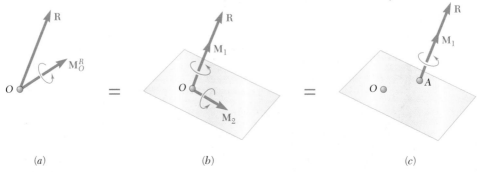

(a)   (b)   (c)

Fig. 3.46

of the wrench. A wrench, therefore, consists of two collinear vectors, namely, a force **R** and a couple vector

$$\mathbf{M}_1 = p\mathbf{R} \tag{3.61}$$

Recalling the expression (3.35) obtained in Sec. 3.9 for the projection of a vector on the line of action of another vector, we note that the projection of $\mathbf{M}_O^R$ on the line of action of **R** is

$$M_1 = \frac{\mathbf{R} \cdot \mathbf{M}_O^R}{R}$$

Thus, the pitch of the wrench can be expressed as†

$$p = \frac{M_1}{R} = \frac{\mathbf{R} \cdot \mathbf{M}_O^R}{R^2} \tag{3.62}$$

To define the axis of the wrench, we can write a relation involving the position vector **r** of an arbitrary point P located on that axis. Attaching the resultant force **R** and couple vector $\mathbf{M}_1$ at P (Fig. 3.47) and expressing that the moment about O of this force-couple system is equal to the moment resultant $\mathbf{M}_O^R$ of the original force system, we write

$$\mathbf{M}_1 + \mathbf{r} \times \mathbf{R} = \mathbf{M}_O^R \tag{3.63}$$

or, recalling Eq. (3.61),

$$p\mathbf{R} + \mathbf{r} \times \mathbf{R} = \mathbf{M}_O^R \tag{3.64}$$

Fig. 3.47

Photo 3.5 The pushing-turning action associated with the tightening of a screw illustrates the collinear lines of action of the force and couple vector that constitute a wrench.

---

†The expressions obtained for the projection of the couple vector on the line of action of **R** and for the pitch of the wrench are independent of the choice of point O. Using the relation (3.53) of Sec. 3.17, we note that if a different point O' had been used, the numerator in (3.62) would have been

$$\mathbf{R} \cdot \mathbf{M}_{O'}^R = \mathbf{R} \cdot (\mathbf{M}_O^R + \mathbf{s} \times \mathbf{R}) = \mathbf{R} \cdot \mathbf{M}_O^R + \mathbf{R} \cdot (\mathbf{s} \times \mathbf{R})$$

Since the mixed triple product $\mathbf{R} \cdot (\mathbf{s} \times \mathbf{R})$ is identically equal to zero, we have

$$\mathbf{R} \cdot \mathbf{M}_{O'}^R = \mathbf{R} \cdot \mathbf{M}_O^R$$

Thus, the scalar product $\mathbf{R} \cdot \mathbf{M}_O^R$ is independent of the choice of point O.

SAMPLE PROBLEM 3.8

A 4.80-m-long beam is subjected to the forces shown. Reduce the given system of forces to (a) an equivalent force-couple system at A, (b) an equivalent force-couple system at B, (c) a single force or resultant.

Note. Since the reactions at the supports are not included in the given system of forces, the given system will not maintain the beam in equilibrium.

SOLUTION

a. Force-Couple System at A. The force-couple system at A equivalent to the given system of forces consists of a force $\mathbf{R}$ and a couple $\mathbf{M}_A^R$ defined as follows:

$$\mathbf{R} = \Sigma \mathbf{F}$$
$$= (150\text{ N})\mathbf{j} - (600\text{ N})\mathbf{j} + (100\text{ N})\mathbf{j} - (250\text{ N})\mathbf{j} = -(600\text{ N})\mathbf{j}$$
$$\mathbf{M}_A^R = \Sigma(\mathbf{r} \times \mathbf{F})$$
$$= (1.6\mathbf{i}) \times (-600\mathbf{j}) + (2.8\mathbf{i}) \times (100\mathbf{j}) + (4.8\mathbf{i}) \times (-250\mathbf{j})$$
$$= -(1880\text{ N} \cdot \text{m})\mathbf{k}$$

The equivalent force-couple system at A is thus

$$\mathbf{R} = 600\text{ N} \downarrow \qquad \mathbf{M}_A^R = 1880\text{ N} \cdot \text{m} \downarrow \quad \blacktriangleleft$$

b. Force-Couple System at B. We propose to find a force-couple system at B equivalent to the force-couple system at A determined in part a. The force $\mathbf{R}$ is unchanged, but a new couple $\mathbf{M}_B^R$ must be determined, the moment of which is equal to the moment about B of the force-couple system determined in part a. Thus, we have

$$\mathbf{M}_B^R = \mathbf{M}_A^R + \overrightarrow{BA} \times \mathbf{R}$$
$$= -(1880\text{ N} \cdot \text{m})\mathbf{k} + (-4.8\text{ m})\mathbf{i} \times (-600\text{ N})\mathbf{j}$$
$$= -(1880\text{ N} \cdot \text{m})\mathbf{k} + (2880\text{ N} \cdot \text{m})\mathbf{k} = +(1000\text{ N} \cdot \text{m})\mathbf{k}$$

The equivalent force-couple system at B is thus

$$\mathbf{R} = 600\text{ N} \downarrow \qquad \mathbf{M}_B^R = 1000\text{ N} \cdot \text{m} \uparrow \quad \blacktriangleleft$$

c. Single Force or Resultant. The resultant of the given system of forces is equal to $\mathbf{R}$, and its point of application must be such that the moment of $\mathbf{R}$ about A is equal to $\mathbf{M}_A^R$. We write

$$\mathbf{r} \times \mathbf{R} = \mathbf{M}_A^R$$
$$x\mathbf{i} \times (-600\text{ N})\mathbf{j} = -(1880\text{ N} \cdot \text{m})\mathbf{k}$$
$$-x(600\text{ N})\mathbf{k} = -(1880\text{ N} \cdot \text{m})\mathbf{k}$$

and conclude that $x = 3.13$ m. Thus, the single force equivalent to the given system is defined as

$$\mathbf{R} = 600\text{ N} \downarrow \qquad x = 3.13\text{ m} \quad \blacktriangleleft$$

SAMPLE PROBLEM 3.9

Four tugboats are used to bring an ocean liner to its pier. Each tugboat exerts a 5000-lb force in the direction shown. Determine (a) the equivalent force-couple system at the foremast O, (b) the point on the hull where a single, more powerful tugboat should push to produce the same effect as the original four tugboats.

SOLUTION

a. Force-Couple System at O. Each of the given forces is resolved into components in the diagram shown (kip units are used). The force-couple system at O equivalent to the given system of forces consists of a force **R** and a couple $\mathbf{M}_O^R$ defined as follows:

$$\mathbf{R} = \Sigma\mathbf{F}$$
$$= (2.50\mathbf{i} - 4.33\mathbf{j}) + (3.00\mathbf{i} - 4.00\mathbf{j}) + (-5.00\mathbf{j}) + (3.54\mathbf{i} + 3.54\mathbf{j})$$
$$= 9.04\mathbf{i} - 9.79\mathbf{j}$$

$$\mathbf{M}_O^R = \Sigma(\mathbf{r} \times \mathbf{F})$$
$$= (-90\mathbf{i} + 50\mathbf{j}) \times (2.50\mathbf{i} - 4.33\mathbf{j})$$
$$\quad + (100\mathbf{i} + 70\mathbf{j}) \times (3.00\mathbf{i} - 4.00\mathbf{j})$$
$$\quad + (400\mathbf{i} + 70\mathbf{j}) \times (-5.00\mathbf{j})$$
$$\quad + (300\mathbf{i} - 70\mathbf{j}) \times (3.54\mathbf{i} + 3.54\mathbf{j})$$
$$= (390 - 125 - 400 - 210 - 2000 + 1062 + 248)\mathbf{k}$$
$$= -1035\mathbf{k}$$

The equivalent force-couple system at O is thus

$$\mathbf{R} = (9.04 \text{ kips})\mathbf{i} - (9.79 \text{ kips})\mathbf{j} \qquad \mathbf{M}_O^R = -(1035 \text{ kip} \cdot \text{ft})\mathbf{k}$$

or
$$\mathbf{R} = 13.33 \text{ kips} \; \measuredangle 47.3° \qquad \mathbf{M}_O^R = 1035 \text{ kip} \cdot \text{ft} \;\downarrow \quad \blacktriangleleft$$

Remark. Since all the forces are contained in the plane of the figure, we could have expected the sum of their moments to be perpendicular to that plane. Note that the moment of each force component could have been obtained directly from the diagram by first forming the product of its magnitude and perpendicular distance to O and then assigning to this product a positive or a negative sign depending upon the sense of the moment.

b. Single Tugboat. The force exerted by a single tugboat must be equal to **R**, and its point of application A must be such that the moment of **R** about O is equal to $\mathbf{M}_O^R$. Observing that the position vector of A is

$$\mathbf{r} = x\mathbf{i} + 70\mathbf{j}$$

we write

$$\mathbf{r} \times \mathbf{R} = \mathbf{M}_O^R$$
$$(x\mathbf{i} + 70\mathbf{j}) \times (9.04\mathbf{i} - 9.79\mathbf{j}) = -1035\mathbf{k}$$
$$-x(9.79)\mathbf{k} - 633\mathbf{k} = -1035\mathbf{k} \qquad x = 41.1 \text{ ft} \quad \blacktriangleleft$$

E(150 mm, −50 mm, 100 mm)

SAMPLE PROBLEM 3.10

Three cables are attached to a bracket as shown. Replace the forces exerted by the cables with an equivalent force-couple system at A.

SOLUTION

We first determine the relative position vectors drawn from point A to the points of application of the various forces and resolve the forces into rectangular components. Observing that $\mathbf{F}_B = (700 \text{ N})\boldsymbol{\lambda}_{BE}$ where

$$\boldsymbol{\lambda}_{BE} = \frac{\overrightarrow{BE}}{BE} = \frac{75\mathbf{i} - 150\mathbf{j} + 50\mathbf{k}}{175}$$

we have, using meters and newtons,

$$\mathbf{r}_{B/A} = \overrightarrow{AB} = 0.075\mathbf{i} + 0.050\mathbf{k} \qquad \mathbf{F}_B = 300\mathbf{i} - 600\mathbf{j} + 200\mathbf{k}$$
$$\mathbf{r}_{C/A} = \overrightarrow{AC} = 0.075\mathbf{i} - 0.050\mathbf{k} \qquad \mathbf{F}_C = 707\mathbf{i} \qquad\qquad - 707\mathbf{k}$$
$$\mathbf{r}_{D/A} = \overrightarrow{AD} = 0.100\mathbf{i} - 0.100\mathbf{j} \qquad \mathbf{F}_D = 600\mathbf{i} + 1039\mathbf{j}$$

The force-couple system at A equivalent to the given forces consists of a force $\mathbf{R} = \Sigma\mathbf{F}$ and a couple $\mathbf{M}_A^R = \Sigma(\mathbf{r} \times \mathbf{F})$. The force $\mathbf{R}$ is readily obtained by adding respectively the x, y, and z components of the forces:

$$\mathbf{R} = \Sigma\mathbf{F} = (1607 \text{ N})\mathbf{i} + (439 \text{ N})\mathbf{j} - (507 \text{ N})\mathbf{k} \quad \blacktriangleleft$$

The computation of $\mathbf{M}_A^R$ will be facilitated if we express the moments of the forces in the form of determinants (Sec. 3.8):

$$\mathbf{r}_{B/A} \times \mathbf{F}_B = \begin{vmatrix} \mathbf{i} & \mathbf{j} & \mathbf{k} \\ 0.075 & 0 & 0.050 \\ 300 & -600 & 200 \end{vmatrix} = 30\mathbf{i} \qquad\qquad -45\mathbf{k}$$

$$\mathbf{r}_{C/A} \times \mathbf{F}_C = \begin{vmatrix} \mathbf{i} & \mathbf{j} & \mathbf{k} \\ 0.075 & 0 & -0.050 \\ 707 & 0 & -707 \end{vmatrix} = \qquad 17.68\mathbf{j}$$

$$\mathbf{r}_{D/A} \times \mathbf{F}_D = \begin{vmatrix} \mathbf{i} & \mathbf{j} & \mathbf{k} \\ 0.100 & -0.100 & 0 \\ 600 & 1039 & 0 \end{vmatrix} = \qquad 163.9\mathbf{k}$$

Adding the expressions obtained, we have

$$\mathbf{M}_A^R = \Sigma(\mathbf{r} \times \mathbf{F}) = (30 \text{ N} \cdot \text{m})\mathbf{i} + (17.68 \text{ N} \cdot \text{m})\mathbf{j} + (118.9 \text{ N} \cdot \text{m})\mathbf{k} \quad \blacktriangleleft$$

The rectangular components of the force $\mathbf{R}$ and the couple $\mathbf{M}_A^R$ are shown in the adjoining sketch.

SAMPLE PROBLEM 3.11

A square foundation mat supports the four columns shown. Determine the magnitude and point of application of the resultant of the four loads.

SOLUTION

We first reduce the given system of forces to a force-couple system at the origin O of the coordinate system. This force-couple system consists of a force $\mathbf{R}$ and a couple vector $\mathbf{M}_O^R$ defined as follows:

$$\mathbf{R} = \Sigma\mathbf{F} \qquad \mathbf{M}_O^R = \Sigma(\mathbf{r} \times \mathbf{F})$$

The position vectors of the points of application of the various forces are determined, and the computations are arranged in tabular form.

r, ft	F, kips	r × F, kip · ft
0	$-40\mathbf{j}$	0
$10\mathbf{i}$	$-12\mathbf{j}$	$-120\mathbf{k}$
$10\mathbf{i} + 5\mathbf{k}$	$-8\mathbf{j}$	$40\mathbf{i} - 80\mathbf{k}$
$4\mathbf{i} + 10\mathbf{k}$	$-20\mathbf{j}$	$200\mathbf{i} - 80\mathbf{k}$
	$\mathbf{R} = -80\mathbf{j}$	$\mathbf{M}_O^R = 240\mathbf{i} - 280\mathbf{k}$

Since the force $\mathbf{R}$ and the couple vector $\mathbf{M}_O^R$ are mutually perpendicular, the force-couple system obtained can be reduced further to a single force $\mathbf{R}$. The new point of application of $\mathbf{R}$ will be selected in the plane of the mat and in such a way that the moment of $\mathbf{R}$ about O will be equal to $\mathbf{M}_O^R$. Denoting by $\mathbf{r}$ the position vector of the desired point of application, and by x and z its coordinates, we write

$$\mathbf{r} \times \mathbf{R} = \mathbf{M}_O^R$$
$$(x\mathbf{i} + z\mathbf{k}) \times (-80\mathbf{j}) = 240\mathbf{i} - 280\mathbf{k}$$
$$-80x\mathbf{k} + 80z\mathbf{i} = 240\mathbf{i} - 280\mathbf{k}$$

from which it follows that

$$-80x = -280 \qquad 80z = 240$$
$$x = 3.50 \text{ ft} \qquad z = 3.00 \text{ ft}$$

We conclude that the resultant of the given system of forces is

$$\mathbf{R} = 80 \text{ kips} \downarrow \qquad \text{at } x = 3.50 \text{ ft}, z = 3.00 \text{ ft} \quad \blacktriangleleft$$

SAMPLE PROBLEM 3.12

Two forces of the same magnitude P act on a cube of side a as shown. Replace the two forces by an equivalent wrench, and determine (a) the magnitude and direction of the resultant force $\mathbf{R}$, (b) the pitch of the wrench, (c) the point where the axis of the wrench intersects the yz plane.

SOLUTION

Equivalent Force-Couple System at O. We first determine the equivalent force-couple system at the origin O. We observe that the position vectors of the points of application E and D of the two given forces are $\mathbf{r}_E = a\mathbf{i} + a\mathbf{j}$ and $\mathbf{r}_D = a\mathbf{j} + a\mathbf{k}$. The resultant $\mathbf{R}$ of the two forces and their moment resultant $\mathbf{M}_O^R$ about O are

$$\mathbf{R} = \mathbf{F}_1 + \mathbf{F}_2 = P\mathbf{i} + P\mathbf{j} = P(\mathbf{i} + \mathbf{j}) \qquad (1)$$
$$\mathbf{M}_O^R = \mathbf{r}_E \times \mathbf{F}_1 + \mathbf{r}_D \times \mathbf{F}_2 = (a\mathbf{i} + a\mathbf{j}) \times P\mathbf{i} + (a\mathbf{j} + a\mathbf{k}) \times P\mathbf{j}$$
$$= -Pa\mathbf{k} - Pa\mathbf{i} = -Pa(\mathbf{i} + \mathbf{k}) \qquad (2)$$

a. Resultant Force R. It follows from Eq. (1) and the adjoining sketch that the resultant force $\mathbf{R}$ has the magnitude $R = P\sqrt{2}$, lies in the xy plane, and forms angles of $45°$ with the x and y axes. Thus

$$R = P\sqrt{2} \qquad \theta_x = \theta_y = 45° \qquad \theta_z = 90° \quad \blacktriangleleft$$

b. Pitch of Wrench. Recalling formula (3.62) of Sec. 3.21 and Eqs. (1) and (2) above, we write

$$p = \frac{\mathbf{R} \cdot \mathbf{M}_O^R}{R^2} = \frac{P(\mathbf{i} + \mathbf{j}) \cdot (-Pa)(\mathbf{i} + \mathbf{k})}{(P\sqrt{2})^2} = \frac{-P^2a(1 + 0 + 0)}{2P^2} \qquad p = -\frac{a}{2} \quad \blacktriangleleft$$

c. Axis of Wrench. It follows from the above and from Eq. (3.61) that the wrench consists of the force $\mathbf{R}$ found in (1) and the couple vector

$$\mathbf{M}_1 = p\mathbf{R} = -\frac{a}{2}P(\mathbf{i} + \mathbf{j}) = -\frac{Pa}{2}(\mathbf{i} + \mathbf{j}) \qquad (3)$$

To find the point where the axis of the wrench intersects the yz plane, we express that the moment of the wrench about O is equal to the moment resultant $\mathbf{M}_O^R$ of the original system:

$$\mathbf{M}_1 + \mathbf{r} \times \mathbf{R} = \mathbf{M}_O^R$$

or, noting that $\mathbf{r} = y\mathbf{j} + z\mathbf{k}$ and substituting for $\mathbf{R}$, $\mathbf{M}_O^R$, and $\mathbf{M}_1$ from Eqs. (1), (2), and (3),

$$-\frac{Pa}{2}(\mathbf{i} + \mathbf{j}) + (y\mathbf{j} + z\mathbf{k}) \times P(\mathbf{i} + \mathbf{j}) = -Pa(\mathbf{i} + \mathbf{k})$$

$$-\frac{Pa}{2}\mathbf{i} - \frac{Pa}{2}\mathbf{j} - Py\mathbf{k} + Pz\mathbf{j} - Pz\mathbf{i} = -Pa\mathbf{i} - Pa\mathbf{k}$$

Equating the coefficients of $\mathbf{k}$, and then the coefficients of $\mathbf{j}$, we find

$$y = a \qquad z = a/2 \quad \blacktriangleleft$$

SOLVING PROBLEMS
ON YOUR OWN

This lesson was devoted to the reduction and simplification of force systems. In solving the problems which follow, you will be asked to perform the operations discussed below.

1. Reducing a force system to a force and a couple at a given point A. The force is the *resultant* **R** of the system and is obtained by adding the various forces; the moment of the couple is the *moment resultant* of the system and is obtained by adding the moments about A of the various forces. We have

$$\mathbf{R} = \Sigma \mathbf{F} \qquad \mathbf{M}_A^R = \Sigma(\mathbf{r} \times \mathbf{F})$$

where the position vector **r** is drawn from A to *any point* on the line of action of **F**.

2. Moving a force-couple system from point A to point B. If you wish to reduce a given force system to a force-couple system at point B after you have reduced it to a force-couple system at point A, you need not recompute the moments of the forces about B. The resultant **R** remains unchanged, and the new moment resultant $\mathbf{M}_B^R$ can be obtained by adding to $\mathbf{M}_A^R$ the moment about B of the force **R** applied at A [Sample Prob. 3.8]. Denoting by **s** the vector drawn from B to A, you can write

$$\mathbf{M}_B^R = \mathbf{M}_A^R + \mathbf{s} \times \mathbf{R}$$

3. Checking whether two force systems are equivalent. First reduce each force system to a force-couple system *at the same, but arbitrary, point A* (as explained in paragraph 1). The two systems are equivalent (that is, they have the same effect on the given rigid body) if the two force-couple systems you have obtained are identical, that is, if

$$\Sigma \mathbf{F} = \Sigma \mathbf{F}' \qquad \text{and} \qquad \Sigma \mathbf{M}_A = \Sigma \mathbf{M}_A'$$

You should recognize that if the first of these equations is not satisfied, that is, if the two systems do not have the same resultant **R**, the two systems cannot be equivalent and there is then no need to check whether or not the second equation is satisfied.

4. Reducing a given force system to a single force. First reduce the given system to a force-couple system consisting of the resultant **R** and the couple vector $\mathbf{M}_A^R$ at some convenient point A (as explained in paragraph 1). You will recall from the previous lesson that further reduction to a single force is possible *only if the*

(continued)

force **R** *and the couple vector* $\mathbf{M}_A^R$ *are mutually perpendicular.* This will certainly be the case for systems of forces which are either *concurrent, coplanar,* or *parallel.* The required single force can then be obtained by moving **R** until its moment about A is equal to $\mathbf{M}_A^R$, as you did in several problems of the preceding lesson. More formally, you can write that the position vector **r** drawn from A to any point on the line of action of the single force **R** must satisfy the equation

$$\mathbf{r} \times \mathbf{R} = \mathbf{M}_A^R$$

This procedure was used in Sample Probs. 3.8, 3.9, and 3.11.

5. Reducing a given force system to a wrench. If the given system is comprised of forces which are not concurrent, coplanar, or parallel, the equivalent force-couple system at a point A will consist of a force **R** and a couple vector $\mathbf{M}_A^R$ which, in general, *are not mutually perpendicular.* (To check whether **R** and $\mathbf{M}_A^R$ are mutually perpendicular, form their scalar product. If this product is zero, they are mutually perpendicular; otherwise, they are not.) If **R** and $\mathbf{M}_A^R$ are not mutually perpendicular, the force-couple system (and thus the given system of forces) *cannot be reduced to a single force.* However, the system can be reduced to a *wrench*— the combination of a force **R** and a couple vector $\mathbf{M}_1$ directed along a common line of action called the *axis of the wrench* (Fig. 3.47). The ratio $p = M_1/R$ is called the *pitch* of the wrench.

To reduce a given force system to a wrench, you should follow these steps:

a. Reduce the given system to an equivalent force-couple system $(\mathbf{R}, \mathbf{M}_O^R)$, typically located at the origin O.

b. Determine the pitch p from Eq. (3.62)

$$p = \frac{M_1}{R} = \frac{\mathbf{R} \cdot \mathbf{M}_O^R}{R^2} \tag{3.62}$$

and the couple vector from $\mathbf{M}_1 = p\mathbf{R}$.

c. Express that the moment about O of the wrench is equal to the moment resultant $\mathbf{M}_O^R$ of the force-couple system at O:

$$\mathbf{M}_1 + \mathbf{r} \times \mathbf{R} = \mathbf{M}_O^R \tag{3.63}$$

This equation allows you to determine the point where the line of action of the wrench intersects a specified plane, since the position vector **r** is directed from O to that point.

These steps are illustrated in Sample Prob. 3.12. Although the determination of a wrench and the point where its axis intersects a plane may appear difficult, the process is simply the application of several of the ideas and techniques developed in this chapter. Thus, once you have mastered the wrench, you can feel confident that you understand much of Chap. 3.

PROBLEMS

Fig. P3.101

3.101 A 3-m-long beam is subjected to a variety of loadings. (*a*) Replace each loading with an equivalent force-couple system at end *A* of the beam. (*b*) Which of the loadings are equivalent?

Fig. P3.102

3.102 A 3-m-long beam is loaded as shown. Determine the loading of Prob. 3.101 that is equivalent to this loading.

3.103 Determine the single equivalent force and the distance from point *A* to its line of action for the beam and loading of (*a*) Prob. 3.101*a*, (*b*) Prob. 3.101*b*, (*c*) Prob. 3.102.

3.104 Five separate force-couple systems act at the corners of a piece of sheet metal, which has been bent into the shape shown. Determine which of these systems is equivalent to a force $\mathbf{F} = (10 \text{ lb})\mathbf{i}$ and a couple of moment $\mathbf{M} = (15 \text{ lb} \cdot \text{ft})\mathbf{j} + (15 \text{ lb} \cdot \text{ft})\mathbf{k}$ located at the origin.

Fig. P3.104

Fig. P3.105

3.105 Three horizontal forces are applied as shown to a vertical cast-iron arm. Determine the resultant of the forces and the distance from the ground to its line of action when (*a*) $P = 200$ N, (*b*) $P = 2400$ N, (*c*) $P = 1000$ N.

3.106 Three stage lights are mounted on a pipe as shown. The lights at *A* and *B* each weigh 4.1 lb, while the one at *C* weighs 3.5 lb. (*a*) If $d = 25$ in., determine the distance from *D* to the line of action of the resultant of the weights of the three lights. (*b*) Determine the value of *d* so that the resultant of the weights passes through the midpoint of the pipe.

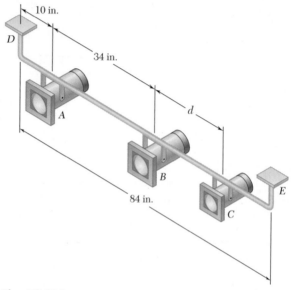

Fig. P3.106

3.107 The weights of two children sitting at ends *A* and *B* of a seesaw are 84 lb and 64 lb, respectively. Where should a third child sit so that the resultant of the weights of the three children will pass through *C* if she weighs (*a*) 60 lb, (*b*) 52 lb?

3.108 A couple of magnitude $M = 54$ lb · in. and the three forces shown are applied to an angle bracket. (*a*) Find the resultant of this system of forces. (*b*) Locate the points where the line of action of the resultant intersects line *AB* and line *BC*.

Fig. P3.107

Fig. P3.108 and P3.109

3.109 A couple **M** and the three forces shown are applied to an angle bracket. Find the moment of the couple if the line of action of the resultant of the force system is to pass through (*a*) point *A*, (*b*) point *B*, (*c*) point *C*.

3.110 A 32-lb motor is mounted on the floor. Find the resultant of the weight and the forces exerted on the belt, and determine where the line of action of the resultant intersects the floor.

3.111 A machine component is subjected to the forces and couples shown. The component is to be held in place by a single rivet that can resist a force but not a couple. For $P = 0$, determine the location of the rivet hole if it is to be located (a) on line FG, (b) on line GH.

Fig. P3.110

Fig. P3.111

3.112 Solve Prob. 3.111, assuming that $P = 60$ N.

3.113 A truss supports the loading shown. Determine the equivalent force acting on the truss and the point of intersection of its line of action with a line drawn through points A and G.

3.114 Four ropes are attached to a crate and exert the forces shown. If the forces are to be replaced with a single equivalent force applied at a point on line AB, determine (a) the equivalent force and the distance from A to the point of application of the force when $\alpha = 30°$, (b) the value of α so that the single equivalent force is applied at point B.

Fig. P3.113

Fig. P3.114

3.115 Solve Prob. 3.114, assuming that the 90-lb force is removed.

3.116 Four forces act on a 700 × 375-mm plate as shown. (a) Find the resultant of these forces. (b) Locate the two points where the line of action of the resultant intersects the edge of the plate.

3.117 Solve Prob. 3.116, assuming that the 760-N force is directed to the right.

Fig. P3.116

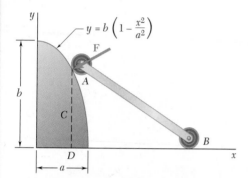

$$y = b\left(1 - \frac{x^2}{a^2}\right)$$

Fig. P3.118

3.118 As follower AB rolls along the surface of member C, it exerts a constant force $\mathbf{F}$ perpendicular to the surface. (*a*) Replace $\mathbf{F}$ with an equivalent force-couple system at the point D obtained by drawing the perpendicular from the point of contact to the x axis. (*b*) For $a = 1$ m and $b = 2$ m, determine the value of x for which the moment of the equivalent force-couple system at D is maximum.

3.119 As plastic bushings are inserted into a 60-mm-diameter cylindrical sheet metal enclosure, the insertion tools exert the forces shown on the enclosure. Each of the forces is parallel to one of the coordinate axes. Replace these forces with an equivalent force-couple system at C.

3.120 Two 150-mm-diameter pulleys are mounted on line shaft AD. The belts at B and C lie in vertical planes parallel to the yz plane. Replace the belt forces shown with an equivalent force-couple system at A.

Fig. P3.119

Fig. P3.120

3.121 Four forces are applied to the machine component $ABDE$ as shown. Replace these forces with an equivalent force-couple system at A.

Fig. P3.121

3.122 While using a pencil sharpener, a student applies the forces and couple shown. (*a*) Determine the forces exerted at *B* and *C* knowing that these forces and the couple are equivalent to a force-couple system at *A* consisting of the force $\mathbf{R} = (2.6 \text{ lb})\mathbf{i} + R_y\mathbf{j} - (0.7 \text{ lb})\mathbf{k}$ and the couple $\mathbf{M}_A^R = M_x\mathbf{i} + (1.0 \text{ lb} \cdot \text{ft})\mathbf{j} - (0.72 \text{ lb} \cdot \text{ft})\mathbf{k}$. (*b*) Find the corresponding values of R_y and M_x.

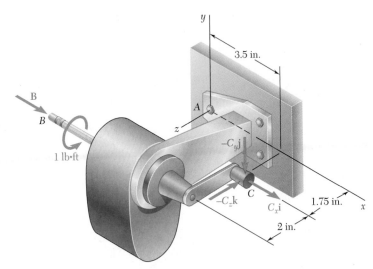

Fig. P3.122

3.123 A blade held in a brace is used to tighten a screw at *A*. (*a*) Determine the forces exerted at *B* and *C*, knowing that these forces are equivalent to a force-couple system at *A* consisting of $\mathbf{R} = -(30 \text{ N})\mathbf{i} + R_y\mathbf{j} + R_z\mathbf{k}$ and $\mathbf{M}_A^R = -(12 \text{ N} \cdot \text{m})\mathbf{i}$. (*b*) Find the corresponding values of R_y and R_z. (*c*) What is the orientation of the slot in the head of the screw for which the blade is least likely to slip when the brace is in the position shown?

Fig. P3.123

3.124 In order to unscrew the tapped faucet A, a plumber uses two pipe wrenches as shown. By exerting a 40-lb force on each wrench, at a distance of 10 in. from the axis of the pipe and in a direction perpendicular to the pipe and to the wrench, he prevents the pipe from rotating, and thus avoids loosening or further tightening the joint between the pipe and the tapped elbow C. Determine (a) the angle θ that the wrench at A should form with the vertical if elbow C is not to rotate about the vertical, (b) the force-couple system at C equivalent to the two 40-lb forces when this condition is satisfied.

Fig. P3.124

3.125 Assuming $\theta = 60°$ in Prob. 3.124, replace the two 40-lb forces with an equivalent force-couple system at D and determine whether the plumber's action tends to tighten or loosen the joint between (a) pipe CD and elbow D, (b) elbow D and pipe DE. Assume all threads to be right-handed.

3.126 As an adjustable brace BC is used to bring a wall into plumb, the force-couple system shown is exerted on the wall. Replace this force-couple system with an equivalent force-couple system at A if $R = 21.2$ lb and $M = 13.25$ lb · ft.

3.127 Three children are standing on a 5 × 5-m raft. If the weights of the children at points A, B, and C are 375 N, 260 N, and 400 N, respectively, determine the magnitude and the point of application of the resultant of the three weights.

3.128 Three children are standing on a 5 × 5-m raft. The weights of the children at points A, B, and C are 375 N, 260 N, and 400 N, respectively. If a fourth child of weight 425 N climbs onto the raft, determine where she should stand if the other children remain in the positions shown and the line of action of the resultant of the four weights is to pass through the center of the raft.

Fig. P3.126

Fig. P3.127 and P3.128

3.129 Four signs are mounted on a frame spanning a highway, and the magnitudes of the horizontal wind forces acting on the signs are as shown. Determine the magnitude and the point of application of the resultant of the four wind forces when $a = 1$ ft and $b = 12$ ft.

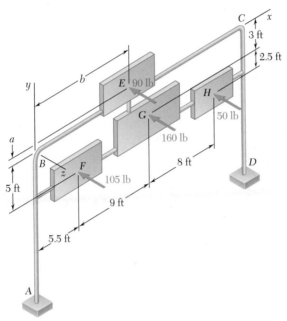

Fig. P3.129 and P3.130

3.130 Four signs are mounted on a frame spanning a highway, and the magnitudes of the horizontal wind forces acting on the signs are as shown. Determine a and b so that the point of application of the resultant of the four forces is at G.

*3.131 A group of students loads a 2×3.3-m flatbed trailer with two $0.66 \times 0.66 \times 0.66$-m boxes and one $0.66 \times 0.66 \times 1.2$-m box. Each of the boxes at the rear of the trailer is positioned so that it is aligned with both the back and a side of the trailer. Determine the smallest load the students should place in a second $0.66 \times 0.66 \times 1.2$-m box and where on the trailer they should secure it, without any part of the box overhanging the sides of the trailer, if each box is uniformly loaded and the line of action of the resultant of the weights of the four boxes is to pass through the point of intersection of the centerlines of the trailer and the axle. (*Hint:* Keep in mind that the box may be placed either on its side or on its end.)

*3.132 Solve Prob. 3.131 if the students want to place as much weight as possible in the fourth box and at least one side of the box must coincide with a side of the trailer.

*3.133 A piece of sheet metal is bent into the shape shown and is acted upon by three forces. If the forces have the same magnitude P, replace them with an equivalent wrench and determine (*a*) the magnitude and the direction of the resultant force **R**, (*b*) the pitch of the wrench, (*c*) the axis of the wrench.

Fig. P3.131

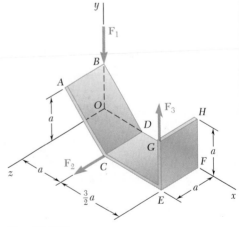

Fig. P3.133

*3.134 Three forces of the same magnitude P act on a cube of side a as shown. Replace the three forces with an equivalent wrench and determine (a) the magnitude and direction of the resultant force **R**, (b) the pitch of the wrench, (c) the axis of the wrench.

*3.135 and *3.136 The forces and couples shown are applied to two screws as a piece of sheet metal is fastened to a block of wood. Reduce the forces and the couples to an equivalent wrench and determine (a) the resultant force **R**, (b) the pitch of the wrench, (c) the point where the axis of the wrench intersects the xz plane.

Fig. P3.134

Fig. P3.135

Fig. P3.136

*3.137 and *3.138 Two bolts at A and B are tightened by applying the forces and couples shown. Replace the two wrenches with a single equivalent wrench and determine (a) the resultant **R**, (b) the pitch of the single equivalent wrench, (c) the point where the axis of the wrench intersects the xz plane.

Fig. P3.137

Fig. P3.138

*3.139 A flagpole is guyed by three cables. If the tensions in the cables have the same magnitude P, replace the forces exerted on the pole with an equivalent wrench and determine (a) the resultant force **R**, (b) the pitch of the wrench, (c) the point where the axis of the wrench intersects the xz plane.

*3.140 Two ropes attached at A and B are used to move the trunk of a fallen tree. Replace the forces exerted by the ropes with an equivalent wrench and determine (a) the resultant force **R**, (b) the pitch of the wrench, (c) the point where the axis of the wrench intersects the yz plane.

Fig. P3.139

Fig. P3.140

*3.141 and *3.142 Determine whether the force-and-couple system shown can be reduced to a single equivalent force **R**. If it can, determine **R** and the point where the line of action of **R** intersects the yz plane. If it cannot be so reduced, replace the given system with an equivalent wrench and determine its resultant, its pitch, and the point where its axis intersects the yz plane.

Fig. P3.141

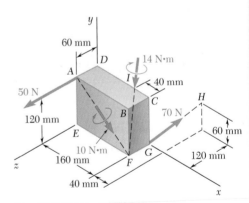

Fig. P3.142

*3.143 Replace the wrench shown with an equivalent system consisting of two forces perpendicular to the y axis and applied respectively at A and B.

*3.144 Show that, in general, a wrench can be replaced with two forces chosen in such a way that one force passes through a given point while the other force lies in a given plane.

*3.145 Show that a wrench can be replaced with two perpendicular forces, one of which is applied at a given point.

*3.146 Show that a wrench can be replaced with two forces, one of which has a prescribed line of action.

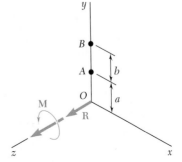

Fig. P3.143

REVIEW AND SUMMARY

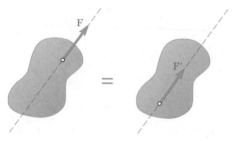

Fig. 3.48

In this chapter we studied the effect of forces exerted on a rigid body. We first learned to distinguish between *external* and *internal* forces [Sec. 3.2] and saw that, according to the *principle of transmissibility*, the effect of an external force on a rigid body remains unchanged if that force is moved along its line of action [Sec. 3.3]. In other words, two forces **F** and **F'** acting on a rigid body at two different points have the same effect on that body if they have the same magnitude, same direction, and same one of action (Fig. 3.48). Two such forces are said to be *equivalent*.

Before proceeding with the discussion of *equivalent systems of forces*, we introduced the concept of the *vector product of two vectors* [Sec. 3.4]. The vector product

$$\mathbf{V} = \mathbf{P} \times \mathbf{Q}$$

Vector product of two vectors

(a)

(b)

Fig. 3.49

of the vectors **P** and **Q** was defined as a vector perpendicular to the plane containing **P** and **Q** (Fig. 3.49), of magnitude

$$V = PQ \sin \theta \tag{3.1}$$

and directed in such a way that a person located at the tip of **V** will observe as counterclockwise the rotation through θ which brings the vector **P** in line with the vector **Q**. The three vectors **P**, **Q**, and **V**—taken in that order—are said to form a *right-handed triad*. It follows that the vector products **Q** × **P** and **P** × **Q** are represented by equal and opposite vectors. We have

$$\mathbf{Q} \times \mathbf{P} = -(\mathbf{P} \times \mathbf{Q}) \tag{3.4}$$

It also follows from the definition of the vector product of two vectors that the vector products of the unit vectors **i**, **j**, and **k** are

$$\mathbf{i} \times \mathbf{i} = 0 \qquad \mathbf{i} \times \mathbf{j} = \mathbf{k} \qquad \mathbf{j} \times \mathbf{i} = -\mathbf{k}$$

Fig. 3.50

and so on. The sign of the vector product of two unit vectors can be obtained by arranging in a circle and in counterclockwise order the three letters representing the unit vectors (Fig. 3.50): The vector product of two unit vectors will be positive if they follow each other in counterclockwise order and negative if they follow each other in clockwise order.

The *rectangular components of the vector product* **V** of two vectors **P** and **Q** were expressed [Sec. 3.5] as

Rectangular components of vector product

$$\begin{aligned} V_x &= P_y Q_z - P_z Q_y \\ V_y &= P_z Q_x - P_x Q_z \\ V_z &= P_x Q_y - P_y Q_x \end{aligned} \tag{3.9}$$

Using a determinant, we also wrote

$$\mathbf{V} = \begin{vmatrix} \mathbf{i} & \mathbf{j} & \mathbf{k} \\ P_x & P_y & P_z \\ Q_x & Q_y & Q_z \end{vmatrix} \qquad (3.10)$$

The *moment of a force* **F** *about a point* O was defined [Sec. 3.6] as the vector product

$$\mathbf{M}_O = \mathbf{r} \times \mathbf{F} \qquad (3.11)$$

where **r** is the *position vector* drawn from O to the point of application A of the force **F** (Fig. 3.51). Denoting by θ the angle between the lines of action of **r** and **F**, we found that the magnitude of the moment of **F** about O can be expressed as

$$M_O = rF \sin \theta = Fd \qquad (3.12)$$

where d represents the perpendicular distance from O to the line of action of **F**.

Moment of a force about a point

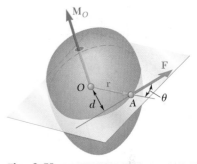

Fig. 3.51

The *rectangular components of the moment* $\mathbf{M}_O$ of a force **F** were expressed [Sec. 3.8] as

$$\begin{aligned} M_x &= yF_z - zF_y \\ M_y &= zF_x - xF_z \\ M_z &= xF_y - yF_x \end{aligned} \qquad (3.18)$$

where x, y, z are the components of the position vector **r** (Fig. 3.52). Using a determinant form, we also wrote

$$\mathbf{M}_O = \begin{vmatrix} \mathbf{i} & \mathbf{j} & \mathbf{k} \\ x & y & z \\ F_x & F_y & F_z \end{vmatrix} \qquad (3.19)$$

In the more general case of the moment about an arbitrary point B of a force **F** applied at A, we had

$$\mathbf{M}_B = \begin{vmatrix} \mathbf{i} & \mathbf{j} & \mathbf{k} \\ x_{A/B} & y_{A/B} & z_{A/B} \\ F_x & F_y & F_z \end{vmatrix} \qquad (3.21)$$

where $x_{A/B}$, $y_{A/B}$, and $z_{A/B}$ denote the components of the vector $\mathbf{r}_{A/B}$:

$$x_{A/B} = x_A - x_B \qquad y_{A/B} = y_A - y_B \qquad z_{A/B} = z_A - z_B$$

In the case of *problems involving only two dimensions*, the force **F** can be assumed to lie in the xy plane. Its moment $\mathbf{M}_B$ about a point B in the same plane is perpendicular to that plane (Fig. 3.53) and is completely defined by the scalar

$$M_B = (x_A - x_B)F_y - (y_A - y_B)F_x \qquad (3.23)$$

Various methods for the computation of the moment of a force about a point were illustrated in Sample Probs. 3.1 through 3.4.

The *scalar product* of two vectors **P** and **Q** [Sec. 3.9] was denoted by **P · Q** and was defined as the scalar quantity

$$\mathbf{P} \cdot \mathbf{Q} = PQ \cos \theta \qquad (3.24)$$

Rectangular components of moment

Fig. 3.52

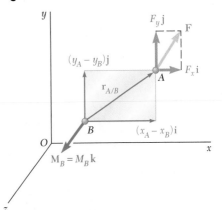

Fig. 3.53

Scalar product of two vectors

Fig. 3.54

Projection of a vector on an axis

where θ is the angle between $\mathbf{P}$ and $\mathbf{Q}$ (Fig. 3.54). By expressing the scalar product of $\mathbf{P}$ and $\mathbf{Q}$ in terms of the rectangular components of the two vectors, we determined that

$$\mathbf{P} \cdot \mathbf{Q} = P_x Q_x + P_y Q_y + P_z Q_z \tag{3.30}$$

The *projection of a vector* $\mathbf{P}$ *on an axis* OL (Fig. 3.55) can be obtained by forming the scalar product of $\mathbf{P}$ and the unit vector $\boldsymbol{\lambda}$ along OL. We have

$$P_{OL} = \mathbf{P} \cdot \boldsymbol{\lambda} \tag{3.36}$$

or, using rectangular components,

$$P_{OL} = P_x \cos \theta_x + P_y \cos \theta_y + P_z \cos \theta_z \tag{3.37}$$

where θ_x, θ_y, and θ_z denote the angles that the axis OL forms with the coordinate axes.

Fig. 3.55

Mixed triple product of three vectors

The *mixed triple product* of the three vectors $\mathbf{S}$, $\mathbf{P}$, and $\mathbf{Q}$ was defined as the scalar expression

$$\mathbf{S} \cdot (\mathbf{P} \times \mathbf{Q}) \tag{3.38}$$

obtained by forming the scalar product of $\mathbf{S}$ with the vector product of $\mathbf{P}$ and $\mathbf{Q}$ [Sec. 3.10]. It was shown that

$$\mathbf{S} \cdot (\mathbf{P} \times \mathbf{Q}) = \begin{vmatrix} S_x & S_y & S_z \\ P_x & P_y & P_z \\ Q_x & Q_y & Q_z \end{vmatrix} \tag{3.41}$$

where the elements of the determinant are the rectangular components of the three vectors.

Moment of a force about an axis

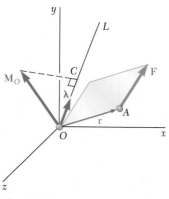

Fig. 3.56

The *moment of a force* $\mathbf{F}$ *about an axis* OL [Sec. 3.11] was defined as the projection OC on OL of the moment $\mathbf{M}_O$ of the force $\mathbf{F}$ (Fig. 3.56), i.e., as the mixed triple product of the unit vector $\boldsymbol{\lambda}$, the position vector $\mathbf{r}$, and the force $\mathbf{F}$:

$$M_{OL} = \boldsymbol{\lambda} \cdot \mathbf{M}_O = \boldsymbol{\lambda} \cdot (\mathbf{r} \times \mathbf{F}) \tag{3.42}$$

Using the determinant form for the mixed triple product, we have

$$M_{OL} = \begin{vmatrix} \lambda_x & \lambda_y & \lambda_z \\ x & y & z \\ F_x & F_y & F_z \end{vmatrix} \tag{3.43}$$

where $\lambda_x, \lambda_y, \lambda_z$ = direction cosines of axis OL
x, y, z = components of $\mathbf{r}$
F_x, F_y, F_z = components of $\mathbf{F}$

An example of the determination of the moment of a force about a skew axis was given in Sample Prob. 3.5.

Two forces **F** and −**F** *having the same magnitude, parallel lines of action, and opposite sense are said to form a couple* [Sec. 3.12]. It was shown that the moment of a couple is independent of the point about which it is computed; it is a vector **M** perpendicular to the plane of the couple and equal in magnitude to the product of the common magnitude F of the forces and the perpendicular distance d between their lines of action (Fig. 3.57).

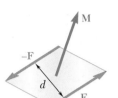

Fig. 3.57

Two couples having the same moment **M** are *equivalent*, i.e., they have the same effect on a given rigid body [Sec. 3.13]. The sum of two couples is itself a couple [Sec. 3.14], and the moment **M** of the resultant couple can be obtained by adding vectorially the moments **M**₁ and **M**₂ of the original couples [Sample Prob. 3.6]. It follows that a couple can be represented by a vector, called a *couple vector*, equal in magnitude and direction to the moment **M** of the couple [Sec. 3.15]. A couple vector is a *free vector* which can be attached to the origin O if so desired and resolved into components (Fig. 3.58).

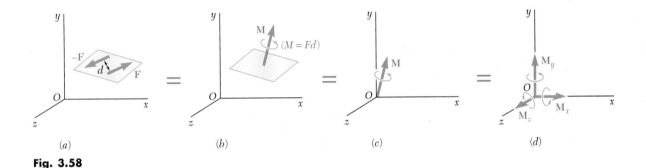

(a)   (b)   (c)   (d)

Fig. 3.58

Any force **F** acting at a point A of a rigid body can be replaced by a *force-couple system* at an arbitrary point O, consisting of the force **F** applied at O and a couple of moment **M**$_O$ equal to the moment about O of the force **F** in its original position [Sec. 3.16]; it should be noted that the force **F** and the couple vector **M**$_O$ are always perpendicular to each other (Fig. 3.59).

Force-couple system

Fig. 3.59

It follows [Sec. 3.17] that *any system of forces can be reduced to a force-couple system at a given point O* by first replacing each of the forces of the system by an equivalent force-couple system at O

Reduction of a system of forces to a force-couple system

(Fig. 3.60) and then adding all the forces and all the couples determined in this manner to obtain a resultant force **R** and a resultant couple vector $\mathbf{M}_O^R$ [Sample Probs. 3.8 through 3.11]. Note that, in general, the resultant **R** and the couple vector $\mathbf{M}_O^R$ will not be perpendicular to each other.

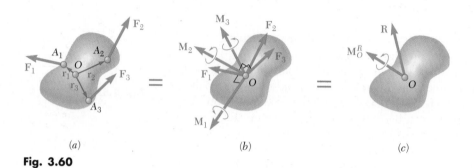

(a)   (b)   (c)

Fig. 3.60

Equivalent systems of forces

We concluded from the above [Sec. 3.18] that, as far as rigid bodies are concerned, *two systems of forces, $\mathbf{F}_1$, $\mathbf{F}_2$, $\mathbf{F}_3$, . . . and $\mathbf{F}_1'$, $\mathbf{F}_2'$, $\mathbf{F}_3'$, . . . , are equivalent if, and only if,*

$$\Sigma \mathbf{F} = \Sigma \mathbf{F}' \qquad \text{and} \qquad \Sigma \mathbf{M}_O = \Sigma \mathbf{M}_O' \qquad (3.57)$$

Further reduction of a system of forces

If the resultant force **R** and the resultant couple vector $\mathbf{M}_O^R$ are perpendicular to each other, the force-couple system at O can be further reduced to a single resultant force [Sec. 3.20]. This will be the case for systems consisting either of (a) concurrent forces (cf. Chap. 2), (b) coplanar forces [Sample Probs. 3.8 and 3.9], or (c) parallel forces [Sample Prob. 3.11]. If the resultant **R** and the couple vector $\mathbf{M}_O^R$ are *not* perpendicular to each other, the system *cannot* be reduced to a single force. It can, however, be reduced to a special type of force-couple system called a *wrench*, consisting of the resultant **R** and a couple vector $\mathbf{M}_1$ directed along **R** [Sec. 3.21 and Sample Prob. 3.12].

3.147 A 300-N force is applied at A as shown. Determine (a) the moment of the 300-N force about D, (b) the smallest force applied at B that creates the same moment about D.

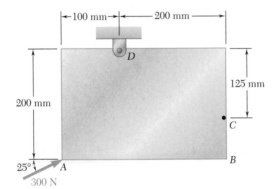

Fig. P3.147

3.148 The tailgate of a car is supported by the hydraulic lift BC. If the lift exerts a 125-lb force directed along its centerline on the ball and socket at B, determine the moment of the force about A.

3.149 The ramp $ABCD$ is supported by cables at corners C and D. The tension in each of the cables is 810 N. Determine the moment about A of the force exerted by (a) the cable at D, (b) the cable at C.

Fig. P3.148

Fig. P3.149

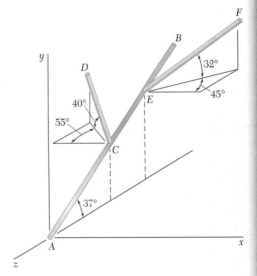

3.150 Section AB of a pipeline lies in the yz plane and forms an angle of 37° with the z axis. Branch lines CD and EF join AB as shown. Determine the angle formed by pipes AB and CD.

Fig. P3.150

Fig. P3.151

3.151 To lift a heavy crate, a man uses a block and tackle attached to the bottom of an I-beam at hook B. Knowing that the moments about the y and the z axes of the force exerted at B by portion AB of the rope are, respectively, 120 N · m and –460 N · m, determine the distance a.

3.152 To loosen a frozen valve, a force $\mathbf{F}$ of magnitude 70 lb is applied to the handle of the valve. Knowing that $\theta = 25°$, $M_x = -61$ lb · ft, and $M_z = -43$ lb · ft, determine ϕ and d.

Fig. P3.152

3.153 The tension in the cable attached to the end C of an adjustable boom ABC is 560 lb. Replace the force exerted by the cable at C with an equivalent force-couple system (a) at A, (b) at B.

Fig. P3.153

Fig. P3.154

3.154 While tapping a hole, a machinist applies the horizontal forces shown to the handle of the tap wrench. Show that these forces are equivalent to a single force, and specify, if possible, the point of application of the single force on the handle.

3.155 Replace the 150-N force with an equivalent force-couple system at *A*.

3.156 A beam supports three loads of given magnitude and a fourth load whose magnitude is a function of position. If $b = 1.5$ m and the loads are to be replaced with a single equivalent force, determine (*a*) the value of *a* so that the distance from support *A* to the line of action of the equivalent force is maximum, (*b*) the magnitude of the equivalent force and its point of application on the beam.

Fig. P3.155

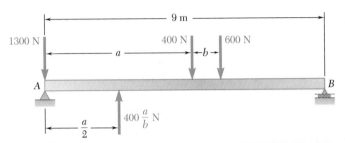

Fig. P3.156

3.157 A mechanic uses a crowfoot wrench to loosen a bolt at *C*. The mechanic holds the socket wrench handle at points *A* and *B* and applies forces at these points. Knowing that these forces are equivalent to a force-couple system at *C* consisting of the force $\mathbf{C} = -(8 \text{ lb})\mathbf{i} + (4 \text{ lb})\mathbf{k}$ and the couple $\mathbf{M}_C = (360 \text{ lb} \cdot \text{in.})\mathbf{i}$, determine the forces applied at *A* and at *B* when $A_z = 2$ lb.

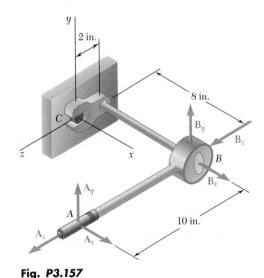

Fig. P3.157

3.158 A concrete foundation mat in the shape of a regular hexagon of side 12 ft supports four column loads as shown. Determine the magnitudes of the additional loads that must be applied at *B* and *F* if the resultant of all six loads is to pass through the center of the mat.

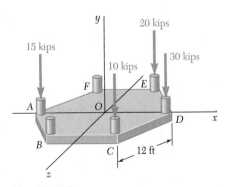

Fig. P3.158

COMPUTER PROBLEMS

Fig. P3.C1

3.C1 A beam AB is subjected to several vertical forces as shown. Write a computer program that can be used to determine the magnitude of the resultant of the forces and the distance x_C to point C, the point where the line of action of the resultant intersects AB. Use this program to solve (a) Sample Prob. 3.8c, (b) Prob. 3.106a.

3.C2 Write a computer program that can be used to determine the magnitude and the point of application of the resultant of the vertical forces P_1, P_2, . . . , P_n that act at points A_1, A_2, . . . , A_n that are located in the xz plane. Use this program to solve (a) Sample Prob. 3.11, (b) Prob. 3.127, (c) Prob. 3.129.

Fig. P3.C2

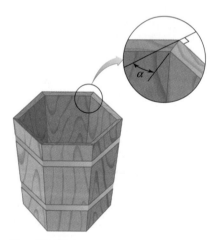

Fig. P3.C3

3.C3 A friend asks for your help in designing flower planter boxes. The boxes are to have 4, 5, 6, or 8 sides, which are to tilt outward at 10°, 20°, or 30°. Write a computer program that can be used to determine the bevel angle α for each of the 12 planter designs. (*Hint:* The bevel angle is equal to one-half of the angle formed by the inward normals of two adjacent sides.)

3.C4 The manufacturer of a spool for hoses wants to determine the moment of the force $\mathbf{F}$ about the axis AA'. The magnitude of the force, in newtons, is defined by the relation $F = 300(1 - x/L)$, where x is the length of hose wound on the 0.6-m-diameter drum and L is the total length of the hose. Write a computer program that can be used to calculate the required moment for a hose 30 m long and 50 mm in diameter. Beginning with $x = 0$, compute the moment after every revolution of the drum until the hose is wound on the drum.

Fig. P3.C4

3.C5 A body is acted upon by a system of n forces. Write a computer program that can be used to calculate the equivalent force-couple system at the origin of the coordinate axes and to determine, if the equivalent force and the equivalent couple are orthogonal, the magnitude and the point of application in the xz plane of the resultant of the original force system. Use this program to solve (*a*) Prob. 3.113, (*b*) Prob. 3.120, (*c*) Prob. 3.127.

3.C6 Two cylindrical ducts, AB and CD, enter a room through two parallel walls. The centerlines of the ducts are parallel to each other but are not perpendicular to the walls. The ducts are to be connected by two flexible elbows and a straight center portion. Write a computer program that can be used to determine the lengths of AB and CD that minimize the distance between the axis of the straight portion and a thermometer mounted on the wall at E. Assume that the elbows are of negligible length and that AB and CD have centerlines defined by $\lambda_{AB} = (7\mathbf{i} - 4\mathbf{j} + 4\mathbf{k})/9$ and $\lambda_{CD} = (-7\mathbf{i} + 4\mathbf{j} - 4\mathbf{k})/9$ and can vary in length from 9 in. to 36 in.

Fig. P3.C5

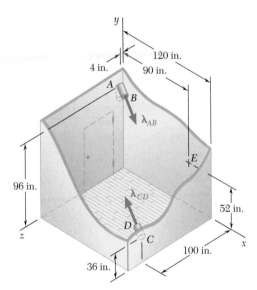

Fig. P3.C6

This telecommunications tower, constructed in the heart of the Barcelona Olympic complex to broadcast the 1992 games, was designed to remain in equilibrium under the vertical force of gravity and the lateral forces exerted by wind.

Equilibrium of Rigid Bodies

4.1 INTRODUCTION

We saw in the preceding chapter that the external forces acting on a rigid body can be reduced to a force-couple system at some arbitrary point O. When the force and the couple are both equal to zero, the external forces form a system equivalent to zero, and the rigid body is said to be in *equilibrium*.

The necessary and sufficient conditions for the equilibrium of a rigid body, therefore, can be obtained by setting $\mathbf{R}$ and $\mathbf{M}_O^R$ equal to zero in the relations (3.52) of Sec. 3.17:

$$\Sigma\mathbf{F} = 0 \qquad \Sigma\mathbf{M}_O = \Sigma(\mathbf{r} \times \mathbf{F}) = 0 \qquad (4.1)$$

Resolving each force and each moment into its rectangular components, we can express the necessary and sufficient conditions for the equilibrium of a rigid body with the following six scalar equations:

$$\Sigma F_x = 0 \qquad \Sigma F_y = 0 \qquad \Sigma F_z = 0 \qquad (4.2)$$
$$\Sigma M_x = 0 \qquad \Sigma M_y = 0 \qquad \Sigma M_z = 0 \qquad (4.3)$$

The equations obtained can be used to determine unknown forces applied to the rigid body or unknown reactions exerted on it by its supports. We note that Eqs. (4.2) express the fact that the components of the external forces in the x, y, and z directions are balanced; Eqs. (4.3) express the fact that the moments of the external forces about the x, y, and z axes are balanced. Therefore, for a rigid body in equilibrium, the system of the external forces will impart no translational or rotational motion to the body considered.

In order to write the equations of equilibrium for a rigid body, it is essential to first identify all of the forces acting on that body and then to draw the corresponding *free-body diagram*. In this chapter we first consider the equilibrium of *two-dimensional structures* subjected to forces contained in their planes and learn how to draw their free-body diagrams. In addition to the forces *applied* to a structure, the *reactions* exerted on the structure by its supports will be considered. A specific reaction will be associated with each type of support. You will learn how to determine whether the structure is properly supported, so that you can know in advance whether the equations of equilibrium can be solved for the unknown forces and reactions.

Later in the chapter, the equilibrium of three-dimensional structures will be considered, and the same kind of analysis will be given to these structures and their supports.

4.2 FREE-BODY DIAGRAM

In solving a problem concerning the equilibrium of a rigid body, it is essential to consider *all* of the forces acting on the body; it is equally important to exclude any force which is not directly applied to the body. Omitting a force or adding an extraneous one would destroy the conditions of equilibrium. Therefore, the first step in the solution of the problem should be to draw a *free-body diagram* of the rigid body under consideration. Free-body diagrams have already been used on many occasions in Chap. 2. However, in view of their importance to the solution of equilibrium problems, we summarize here the various steps which must be followed in drawing a free-body diagram.

1. A clear decision should be made regarding the choice of the free body to be used. This body is then detached from the ground and is separated from all other bodies. The contour of the body thus isolated is sketched.

2. All external forces should be indicated on the free-body diagram. These forces represent the actions exerted *on* the free body *by* the ground and *by* the bodies which have been detached; they should be applied at the various points where the free body was supported by the ground or was connected to the other bodies. The *weight* of the free body should also be included among the external forces, since it represents the attraction exerted by the earth on the various particles forming the free body. As will be seen in Chap. 5, the weight should be applied at the center of gravity of the body. When the free body is made of several parts, the forces the various parts exert on each other should *not* be included among the external forces. These forces are internal forces as far as the free body is concerned.

3. The magnitudes and directions of the *known external forces* should be clearly marked on the free-body diagram. When indicating the directions of these forces, it must be remembered that the forces shown on the free-body diagram must be those which are exerted *on*, and not *by*, the free body. Known external forces generally include the *weight* of the free body and *forces applied* for a given purpose.

4. *Unknown external forces* usually consist of the *reactions*, through which the ground and other bodies oppose a possible motion of the free body. The reactions constrain the free body to remain in the same position, and, for that reason, are sometimes called *constraining forces*. Reactions are exerted at the points where the free body is *supported by* or *connected to* other bodies and should be clearly indicated. Reactions are discussed in detail in Secs. 4.3 and 4.8.

5. The free-body diagram should also include dimensions, since these may be needed in the computation of moments of forces. Any other detail, however, should be omitted.

Photo 4.1 A free-body diagram of the tractor shown would include all of the external forces acting on the tractor: the weight of the tractor, the weight of the load in the bucket, and the forces exerted by the ground on the tires.

Photo 4.2 In Chap. 6, we will discuss how to determine the internal forces in structures made of several connected pieces, such as the forces in the members that support the bucket of the tractor of Photo 4.1.

Photo 4.3 As the link of the awning window opening mechanism is extended, the force it exerts on the slider results in a normal force being applied to the rod, which causes the window to open.

Photo 4.4 The abutment-mounted rocker bearing shown is used to support the roadway of a bridge.

Photo 4.5 Shown is the rocker expansion bearing of a plate girder bridge. The convex surface of the rocker allows the support of the girder to move horizontally.

EQUILIBRIUM IN TWO DIMENSIONS

4.3 REACTIONS AT SUPPORTS AND CONNECTIONS FOR A TWO-DIMENSIONAL STRUCTURE

In the first part of this chapter, the equilibrium of a two-dimensional structure is considered; i.e., it is assumed that the structure being analyzed and the forces applied to it are contained in the same plane. Clearly, the reactions needed to maintain the structure in the same position will also be contained in this plane.

The reactions exerted on a two-dimensional structure can be divided into three groups corresponding to three types of *supports*, or *connections:*

1. *Reactions Equivalent to a Force with Known Line of Action.* Supports and connections causing reactions of this type include *rollers, rockers, frictionless surfaces, short links and cables, collars on frictionless rods,* and *frictionless pins in slots.* Each of these supports and connections can prevent motion in one direction only. They are shown in Fig. 4.1, together with the reactions they produce. Each of these reactions involves *one unknown,* namely, the magnitude of the reaction; this magnitude should be denoted by an appropriate letter. The line of action of the reaction is known and should be indicated clearly in the free-body diagram. The sense of the reaction must be as shown in Fig. 4.1 for the cases of a frictionless surface (toward the free body) or a cable (away from the free body). The reaction can be directed either way in the case of double-track rollers, links, collars on rods, and pins in slots. Single-track rollers and rockers are generally assumed to be reversible, and thus the corresponding reactions can also be directed either way.

2. *Reactions Equivalent to a Force of Unknown Direction and Magnitude.* Supports and connections causing reactions of this type include *frictionless pins in fitted holes, hinges,* and *rough surfaces.* They can prevent translation of the free body in all directions, but they cannot prevent the body from rotating about the connection. Reactions of this group involve *two unknowns* and are usually represented by their *x* and *y* components. In the case of a rough surface, the component normal to the surface must be directed away from the surface.

3. *Reactions Equivalent to a Force and a Couple.* These reactions are caused by *fixed supports,* which oppose any motion of the free body and thus constrain it completely. Fixed supports actually produce forces over the entire surface of contact; these forces, however, form a system which can be reduced to a force and a couple. Reactions of this group involve *three unknowns,* consisting usually of the two components of the force and the moment of the couple.

Support or Connection			Reaction	Number of Unknowns
Rollers	Rocker	Frictionless surface	Force with known line of action	1
Short cable		Short link	Force with known line of action	1
Collar on frictionless rod		Frictionless pin in slot	90° Force with known line of action	1
Frictionless pin or hinge		Rough surface	or α Force of unknown direction	2
Fixed support			or α Force and couple	3

Fig. 4.1 Reactions at supports and connections.

When the sense of an unknown force or couple is not readily apparent, no attempt should be made to determine it. Instead, the sense of the force or couple should be arbitrarily assumed; the sign of the answer obtained will indicate whether the assumption is correct or not.

4.4 EQUILIBRIUM OF A RIGID BODY IN TWO DIMENSIONS

The conditions stated in Sec. 4.1 for the equilibrium of a rigid body become considerably simpler for the case of a two-dimensional structure. Choosing the x and y axes to be in the plane of the structure, we have

$$F_z = 0 \qquad M_x = M_y = 0 \qquad M_z = M_O$$

for each of the forces applied to the structure. Thus, the six equations of equilibrium derived in Sec. 4.1 reduce to

$$\Sigma F_x = 0 \qquad \Sigma F_y = 0 \qquad \Sigma M_O = 0 \qquad (4.4)$$

and to three trivial identities, $0 = 0$. Since $\Sigma M_O = 0$ must be satisfied regardless of the choice of the origin O, we can write the equations of equilibrium for a two-dimensional structure in the more general form

$$\Sigma F_x = 0 \qquad \Sigma F_y = 0 \qquad \Sigma M_A = 0 \qquad (4.5)$$

where A is any point in the plane of the structure. The three equations obtained can be solved for no more than *three unknowns*.

We saw in the preceding section that unknown forces include reactions and that the number of unknowns corresponding to a given reaction depends upon the type of support or connection causing that reaction. Referring to Sec. 4.3, we observe that the equilibrium equations (4.5) can be used to determine the reactions associated with two rollers and one cable, one fixed support, or one roller and one pin in a fitted hole, etc.

Consider Fig. 4.2a, in which the truss shown is subjected to the given forces **P**, **Q**, and **S**. The truss is held in place by a pin at A and a roller at B. The pin prevents point A from moving by exerting on the truss a force which can be resolved into the components $\mathbf{A}_x$ and $\mathbf{A}_y$; the roller keeps the truss from rotating about A by exerting the vertical force **B**. The free-body diagram of the truss is shown in Fig. 4.2b; it includes the reactions $\mathbf{A}_x$, $\mathbf{A}_y$, and **B** as well as the applied forces **P**, **Q**, **S** and the weight **W** of the truss. Expressing that the sum of the moments about A of all of the forces shown in Fig. 4.2b is zero, we write the equation $\Sigma M_A = 0$, which can be used to determine the magnitude B since it does not contain A_x or A_y. Next, expressing that the sum of the x components and the sum of the y components of the forces are zero, we write the equations $\Sigma F_x = 0$ and $\Sigma F_y = 0$, from which we can obtain the components A_x and A_y, respectively.

An additional equation could be obtained by expressing that the sum of the moments of the external forces about a point other than A is zero. We could write, for instance, $\Sigma M_B = 0$. Such a statement, however, does not contain any new information, since it has already been established that the system of the forces shown in Fig. 4.2b is equivalent to zero. The additional equation *is not independent* and cannot be used to determine a fourth unknown. It will be useful,

(a)

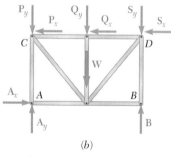

(b)

Fig. 4.2

however, for checking the solution obtained from the original three equations of equilibrium.

While the three equations of equilibrium cannot be *augmented* by additional equations, any of them can be *replaced* by another equation. Therefore, an alternative system of equations of equilibrium is

$$\Sigma F_x = 0 \qquad \Sigma M_A = 0 \qquad \Sigma M_B = 0 \qquad (4.6)$$

where the second point about which the moments are summed (in this case, point B) cannot lie on the line parallel to the y axis that passes through point A (Fig. 4.2b). These equations are sufficient conditions for the equilibrium of the truss. The first two equations indicate that the external forces must reduce to a single vertical force at A. Since the third equation requires that the moment of this force be zero about a point B which is not on its line of action, the force must be zero, and the rigid body is in equilibrium.

A third possible set of equations of equilibrium is

$$\Sigma M_A = 0 \qquad \Sigma M_B = 0 \qquad \Sigma M_C = 0 \qquad (4.7)$$

where the points A, B, and C do not lie in a straight line (Fig. 4.2b). The first equation requires that the external forces reduce to a single force at A; the second equation requires that this force pass through B; and the third equation requires that it pass through C. Since the points A, B, C do not lie in a straight line, the force must be zero, and the rigid body is in equilibrium.

The equation $\Sigma M_A = 0$, which expresses that the sum of the moments of the forces about pin A is zero, possesses a more definite physical meaning than either of the other two equations (4.7). These two equations express a similar idea of balance, but with respect to points about which the rigid body is not actually hinged. They are, however, as useful as the first equation, and our choice of equilibrium equations should not be unduly influenced by the physical meaning of these equations. Indeed, it will be desirable in practice to choose equations of equilibrium containing only one unknown, since this eliminates the necessity of solving simultaneous equations. Equations containing only one unknown can be obtained by summing moments about the point of intersection of the lines of action of two unknown forces or, if these forces are parallel, by summing components in a direction perpendicular to their common direction. For example, in Fig. 4.3, in which the truss shown is held by rollers at A and B and a short link at D, the reactions at A and B can be eliminated by summing x components. The reactions at A and D will be eliminated by summing moments about C, and the reactions at B and D by summing moments about D. The equations obtained are

$$\Sigma F_x = 0 \qquad \Sigma M_C = 0 \qquad \Sigma M_D = 0$$

Each of these equations contains only one unknown.

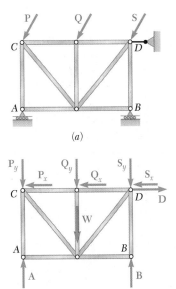

Fig. 4.3

4.5 STATICALLY INDETERMINATE REACTIONS. PARTIAL CONSTRAINTS

In the two examples considered in the preceding section (Figs. 4.2 and 4.3), the types of supports used were such that the rigid body could not possibly move under the given loads or under any other loading conditions. In such cases, the rigid body is said to be *completely constrained*. We also recall that the reactions corresponding to these supports involved *three unknowns* and could be determined by solving the three equations of equilibrium. When such a situation exists, the reactions are said to be *statically determinate*.

Consider Fig. 4.4*a*, in which the truss shown is held by pins at *A* and *B*. These supports provide more constraints than are necessary to keep the truss from moving under the given loads or under any other loading conditions. We also note from the free-body diagram of Fig. 4.4*b* that the corresponding reactions involve *four unknowns*. Since, as was pointed out in Sec. 4.4, only three independent equilibrium equations are available, there are *more unknowns than equations*; thus, all of the unknowns cannot be determined. While the equations $\Sigma M_A = 0$ and $\Sigma M_B = 0$ yield the vertical components B_y and A_y, respectively, the equation $\Sigma F_x = 0$ gives only the sum $A_x + B_x$ of the horizontal components of the reactions at *A* and *B*. The components A_x and B_x are said to be *statically indeterminate*. They could be determined by considering the deformations produced in the truss by the given loading, but this method is beyond the scope of statics and belongs to the study of mechanics of materials.

The supports used to hold the truss shown in Fig. 4.5*a* consist of rollers at *A* and *B*. Clearly, the constraints provided by these supports are not sufficient to keep the truss from moving. While any vertical motion is prevented, the truss is free to move horizontally. The truss is said to be *partially constrained*.† Turning our attention to Fig. 4.5*b*, we note that the reactions at *A* and *B* involve only *two unknowns*. Since three equations of equilibrium must still be satisfied, there are *fewer unknowns than equations*, and, in general, one of the equilibrium equations will not be satisfied. While the equations $\Sigma M_A = 0$ and $\Sigma M_B = 0$ can be satisfied by a proper choice of reactions at *A* and *B*, the equation $\Sigma F_x = 0$ will not be satisfied unless the sum of the horizontal components of the applied forces happens to be zero. We thus observe that the equilibrium of the truss of Fig. 4.5 cannot be maintained under general loading conditions.

It appears from the above that if a rigid body is to be completely constrained and if the reactions at its supports are to be statically determinate, *there must be as many unknowns as there are equations of equilibrium*. When this condition is *not* satisfied, we can be certain that either the rigid body is not completely constrained or that the reactions at its supports are not statically determinate; it is also possible that the rigid body is not completely constrained *and* that the reactions are statically indeterminate.

We should note, however, that, while *necessary*, the above condition is *not sufficient*. In other words, the fact that the number of

(a)

(b)

Fig. 4.4 Statically indeterminate reactions.

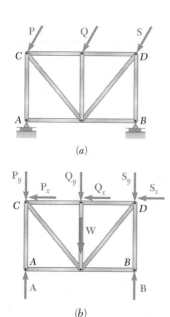

(a)

(b)

Fig. 4.5 Partial constraints.

---

†Partially constrained bodies are often referred to as *unstable*. However, to avoid confusion between this type of instability, due to insufficient constraints, and the type of instability considered in Chap. 10, which relates to the behavior of a rigid body when its equilibrium is disturbed, we shall restrict the use of the words *stable* and *unstable* to the latter case.

unknowns is equal to the number of equations is no guarantee that the body is completely constrained or that the reactions at its supports are statically determinate. Consider Fig. 4.6a, in which the truss shown is held by rollers at A, B, and E. While there are three unknown reactions, $\mathbf{A}$, $\mathbf{B}$, and $\mathbf{E}$ (Fig. 4.6b), the equation $\Sigma F_x = 0$ will not be satisfied unless the sum of the horizontal components of the applied forces happens to be zero. Although there are a sufficient number of constraints, these constraints are not properly arranged, and the truss is free to move horizontally. We say that the truss is *improperly constrained*. Since only two equilibrium equations are left for determining three unknowns, the reactions will be statically indeterminate. Thus, improper constraints also produce static indeterminacy.

Another example of improper constraints—and of static indeterminacy—is provided by the truss shown in Fig. 4.7. This truss is held by a pin at A and by rollers at B and C, which altogether involve four unknowns. Since only three independent equilibrium equations are available, the reactions at the supports are statically indeterminate. On the other hand, we note that the equation $\Sigma M_A = 0$ cannot be satisfied under general loading conditions, since the lines of action of the reactions $\mathbf{B}$ and $\mathbf{C}$ pass through A. We conclude that the truss can rotate about A and that it is improperly constrained.†

The examples of Figs. 4.6 and 4.7 lead us to conclude that *a rigid body is improperly constrained whenever the supports*, even though they may provide a sufficient number of reactions, *are arranged in such a way that the reactions must be either concurrent or parallel.*‡

In summary, to be sure that a two-dimensional rigid body is completely constrained and that the reactions at its supports are statically determinate, we should verify that the reactions involve three—and only three—unknowns and that the supports are arranged in such a way that they do not require the reactions to be either concurrent or parallel.

Supports involving statically indeterminate reactions should be used with care in the *design* of structures and only with a full knowledge of the problems they may cause. On the other hand, the *analysis* of structures possessing statically indeterminate reactions often can be partially carried out by the methods of statics. In the case of the truss of Fig. 4.4, for example, the vertical components of the reactions at A and B were obtained from the equilibrium equations.

For obvious reasons, supports producing partial or improper constraints should be avoided in the design of stationary structures. However, a partially or improperly constrained structure will not necessarily collapse; under particular loading conditions, equilibrium can be maintained. For example, the trusses of Figs. 4.5 and 4.6 will be in equilibrium if the applied forces $\mathbf{P}$, $\mathbf{Q}$, and $\mathbf{S}$ are vertical. Besides, structures which are designed to move *should* be only partially constrained. A railroad car, for instance, would be of little use if it were completely constrained by having its brakes applied permanently.

†Rotation of the truss about A requires some "play" in the supports at B and C. In practice such play will always exist. In addition, we note that if the play is kept small, the displacements of the rollers B and C and, thus, the distances from A to the lines of action of the reactions $\mathbf{B}$ and $\mathbf{C}$ will also be small. The equation $\Sigma M_A = 0$ then requires that $\mathbf{B}$ and $\mathbf{C}$ be very large, a situation which can result in the failure of the supports at B and C.

‡Because this situation arises from an inadequate arrangement or *geometry* of the supports, it is often referred to as *geometric instability*.

Fig. 4.6 Improper constraints.

Fig. 4.7 Improper constraints.

SAMPLE PROBLEM 4.1

A fixed crane has a mass of 1000 kg and is used to lift a 2400-kg crate. It is held in place by a pin at A and a rocker at B. The center of gravity of the crane is located at G. Determine the components of the reactions at A and B.

SOLUTION

Free-Body Diagram. A free-body diagram of the crane is drawn. By multiplying the masses of the crane and of the crate by $g = 9.81$ m/s², we obtain the corresponding weights, that is, 9810 N or 9.81 kN, and 23 500 N or 23.5 kN. The reaction at pin A is a force of unknown direction; it is represented by its components A_x and A_y. The reaction at the rocker B is perpendicular to the rocker surface; thus, it is horizontal. We assume that A_x, A_y, and B act in the directions shown.

Determination of B. We express that the sum of the moments of all external forces about point A is zero. The equation obtained will contain neither A_x nor A_y, since the moments of A_x and A_y about A are zero. Multiplying the magnitude of each force by its perpendicular distance from A, we write

$$+\gamma\Sigma M_A = 0: \quad +B(1.5 \text{ m}) - (9.81 \text{ kN})(2 \text{ m}) - (23.5 \text{ kN})(6 \text{ m}) = 0$$
$$B = +107.1 \text{ kN} \qquad \mathbf{B} = 107.1 \text{ kN} \rightarrow \quad \blacktriangleleft$$

Since the result is positive, the reaction is directed as assumed.

Determination of A_x. The magnitude of A_x is determined by expressing that the sum of the horizontal components of all external forces is zero.

$$\xrightarrow{+}\Sigma F_x = 0: \quad A_x + B = 0$$
$$A_x + 107.1 \text{ kN} = 0$$
$$A_x = -107.1 \text{ kN} \qquad \mathbf{A}_x = 107.1 \text{ kN} \leftarrow \quad \blacktriangleleft$$

Since the result is negative, the sense of A_x is opposite to that assumed originally.

Determination of A_y. The sum of the vertical components must also equal zero.

$$+\uparrow\Sigma F_y = 0: \quad A_y - 9.81 \text{ kN} - 23.5 \text{ kN} = 0$$
$$A_y = +33.3 \text{ kN} \qquad \mathbf{A}_y = 33.3 \text{ kN} \uparrow \quad \blacktriangleleft$$

Adding vectorially the components $\mathbf{A}_x$ and $\mathbf{A}_y$, we find that the reaction at A is 112.2 kN ⦟17.3°.

Check. The values obtained for the reactions can be checked by recalling that the sum of the moments of all of the external forces about any point must be zero. For example, considering point B, we write

$$+\gamma\Sigma M_B = -(9.81 \text{ kN})(2 \text{ m}) - (23.5 \text{ kN})(6 \text{ m}) + (107.1 \text{ kN})(1.5 \text{ m}) = 0$$

Three loads are applied to a beam as shown. The beam is supported by a roller at A and by a pin at B. Neglecting the weight of the beam, determine the reactions at A and B when $P = 15$ kips.

SOLUTION

Free-Body Diagram. A free-body diagram of the beam is drawn. The reaction at A is vertical and is denoted by **A**. The reaction at B is represented by components $\mathbf{B}_x$ and $\mathbf{B}_y$. Each component is assumed to act in the direction shown.

Equilibrium Equations. We write the following three equilibrium equations and solve for the reactions indicated:

$$\xrightarrow{+}\Sigma F_x = 0: \qquad\qquad B_x = 0 \qquad\qquad \mathbf{B}_x = 0 \;\blacktriangleleft$$

$$+\uparrow\Sigma M_A = 0:$$
$$-(15 \text{ kips})(3 \text{ ft}) + B_y(9 \text{ ft}) - (6 \text{ kips})(11 \text{ ft}) - (6 \text{ kips})(13 \text{ ft}) = 0$$
$$B_y = +21.0 \text{ kips} \qquad \mathbf{B}_y = 21.0 \text{ kips} \uparrow \;\blacktriangleleft$$

$$+\uparrow\Sigma M_B = 0:$$
$$-A(9 \text{ ft}) + (15 \text{ kips})(6 \text{ ft}) - (6 \text{ kips})(2 \text{ ft}) - (6 \text{ kips})(4 \text{ ft}) = 0$$
$$A = +6.00 \text{ kips} \qquad \mathbf{A} = 6.00 \text{ kips} \uparrow \;\blacktriangleleft$$

Check. The results are checked by adding the vertical components of all of the external forces:

$$+\uparrow\Sigma F_y = +6.00 \text{ kips} - 15 \text{ kips} + 21.0 \text{ kips} - 6 \text{ kips} - 6 \text{ kips} = 0$$

Remark. In this problem the reactions at both A and B are vertical; however, these reactions are vertical for different reasons. At A, the beam is supported by a roller; hence the reaction cannot have any horizontal component. At B, the horizontal component of the reaction is zero because it must satisfy the equilibrium equation $\Sigma F_x = 0$ and because none of the other forces acting on the beam has a horizontal component.

We could have noticed at first glance that the reaction at B was vertical and dispensed with the horizontal component $\mathbf{B}_x$. This, however, is a bad practice. In following it, we would run the risk of forgetting the component $\mathbf{B}_x$ when the loading conditions require such a component (i.e., when a horizontal load is included). Also, the component $\mathbf{B}_x$ was found to be zero by using and solving an equilibrium equation, $\Sigma F_x = 0$. By setting $\mathbf{B}_x$ equal to zero immediately, we might not realize that we actually make use of this equation and thus might lose track of the number of equations available for solving the problem.

SAMPLE PROBLEM 4.3

A loading car is at rest on a track forming an angle of 25° with the vertical. The gross weight of the car and its load is 5500 lb, and it is applied at a point 30 in. from the track, halfway between the two axles. The car is held by a cable attached 24 in. from the track. Determine the tension in the cable and the reaction at each pair of wheels.

SOLUTION

Free-Body Diagram. A free-body diagram of the car is drawn. The reaction at each wheel is perpendicular to the track, and the tension force **T** is parallel to the track. For convenience, we choose the x axis parallel to the track and the y axis perpendicular to the track. The 5500-lb weight is then resolved into x and y components.

$$W_x = +(5500 \text{ lb}) \cos 25° = +4980 \text{ lb}$$
$$W_y = -(5500 \text{ lb}) \sin 25° = -2320 \text{ lb}$$

Equilibrium Equations. We take moments about A to eliminate **T** and $\mathbf{R_1}$ from the computation.

$+\curvearrowleft \Sigma M_A = 0:$ $\quad -(2320 \text{ lb})(25 \text{ in.}) - (4980 \text{ lb})(6 \text{ in.}) + R_2(50 \text{ in.}) = 0$
$\qquad\qquad\qquad R_2 = +1758 \text{ lb}$ $\qquad\qquad \mathbf{R_2} = 1758 \text{ lb} \nearrow$ ◀

Now, taking moments about B to eliminate **T** and $\mathbf{R_2}$ from the computation, we write

$+\curvearrowleft \Sigma M_B = 0:$ $\quad (2320 \text{ lb})(25 \text{ in.}) - (4980 \text{ lb})(6 \text{ in.}) - R_1(50 \text{ in.}) = 0$
$\qquad\qquad\qquad R_1 = +562 \text{ lb}$ $\qquad\qquad \mathbf{R_1} = +562 \text{ lb} \nearrow$ ◀

The value of T is found by writing

$\searrow + \Sigma F_x = 0:$ $\quad +4980 \text{ lb} - T = 0$
$\qquad\qquad\qquad T = +4980 \text{ lb}$ $\qquad\qquad \mathbf{T} = 4980 \text{ lb} \nwarrow$ ◀

The computed values of the reactions are shown in the adjacent sketch.

Check. The computations are verified by writing

$$\nearrow + \Sigma F_y = +562 \text{ lb} + 1758 \text{ lb} - 2320 \text{ lb} = 0$$

The solution could also have been checked by computing moments about any point other than A or B.

SAMPLE PROBLEM 4.4

The frame shown supports part of the roof of a small building. Knowing that the tension in the cable is 150 kN, determine the reaction at the fixed end E.

SOLUTION

Free-Body Diagram. A free-body diagram of the frame and of the cable BDF is drawn. The reaction at the fixed end E is represented by the force components E_x and E_y and the couple $\mathbf{M}_E$. The other forces acting on the free body are the four 20-kN loads and the 150-kN force exerted at end F of the cable.

Equilibrium Equations. Noting that $DF = \sqrt{(4.5\text{ m})^2 + (6\text{ m})^2} = 7.5$ m, we write

$$\xrightarrow{+}\Sigma F_x = 0: \qquad E_x + \frac{4.5}{7.5}(150\text{ kN}) = 0$$

$$E_x = -90.0\text{ kN} \qquad \mathbf{E}_x = 90.0\text{ kN} \leftarrow \quad \blacktriangleleft$$

$$+\uparrow\Sigma F_y = 0: \qquad E_y - 4(20\text{ kN}) - \frac{6}{7.5}(150\text{ kN}) = 0$$

$$E_y = +200\text{ kN} \qquad \mathbf{E}_y = 200\text{ kN} \uparrow \quad \blacktriangleleft$$

$$+\curvearrowleft\Sigma M_E = 0: \quad (20\text{ kN})(7.2\text{ m}) + (20\text{ kN})(5.4\text{ m}) + (20\text{ kN})(3.6\text{ m})$$

$$+ (20\text{ kN})(1.8\text{ m}) - \frac{6}{7.5}(150\text{ kN})(4.5\text{ m}) + M_E = 0$$

$$M_E = +180.0\text{ kN}\cdot\text{m} \qquad \mathbf{M}_E = 180.0\text{ kN}\cdot\text{m} \curvearrowleft \quad \blacktriangleleft$$

SAMPLE PROBLEM 4.5

A 400-lb weight is attached at A to the lever shown. The constant of the spring BC is $k = 250$ lb/in., and the spring is unstretched when $\theta = 0$. Determine the position of equilibrium.

SOLUTION

Free-Body Diagram. We draw a free-body diagram of the lever and cylinder. Denoting by s the deflection of the spring from its undeformed position, and noting that $s = r\theta$, we have $F = ks = kr\theta$.

Equilibrium Equation. Summing the moments of $\mathbf{W}$ and $\mathbf{F}$ about O, we write

$$+\curvearrowleft\Sigma M_O = 0: \qquad Wl\sin\theta - r(kr\theta) = 0 \qquad \sin\theta = \frac{kr^2}{Wl}\theta$$

Substituting the given data, we obtain

$$\sin\theta = \frac{(250\text{ lb/in.})(3\text{ in.})^2}{(400\text{ lb})(8\text{ in.})}\theta \qquad \sin\theta = 0.703\,\theta$$

Solving by trial and error, we find

$$\theta = 0 \qquad \theta = 80.3° \quad \blacktriangleleft$$

SOLVING PROBLEMS
ON YOUR OWN

You saw that the external forces acting on a rigid body in equilibrium form a system equivalent to zero. To solve an equilibrium problem your first task is to draw a neat, reasonably large *free-body diagram* on which you will show all external forces. Both known and unknown forces must be included.

For a two-dimensional rigid body, the reactions at the supports can involve one, two, or three unknowns depending on the type of support (Fig. 4.1). For the successful solution of a problem, a correct free-body diagram is essential. Never proceed with the solution of a problem until you are sure that your free-body diagram includes all loads, all reactions, and the weight of the body (if appropriate).

1. You can write three equilibrium equations and solve them for *three unknowns.* The three equations might be

$$\Sigma F_x = 0 \qquad \Sigma F_y = 0 \qquad \Sigma M_O = 0$$

However, there are usually several sets of equations that you can write, such as

$$\Sigma F_x = 0 \qquad \Sigma M_A = 0 \qquad \Sigma M_B = 0$$

where point B is chosen in such a way that the line AB is not parallel to the y axis, or

$$\Sigma M_A = 0 \qquad \Sigma M_B = 0 \qquad \Sigma M_C = 0$$

where the points A, B, and C do not lie in a straight line.

2. To simplify your solution, it may be helpful to use one of the following solution techniques if applicable.

    a. By summing moments about the point of intersection of the lines of action of two unknown forces, you will obtain an equation in a single unknown.

    b. By summing components in a direction perpendicular to two unknown parallel forces, you will obtain an equation in a single unknown.

3. After drawing your free-body diagram, you may find that one of the following special situations exists.

    a. The reactions involve fewer than three unknowns; the body is said to be *partially constrained* and motion of the body is possible.

    b. The reactions involve more than three unknowns; the reactions are said to be *statically indeterminate.* While you may be able to calculate one or two reactions, you cannot determine all of the reactions.

    c. The reactions pass through a single point or are parallel; the body is said to be *improperly constrained* and motion can occur under a general loading condition.

PROBLEMS

FREE BODY PRACTICE PROBLEMS

4.F1 For the frame and loading shown, draw the free-body diagram needed to determine the reactions at A and E when $\alpha = 30°$.

4.F2 Neglecting friction, draw the free-body diagram needed to determine the tension in cable ABD and the reaction at C when $\theta = 60°$.

Fig. P4.F1

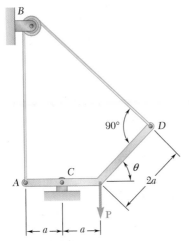

Fig. P4.F2

4.F3 Bar AC supports two 400-N loads as shown. Rollers at A and C rest against frictionless surfaces and a cable BD is attached at B. Draw the free-body diagram needed to determine the tension in cable BD and the reactions at A and C.

Fig. P4.F3

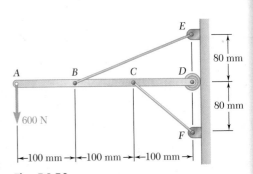

Fig. P4.F4

4.F4 Draw the free-body diagram needed to determine the tension in each cable and the reaction at D.

173

Fig. P4.1

END-OF-SECTION PROBLEMS

4.1 Two crates, each of mass 350 kg, are placed as shown in the bed of a 1400-kg pickup truck. Determine the reactions at each of the two (*a*) rear wheels *A*, (*b*) front wheels *B*.

4.2 Solve Prob. 4.1, assuming that crate *D* is removed and that the position of crate *C* is unchanged.

4.3 A T-shaped bracket supports the four loads shown. Determine the reactions at *A* and *B* (*a*) if *a* = 10 in., (*b*) if *a* = 7 in.

Fig. P4.3

4.4 For the bracket and loading of Prob. 4.3, determine the smallest distance *a* if the bracket is not to move.

4.5 A hand truck is used to move two kegs, each of mass 40 kg. Neglecting the mass of the hand truck, determine (*a*) the vertical force **P** that should be applied to the handle to maintain equilibrium when $\alpha = 35°$, (*b*) the corresponding reaction at each of the two wheels.

4.6 Solve Prob. 4.5 when $\alpha = 40°$.

4.7 A 3200-lb forklift truck is used to lift a 1700-lb crate. Determine the reaction at each of the two (*a*) front wheels *A*, (*b*) rear wheels *B*.

Fig. P4.5

Fig. P4.7

Fig. P4.8

4.8 For the beam and loading shown, determine (*a*) the reaction at *A*, (*b*) the tension in cable *BC*.

4.9 For the beam and loading shown, determine the range of the distance a for which the reaction at B does not exceed 100 lb downward or 200 lb upward.

4.10 The maximum allowable value of each of the reactions is 180 N. Neglecting the weight of the beam, determine the range of the distance d for which the beam is safe.

Fig. P4.9

Fig. P4.10

4.11 Three loads are applied as shown to a light beam supported by cables attached at B and D. Neglecting the weight of the beam, determine the range of values of Q for which neither cable becomes slack when $P = 0$.

4.12 Three loads are applied as shown to a light beam supported by cables attached at B and D. Knowing that the maximum allowable tension in each cable is 4 kN and neglecting the weight of the beam, determine the range of values of Q for which the loading is safe when $P = 0$.

4.13 For the beam of Prob. 4.12, determine the range of values of Q for which the loading is safe when $P = 1$ kN.

Fig. P4.11 and P4.12

4.14 For the beam of Sample Prob. 4.2, determine the range of values of P for which the beam will be safe, knowing that the maximum allowable value of each of the reactions is 30 kips and that the reaction at A must be directed upward.

4.15 The bracket BCD is hinged at C and attached to a control cable at B. For the loading shown, determine (a) the tension in the cable, (b) the reaction at C.

Fig. P4.15

4.16 Solve Prob. 4.15, assuming that $a = 0.32$ m.

4.17 The lever BCD is hinged at C and attached to a control rod at B. If $P = 100$ lb, determine (a) the tension in rod AB, (b) the reaction at C.

4.18 The lever BCD is hinged at C and attached to a control rod at B. Determine the maximum force **P** that can be safely applied at D if the maximum allowable value of the reaction at C is 250 lb.

Fig. P4.17 and P4.18

4.19 Two links AB and DE are connected by a bell crank as shown. Knowing that the tension in link AB is 720 N, determine (a) the tension in link DE, (b) the reaction at C.

Fig. P4.19 and P4.20

4.20 Two links AB and DE are connected by a bell crank as shown. Determine the maximum force that can be safely exerted by link AB on the bell crank if the maximum allowable value for the reaction at C is 1600 N.

4.21 Determine the reactions at A and C when (a) $\alpha = 0$, (b) $\alpha = 30°$.

4.22 Determine the reactions at A and B when (a) $\alpha = 0$, (b) $\alpha = 90°$, (c) $\alpha = 30°$.

4.23 Determine the reactions at A and B when (a) $h = 0$, (b) $h = 200$ mm.

Fig. P4.21

Fig. P4.22

Fig. P4.23

4.24 A lever AB is hinged at C and attached to a control cable at A. If the lever is subjected to a 75-lb vertical force at B, determine (a) the tension in the cable, (b) the reaction at C.

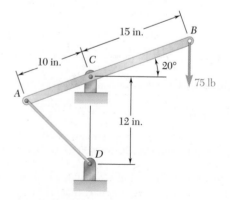

Fig. P4.24

4.25 and 4.26 For each of the plates and loadings shown, determine the reactions at A and B.

(a)   (b)

Fig. P4.25

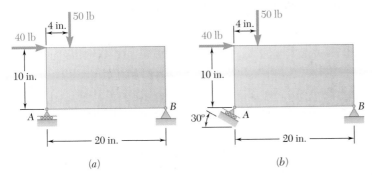

(a)   (b)

Fig. P4.26

4.27 A rod AB hinged at A and attached at B to cable BD supports the loads shown. Knowing that $d = 200$ mm, determine (a) the tension in cable BD, (b) the reaction at A.

Fig. P4.27 and P4.28

4.28 A rod AB, hinged at A and attached at B to cable BD, supports the loads shown. Knowing that $d = 150$ mm, determine (a) the tension in cable BD, (b) the reaction at A.

4.29 A force **P** of magnitude 90 lb is applied to member ACE, which is supported by a frictionless pin at D and by the cable ABE. Since the cable passes over a small pulley at B, the tension may be assumed to be the same in portions AB and BE of the cable. For the case when $a = 3$ in., determine (a) the tension in the cable, (b) the reaction at D.

4.30 Solve Prob. 4.29 for $a = 6$ in.

Fig. P4.29

Fig. P4.31

4.31 Neglecting friction, determine the tension in cable ABD and the reaction at support C.

4.32 Neglecting friction and the radius of the pulley, determine (a) the tension in cable ADB, (b) the reaction at C.

Fig. P4.32

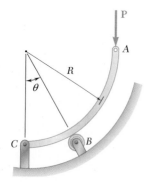

Fig. P4.33 and P4.34

4.33 Rod ABC is bent in the shape of an arc of circle of radius R. Knowing the $\theta = 30°$, determine the reaction (a) at B, (b) at C.

4.34 Rod ABC is bent in the shape of an arc of circle of radius R. Knowing the $\theta = 60°$, determine the reaction (a) at B, (b) at C.

4.35 A movable bracket is held at rest by a cable attached at C and by frictionless rollers at A and B. For the loading shown, determine (a) the tension in the cable, (b) the reactions at A and B.

Fig. P4.35

4.36 A light bar AB supports a 15-kg block at its midpoint C. Rollers at A and B rest against frictionless surfaces, and a horizontal cable AD is attached at A. Determine (a) the tension in cable AD, (b) the reactions at A and B.

Fig. P4.36

4.37 A light bar *AD* is suspended from a cable *BE* and supports a 50-lb block at *C*. The ends *A* and *D* of the bar are in contact with frictionless vertical walls. Determine the tension in cable *BE* and the reactions at *A* and *D*.

4.38 A light rod *AD* is supported by frictionless pegs at *B* and *C* and rests against a frictionless wall at *A*. A vertical 120-lb force is applied at *D*. Determine the reactions at *A*, *B*, and *C*.

Fig. P4.37

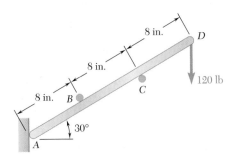

Fig. P4.38

4.39 Bar *AD* is attached at *A* and *C* to collars that can move freely on the rods shown. If the cord *BE* is vertical ($\alpha = 0$), determine the tension in the cord and the reactions at *A* and *C*.

Fig. P4.39

4.40 Solve Prob. 4.39 if the cord *BE* is parallel to the rods ($\alpha = 30°$).

4.41 The T-shaped bracket shown is supported by a small wheel at *E* and pegs at *C* and *D*. Neglecting the effect of friction, determine the reactions at *C*, *D*, and *E* when $\theta = 30°$.

4.42 The T-shaped bracket shown is supported by a small wheel at *E* and pegs at *C* and *D*. Neglecting the effect of friction, determine (*a*) the smallest value of θ for which the equilibrium of the bracket is maintained, (*b*) the corresponding reactions at *C*, *D*, and *E*.

Fig. P4.41 and P4.42

4.43 Beam *AD* carries the two 40-lb loads shown. The beam is held by a fixed support at *D* and by the cable *BE* that is attached to the counterweight *W*. Determine the reaction at *D* when (*a*) *W* = 100 lb, (*b*) *W* = 90 lb.

4.44 For the beam and loading shown, determine the range of values of *W* for which the magnitude of the couple at *D* does not exceed 40 lb · ft.

Fig. P4.43 and P4.44

4.45 An 8-kg mass can be supported in the three different ways shown. Knowing that the pulleys have a 100-mm radius, determine the reaction at A in each case.

(a) (b) (c)

Fig. P4.45

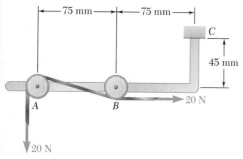

Fig. P4.46

4.46 A tension of 20 N is maintained in a tape as it passes through the support system shown. Knowing that the radius of each pulley is 10 mm, determine the reaction at C.

4.47 Solve Prob. 4.46, assuming that 15-mm-radius pulleys are used.

4.48 The rig shown consists of a 1200-lb horizontal member ABC and a vertical member DBE welded together at B. The rig is being used to raise a 3600-lb crate at a distance $x = 12$ ft from the vertical member DBE. If the tension in the cable is 4 kips, determine the reaction at E, assuming that the cable is (a) anchored at F as shown in the figure, (b) attached to the vertical member at a point located 1 ft above E.

Fig. P4.48

4.49 For the rig and crate of Prob. 4.48, and assuming that the cable is anchored at F as shown, determine (a) the required tension in cable $ADCF$ if the maximum value of the couple at E as x varies from 1.5 to 17.5 ft is to be as small as possible, (b) the corresponding maximum value of the couple.

4.50 A 6-m telephone pole weighing 1600 N is used to support the ends of two wires. The wires form the angles shown with the horizontal and the tensions in the wires are, respectively, $T_1 = 600$ N and $T_2 = 375$ N. Determine the reaction at the fixed end A.

4.51 and 4.52 A vertical load **P** is applied at end B of rod BC. (*a*) Neglecting the weight of the rod, express the angle θ corresponding to the equilibrium position in terms of P, l, and the counterweight W. (*b*) Determine the value of θ corresponding to equilibrium if $P = 2W$.

Fig. P4.50

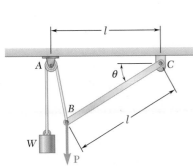

Fig. P4.51

Fig. P4.52

4.53 A slender rod AB, of weight W, is attached to blocks A and B, which move freely in the guides shown. The blocks are connected by an elastic cord that passes over a pulley at C. (*a*) Express the tension in the cord in terms of W and θ. (*b*) Determine the value of θ for which the tension in the cord is equal to $3W$.

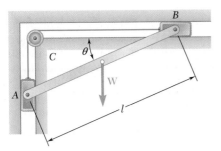

Fig. P4.53

4.54 Rod AB is acted upon by a couple **M** and two forces, each of magnitude P. (*a*) Derive an equation in θ, P, M, and l that must be satisfied when the rod is in equilibrium. (*b*) Determine the value of θ corresponding to equilibrium when $M = 150$ N $\cdot$ m, $P = 200$ N, and $l = 600$ mm.

Fig. P4.54

4.55 Solve Sample Prob. 4.5, assuming that the spring is unstretched when $\theta = 90°$.

Fig. P4.56

4.56 A slender rod AB, of weight W, is attached to blocks A and B that move freely in the guides shown. The constant of the spring is k, and the spring is unstretched when $\theta = 0$. (a) Neglecting the weight of the blocks, derive an equation in W, k, l, and θ that must be satisfied when the rod is in equilibrium. (b) Determine the value of θ when $W = 75$ lb, $l = 30$ in., and $k = 3$ lb/in.

4.57 A vertical load **P** is applied at end B of rod BC. The constant of the spring is k, and the spring is unstretched when $\theta = 60°$. (a) Neglecting the weight of the rod, express the angle θ corresponding to the equilibrium position in terms of P, k, and l. (b) Determine the value of θ corresponding to equilibrium if $P = \frac{1}{4}kl$.

Fig. P4.57

Fig. P4.58

4.58 A collar B of weight W can move freely along the vertical rod shown. The constant of the spring is k, and the spring is unstretched when $\theta = 0$. (a) Derive an equation in θ, W, k, and l that must be satisfied when the collar is in equilibrium. (b) Knowing that $W = 300$ N, $l = 500$ mm, and $k = 800$ N/m, determine the value of θ corresponding to equilibrium.

4.59 Eight identical 500×750-mm rectangular plates, each of mass $m = 40$ kg, are held in a vertical plane as shown. All connections consist of frictionless pins, rollers, or short links. In each case, determine whether (a) the plate is completely, partially, or improperly constrained, (b) the reactions are statically determinate or indeterminate, (c) the equilibrium of the plate is maintained in the position shown. Also, wherever possible, compute the reactions.

Fig. P4.59

4.60 The bracket *ABC* can be supported in the eight different ways shown. All connections consist of smooth pins, rollers, or short links. For each case, answer the questions listed in Prob. 4.59, and, wherever possible, compute the reactions, assuming that the magnitude of the force **P** is 100 lb.

Fig. P4.60

4.6 EQUILIBRIUM OF A TWO-FORCE BODY

A particular case of equilibrium which is of considerable interest is that of a rigid body subjected to two forces. Such a body is commonly called a *two-force body*. It will be shown that *if a two-force body is in equilibrium, the two forces must have the same magnitude, the same line of action, and opposite sense.*

Consider a corner plate subjected to two forces **F**$_1$ and **F**$_2$ acting at *A* and *B*, respectively (Fig. 4.8*a*). If the plate is to be in equilibrium, the sum of the moments of **F**$_1$ and **F**$_2$ about any axis must be zero. First, we sum moments about *A*. Since the moment of **F**$_1$ is obviously zero, the moment of **F**$_2$ must also be zero and the line of action of **F**$_2$ must pass through *A* (Fig. 4.8*b*). Summing moments about *B*, we prove similarly that the line of action of **F**$_1$ must pass through *B* (Fig. 4.8*c*). Therefore, both forces have the same line of action (line *AB*). From either of the equations $\Sigma F_x = 0$ and $\Sigma F_y = 0$ it is seen that they must also have the same magnitude but opposite sense.

Fig. 4.8

(a)   (b)   (c)

Fig. 4.8 (repeated)

If several forces act at two points A and B, the forces acting at A can be replaced by their resultant $\mathbf{F}_1$ and those acting at B can be replaced by their resultant $\mathbf{F}_2$. Thus a two-force body can be more generally defined as *a rigid body subjected to forces acting at only two points*. The resultants $\mathbf{F}_1$ and $\mathbf{F}_2$ then must have the same line of action, the same magnitude, and opposite sense (Fig. 4.8).

In the study of structures, frames, and machines, you will see how the recognition of two-force bodies simplifies the solution of certain problems.

4.7 EQUILIBRIUM OF A THREE-FORCE BODY

Another case of equilibrium that is of great interest is that of a *three-force body*, i.e., a rigid body subjected to three forces or, more generally, *a rigid body subjected to forces acting at only three points*. Consider a rigid body subjected to a system of forces which can be reduced to three forces $\mathbf{F}_1$, $\mathbf{F}_2$, and $\mathbf{F}_3$ acting at A, B, and C, respectively (Fig. 4.9a). It will be shown that if the body is in equilibrium, *the lines of action of the three forces must be either concurrent or parallel.*

Since the rigid body is in equilibrium, the sum of the moments of $\mathbf{F}_1$, $\mathbf{F}_2$, and $\mathbf{F}_3$ about any axis must be zero. Assuming that the lines of action of $\mathbf{F}_1$ and $\mathbf{F}_2$ intersect and denoting their point of intersection by D, we sum moments about D (Fig. 4.9b). Since the moments of $\mathbf{F}_1$ and $\mathbf{F}_2$ about D are zero, the moment of $\mathbf{F}_3$ about D must also be zero, and the line of action of $\mathbf{F}_3$ must pass through D (Fig. 4.9c). Therefore, the three lines of action are concurrent. The only exception occurs when none of the lines intersect; the lines of action are then parallel.

Although problems concerning three-force bodies can be solved by the general methods of Secs. 4.3 to 4.5, the property just established can be used to solve them either graphically or mathematically from simple trigonometric or geometric relations.

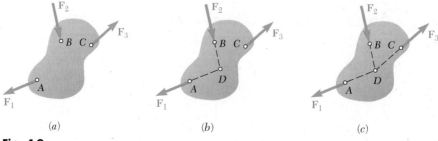

(a)   (b)   (c)

Fig. 4.9

SAMPLE PROBLEM 4.6

A man raises a 10-kg joist, of length 4 m, by pulling on a rope. Find the tension T in the rope and the reaction at A.

SOLUTION

Free-Body Diagram. The joist is a three-force body, since it is acted upon by three forces: its weight **W**, the force **T** exerted by the rope, and the reaction **R** of the ground at A. We note that

$$W = mg = (10 \text{ kg})(9.81 \text{ m/s}^2) = 98.1 \text{ N}$$

Three-Force Body. Since the joist is a three-force body, the forces acting on it must be concurrent. The reaction **R**, therefore, will pass through the point of intersection C of the lines of action of the weight **W** and the tension force **T**. This fact will be used to determine the angle α that **R** forms with the horizontal.

Drawing the vertical BF through B and the horizontal CD through C, we note that

$$AF = BF = (AB) \cos 45° = (4 \text{ m}) \cos 45° = 2.828 \text{ m}$$
$$CD = EF = \tfrac{1}{2}(AF) = 1.414 \text{ m}$$
$$BD = (CD) \cot (45° + 25°) = (1.414 \text{ m}) \tan 20° = 0.515 \text{ m}$$
$$CE = DF = BF - BD = 2.828 \text{ m} - 0.515 \text{ m} = 2.313 \text{ m}$$

We write

$$\tan \alpha = \frac{CE}{AE} = \frac{2.313 \text{ m}}{1.414 \text{ m}} = 1.636$$

$$\alpha = 58.6° \quad \blacktriangleleft$$

We now know the direction of all the forces acting on the joist.

Force Triangle. A force triangle is drawn as shown, and its interior angles are computed from the known directions of the forces. Using the law of sines, we write

$$\frac{T}{\sin 31.4°} = \frac{R}{\sin 110°} = \frac{98.1 \text{ N}}{\sin 38.6°}$$

$$T = 81.9 \text{ N} \quad \blacktriangleleft$$
$$R = 147.8 \text{ N} \; \measuredangle 58.6° \quad \blacktriangleleft$$

SOLVING PROBLEMS
ON YOUR OWN

The preceding sections covered two particular cases of equilibrium of a rigid body.

1. A two-force body is a body subjected to forces at only two points. The resultants of the forces acting at each of these points must have the *same magnitude, the same line of action, and opposite sense.* This property will allow you to simplify the solutions of some problems by replacing the two unknown components of a reaction by a single force of unknown magnitude but of *known direction.*

2. A three-force body is subjected to forces at only three points. The resultants of the forces acting at each of these points must be *concurrent or parallel.* To solve a problem involving a three-force body with concurrent forces, draw your free-body diagram showing that these three forces pass through the same point. The use of simple geometry may then allow you to complete the solution by using a force triangle [Sample Prob. 4.6].

Although the principle noted above for the solution of problems involving three-force bodies is easily understood, it can be difficult to sketch the needed geometric constructions. If you encounter difficulty, first draw a reasonably large free-body diagram and then seek a relation between known or easily calculated lengths and a dimension that involves an unknown. This was done in Sample Prob. 4.6, where the easily calculated dimensions AE and CE were used to determine the angle α.

PROBLEMS

4.61 Determine the reactions at A and B when $a = 150$ mm.

4.62 Determine the value of a for which the magnitude of the reaction at B is equal to 800 N.

4.63 Using the method of Sec. 4.7, solve Prob. 4.22b.

4.64 A 500-lb cylindrical tank, 8 ft in diameter, is to be raised over a 2-ft obstruction. A cable is wrapped around the tank and pulled horizontally as shown. Knowing that the corner of the obstruction at A is rough, find the required tension in the cable and the reaction at A.

Fig. P4.61 and P4.62

Fig. P4.64

Fig. P4.65

4.65 For the frame and loading shown, determine the reactions at A and C.

4.66 For the frame and loading shown, determine the reactions at C and D.

Fig. P4.66

4.67 Determine the reactions at B and D when $b = 60$ mm.

4.68 Determine the reactions at B and D when $b = 120$ mm.

Fig. P4.67 and P4.68

4.69 A T-shaped bracket supports a 300-N load as shown. Determine the reactions at A and C when $\alpha = 45°$.

300 mm

B

α 300 N

A

C

150 mm

250 mm

Fig. P4.69 and P4.70

4.70 A T-shaped bracket supports a 300-N load as shown. Determine the reactions at A and C when $\alpha = 60°$.

4.71 A 40-lb roller, of diameter 8 in., which is to be used on a tile floor, is resting directly on the subflooring as shown. Knowing that the thickness of each tile is 0.3 in., determine the force **P** required to move the roller onto the tiles if the roller is (a) pushed to the left, (b) pulled to the right.

P

30°

Fig. P4.71

4.72 One end of rod AB rests in the corner A and the other end is attached to cord BD. If the rod supports a 40-lb load at its midpoint C, find the reaction at A and the tension in the cord.

4.73 A 50-kg crate is attached to the trolley-beam system shown. Knowing that $a = 1.5$ m, determine (a) the tension in cable CD, (b) the reaction at B.

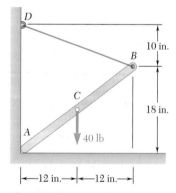

D

10 in.

B

C

18 in.

A

40 lb

12 in. 12 in.

Fig. P4.72

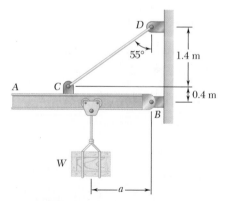

D

55°

1.4 m

A   C

0.4 m

B

W

a

Fig. P4.73

4.74 Solve Prob. 4.73, assuming that $a = 3$ m.

4.75 Determine the reactions at A and B when $\beta = 50°$.

Fig. P4.75 and P4.76

4.76 Determine the reactions at A and B when $\beta = 80°$.

4.77 Knowing that $\theta = 30°$, determine the reaction (a) at B, (b) at C.

4.78 Knowing that $\theta = 60°$, determine the reaction (a) at B, (b) at C.

Fig. P4.77 and P4.78

4.79 Using the method of Sec. 4.7, solve Prob. 4.23.

4.80 Using the method of Sec. 4.7, solve Prob. 4.24.

4.81 and 4.82 Member ABC is supported by a pin and bracket at B and by an inextensible cord attached at A and C and passing over a frictionless pulley at D. The tension may be assumed to be the same in portions AD and CD of the cord. For the loading shown and neglecting the size of the pulley, determine the tension in the cord and the reaction at B.

Fig. P4.81

Fig. P4.82

4.83 A thin ring of mass 2 kg and radius $r = 140$ mm is held against a frictionless wall by a 125-mm string AB. Determine (a) the distance d, (b) the tension in the string, (c) the reaction at C.

Fig. P4.83

Fig. P4.84

Fig. P4.86

Fig. P4.89 and P4.90

4.84 A uniform rod AB of length $2R$ rests inside a hemispherical bowl of radius R as shown. Neglecting friction, determine the angle θ corresponding to equilibrium.

4.85 A slender rod BC of length L and weight W is held by two cables as shown. Knowing that cable AB is horizontal and that the rod forms an angle of $40°$ with the horizontal, determine (a) the angle θ that cable CD forms with the horizontal, (b) the tension in each cable.

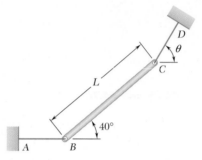

Fig. P4.85

4.86 A slender rod of length L and weight W is attached to a collar at A and is fitted with a small wheel at B. Knowing that the wheel rolls freely along a cylindrical surface of radius R, and neglecting friction, derive an equation in θ, L, and R that must be satisfied when the rod is in equilibrium.

4.87 Knowing that for the rod of Prob. 4.86, $L = 15$ in., $R = 20$ in., and $W = 10$ lb, determine (a) the angle θ corresponding to equilibrium, (b) the reactions at A and B.

4.88 Rod AB is bent into the shape of an arc of circle and is lodged between two pegs D and E. It supports a load $\mathbf{P}$ at end B. Neglecting friction and the weight of the rod, determine the distance c corresponding to equilibrium when $a = 20$ mm and $R = 100$ mm.

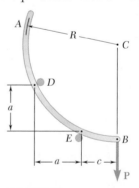

Fig. P4.88

4.89 A slender rod of length L is attached to collars that can slide freely along the guides shown. Knowing that the rod is in equilibrium, derive an expression for the angle θ in terms of the angle β.

4.90 An 8-kg slender rod of length L is attached to collars that can slide freely along the guides shown. Knowing that the rod is in equilibrium and that $\beta = 30°$, determine (a) the angle θ that the rod forms with the vertical, (b) the reactions at A and B.

4.8 EQUILIBRIUM OF A RIGID BODY IN THREE DIMENSIONS

We saw in Sec. 4.1 that six scalar equations are required to express the conditions for the equilibrium of a rigid body in the general three-dimensional case:

$$\Sigma F_x = 0 \qquad \Sigma F_y = 0 \qquad \Sigma F_z = 0 \qquad (4.2)$$
$$\Sigma M_x = 0 \qquad \Sigma M_y = 0 \qquad \Sigma M_z = 0 \qquad (4.3)$$

These equations can be solved for no more than *six unknowns*, which generally will represent reactions at supports or connections.

In most problems the scalar equations (4.2) and (4.3) will be more conveniently obtained if we first express in vector form the conditions for the equilibrium of the rigid body considered. We write

$$\Sigma \mathbf{F} = 0 \qquad \Sigma \mathbf{M}_O = \Sigma(\mathbf{r} \times \mathbf{F}) = 0 \qquad (4.1)$$

and express the forces $\mathbf{F}$ and position vectors $\mathbf{r}$ in terms of scalar components and unit vectors. Next, we compute all vector products, either by direct calculation or by means of determinants (see Sec. 3.8). We observe that as many as three unknown reaction components may be eliminated from these computations through a judicious choice of the point O. By equating to zero the coefficients of the unit vectors in each of the two relations (4.1), we obtain the desired scalar equations.†

4.9 REACTIONS AT SUPPORTS AND CONNECTIONS FOR A THREE-DIMENSIONAL STRUCTURE

The reactions on a three-dimensional structure range from the single force of known direction exerted by a frictionless surface to the force-couple system exerted by a fixed support. Consequently, in problems involving the equilibrium of a three-dimensional structure, there can be between one and six unknowns associated with the reaction at each support or connection. Various types of supports and

---

†In some problems, it will be found convenient to eliminate the reactions at two points A and B from the solution by writing the equilibrium equation $\Sigma M_{AB} = 0$, which involves the determination of the moments of the forces about the axis AB joining points A and B (see Sample Prob. 4.10).

Photo 4.6 Universal joints, easily seen on the drive shafts of rear-wheel-drive cars and trucks, allow rotational motion to be transferred between two noncollinear shafts.

Photo 4.7 The pillow block bearing shown supports the shaft of a fan used in an industrial facility.

connections are shown in Fig. 4.10 with their corresponding reactions. A simple way of determining the type of reaction corresponding to a given support or connection and the number of unknowns involved is to find which of the six fundamental motions (translation in the x, y, and z directions, rotation about the x, y, and z axes) are allowed and which motions are prevented.

Ball supports, frictionless surfaces, and cables, for example, prevent translation in one direction only and thus exert a single force whose line of action is known; each of these supports involves one unknown, namely, the magnitude of the reaction. Rollers on rough surfaces and wheels on rails prevent translation in two directions; the corresponding reactions consist of two unknown force components. Rough surfaces in direct contact and ball-and-socket supports prevent translation in three directions; these supports involve three unknown force components.

Some supports and connections can prevent rotation as well as translation; the corresponding reactions include couples as well as forces. For example, the reaction at a fixed support, which prevents any motion (rotation as well as translation), consists of three unknown forces and three unknown couples. A universal joint, which is designed to allow rotation about two axes, will exert a reaction consisting of three unknown force components and one unknown couple.

Other supports and connections are primarily intended to prevent translation; their design, however, is such that they also prevent some rotations. The corresponding reactions consist essentially of force components but *may* also include couples. One group of supports of this type includes hinges and bearings designed to support radial loads only (for example, journal bearings, roller bearings). The corresponding reactions consist of two force components but may also include two couples. Another group includes pin-and-bracket supports, hinges, and bearings designed to support an axial thrust as well as a radial load (for example, ball bearings). The corresponding reactions consist of three force components but may include two couples. However, these supports will not exert any appreciable couples under normal conditions of use. Therefore, *only* force components should be included in their analysis *unless* it is found that couples are necessary to maintain the equilibrium of the rigid body, or unless the support is known to have been specifically designed to exert a couple (see Probs. 4.119 through 4.122).

If the reactions involve more than six unknowns, there are more unknowns than equations, and some of the reactions are *statically indeterminate*. If the reactions involve fewer than six unknowns, there are more equations than unknowns, and some of the equations of equilibrium cannot be satisfied under general loading conditions; the rigid body is only *partially constrained*. Under the particular loading conditions corresponding to a given problem, however, the extra equations often reduce to trivial identities, such as $0 = 0$, and can be disregarded; although only partially constrained, the rigid body remains in equilibrium (see Sample Probs. 4.7 and 4.8). Even with six or more unknowns, it is possible that some equations of equilibrium will not be satisfied. This can occur when the reactions associated with the given supports either are parallel or intersect the same line; the rigid body is then *improperly constrained*.

Fig. 4.10 Reactions at supports and connections.

SAMPLE PROBLEM 4.7

A 20-kg ladder used to reach high shelves in a storeroom is supported by two flanged wheels A and B mounted on a rail and by an unflanged wheel C resting against a rail fixed to the wall. An 80-kg man stands on the ladder and leans to the right. The line of action of the combined weight $\mathbf{W}$ of the man and ladder intersects the floor at point D. Determine the reactions at A, B, and C.

SOLUTION

Free-Body Diagram. A free-body diagram of the ladder is drawn. The forces involved are the combined weight of the man and ladder,

$$\mathbf{W} = -mg\mathbf{j} = -(80 \text{ kg} + 20 \text{ kg})(9.81 \text{ m/s}^2)\mathbf{j} = -(981 \text{ N})\mathbf{j}$$

and five unknown reaction components, two at each flanged wheel and one at the unflanged wheel. The ladder is thus only partially constrained; it is free to roll along the rails. It is, however, in equilibrium under the given load since the equation $\Sigma F_x = 0$ is satisfied.

Equilibrium Equations. We express that the forces acting on the ladder form a system equivalent to zero:

$$\Sigma\mathbf{F} = 0: \qquad A_y\mathbf{j} + A_z\mathbf{k} + B_y\mathbf{j} + B_z\mathbf{k} - (981 \text{ N})\mathbf{j} + C\mathbf{k} = 0$$
$$(A_y + B_y - 981 \text{ N})\mathbf{j} + (A_z + B_z + C)\mathbf{k} = 0 \qquad (1)$$
$$\Sigma\mathbf{M}_A = \Sigma(\mathbf{r} \times \mathbf{F}) = 0: \qquad 1.2\mathbf{i} \times (B_y\mathbf{j} + B_z\mathbf{k}) + (0.9\mathbf{i} - 0.6\mathbf{k}) \times (-981\mathbf{j})$$
$$+ (0.6\mathbf{i} + 3\mathbf{j} - 1.2\mathbf{k}) \times C\mathbf{k} = 0$$

Computing the vector products, we have†

$$1.2B_y\mathbf{k} - 1.2B_z\mathbf{j} - 882.9\mathbf{k} - 588.6\mathbf{i} - 0.6C\mathbf{j} + 3C\mathbf{i} = 0$$
$$(3C - 588.6)\mathbf{i} - (1.2B_z + 0.6C)\mathbf{j} + (1.2B_y - 882.9)\mathbf{k} = 0 \qquad (2)$$

Setting the coefficients of $\mathbf{i}$, $\mathbf{j}$, $\mathbf{k}$ equal to zero in Eq. (2), we obtain the following three scalar equations, which express that the sum of the moments about each coordinate axis must be zero:

$$\begin{aligned} 3C - 588.6 &= 0 & C &= +196.2 \text{ N} \\ 1.2B_z + 0.6C &= 0 & B_z &= -98.1 \text{ N} \\ 1.2B_y - 882.9 &= 0 & B_y &= +736 \text{ N} \end{aligned}$$

The reactions at B and C are therefore

$$\mathbf{B} = +(736 \text{ N})\mathbf{j} - (98.1 \text{ N})\mathbf{k} \qquad \mathbf{C} = +(196.2 \text{ N})\mathbf{k} \quad \blacktriangleleft$$

Setting the coefficients of $\mathbf{j}$ and $\mathbf{k}$ equal to zero in Eq. (1), we obtain two scalar equations expressing that the sums of the components in the y and z directions are zero. Substituting for B_y, B_z, and C the values obtained above, we write

$$\begin{aligned} A_y + B_y - 981 &= 0 & A_y + 736 - 981 &= 0 & A_y &= +245 \text{ N} \\ A_z + B_z + C &= 0 & A_z - 98.1 + 196.2 &= 0 & A_z &= -98.1 \text{ N} \end{aligned}$$

We conclude that the reaction at A is $\qquad \mathbf{A} = +(245 \text{ N})\mathbf{j} - (98.1 \text{ N})\mathbf{k} \quad \blacktriangleleft$

---

†The moments in this sample problem and in Sample Probs. 4.8 and 4.9 can also be expressed in the form of determinants (see Sample Prob. 3.10).

SAMPLE PROBLEM 4.8

A 5 × 8-ft sign of uniform density weighs 270 lb and is supported by a ball-and-socket joint at A and by two cables. Determine the tension in each cable and the reaction at A.

SOLUTION

Free-Body Diagram. A free-body diagram of the sign is drawn. The forces acting on the free body are the weight $\mathbf{W} = -(270 \text{ lb})\mathbf{j}$ and the reactions at A, B, and E. The reaction at A is a force of unknown direction and is represented by three unknown components. Since the directions of the forces exerted by the cables are known, these forces involve only one unknown each, namely, the magnitudes T_{BD} and T_{EC}. Since there are only five unknowns, the sign is partially constrained. It can rotate freely about the x axis; it is, however, in equilibrium under the given loading, since the equation $\Sigma M_x = 0$ is satisfied.

The components of the forces $\mathbf{T}_{BD}$ and $\mathbf{T}_{EC}$ can be expressed in terms of the unknown magnitudes T_{BD} and T_{EC} by writing

$$\overrightarrow{BD} = -(8 \text{ ft})\mathbf{i} + (4 \text{ ft})\mathbf{j} - (8 \text{ ft})\mathbf{k} \qquad BD = 12 \text{ ft}$$
$$\overrightarrow{EC} = -(6 \text{ ft})\mathbf{i} + (3 \text{ ft})\mathbf{j} + (2 \text{ ft})\mathbf{k} \qquad EC = 7 \text{ ft}$$

$$\mathbf{T}_{BD} = T_{BD}\left(\frac{\overrightarrow{BD}}{BD}\right) = T_{BD}(-\tfrac{2}{3}\mathbf{i} + \tfrac{1}{3}\mathbf{j} - \tfrac{2}{3}\mathbf{k})$$

$$\mathbf{T}_{EC} = T_{EC}\left(\frac{\overrightarrow{EC}}{EC}\right) = T_{EC}(-\tfrac{6}{7}\mathbf{i} + \tfrac{3}{7}\mathbf{j} - \tfrac{2}{7}\mathbf{k})$$

Equilibrium Equations. We express that the forces acting on the sign form a system equivalent to zero:

$$\Sigma \mathbf{F} = 0: \qquad A_x\mathbf{i} + A_y\mathbf{j} + A_z\mathbf{k} + \mathbf{T}_{BD} + \mathbf{T}_{EC} - (270 \text{ lb})\mathbf{j} = 0$$
$$(A_x - \tfrac{2}{3}T_{BD} - \tfrac{6}{7}T_{EC})\mathbf{i} + (A_y + \tfrac{1}{3}T_{BD} + \tfrac{3}{7}T_{EC} - 270 \text{ lb})\mathbf{j}$$
$$+ (A_z - \tfrac{2}{3}T_{BD} + \tfrac{2}{7}T_{EC})\mathbf{k} = 0 \quad (1)$$

$$\Sigma \mathbf{M}_A = \Sigma(\mathbf{r} \times \mathbf{F}) = 0:$$
$$(8\text{ft})\mathbf{i} \times T_{BD}(-\tfrac{2}{3}\mathbf{i} + \tfrac{1}{3}\mathbf{j} - \tfrac{2}{3}\mathbf{k}) + (6\text{ft})\mathbf{i} \times T_{EC}(-\tfrac{6}{7}\mathbf{i} + \tfrac{3}{7}\mathbf{j} + \tfrac{2}{7}\mathbf{k})$$
$$+ (4\text{ft})\mathbf{i} \times (-270\text{lb})\mathbf{j} = 0$$

$$(2.667T_{BD} + 2.571T_{EC} - 1080 \text{ lb})\mathbf{k} + (5.333T_{BD} - 1.714T_{EC})\mathbf{j} = 0 \quad (2)$$

Setting the coefficients of $\mathbf{j}$ and $\mathbf{k}$ equal to zero in Eq. (2), we obtain two scalar equations which can be solved for T_{BD} and T_{EC}:

$$T_{BD} = 101.3 \text{ lb} \qquad T_{EC} = 315 \text{ lb} \quad \blacktriangleleft$$

Setting the coefficients of $\mathbf{i}$, $\mathbf{j}$, and $\mathbf{k}$ equal to zero in Eq. (1), we obtain three more equations, which yield the components of $\mathbf{A}$. We have

$$\mathbf{A} = +(338 \text{ lb})\mathbf{i} + (101.2 \text{ lb})\mathbf{j} - (22.5 \text{ lb})\mathbf{k} \quad \blacktriangleleft$$

SAMPLE PROBLEM 4.9

A uniform pipe cover of radius $r = 240$ mm and mass 30 kg is held in a horizontal position by the cable CD. Assuming that the bearing at B does not exert any axial thrust, determine the tension in the cable and the reactions at A and B.

SOLUTION

Free-Body Diagram. A free-body diagram is drawn with the coordinate axes shown. The forces acting on the free body are the weight of the cover,

$$\mathbf{W} = -mg\mathbf{j} = -(30 \text{ kg})(9.81 \text{ m/s}^2)\mathbf{j} = -(294 \text{ N})\mathbf{j}$$

and reactions involving six unknowns, namely, the magnitude of the force $\mathbf{T}$ exerted by the cable, three force components at hinge A, and two at hinge B. The components of $\mathbf{T}$ are expressed in terms of the unknown magnitude T by resolving the vector $\overrightarrow{DC}$ into rectangular components and writing

$$\overrightarrow{DC} = -(480 \text{ mm})\mathbf{i} + (240 \text{ mm})\mathbf{j} - (160 \text{ mm})\mathbf{k} \qquad DC = 560 \text{ mm}$$

$$\mathbf{T} = T\frac{\overrightarrow{DC}}{DC} = -\tfrac{6}{7}T\mathbf{i} + \tfrac{3}{7}T\mathbf{j} - \tfrac{2}{7}T\mathbf{k}$$

Equilibrium Equations. We express that the forces acting on the pipe cover form a system equivalent to zero:

$$\Sigma\mathbf{F} = 0: \qquad A_x\mathbf{i} + A_y\mathbf{j} + A_z\mathbf{k} + B_x\mathbf{i} + B_y\mathbf{j} + \mathbf{T} - (294 \text{ N})\mathbf{j} = 0$$
$$(A_x + B_x - \tfrac{6}{7}T)\mathbf{i} + (A_y + B_y + \tfrac{3}{7}T - 294 \text{ N})\mathbf{j} + (A_z - \tfrac{2}{7}T)\mathbf{k} = 0 \quad (1)$$

$$\Sigma\mathbf{M}_B = \Sigma(\mathbf{r} \times \mathbf{F}) = 0:$$
$$2r\mathbf{k} \times (A_x\mathbf{i} + A_y\mathbf{j} + A_z\mathbf{k})$$
$$+ (2r\mathbf{i} + r\mathbf{k}) \times (-\tfrac{6}{7}T\mathbf{i} + \tfrac{3}{7}T\mathbf{j} - \tfrac{2}{7}T\mathbf{k})$$
$$+ (r\mathbf{i} + r\mathbf{k}) \times (-294 \text{ N})\mathbf{j} = 0$$
$$(-2A_y - \tfrac{3}{7}T + 294 \text{ N})r\mathbf{i} + (2A_x - \tfrac{2}{7}T)r\mathbf{j} + (\tfrac{6}{7}T - 294 \text{ N})r\mathbf{k} = 0 \quad (2)$$

Setting the coefficients of the unit vectors equal to zero in Eq. (2), we write three scalar equations, which yield

$$A_x = +49.0 \text{ N} \qquad A_y = +73.5 \text{ N} \qquad T = 343 \text{ N} \quad \blacktriangleleft$$

Setting the coefficients of the unit vectors equal to zero in Eq. (1), we obtain three more scalar equations. After substituting the values of T, A_x, and A_y into these equations, we obtain

$$A_z = +98.0 \text{ N} \qquad B_x = +245 \text{ N} \qquad B_y = +73.5 \text{ N}$$

The reactions at A and B are therefore

$$\mathbf{A} = +(49.0 \text{ N})\mathbf{i} + (73.5 \text{ N})\mathbf{j} + (98.0 \text{ N})\mathbf{k} \quad \blacktriangleleft$$
$$\mathbf{B} = +(245 \text{ N})\mathbf{i} + (73.5 \text{ N})\mathbf{j} \quad \blacktriangleleft$$

SAMPLE PROBLEM 4.10

A 450-lb load hangs from the corner C of a rigid piece of pipe $ABCD$ which has been bent as shown. The pipe is supported by the ball-and-socket joints A and D, which are fastened, respectively, to the floor and to a vertical wall, and by a cable attached at the midpoint E of the portion BC of the pipe and at a point G on the wall. Determine (a) where G should be located if the tension in the cable is to be minimum, (b) the corresponding minimum value of the tension.

SOLUTION

Free-Body Diagram. The free-body diagram of the pipe includes the load $\mathbf{W} = (-450 \text{ lb})\mathbf{j}$, the reactions at A and D, and the force $\mathbf{T}$ exerted by the cable. To eliminate the reactions at A and D from the computations, we express that the sum of the moments of the forces about AD is zero. Denoting by $\boldsymbol{\lambda}$ the unit vector along AD, we write

$$\Sigma M_{AD} = 0: \quad \boldsymbol{\lambda} \cdot (\overrightarrow{AE} \times \mathbf{T}) + \boldsymbol{\lambda} \cdot (\overrightarrow{AC} \times \mathbf{W}) = 0 \quad (1)$$

The second term in Eq. (1) can be computed as follows:

$$\overrightarrow{AC} \times \mathbf{W} = (12\mathbf{i} + 12\mathbf{j}) \times (-450\mathbf{j}) = -5400\mathbf{k}$$

$$\boldsymbol{\lambda} = \frac{\overrightarrow{AD}}{AD} = \frac{12\mathbf{i} + 12\mathbf{j} - 6\mathbf{k}}{18} = \tfrac{2}{3}\mathbf{i} + \tfrac{2}{3}\mathbf{j} - \tfrac{1}{3}\mathbf{k}$$

$$\boldsymbol{\lambda} \cdot (\overrightarrow{AC} \times \mathbf{W}) = (\tfrac{2}{3}\mathbf{i} + \tfrac{2}{3}\mathbf{j} - \tfrac{1}{3}\mathbf{k}) \cdot (-5400\mathbf{k}) = +1800$$

Substituting the value obtained into Eq. (1), we write

$$\boldsymbol{\lambda} \cdot (\overrightarrow{AE} \times \mathbf{T}) = -1800 \text{ lb} \cdot \text{ft} \quad (2)$$

Minimum Value of Tension. Recalling the commutative property for mixed triple products, we rewrite Eq. (2) in the form

$$\mathbf{T} \cdot (\boldsymbol{\lambda} \times \overrightarrow{AE}) = -1800 \text{ lb} \cdot \text{ft} \quad (3)$$

which shows that the projection of $\mathbf{T}$ on the vector $\boldsymbol{\lambda} \times \overrightarrow{AE}$ is a constant. It follows that $\mathbf{T}$ is minimum when parallel to the vector

$$\boldsymbol{\lambda} \times \overrightarrow{AE} = (\tfrac{2}{3}\mathbf{i} + \tfrac{2}{3}\mathbf{j} - \tfrac{1}{3}\mathbf{k}) \times (6\mathbf{i} + 12\mathbf{j}) = 4\mathbf{i} - 2\mathbf{j} + 4\mathbf{k}$$

Since the corresponding unit vector is $\tfrac{2}{3}\mathbf{i} - \tfrac{1}{3}\mathbf{j} + \tfrac{2}{3}\mathbf{k}$, we write

$$\mathbf{T}_{\min} = T(\tfrac{2}{3}\mathbf{i} - \tfrac{1}{3}\mathbf{j} + \tfrac{2}{3}\mathbf{k}) \quad (4)$$

Substituting for $\mathbf{T}$ and $\boldsymbol{\lambda} \times \overrightarrow{AE}$ in Eq. (3) and computing the dot products, we obtain $6T = -1800$ and, thus, $T = -300$. Carrying this value into (4), we obtain

$$\mathbf{T}_{\min} = -200\mathbf{i} + 100\mathbf{j} - 200\mathbf{k} \qquad T_{\min} = 300 \text{ lb} \quad \blacktriangleleft$$

Location of G. Since the vector $\overrightarrow{EG}$ and the force $\mathbf{T}_{\min}$ have the same direction, their components must be proportional. Denoting the coordinates of G by x, y, 0, we write

$$\frac{x - 6}{-200} = \frac{y - 12}{+100} = \frac{0 - 6}{-200} \qquad x = 0 \qquad y = 15 \text{ ft} \quad \blacktriangleleft$$

SOLVING PROBLEMS
ON YOUR OWN

The equilibrium of a *three-dimensional body* was considered in the sections you just completed. It is again most important that you draw a complete *free-body diagram* as the first step of your solution.

1. As you draw the free-body diagram, pay particular attention to the reactions at the supports. The number of unknowns at a support can range from one to six (Fig. 4.10). To decide whether an unknown reaction or reaction component exists at a support, ask yourself whether the support prevents motion of the body in a certain direction or about a certain axis.

   a. If motion is prevented in a certain direction, include in your free-body diagram an unknown *reaction* or *reaction component* that acts in the *same direction*.

   b. If a support prevents rotation about a certain axis, include in your free-body diagram a *couple* of unknown magnitude that acts about the *same axis*.

2. The external forces acting on a three-dimensional body form a system equivalent to zero. Writing $\Sigma \mathbf{F} = 0$ and $\Sigma \mathbf{M}_A = 0$ about an appropriate point A, and setting the coefficients of $\mathbf{i}$, $\mathbf{j}$, $\mathbf{k}$ in both equations equal to zero will provide you with six scalar equations. In general, these equations will contain six unknowns and may be solved for these unknowns.

3. After completing your free-body diagram, you may want to seek equations involving as few unknowns as possible. The following strategies may help you.

   a. By summing moments about a ball-and-socket support or a hinge, you will obtain equations from which three unknown reaction components have been eliminated [Sample Probs. 4.8 and 4.9].

   b. If you can draw an axis through the points of application of all but one of the unknown reactions, summing moments about that axis will yield an equation in a single unknown [Sample Prob. 4.10].

4. After drawing your free-body diagram, you may find that one of the following situations exists.

   a. The reactions involve fewer than six unknowns; the body is said to be *partially constrained* and motion of the body is possible. However, you may be able to determine the reactions for a given loading condition [Sample Prob. 4.7].

   b. The reactions involve more than six unknowns; the reactions are said to be *statically indeterminate*. Although you may be able to calculate one or two reactions, you cannot determine all of the reactions [Sample Prob. 4.10].

   c. The reactions are parallel or intersect the same line; the body is said to be *improperly constrained*, and motion can occur under a general loading condition.

PROBLEMS

4.F5 A 4 × 8-ft sheet of plywood weighing 34 lb has been temporarily placed among three pipe supports. The lower edge of the sheet rests on small collars at A and B and its upper edge leans against pipe C. Neglecting friction on all surfaces, draw the free-body diagram needed to determine the reactions at A, B, and C.

Fig. P4.F5

4.F6 Two transmission belts pass over sheaves welded to an axle supported by bearings at B and D. The sheave at A has a radius of 2.5 in. and the sheave at C has a radius of 2 in. Knowing that the system rotates at a constant rate, draw the free-body diagram needed to determine the tension T and the reactions at B and D. Assume that the bearing at D does not exert any axial thrust and neglect the weights of the sheaves and axle.

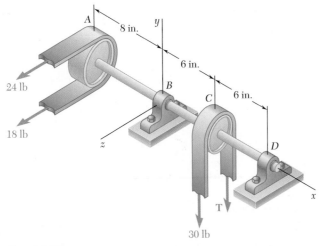

Fig. P4.F6

4.F7 The 6-m pole ABC is acted upon by a 455-N force as shown. The pole is held by a ball-and-socket joint at A and by two cables BD and BE. Draw the free-body diagram needed to determine the tension in each cable and the reaction at A.

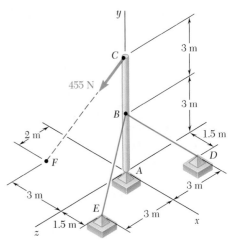

Fig. P4.F7

END-OF-SECTION PROBLEMS

4.91 A 200-mm lever and a 240-mm-diameter pulley are welded to the axle *BE* that is supported by bearings at *C* and *D*. If a 720-N vertical load is applied at *A* when the lever is horizontal, determine (*a*) the tension in the cord, (*b*) the reactions at *C* and *D*. Assume that the bearing at *D* does not exert any axial thrust.

Fig. P4.91

4.92 Solve Prob. 4.91, assuming that the axle has been rotated clockwise in its bearings by 30° and that the 720-N load remains vertical.

4.93 A 4 × 8-ft sheet of plywood weighing 40 lb has been temporarily propped against column *CD*. It rests at *A* and *B* on small wooden blocks and against protruding nails. Neglecting friction at all surfaces of contact, determine the reactions at *A*, *B*, and *C*.

Fig. P4.93

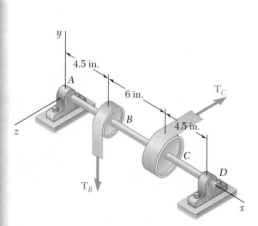

Fig. P4.94

4.94 Two tape spools are attached to an axle supported by bearings at *A* and *D*. The radius of spool *B* is 1.5 in. and the radius of spool *C* is 2 in. Knowing that $T_B = 20$ lb and that the system rotates at a constant rate, determine the reactions at *A* and *D*. Assume that the bearing at *A* does not exert any axial thrust and neglect the weights of the spools and axle.

4.95 Two transmission belts pass over a double-sheaved pulley that is attached to an axle supported by bearings at A and D. The radius of the inner sheave is 125 mm and the radius of the outer sheave is 250 mm. Knowing that when the system is at rest, the tension is 90 N in both portions of belt B and 150 N in both portions of belt C, determine the reactions at A and D. Assume that the bearing at D does not exert any axial thrust.

Fig. P4.95

4.96 Solve Prob. 4.95, assuming that the pulley rotates at a constant rate and that $T_B = 104$ N, $T_B' = 84$ N, and $T_C = 175$ N.

4.97 Two steel pipes AB and BC, each having a mass per unit length of 8 kg/m, are welded together at B and supported by three vertical wires. Knowing that $a = 0.4$ m, determine the tension in each wire.

Fig. P4.97

4.98 For the pipe assembly of Prob. 4.97, determine (a) the largest permissible value of a if the assembly is not to tip, (b) the corresponding tension in each wire.

4.99 The 45-lb square plate shown is supported by three vertical wires. Determine the tension in each wire.

Fig. P4.99

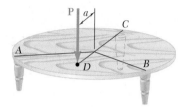

Fig. P4.100

4.100 The table shown weighs 30 lb and has a diameter of 4 ft. It is supported by three legs equally spaced around the edge. A vertical load **P** of magnitude 100 lb is applied to the top of the table at D. Determine the maximum value of a if the table is not to tip over. Show, on a sketch, the area of the table over which **P** can act without tipping the table.

4.101 An opening in a floor is covered by a 1×1.2-m sheet of plywood of mass 18 kg. The sheet is hinged at A and B and is maintained in a position slightly above the floor by a small block C. Determine the vertical component of the reaction (a) at A, (b) at B, (c) at C.

Fig. P4.101

4.102 Solve Prob. 4.101, assuming that the small block C is moved and placed under edge DE at a point 0.15 m from corner E.

4.103 The rectangular plate shown weighs 80 lb and is supported by three vertical wires. Determine the tension in each wire.

Fig. P4.103 and P4.104

4.104 The rectangular plate shown weighs 80 lb and is supported by three vertical wires. Determine the weight and location of the lightest block that should be placed on the plate if the tensions in the three wires are to be equal.

4.105 A 2.4-m boom is held by a ball-and-socket joint at C and by two cables AD and AE. Determine the tension in each cable and the reaction at C.

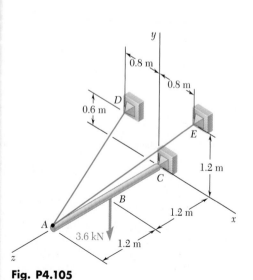

Fig. P4.105

4.106 Solve Prob. 4.105, assuming that the 3.6-kN load is applied at point *A*.

4.107 A 10-ft boom is acted upon by the 840-lb force shown. Determine the tension in each cable and the reaction at the ball-and-socket joint at *A*.

4.108 A 12-m pole supports a horizontal cable *CD* and is held by a ball and socket at *A* and two cables *BE* and *BF*. Knowing that the tension in cable *CD* is 14 kN and assuming that *CD* is parallel to the *x* axis ($\phi = 0$), determine the tension in cables *BE* and *BF* and the reaction at *A*.

Fig. P4.107

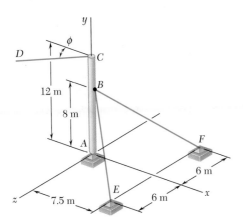

Fig. P4.108

4.109 Solve Prob. 4.108, assuming that cable *CD* forms an angle $\phi = 25°$ with the vertical *xy* plane.

4.110 A 48-in. boom is held by a ball-and-socket joint at *C* and by two cables *BF* and *DAE*; cable *DAE* passes around a frictionless pulley at *A*. For the loading shown, determine the tension in each cable and the reaction at *C*.

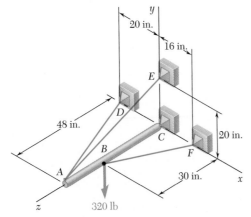

Fig. P4.110

4.111 Solve Prob. 4.110, assuming that the 320-lb load is applied at *A*.

4.112 A 600-lb crate hangs from a cable that passes over a pulley B and is attached to a support at H. The 200-lb boom AB is supported by a ball-and-socket joint at A and by two cables DE and DF. The center of gravity of the boom is located at G. Determine (a) the tension in cables DE and DF, (b) the reaction at A.

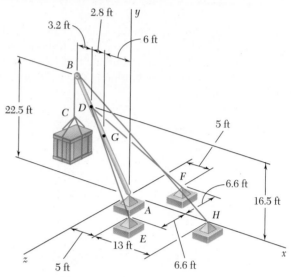

Fig. P4.112

4.113 A 100-kg uniform rectangular plate is supported in the position shown by hinges A and B and by cable DCE that passes over a frictionless hook at C. Assuming that the tension is the same in both parts of the cable, determine (a) the tension in the cable, (b) the reactions at A and B. Assume that the hinge at B does not exert any axial thrust.

4.114 Solve Prob. 4.113, assuming that cable DCE is replaced by a cable attached to point E and hook C.

4.115 The rectangular plate shown weighs 75 lb and is held in the position shown by hinges at A and B and by cable EF. Assuming that the hinge at B does not exert any axial thrust, determine (a) the tension in the cable, (b) the reactions at A and B.

Fig. P4.113

Fig. P4.115

4.116 Solve Prob. 4.115, assuming that cable EF is replaced by a cable attached at points E and H.

4.117 A 20-kg cover for a roof opening is hinged at corners A and B. The roof forms an angle of 30° with the horizontal, and the cover is maintained in a horizontal position by the brace CE. Determine (a) the magnitude of the force exerted by the brace, (b) the reactions at the hinges. Assume that the hinge at A does not exert any axial thrust.

4.118 The bent rod ABEF is supported by bearings at C and D and by wire AH. Knowing that portion AB of the rod is 250 mm long, determine (a) the tension in wire AH, (b) the reactions at C and D. Assume that the bearing at D does not exert any axial thrust.

Fig. P4.117

Fig. P4.118

4.119 Solve Prob. 4.115, assuming that the hinge at B is removed and that the hinge at A can exert couples about axes parallel to the y and z axes.

4.120 Solve Prob. 4.118, assuming that the bearing at D is removed and that the bearing at C can exert couples about axes parallel to the y and z axes.

4.121 The assembly shown is welded to collar A that fits on the vertical pin shown. The pin can exert couples about the x and z axes but does not prevent motion about or along the y axis. For the loading shown, determine the tension in each cable and the reaction at A.

Fig. P4.121

Fig. P4.122

4.122 The assembly shown is used to control the tension T in a tape that passes around a frictionless spool at E. Collar C is welded to rods ABC and CDE. It can rotate about shaft FG but its motion along the shaft is prevented by a washer S. For the loading shown, determine (a) the tension T in the tape, (b) the reaction at C.

4.123 The rigid L-shaped member ABF is supported by a ball-and-socket joint at A and by three cables. For the loading shown, determine the tension in each cable and the reaction at A.

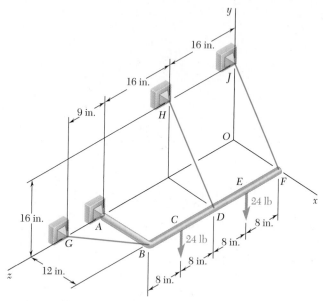

Fig. P4.123

4.124 Solve Prob. 4.123, assuming that the load at C has been removed.

4.125 The rigid L-shaped member ABC is supported by a ball-and-socket joint at A and by three cables. If a 1.8-kN load is applied at F, determine the tension in each cable.

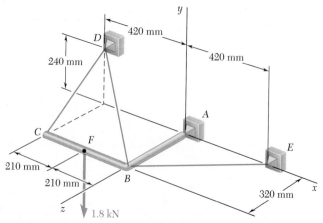

Fig. P4.125

4.126 Solve Prob. 4.125, assuming that the 1.8-kN load is applied at C.

4.127 The assembly shown consists of an 80-mm rod AF that is welded to a cross consisting of four 200-mm arms. The assembly is supported by a ball-and-socket joint at F and by three short links, each of which forms an angle of 45° with the vertical. For the loading shown, determine (a) the tension in each link, (b) the reaction at F.

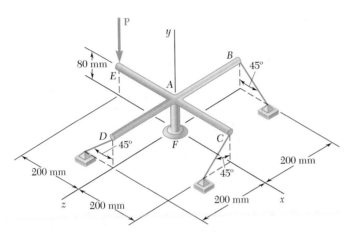

Fig. P4.127

4.128 The uniform 10-kg rod AB is supported by a ball-and-socket joint at A and by the cord CG that is attached to the midpoint G of the rod. Knowing that the rod leans against a frictionless vertical wall at B, determine (a) the tension in the cord, (b) the reactions at A and B.

Fig. P4.128

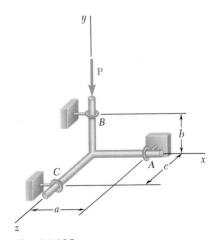

Fig. P4.129

4.129 Three rods are welded together to form a "corner" that is supported by three eyebolts. Neglecting friction, determine the reactions at A, B, and C when $P = 240$ lb, $a = 12$ in., $b = 8$ in., and $c = 10$ in.

4.130 Solve Prob. 4.129, assuming that the force **P** is removed and is replaced by a couple **M** = +(600 lb · in.)**j** acting at B.

4.131 In order to clean the clogged drainpipe AE, a plumber has discon-
nected both ends of the pipe and inserted a power snake through
the opening at A. The cutting head of the snake is connected by
a heavy cable to an electric motor that rotates at a constant speed
as the plumber forces the cable into the pipe. The forces exerted
by the plumber and the motor on the end of the cable can be
represented by the wrench $\mathbf{F} = -(48\text{ N})\mathbf{k}$, $\mathbf{M} = -(90\text{ N}\cdot\text{m})\mathbf{k}$.
Determine the additional reactions at B, C, and D caused by the
cleaning operation. Assume that the reaction at each support consists of two force components perpendicular to the pipe.

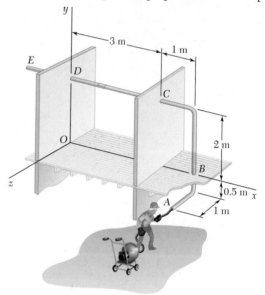

Fig. P4.131

4.132 Solve Prob. 4.131, assuming that the plumber exerts a force $\mathbf{F} = -(48\text{ N})\mathbf{k}$ and that the motor is turned off ($\mathbf{M} = 0$).

4.133 The 50-kg plate $ABCD$ is supported by hinges along edge AB and
by wire CE. Knowing that the plate is uniform, determine the tension in the wire.

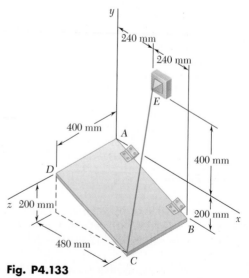

Fig. P4.133

4.134 Solve Prob. 4.133, assuming that wire CE is replaced by a wire
connecting E and D.

4.135 Two rectangular plates are welded together to form the assembly shown. The assembly is supported by ball-and-socket joints at B and D and by a ball on a horizontal surface at C. For the loading shown, determine the reaction at C.

Fig. P4.135

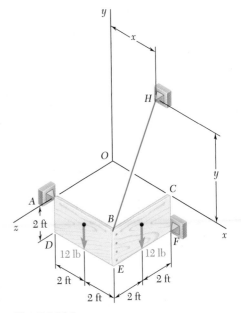

Fig. P4.136

4.136 Two 2×4-ft plywood panels, each of weight 12 lb, are nailed together as shown. The panels are supported by ball-and-socket joints at A and F and by the wire BH. Determine (a) the location of H in the xy plane if the tension in the wire is to be minimum, (b) the corresponding minimum tension.

4.137 Solve Prob. 4.136, subject to the restriction that H must lie on the y axis.

4.138 The frame ACD is supported by ball-and-socket joints at A and D and by a cable that passes through a ring at B and is attached to hooks at G and H. Knowing that the frame supports at point C a load of magnitude $P = 268$ N, determine the tension in the cable.

4.139 Solve Prob. 4.138, assuming that cable GBH is replaced by a cable GB attached at G and B.

4.140 The bent rod $ABDE$ is supported by ball-and-socket joints at A and E and by the cable DF. If a 60-lb load is applied at C as shown, determine the tension in the cable.

Fig. P4.138

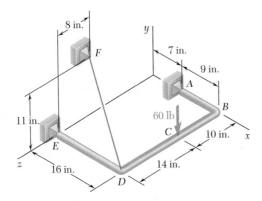

Fig. P4.140

4.141 Solve Prob. 4.140, assuming that cable DF is replaced by a cable connecting B and F.

REVIEW AND SUMMARY

Equilibrium equations

This chapter was devoted to the study of the *equilibrium of rigid bodies*, i.e., to the situation when the external forces acting on a rigid body *form a system equivalent to zero* [Sec. 4.1]. We then have

$$\Sigma \mathbf{F} = 0 \qquad \Sigma \mathbf{M}_O = \Sigma(\mathbf{r} \times \mathbf{F}) = 0 \qquad (4.1)$$

Resolving each force and each moment into its rectangular components, we can express the necessary and sufficient conditions for the equilibrium of a rigid body with the following six scalar equations:

$$\Sigma F_x = 0 \qquad \Sigma F_y = 0 \qquad \Sigma F_z = 0 \qquad (4.2)$$
$$\Sigma M_x = 0 \qquad \Sigma M_y = 0 \qquad \Sigma M_z = 0 \qquad (4.3)$$

These equations can be used to determine unknown forces applied to the rigid body or unknown reactions exerted by its supports.

Free-body diagram

When solving a problem involving the equilibrium of a rigid body, it is essential to consider *all* of the forces acting on the body. Therefore, the first step in the solution of the problem should be to draw a *free-body diagram* showing the body under consideration and all of the unknown as well as known forces acting on it [Sec. 4.2].

Equilibrium of a two-dimensional structure

In the first part of the chapter, we considered the *equilibrium of a two-dimensional structure;* i.e., we assumed that the structure considered and the forces applied to it were contained in the same plane. We saw that each of the reactions exerted on the structure by its supports could involve one, two, or three unknowns, depending upon the type of support [Sec. 4.3].

In the case of a two-dimensional structure, Eqs. (4.1), or Eqs. (4.2) and (4.3), reduce to *three equilibrium equations*, namely

$$\Sigma F_x = 0 \qquad \Sigma F_y = 0 \qquad \Sigma M_A = 0 \qquad (4.5)$$

where A is an arbitrary point in the plane of the structure [Sec. 4.4]. These equations can be used to solve for three unknowns. While the three equilibrium equations (4.5) cannot be *augmented* with additional equations, any of them can be *replaced* by another equation. Therefore, we can write alternative sets of equilibrium equations, such as

$$\Sigma F_x = 0 \qquad \Sigma M_A = 0 \qquad \Sigma M_B = 0 \qquad (4.6)$$

where point B is chosen in such a way that the line AB is not parallel to the y axis, or

$$\Sigma M_A = 0 \qquad \Sigma M_B = 0 \qquad \Sigma M_C = 0 \qquad (4.7)$$

where the points A, B, and C do not lie in a straight line.

Since any set of equilibrium equations can be solved for only three unknowns, the reactions at the supports of a rigid two-dimensional structure cannot be completely determined if they involve *more than three unknowns*; they are said to be *statically indeterminate* [Sec. 4.5]. On the other hand, if the reactions involve *fewer than three unknowns*, equilibrium will not be maintained under general loading conditions; the structure is said to be *partially constrained*. The fact that the reactions involve exactly three unknowns is no guarantee that the equilibrium equations can be solved for all three unknowns. If the supports are arranged in such a way that the reactions are *either concurrent or parallel*, the reactions are statically indeterminate, and the structure is said to be *improperly constrained*.

Statical indeterminacy

Partial constraints

Improper constraints

Two particular cases of equilibrium of a rigid body were given special attention. In Sec. 4.6, a *two-force body* was defined as a rigid body subjected to forces at only two points, and it was shown that the resultants $\mathbf{F}_1$ and $\mathbf{F}_2$ of these forces must have the *same magnitude, the same line of action, and opposite sense* (Fig. 4.11), a property which will simplify the solution of certain problems in later chapters. In Sec. 4.7, a *three-force body* was defined as a rigid body subjected to forces at only three points, and it was shown that the resultants $\mathbf{F}_1$, $\mathbf{F}_2$, and $\mathbf{F}_3$ of these forces must be *either concurrent* (Fig. 4.12) *or parallel*. This property provides us with an alternative approach to the solution of problems involving a three-force body [Sample Prob. 4.6].

Two-force body

Three-force body

Fig. 4.11

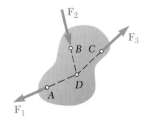

Fig. 4.12

In the second part of the chapter, we considered the *equilibrium of a three-dimensional body* and saw that each of the reactions exerted on the body by its supports could involve between one and six unknowns, depending upon the type of support [Sec. 4.8].

Equilibrium of a three-dimensional body

In the general case of the equilibrium of a three-dimensional body, all of the six scalar equilibrium equations (4.2) and (4.3) listed at the beginning of this review should be used and solved for *six unknowns* [Sec. 4.9]. In most problems, however, these equations will be more conveniently obtained if we first write

$$\Sigma\mathbf{F} = 0 \qquad \Sigma\mathbf{M}_O = \Sigma(\mathbf{r} \times \mathbf{F}) = 0 \qquad (4.1)$$

and express the forces $\mathbf{F}$ and position vectors $\mathbf{r}$ in terms of scalar components and unit vectors. The vector products can then be computed either directly or by means of determinants, and the desired scalar equations obtained by equating to zero the coefficients of the unit vectors [Sample Probs. 4.7 through 4.9].

We noted that as many as three unknown reaction components may be eliminated from the computation of $\Sigma \mathbf{M}_O$ in the second of the relations (4.1) through a judicious choice of point O. Also, the reactions at two points A and B can be eliminated from the solution of some problems by writing the equation $\Sigma M_{AB} = 0$, which involves the computation of the moments of the forces about an axis AB joining points A and B [Sample Prob. 4.10].

If the reactions involve more than six unknowns, some of the reactions are *statically indeterminate;* if they involve fewer than six unknowns, the rigid body is only *partially constrained.* Even with six or more unknowns, the rigid body will be *improperly constrained* if the reactions associated with the given supports either are parallel or intersect the same line.

4.142 A gardener uses a 60-N wheelbarrow to transport a 250-N bag of fertilizer. What force must she exert on each handle?

250 N

60 N

0.15 m | 0.15 m | 0.7 m

Fig. P4.142

4.143 The required tension in cable AB is 200 lb. Determine (*a*) the vertical force **P** that must be applied to the pedal, (*b*) the corresponding reaction at C.

P | 15 in.

D

C

60°

7 in.

A | B

Fig. P4.143

4.144 A lever AB is hinged at C and attached to a control cable at A. If the lever is subjected to a 500-N horizontal force at B, determine (*a*) the tension in the cable, (*b*) the reaction at C.

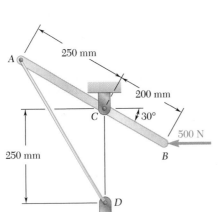

250 mm

A

200 mm

30°

C

500 N

250 mm

B

D

Fig. P4.144

4.145 A force **P** of magnitude 280 lb is applied to member $ABCD$, which is supported by a pin at A and by the cable CED. Neglecting friction and considering the case when $a = 3$ in., determine (*a*) the tension in the cable, (*b*) the reaction at A.

P

5 in.

B | C

12 in.

A

12 in.

D

E

a | 12 in.

Fig. P4.145

4.146 Two slots have been cut in plate *DEF*, and the plate has been placed so that the slots fit two fixed, frictionless pins *A* and *B*. Knowing that $P = 15$ lb, determine (*a*) the force each pin exerts on the plate, (*b*) the reaction at *F*.

Fig. P4.146

4.147 Knowing that the tension in wire *BD* is 1300 N, determine the reaction at the fixed support *C* of the frame shown.

4.148 The spanner shown is used to rotate a shaft. A pin fits in a hole at *A*, while a flat, frictionless surface rests against the shaft at *B*. If a 60-lb force **P** is exerted on the spanner at *D*, find the reactions at *A* and *B*.

Fig. P4.147

Fig. P4.148

4.149 Rod *AB* is supported by a pin and bracket at *A* and rests against a frictionless peg at *C*. Determine the reactions at *A* and *C* when a 170-N vertical force is applied at *B*.

4.150 The 24-lb square plate shown is supported by three vertical wires. Determine (*a*) the tension in each wire when $a = 10$ in., (*b*) the value of *a* for which the tension in each wire is 8 lb.

Fig. P4.149

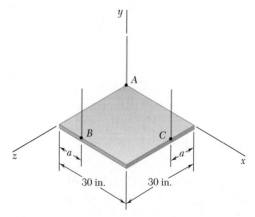

Fig. P4.150

4.151 Frame *ABCD* is supported by a ball-and-socket joint at *A* and by three cables. For *a* = 150 mm, determine the tension in each cable and the reaction at *A*.

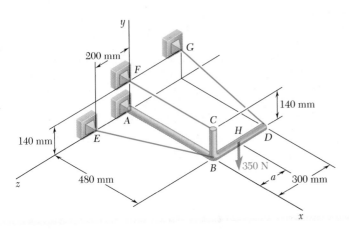

Fig. P4.151

4.152 The pipe *ACDE* is supported by ball-and-socket joints at *A* and *E* and by the wire *DF*. Determine the tension in the wire when a 640-N load is applied at *B* as shown.

Fig. P4.152

4.153 A force **P** is applied to a bent rod *ABC*, which may be supported in four different ways as shown. In each case, if possible, determine the reactions at the supports.

Fig. P4.153

COMPUTER PROBLEMS

4.C1 The position of the L-shaped rod shown is controlled by a cable attached at B. Knowing that the rod supports a load of magnitude $P = 50$ lb, write a computer program that can be used to calculate the tension T in the cable for values of θ from 0 to 120° using 10° increments. Using appropriate smaller increments, calculate the maximum tension T and the corresponding value of θ.

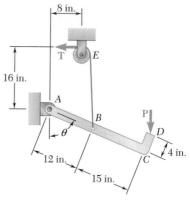

Fig. P4.C1

4.C2 The position of the 10-kg rod AB is controlled by the block shown, which is slowly moved to the left by the force $\mathbf{P}$. Neglecting the effect of friction, write a computer program that can be used to calculate the magnitude P of the force for values of x decreasing from 750 mm to 0 using 50-mm increments. Using appropriate smaller increments, determine the maximum value of P and the corresponding value of x.

Fig. P4.C2

4.C3 and 4.C4 The constant of spring AB is k, and the spring is unstretched when $\theta = 0$. Knowing that $R = 10$ in., $a = 20$ in., and $k = 5$ lb/in., write a computer program that can be used to calculate the weight W corresponding to equilibrium for values of θ from 0 to 90° using 10° increments. Using appropriate smaller increments, determine the value of θ corresponding to equilibrium when $W = 5$ lb.

Fig. P4.C3

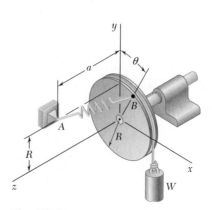

Fig. P4.C4

4.C5 A 200 × 250-mm panel of mass 20 kg is supported by hinges along edge *AB*. Cable *CDE* is attached to the panel at *C*, passes over a small pulley at *D*, and supports a cylinder of mass *m*. Neglecting the effect of friction, write a computer program that can be used to calculate the mass of the cylinder corresponding to equilibrium for values of θ from 0 to 90° using 10° increments. Using appropriate smaller increments, determine the value of θ corresponding to equilibrium when *m* = 10 kg.

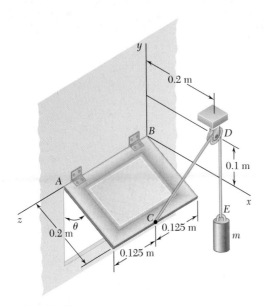

Fig. P4.C5

4.C6 The derrick shown supports a 2000-kg crate. It is held by a ball-and-socket joint at *A* and by two cables attached at *D* and *E*. Knowing that the derrick stands in a vertical plane forming an angle ϕ with the *xy* plane, write a computer program that can be used to calculate the tension in each cable for values of ϕ from 0 to 60° using 5° increments. Using appropriate smaller increments, determine the value of ϕ for which the tension in cable *BE* is maximum.

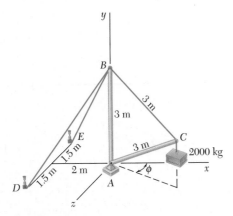

Fig. P4.C6

The Revelstoke Dam, located on the Columbia River in British Columbia, is subjected to three different kinds of distributed forces: the weights of its constituent elements, the pressure forces exerted by the water of its submerged face, and the pressure forces exerted by the ground on its base.

CHAPTER

Distributed Forces: Centroids and Centers of Gravity

5.1   INTRODUCTION

We have assumed so far that the attraction exerted by the earth on a rigid body could be represented by a single force **W**. This force, called the force of gravity or the weight of the body, was to be applied at the *center of gravity* of the body (Sec. 3.2). Actually, the earth exerts a force on each of the particles forming the body. The action of the earth on a rigid body should thus be represented by a large number of small forces distributed over the entire body. You will learn in this chapter, however, that all of these small forces can be replaced by a single equivalent force **W**. You will also learn how to determine the center of gravity, i.e., the point of application of the resultant **W**, for bodies of various shapes.

In the first part of the chapter, two-dimensional bodies, such as flat plates and wires contained in a given plane, are considered. Two concepts closely associated with the determination of the center of gravity of a plate or a wire are introduced: the concept of the *centroid* of an area or a line and the concept of the *first moment* of an area or a line with respect to a given axis.

You will also learn that the computation of the area of a surface of revolution or of the volume of a body of revolution is directly related to the determination of the centroid of the line or area used to generate that surface or body of revolution (theorems of Pappus-Guldinus). And, as is shown in Secs. 5.8 and 5.9, the determination of the centroid of an area simplifies the analysis of beams subjected to distributed loads and the computation of the forces exerted on submerged rectangular surfaces, such as hydraulic gates and portions of dams.

In the last part of the chapter, you will learn how to determine the center of gravity of a three-dimensional body as well as the centroid of a volume and the first moments of that volume with respect to the coordinate planes.

AREAS AND LINES

5.2   CENTER OF GRAVITY OF A TWO-DIMENSIONAL BODY

Let us first consider a flat horizontal plate (Fig. 5.1). We can divide the plate into n small elements. The coordinates of the first element

Photo 5.1 The precise balancing of the components of a mobile requires an understanding of centers of gravity and centroids, the main topics of this chapter.

$$\Sigma M_y: \quad \bar{x} W = \Sigma x \, \Delta W$$

$$\Sigma M_x: \quad \bar{y} W = \Sigma y \, \Delta W$$

Fig. 5.1   Center of gravity of a plate.

are denoted by x_1 and y_1, those of the second element by x_2 and y_2, etc. The forces exerted by the earth on the elements of the plate will be denoted, respectively, by $\Delta \mathbf{W}_1$, $\Delta \mathbf{W}_2$, ... , $\Delta \mathbf{W}_n$. These forces or weights are directed toward the center of the earth; however, for all practical purposes they can be assumed to be parallel. Their resultant is therefore a single force in the same direction. The magnitude W of this force is obtained by adding the magnitudes of the elemental weights,

$$\Sigma F_z: \qquad W = \Delta W_1 + \Delta W_2 + \cdots + \Delta W_n$$

To obtain the coordinates $\bar{x}$ and $\bar{y}$ of the point G where the resultant $\mathbf{W}$ should be applied, we write that the moments of $\mathbf{W}$ about the y and x axes are equal to the sum of the corresponding moments of the elemental weights,

$$\Sigma M_y: \qquad \bar{x} W = x_1 \Delta W_1 + x_2 \Delta W_2 + \cdots + x_n \Delta W_n$$
$$\Sigma M_x: \qquad \bar{y} W = y_1 \Delta W_1 + y_2 \Delta W_2 + \cdots + y_n \Delta W_n \qquad (5.1)$$

If we now increase the number of elements into which the plate is divided and simultaneously decrease the size of each element, we obtain in the limit the following expressions:

$$W = \int dW \qquad \bar{x} W = \int x \, dW \qquad \bar{y} W = \int y \, dW \qquad (5.2)$$

These equations define the weight $\mathbf{W}$ and the coordinates $\bar{x}$ and $\bar{y}$ of the center of gravity G of a flat plate. The same equations can be derived for a wire lying in the xy plane (Fig. 5.2). We note that the center of gravity G of a wire is usually not located on the wire.

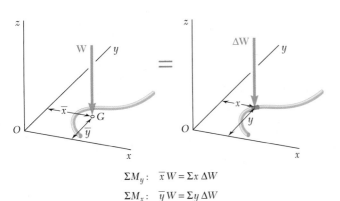

$$\Sigma M_y: \quad \bar{x} W = \Sigma x \, \Delta W$$
$$\Sigma M_x: \quad \bar{y} W = \Sigma y \, \Delta W$$

Fig. 5.2 Center of gravity of a wire.

5.3 CENTROIDS OF AREAS AND LINES

In the case of a flat homogeneous plate of uniform thickness, the magnitude ΔW of the weight of an element of the plate can be expressed as

$$\Delta W = \gamma t \, \Delta A$$

where γ = specific weight (weight per unit volume) of the material
t = thickness of the plate
ΔA = area of the element

Similarly, we can express the magnitude W of the weight of the entire plate as

$$W = \gamma t A$$

where A is the total area of the plate.

If U.S. customary units are used, the specific weight γ should be expressed in lb/ft^3, the thickness t in feet, and the areas ΔA and A in square feet. We observe that ΔW and W will then be expressed in pounds. If SI units are used, γ should be expressed in N/m^3, t in meters, and the areas ΔA and A in square meters; the weights ΔW and W will then be expressed in newtons.†

Substituting for ΔW and W in the moment equations (5.1) and dividing throughout by γt, we obtain

ΣM_y: $\bar{x}A = x_1 \, \Delta A_1 + x_2 \, \Delta A_2 + \cdots + x_n \, \Delta A_n$
ΣM_x: $\bar{y}A = y_1 \, \Delta A_1 + y_2 \, \Delta A_2 + \cdots + y_n \, \Delta A_n$

If we increase the number of elements into which the area A is divided and simultaneously decrease the size of each element, we obtain in the limit

$$\bar{x}A = \int x \, dA \qquad \bar{y}A = \int y \, dA \tag{5.3}$$

These equations define the coordinates $\bar{x}$ and $\bar{y}$ of the center of gravity of a homogeneous plate. The point whose coordinates are $\bar{x}$ and $\bar{y}$ is also known as the *centroid C of the area A* of the plate (Fig. 5.3). If the plate is not homogeneous, these equations cannot be used to determine the center of gravity of the plate; they still define, however, the centroid of the area.

In the case of a homogeneous wire of uniform cross section, the magnitude ΔW of the weight of an element of wire can be expressed as

$$\Delta W = \gamma a \, \Delta L$$

where γ = specific weight of the material
a = cross-sectional area of the wire
ΔL = length of the element

---

†It should be noted that in the SI system of units a given material is generally characterized by its density ρ (mass per unit volume) rather than by its specific weight γ. The specific weight of the material can then be obtained from the relation

$$\gamma = \rho g$$

where g = 9.81 m/s^2. Since ρ is expressed in kg/m^3, we observe that γ will be expressed in (kg/m^3)(m/s^2), that is, in N/m^3.

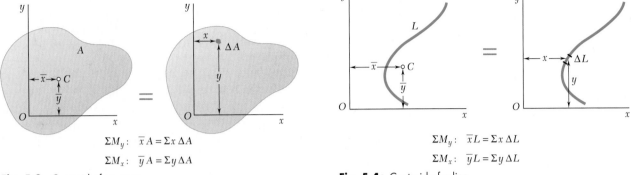

$$\Sigma M_y : \quad \bar{x} A = \Sigma x \, \Delta A$$
$$\Sigma M_x : \quad \bar{y} A = \Sigma y \, \Delta A$$

Fig. 5.3 Centroid of an area.

$$\Sigma M_y : \quad \bar{x} L = \Sigma x \, \Delta L$$
$$\Sigma M_x : \quad \bar{y} L = \Sigma y \, \Delta L$$

Fig. 5.4 Centroid of a line.

The center of gravity of the wire then coincides with the *centroid C of the line L* defining the shape of the wire (Fig. 5.4). The coordinates $\bar{x}$ and $\bar{y}$ of the centroid of the line L are obtained from the equations

$$\bar{x} L = \int x \, dL \qquad \bar{y} L = \int y \, dL \tag{5.4}$$

5.4 FIRST MOMENTS OF AREAS AND LINES

The integral $\int x \, dA$ in Eqs. (5.3) of the preceding section is known as the *first moment of the area A with respect to the y axis* and is denoted by Q_y. Similarly, the integral $\int y \, dA$ defines the *first moment of A with respect to the x axis* and is denoted by Q_x. We write

$$Q_y = \int x \, dA \qquad Q_x = \int y \, dA \tag{5.5}$$

Comparing Eqs. (5.3) with Eqs. (5.5), we note that the first moments of the area A can be expressed as the products of the area and the coordinates of its centroid:

$$Q_y = \bar{x} A \qquad Q_x = \bar{y} A \tag{5.6}$$

It follows from Eqs. (5.6) that the coordinates of the centroid of an area can be obtained by dividing the first moments of that area by the area itself. The first moments of the area are also useful in mechanics of materials for determining the shearing stresses in beams under transverse loadings. Finally, we observe from Eqs. (5.6) that if the centroid of an area is located on a coordinate axis, the first moment of the area with respect to that axis is zero. Conversely, if the first moment of an area with respect to a coordinate axis is zero, then the centroid of the area is located on that axis.

Relations similar to Eqs. (5.5) and (5.6) can be used to define the first moments of a line with respect to the coordinate axes and

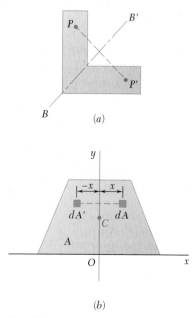

Fig. 5.5

to express these moments as the products of the length L of the line and the coordinates $\bar{x}$ and $\bar{y}$ of its centroid.

An area A is said to be *symmetric with respect to an axis BB′* if for every point P of the area there exists a point P' of the same area such that the line PP' is perpendicular to BB' and is divided into two equal parts by that axis (Fig. 5.5a). A line L is said to be symmetric with respect to an axis BB' if it satisfies similar conditions. When an area A or a line L possesses an axis of symmetry BB', its first moment with respect to BB' is zero, and its centroid is located on that axis. For example, in the case of the area A of Fig. 5.5b, which is symmetric with respect to the y axis, we observe that for every element of area dA of abscissa x there exists an element dA' of equal area and with abscissa $-x$. It follows that the integral in the first of Eqs. (5.5) is zero and, thus, that $Q_y = 0$. It also follows from the first of the relations (5.3) that $\bar{x} = 0$. Thus, if an area A or a line L possesses an axis of symmetry, its centroid C is located on that axis.

We further note that if an area or line possesses two axes of symmetry, its centroid C must be located at the intersection of the two axes (Fig. 5.6). This property enables us to determine immediately the centroid of areas such as circles, ellipses, squares, rectangles, equilateral triangles, or other symmetric figures as well as the centroid of lines in the shape of the circumference of a circle, the perimeter of a square, etc.

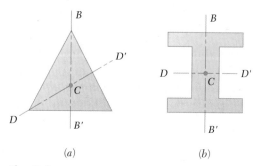

Fig. 5.6

An area A is said to be *symmetric with respect to a center O* if for every element of area dA of coordinates x and y there exists an element dA' of equal area with coordinates $-x$ and $-y$ (Fig. 5.7). It then follows that the integrals in Eqs. (5.5) are both zero and that $Q_x = Q_y = 0$. It also follows from Eqs. (5.3) that $\bar{x} = \bar{y} = 0$, that is, that the centroid of the area coincides with its center of symmetry O. Similarly, if a line possesses a center of symmetry O, the centroid of the line will coincide with the center O.

It should be noted that a figure possessing a center of symmetry does not necessarily possess an axis of symmetry (Fig. 5.7), while a figure possessing two axes of symmetry does not necessarily possess a center of symmetry (Fig. 5.6a). However, if a figure possesses two axes of symmetry at a right angle to each other, the point of intersection of these axes is a center of symmetry (Fig. 5.6b).

Determining the centroids of unsymmetrical areas and lines and of areas and lines possessing only one axis of symmetry will be discussed in Secs. 5.6 and 5.7. Centroids of common shapes of areas and lines are shown in Fig. 5.8A and B.

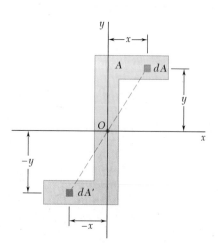

Fig. 5.7

Shape		$\bar{x}$	$\bar{y}$	Area
Triangular area			$\dfrac{h}{3}$	$\dfrac{bh}{2}$
Quarter-circular area		$\dfrac{4r}{3\pi}$	$\dfrac{4r}{3\pi}$	$\dfrac{\pi r^2}{4}$
Semicircular area		0	$\dfrac{4r}{3\pi}$	$\dfrac{\pi r^2}{2}$
Quarter-elliptical area		$\dfrac{4a}{3\pi}$	$\dfrac{4b}{3\pi}$	$\dfrac{\pi ab}{4}$
Semielliptical area		0	$\dfrac{4b}{3\pi}$	$\dfrac{\pi ab}{2}$
Semiparabolic area		$\dfrac{3a}{8}$	$\dfrac{3h}{5}$	$\dfrac{2ah}{3}$
Parabolic area		0	$\dfrac{3h}{5}$	$\dfrac{4ah}{3}$
Parabolic spandrel		$\dfrac{3a}{4}$	$\dfrac{3h}{10}$	$\dfrac{ah}{3}$
General spandrel		$\dfrac{n+1}{n+2}a$	$\dfrac{n+1}{4n+2}h$	$\dfrac{ah}{n+1}$
Circular sector		$\dfrac{2r\sin\alpha}{3\alpha}$	0	αr^2

Fig. 5.8A Centroids of common shapes of areas.

Shape		$\bar{x}$	$\bar{y}$	Length
Quarter-circular arc		$\dfrac{2r}{\pi}$	$\dfrac{2r}{\pi}$	$\dfrac{\pi r}{2}$
Semicircular arc		0	$\dfrac{2r}{\pi}$	πr
Arc of circle		$\dfrac{r \sin \alpha}{\alpha}$	0	$2\alpha r$

Fig. 5.8B Centroids of common shapes of lines.

5.5 COMPOSITE PLATES AND WIRES

In many instances, a flat plate can be divided into rectangles, triangles, or the other common shapes shown in Fig. 5.8A. The abscissa $\overline{X}$ of its center of gravity G can be determined from the abscissas $\bar{x}_1, \bar{x}_2, \ldots, \bar{x}_n$ of the centers of gravity of the various parts by expressing that the moment of the weight of the whole plate about the y axis is equal to the sum of the moments of the weights of the various parts about the same axis (Fig. 5.9). The ordinate $\overline{Y}$ of the center of gravity of the plate is found in a similar way by equating moments about the x axis. We write

$$\Sigma M_y: \quad \overline{X}(W_1 + W_2 + \cdots + W_n) = \bar{x}_1 W_1 + \bar{x}_2 W_2 + \cdots + \bar{x}_n W_n$$
$$\Sigma M_x: \quad \overline{Y}(W_1 + W_2 + \cdots + W_n) = \bar{y}_1 W_1 + \bar{y}_2 W_2 + \cdots + \bar{y}_n W_n$$

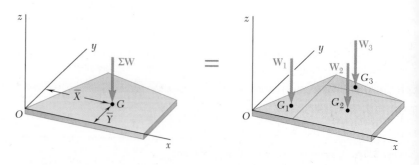

$$\Sigma M_y: \quad \overline{X}\,\Sigma W = \Sigma \bar{x}\, W$$
$$\Sigma M_x: \quad \overline{Y}\,\Sigma W = \Sigma \bar{y}\, W$$

Fig. 5.9 Center of gravity of a composite plate.

or, for short,

$$\overline{X}\Sigma W = \Sigma \overline{x}\,W \qquad \overline{Y}\Sigma W = \Sigma \overline{y}\,W \qquad (5.7)$$

These equations can be solved for the coordinates $\overline{X}$ and $\overline{Y}$ of the center of gravity of the plate.

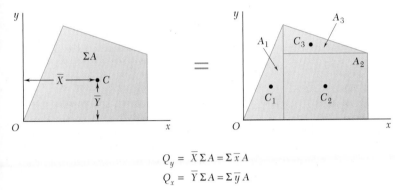

$$Q_y = \overline{X}\Sigma A = \Sigma \overline{x}\,A$$
$$Q_x = \overline{Y}\Sigma A = \Sigma \overline{y}\,A$$

Fig. 5.10 Centroid of a composite area.

If the plate is homogeneous and of uniform thickness, the center of gravity coincides with the centroid C of its area. The abscissa $\overline{X}$ of the centroid of the area can be determined by noting that the first moment Q_y of the composite area with respect to the y axis can be expressed both as the product of $\overline{X}$ and the total area and as the sum of the first moments of the elementary areas with respect to the y axis (Fig. 5.10). The ordinate $\overline{Y}$ of the centroid is found in a similar way by considering the first moment Q_x of the composite area. We have

$$Q_y = \overline{X}(A_1 + A_2 + \cdots + A_n) = \overline{x}_1 A_1 + \overline{x}_2 A_2 + \cdots + \overline{x}_n A_n$$
$$Q_x = \overline{Y}(A_1 + A_2 + \cdots + A_n) = \overline{y}_1 A_1 + \overline{y}_2 A_2 + \cdots + \overline{y}_n A_n$$

or, for short,

$$Q_y = \overline{X}\Sigma A = \Sigma \overline{x}A \qquad Q_x = \overline{Y}\Sigma A = \Sigma \overline{y}A \qquad (5.8)$$

These equations yield the first moments of the composite area, or they can be used to obtain the coordinates $\overline{X}$ and $\overline{Y}$ of its centroid.

Care should be taken to assign the appropriate sign to the moment of each area. First moments of areas, like moments of forces, can be positive or negative. For example, an area whose centroid is located to the left of the y axis will have a negative first moment with respect to that axis. Also, the area of a hole should be assigned a negative sign (Fig. 5.11).

Similarly, it is possible in many cases to determine the center of gravity of a composite wire or the centroid of a composite line by dividing the wire or line into simpler elements (see Sample Prob. 5.2).

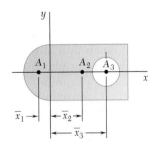

	$\overline{x}$	A	$\overline{x}A$
A_1 Semicircle	$-$	$+$	$-$
A_2 Full rectangle	$+$	$+$	$+$
A_3 Circular hole	$+$	$-$	$-$

Fig. 5.11

For the plane area shown, determine (a) the first moments with respect to the x and y axes, (b) the location of the centroid.

SOLUTION

Components of Area. The area is obtained by adding a rectangle, a triangle, and a semicircle and by then subtracting a circle. Using the coordinate axes shown, the area and the coordinates of the centroid of each of the component areas are determined and entered in the table below. The area of the circle is indicated as negative, since it is to be subtracted from the other areas. We note that the coordinate $\bar{y}$ of the centroid of the triangle is negative for the axes shown. The first moments of the component areas with respect to the coordinate axes are computed and entered in the table.

Component	A, mm^2	$\bar{x}$, mm	$\bar{y}$, mm	$\bar{x}A$, mm^3	$\bar{y}A$, mm^3
Rectangle	$(120)(80) = 9.6 \times 10^3$	60	40	$+576 \times 10^3$	$+384 \times 10^3$
Triangle	$\frac{1}{2}(120)(60) = 3.6 \times 10^3$	40	-20	$+144 \times 10^3$	-72×10^3
Semicircle	$\frac{1}{2}\pi(60)^2 = 5.655 \times 10^3$	60	105.46	$+339.3 \times 10^3$	$+596.4 \times 10^3$
Circle	$-\pi(40)^2 = -5.027 \times 10^3$	60	80	-301.6×10^3	-402.2×10^3
	$\Sigma A = 13.828 \times 10^3$			$\Sigma \bar{x}A = +757.7 \times 10^3$	$\Sigma \bar{y}A = +506.2 \times 10^3$

a. First Moments of the Area. Using Eqs. (5.8), we write

$$Q_x = \Sigma \bar{y}A = 506.2 \times 10^3 \text{ mm}^3 \qquad Q_x = 506 \times 10^3 \text{ mm}^3 \blacktriangleleft$$
$$Q_y = \Sigma \bar{x}A = 757.7 \times 10^3 \text{ mm}^3 \qquad Q_y = 758 \times 10^3 \text{ mm}^3 \blacktriangleleft$$

b. Location of Centroid. Substituting the values given in the table into the equations defining the centroid of a composite area, we obtain

$$\bar{X}\Sigma A = \Sigma \bar{x}A: \quad \bar{X}(13.828 \times 10^3 \text{ mm}^2) = 757.7 \times 10^3 \text{ mm}^3$$
$$\bar{X} = 54.8 \text{ mm} \blacktriangleleft$$

$$\bar{Y}\Sigma A = \Sigma \bar{y}A: \quad \bar{Y}(13.828 \times 10^3 \text{ mm}^2) = 506.2 \times 10^3 \text{ mm}^3$$
$$\bar{Y} = 36.6 \text{ mm} \blacktriangleleft$$

SAMPLE PROBLEM 5.2

The figure shown is made from a piece of thin, homogeneous wire. Determine the location of its center of gravity.

SOLUTION

Since the figure is formed of homogeneous wire, its center of gravity coincides with the centroid of the corresponding line. Therefore, that centroid will be determined. Choosing the coordinate axes shown, with origin at A, we determine the coordinates of the centroid of each line segment and compute the first moments with respect to the coordinate axes.

Segment	L, in.	$\bar{x}$, in.	$\bar{y}$, in.	$\bar{x}L$, in^2	$\bar{y}L$, in^2
AB	24	12	0	288	0
BC	26	12	5	312	130
CA	10	0	5	0	50
	$\Sigma L = 60$			$\Sigma \bar{x}L = 600$	$\Sigma \bar{y}L = 180$

Substituting the values obtained from the table into the equations defining the centroid of a composite line, we obtain

$$\bar{X}\Sigma L = \Sigma \bar{x}L: \qquad \bar{X}(60 \text{ in.}) = 600 \text{ in}^2 \qquad\qquad \bar{X} = 10 \text{ in.} \blacktriangleleft$$
$$\bar{Y}\Sigma L = \Sigma \bar{y}L: \qquad \bar{Y}(60 \text{ in.}) = 180 \text{ in}^2 \qquad\qquad \bar{Y} = 3 \text{ in.} \blacktriangleleft$$

SAMPLE PROBLEM 5.3

A uniform semicircular rod of weight W and radius r is attached to a pin at A and rests against a frictionless surface at B. Determine the reactions at A and B.

SOLUTION

Free-Body Diagram. A free-body diagram of the rod is drawn. The forces acting on the rod are its weight $\mathbf{W}$, which is applied at the center of gravity G (whose position is obtained from Fig. 5.8B); a reaction at A, represented by its components $\mathbf{A}_x$ and $\mathbf{A}_y$; and a horizontal reaction at B.

Equilibrium Equations

$$+\curvearrowleft \Sigma M_A = 0: \qquad B(2r) - W\left(\frac{2r}{\pi}\right) = 0$$

$$B = +\frac{W}{\pi} \qquad\qquad \mathbf{B} = \frac{W}{\pi} \rightarrow \quad \blacktriangleleft$$

$$\xrightarrow{+}\Sigma F_x = 0: \qquad A_x + B = 0$$

$$A_x = -B = -\frac{W}{\pi} \qquad \mathbf{A}_x = \frac{W}{\pi} \leftarrow$$

$$+\uparrow\Sigma F_y = 0: \qquad A_y - W = 0 \qquad \mathbf{A}_y = W \uparrow$$

Adding the two components of the reaction at A:

$$A = \left[W^2 + \left(\frac{W}{\pi}\right)^2\right]^{1/2} \qquad A = W\left(1 + \frac{1}{\pi^2}\right)^{1/2} \quad \blacktriangleleft$$

$$\tan \alpha = \frac{W}{W/\pi} = \pi \qquad\qquad \alpha = \tan^{-1}\pi \quad \blacktriangleleft$$

The answers can also be expressed as follows:

$$\mathbf{A} = 1.049W \measuredangle 72.3° \qquad \mathbf{B} = 0.318W\rightarrow \quad \blacktriangleleft$$

SOLVING PROBLEMS
ON YOUR OWN

In this lesson we developed the general equations for locating the centers of gravity of two-dimensional bodies and wires [Eqs. (5.2)] and the centroids of plane areas [Eqs. (5.3)] and lines [Eqs. (5.4)]. In the following problems, you will have to locate the centroids of composite areas and lines or determine the first moments of the area for composite plates [Eqs. (5.8)].

1. Locating the centroids of composite areas and lines. Sample Problems 5.1 and 5.2 illustrate the procedure you should follow when solving problems of this type. There are, however, several points that should be emphasized.

    a. The first step in your solution should be to decide how to construct the given area or line from the common shapes of Fig. 5.8. You should recognize that for plane areas it is often possible to construct a particular shape in more than one way. Also, showing the different components (as is done in Sample Prob. 5.1) will help you to correctly establish their centroids and areas or lengths. Do not forget that you can subtract areas as well as add them to obtain a desired shape.

    b. We strongly recommend that for each problem you construct a table containing the areas or lengths and the respective coordinates of the centroids. It is essential for you to remember that areas which are "removed" (for example, holes) are treated as negative. Also, the sign of negative coordinates must be included. Therefore, you should always carefully note the location of the origin of the coordinate axes.

    c. When possible, use symmetry [Sec. 5.4] to help you determine the location of a centroid.

    d. In the formulas for the circular sector and for the arc of a circle in Fig. 5.8, the angle α must always be expressed in radians.

2. Calculating the first moments of an area. The procedures for locating the centroid of an area and for determining the first moments of an area are similar; however, for the latter it is not necessary to compute the total area. Also, as noted in Sec. 5.4, you should recognize that the first moment of an area relative to a centroidal axis is zero.

3. Solving problems involving the center of gravity. The bodies considered in the following problems are homogeneous; thus, their centers of gravity and centroids coincide. In addition, when a body that is suspended from a single pin is in equilibrium, the pin and the body's center of gravity must lie on the same vertical line.

It may appear that many of the problems in this lesson have little to do with the study of mechanics. However, being able to locate the centroid of composite shapes will be essential in several topics that you will soon encounter.

PROBLEMS

5.1 through 5.9 Locate the centroid of the plane area shown.

Fig. P5.1

Fig. P5.2

Fig. P5.3

Fig. P5.4

Fig. P5.5

Fig. P5.6

Fig. P5.7

Fig. P5.8

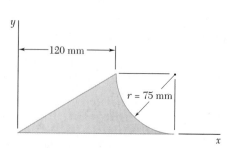

Fig. P5.9

5.10 through 5.15 Locate the centroid of the plane area shown.

Fig. P5.10

Fig. P5.11

Fig. P5.12

Fig. P5.13

Fig. P5.14

Fig. P5.15

5.16 Determine the x coordinate of the centroid of the trapezoid shown in terms of h_1, h_2, and a.

Fig. P5.16

5.17 For the plane area of Prob. 5.5, determine the ratio a/r so that the centroid of the area is located at point B.

5.18 Determine the y coordinate of the centroid of the shaded area in terms of r_1, r_2, and α.

Fig. P5.18 and P5.19

5.19 Show that as r_1 approaches r_2, the location of the centroid approaches that for an arc of circle of radius $(r_1 + r_2)/2$.

5.20 and 5.21 The horizontal x axis is drawn through the centroid C of the area shown, and it divides the area into two component areas A_1 and A_2. Determine the first moment of each component area with respect to the x axis, and explain the results obtained.

Fig. P5.20

Dimensions in mm

Fig. P5.21

5.22 A composite beam is constructed by bolting four plates to four $60 \times 60 \times 12$-mm angles as shown. The bolts are equally spaced along the beam, and the beam supports a vertical load. As proved in mechanics of materials, the shearing forces exerted on the bolts at A and B are proportional to the first moments with respect to the centroidal x axis of the red shaded areas shown, respectively, in parts a and b of the figure. Knowing that the force exerted on the bolt at A is 280 N, determine the force exerted on the bolt at B.

Fig. P5.22

5.23 The first moment of the shaded area with respect to the x axis is denoted by Q_x. (a) Express Q_x in terms of b, c, and the distance y from the base of the shaded area to the x axis. (b) For what value of y is Q_x maximum, and what is that maximum value?

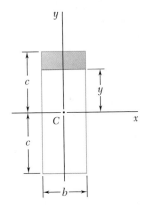

Fig. P5.23

5.24 through 5.27   A thin, homogeneous wire is bent to form the perimeter of the figure indicated. Locate the center of gravity of the wire figure thus formed.

    5.24   Fig. P5.2.
    5.25   Fig. P5.3.
    5.26   Fig. P5.4.
    5.27   Fig. P5.5.

5.28 The homogeneous wire $ABCD$ is bent as shown and is attached to a hinge at C. Determine the length L for which portion BCD of the wire is horizontal.

5.29 The homogeneous wire $ABCD$ is bent as shown and is attached to a hinge at C. Determine the length L for which portion AB of the wire is horizontal.

Fig. P5.28 and P5.29

5.30 The homogeneous wire ABC is bent into a semicircular arc and a straight section as shown and is attached to a hinge at A. Determine the value of θ for which the wire is in equilibrium for the indicated position.

Fig. P5.30

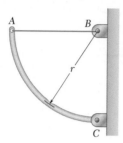

Fig. P5.31

5.31 A uniform circular rod of weight 8 lb and radius 10 in. is attached to a pin at C and to the cable AB. Determine (a) the tension in the cable, (b) the reaction at C.

5.32 Determine the distance h for which the centroid of the shaded area is as far above line BB' as possible when (a) $k = 0.10$, (b) $k = 0.80$.

Fig. P5.32 and P5.33

5.33 Knowing that the distance h has been selected to maximize the distance $\bar{y}$ from line BB' to the centroid of the shaded area, show that $\bar{y} = 2h/3$.

5.6 DETERMINATION OF CENTROIDS BY INTEGRATION

The centroid of an area bounded by analytical curves (i.e., curves defined by algebraic equations) is usually determined by evaluating the integrals in Eqs. (5.3) of Sec. 5.3:

$$\bar{x}A = \int x\, dA \qquad \bar{y}A = \int y\, dA \qquad (5.3)$$

If the element of area dA is a small rectangle of sides dx and dy, the evaluation of each of these integrals requires a *double integration* with respect to x and y. A double integration is also necessary if polar coordinates are used for which dA is a small element of sides dr and $r\, d\theta$.

   In most cases, however, it is possible to determine the coordinates of the centroid of an area by performing a single integration. This is achieved by choosing dA to be a thin rectangle or strip or a thin sector or pie-shaped element (Fig. 5.12); the centroid of the thin rectangle is located at its center, and the centroid of the thin sector is located at a distance $\frac{2}{3}r$ from its vertex (as it is for a triangle). The coordinates of the centroid of the area under consideration are then obtained by expressing that the first moment of the entire area with respect to each of the coordinate axes is equal to the sum (or integral) of the corresponding moments of the elements of area.

Denoting by $\bar{x}_{el}$ and $\bar{y}_{el}$ the coordinates of the centroid of the element dA, we write

$$Q_y = \bar{x}A = \int \bar{x}_{el}\,dA$$

$$Q_x = \bar{y}A = \int \bar{y}_{el}\,dA$$

(5.9)

If the area A is not already known, it can also be computed from these elements.

The coordinates $\bar{x}_{el}$ and $\bar{y}_{el}$ of the centroid of the element of area dA should be expressed in terms of the coordinates of a point located on the curve bounding the area under consideration. Also, the area of the element dA should be expressed in terms of the coordinates of that point and the appropriate differentials. This has been done in Fig. 5.12 for three common types of elements; the pie-shaped element of part c should be used when the equation of the curve bounding the area is given in polar coordinates. The appropriate expressions should be substituted into formulas (5.9), and the equation of the bounding curve should be used to express one of the coordinates in terms of the other. The integration is thus reduced to a single integration. Once the area has been determined and the integrals in Eqs. (5.9) have been evaluated, these equations can be solved for the coordinates $\bar{x}$ and $\bar{y}$ of the centroid of the area.

When a line is defined by an algebraic equation, its centroid can be determined by evaluating the integrals in Eqs. (5.4) of Sec. 5.3:

$$\bar{x}L = \int x\,dL \qquad \bar{y}L = \int y\,dL$$

(5.4)

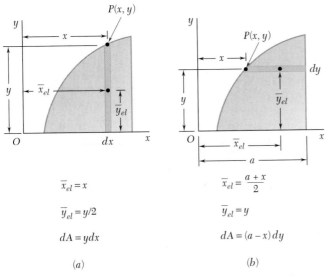

$$\bar{x}_{el} = x$$

$$\bar{y}_{el} = y/2$$

$$dA = y\,dx$$

(a)

$$\bar{x}_{el} = \frac{a+x}{2}$$

$$\bar{y}_{el} = y$$

$$dA = (a-x)\,dy$$

(b)

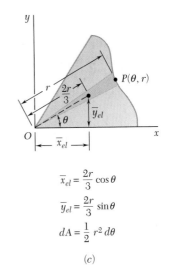

$$\bar{x}_{el} = \frac{2r}{3}\cos\theta$$

$$\bar{y}_{el} = \frac{2r}{3}\sin\theta$$

$$dA = \frac{1}{2}r^2\,d\theta$$

(c)

Fig. 5.12 Centroids and areas of differential elements.

The differential length dL should be replaced by one of the following expressions, depending upon which coordinate, x, y, or θ, is chosen as the independent variable in the equation used to define the line (these expressions can be derived using the Pythagorean theorem):

$$dL = \sqrt{1 + \left(\frac{dy}{dx}\right)^2}\,dx \qquad dL = \sqrt{1 + \left(\frac{dx}{dy}\right)^2}\,dy$$

$$dL = \sqrt{r^2 + \left(\frac{dr}{d\theta}\right)^2}\,d\theta$$

After the equation of the line has been used to express one of the coordinates in terms of the other, the integration can be performed, and Eqs. (5.4) can be solved for the coordinates $\bar{x}$ and $\bar{y}$ of the centroid of the line.

5.7 THEOREMS OF PAPPUS-GULDINUS

These theorems, which were first formulated by the Greek geometer Pappus during the third century A.D. and later restated by the Swiss mathematician Guldinus, or Guldin, (1577–1643) deal with surfaces and bodies of revolution.

A *surface of revolution* is a surface which can be generated by rotating a plane curve about a fixed axis. For example (Fig. 5.13), the

Photo 5.2 The storage tanks shown are all bodies of revolution. Thus, their surface areas and volumes can be determined using the theorems of Pappus-Guldinus.

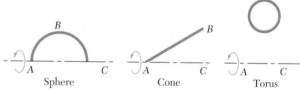

Fig. 5.13

surface of a sphere can be obtained by rotating a semicircular arc ABC about the diameter AC, the surface of a cone can be produced by rotating a straight line AB about an axis AC, and the surface of a torus or ring can be generated by rotating the circumference of a circle about a nonintersecting axis. A *body of revolution* is a body which can be generated by rotating a plane area about a fixed axis. As shown in Fig. 5.14, a sphere, a cone, and a torus can each be generated by rotating the appropriate shape about the indicated axis.

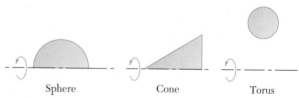

Fig. 5.14

THEOREM I. *The area of a surface of revolution is equal to the length of the generating curve times the distance traveled by the centroid of the curve while the surface is being generated.*

Proof. Consider an element dL of the line L (Fig. 5.15), which is revolved about the x axis. The area dA generated by the element

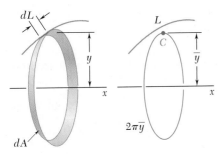

Fig. 5.15

dL is equal to $2\pi y\ dL$. Thus, the entire area generated by L is $A = \int 2\pi y\ dL$. Recalling that we found in Sec. 5.3 that the integral $\int y\ dL$ is equal to $\bar{y}L$, we therefore have

$$A = 2\pi\bar{y}L \tag{5.10}$$

where $2\pi\bar{y}$ is the distance traveled by the centroid of L (Fig. 5.15). It should be noted that the generating curve must not cross the axis about which it is rotated; if it did, the two sections on either side of the axis would generate areas having opposite signs, and the theorem would not apply.

THEOREM II. *The volume of a body of revolution is equal to the generating area times the distance traveled by the centroid of the area while the body is being generated.*

Proof. Consider an element dA of the area A which is revolved about the x axis (Fig. 5.16). The volume dV generated by the element dA is equal to $2\pi y\ dA$. Thus, the entire volume generated by A is $V = \int 2\pi y\ dA$, and since the integral $\int y\ dA$ is equal to $\bar{y}A$ (Sec. 5.3), we have

$$V = 2\pi\bar{y}A \tag{5.11}$$

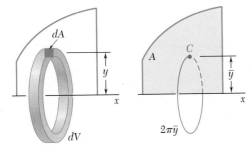

Fig. 5.16

where $2\pi\bar{y}$ is the distance traveled by the centroid of A. Again, it should be noted that the theorem does not apply if the axis of rotation intersects the generating area.

The theorems of Pappus-Guldinus offer a simple way to compute the areas of surfaces of revolution and the volumes of bodies of revolution. Conversely, they can also be used to determine the centroid of a plane curve when the area of the surface generated by the curve is known or to determine the centroid of a plane area when the volume of the body generated by the area is known (see Sample Prob. 5.8).

SAMPLE PROBLEM 5.4

Determine by direct integration the location of the centroid of a parabolic spandrel.

SOLUTION

Determination of the Constant k. The value of k is determined by substituting $x = a$ and $y = b$ into the given equation. We have $b = ka^2$ or $k = b/a^2$. The equation of the curve is thus

$$y = \frac{b}{a^2}x^2 \qquad \text{or} \qquad x = \frac{a}{b^{1/2}}y^{1/2}$$

Vertical Differential Element. We choose the differential element shown and find the total area of the figure.

$$A = \int dA = \int y\, dx = \int_0^a \frac{b}{a^2}x^2\, dx = \left[\frac{b}{a^2}\frac{x^3}{3}\right]_0^a = \frac{ab}{3}$$

The first moment of the differential element with respect to the y axis is $\bar{x}_{el}\, dA$; hence, the first moment of the entire area with respect to this axis is

$$Q_y = \int \bar{x}_{el}\, dA = \int xy\, dx = \int_0^a x\left(\frac{b}{a^2}x^2\right)dx = \left[\frac{b}{a^2}\frac{x^4}{4}\right]_0^a = \frac{a^2b}{4}$$

Since $Q_y = \bar{x}A$, we have

$$\bar{x}A = \int \bar{x}_{el}\, dA \qquad \bar{x}\frac{ab}{3} = \frac{a^2b}{4} \qquad \bar{x} = \tfrac{3}{4}a \quad \blacktriangleleft$$

Likewise, the first moment of the differential element with respect to the x axis is $\bar{y}_{el}\, dA$, and the first moment of the entire area is

$$Q_x = \int \bar{y}_{el}\, dA = \int \frac{y}{2}y\, dx = \int_0^a \frac{1}{2}\left(\frac{b}{a^2}x^2\right)^2 dx = \left[\frac{b^2}{2a^4}\frac{x^5}{5}\right]_0^a = \frac{ab^2}{10}$$

Since $Q_x = \bar{y}A$, we have

$$\bar{y}A = \int \bar{y}_{el}\, dA \qquad \bar{y}\frac{ab}{3} = \frac{ab^2}{10} \qquad \bar{y} = \tfrac{3}{10}b \quad \blacktriangleleft$$

Horizontal Differential Element. The same results can be obtained by considering a horizontal element. The first moments of the area are

$$Q_y = \int \bar{x}_{el}\, dA = \int \frac{a+x}{2}(a-x)\, dy = \int_0^b \frac{a^2 - x^2}{2}\, dy$$

$$= \frac{1}{2}\int_0^b \left(a^2 - \frac{a^2}{b}y\right)dy = \frac{a^2b}{4}$$

$$Q_x = \int \bar{y}_{el}\, dA = \int y(a-x)\, dy = \int y\left(a - \frac{a}{b^{1/2}}y^{1/2}\right)dy$$

$$= \int_0^b \left(ay - \frac{a}{b^{1/2}}y^{3/2}\right)dy = \frac{ab^2}{10}$$

To determine $\bar{x}$ and $\bar{y}$, the expressions obtained are again substituted into the equations defining the centroid of the area.

SAMPLE PROBLEM 5.5

Determine the location of the centroid of the arc of circle shown.

SOLUTION

Since the arc is symmetrical with respect to the x axis, $\bar{y} = 0$. A differential element is chosen as shown, and the length of the arc is determined by integration.

$$L = \int dL = \int_{-\alpha}^{\alpha} r \, d\theta = r \int_{-\alpha}^{\alpha} d\theta = 2r\alpha$$

The first moment of the arc with respect to the y axis is

$$Q_y = \int x \, dL = \int_{-\alpha}^{\alpha} (r \cos \theta)(r \, d\theta) = r^2 \int_{-\alpha}^{\alpha} \cos \theta \, d\theta$$
$$= r^2 [\sin \theta]_{-\alpha}^{\alpha} = 2r^2 \sin \alpha$$

Since $Q_y = \bar{x}L$, we write

$$\bar{x}(2r\alpha) = 2r^2 \sin \alpha \qquad \bar{x} = \frac{r \sin \alpha}{\alpha} \quad \blacktriangleleft$$

SAMPLE PROBLEM 5.6

Determine the area of the surface of revolution shown, which is obtained by rotating a quarter-circular arc about a vertical axis.

SOLUTION

According to Theorem I of Pappus-Guldinus, the area generated is equal to the product of the length of the arc and the distance traveled by its centroid. Referring to Fig. 5.8B, we have

$$\bar{x} = 2r - \frac{2r}{\pi} = 2r\left(1 - \frac{1}{\pi}\right)$$

$$A = 2\pi\bar{x}L = 2\pi\left[2r\left(1 - \frac{1}{\pi}\right)\right]\left(\frac{\pi r}{2}\right)$$

$$A = 2\pi r^2(\pi - 1) \quad \blacktriangleleft$$

SAMPLE PROBLEM 5.7

The outside diameter of a pulley is 0.8 m, and the cross section of its rim is as shown. Knowing that the pulley is made of steel and that the density of steel is $\rho = 7.85 \times 10^3$ kg/m³, determine the mass and the weight of the rim.

SOLUTION

The volume of the rim can be found by applying Theorem II of Pappus-Guldinus, which states that the volume equals the product of the given cross-sectional area and the distance traveled by its centroid in one complete revolution. However, the volume can be more easily determined if we observe that the cross section can be formed from rectangle I, whose area is positive, and rectangle II, whose area is negative.

	Area, mm²	$\bar{y}$, mm	Distance Traveled by C, mm	Volume, mm³
I	+5000	375	$2\pi(375) = 2356$	$(5000)(2356) = 11.78 \times 10^6$
II	−1800	365	$2\pi(365) = 2293$	$(-1800)(2293) = -4.13 \times 10^6$
				Volume of rim $= 7.65 \times 10^6$

Since 1 mm $= 10^{-3}$ m, we have 1 mm³ $= (10^{-3}$ m$)^3 = 10^{-9}$ m³, and we obtain $V = 7.65 \times 10^6$ mm³ $= (7.65 \times 10^6)(10^{-9}$ m³$) = 7.65 \times 10^{-3}$ m³.

$$m = \rho V = (7.85 \times 10^3 \text{ kg/m}^3)(7.65 \times 10^{-3} \text{ m}^3) \qquad m = 60.0 \text{ kg} \blacktriangleleft$$
$$W = mg = (60.0 \text{ kg})(9.81 \text{ m/s}^2) = 589 \text{ kg} \cdot \text{m/s}^2 \qquad W = 589 \text{ N} \blacktriangleleft$$

SAMPLE PROBLEM 5.8

Using the theorems of Pappus-Guldinus, determine (a) the centroid of a semicircular area, (b) the centroid of a semicircular arc. We recall that the volume and the surface area of a sphere are $\frac{4}{3}\pi r^3$ and $4\pi r^2$, respectively.

SOLUTION

The volume of a sphere is equal to the product of the area of a semicircle and the distance traveled by the centroid of the semicircle in one revolution about the x axis.

$$V = 2\pi\bar{y}A \qquad \tfrac{4}{3}\pi r^3 = 2\pi\bar{y}(\tfrac{1}{2}\pi r^2) \qquad \bar{y} = \frac{4r}{3\pi} \blacktriangleleft$$

Likewise, the area of a sphere is equal to the product of the length of the generating semicircle and the distance traveled by its centroid in one revolution.

$$A = 2\pi\bar{y}L \qquad 4\pi r^2 = 2\pi\bar{y}(\pi r) \qquad \bar{y} = \frac{2r}{\pi} \blacktriangleleft$$

SOLVING PROBLEMS ON YOUR OWN

In the problems for this lesson, you will use the equations

$$\bar{x}A = \int x\, dA \qquad \bar{y}A = \int y\, dA \tag{5.3}$$

$$\bar{x}L = \int x\, dL \qquad \bar{y}L = \int y\, dL \tag{5.4}$$

to locate the centroids of plane areas and lines, respectively. You will also apply the theorems of Pappus-Guldinus (Sec. 5.7) to determine the areas of surfaces of revolution and the volumes of bodies of revolution.

1. Determining by direct integration the centroids of areas and lines. When solving problems of this type, you should follow the method of solution shown in Sample Probs. 5.4 and 5.5: compute A or L, determine the first moments of the area or the line, and solve Eqs. (5.3) or (5.4) for the coordinates of the centroid. In addition, you should pay particular attention to the following points.

a. Begin your solution by carefully defining or determining each term in the applicable integral formulas. We strongly encourage you to show on your sketch of the given area or line your choice for dA or dL and the distances to its centroid.

b. As explained in Sec. 5.6, the x and the y in the above equations represent the *coordinates of the centroid* of the differential elements dA and dL. It is important to recognize that the coordinates of the centroid of dA are not equal to the coordinates of a point located on the curve bounding the area under consideration. You should carefully study Fig. 5.12 until you fully understand this important point.

c. To possibly simplify or minimize your computations, always examine the shape of the given area or line before defining the differential element that you will use. For example, sometimes it may be preferable to use horizontal rectangular elements instead of vertical ones. Also, it will usually be advantageous to use polar coordinates when a line or an area has circular symmetry.

d. Although most of the integrations in this lesson are straightforward, at times it may be necessary to use more advanced techniques, such as trigonometric substitution or integration by parts. Of course, using a table of integrals is the fastest method to evaluate difficult integrals.

2. Applying the theorems of Pappus-Guldinus. As shown in Sample Probs. 5.6 through 5.8, these simple, yet very useful theorems allow you to apply your knowledge of centroids to the computation of areas and volumes. Although the theorems refer to the distance traveled by the centroid and to the length of the generating curve or to the generating area, the resulting equations [Eqs. (5.10) and (5.11)] contain the products of these quantities, which are simply the first moments of a line ($\bar{y}L$) and an area ($\bar{y}A$), respectively. Thus, for those problems for which the generating line or area consists of more than one common shape, you need only determine $\bar{y}L$ or $\bar{y}A$; you do not have to calculate the length of the generating curve or the generating area.

PROBLEMS

5.34 through 5.36 Determine by direct integration the centroid of the area shown. Express your answer in terms of a and h.

Fig. P5.34

Fig. *P5.35*

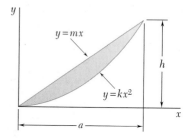

Fig. P5.36

5.37 through 5.39 Determine by direct integration the centroid of the area shown.

Fig. P5.37

Fig. P5.38

Fig. *P5.39*

5.40 and 5.41 Determine by direct integration the centroid of the area shown. Express your answer in terms of a and b.

Fig. P5.40

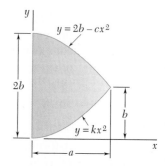

Fig. P5.41

5.42 Determine by direct integration the centroid of the area shown.

5.43 and 5.44 Determine by direct integration the centroid of the area shown. Express your answer in terms of a and b.

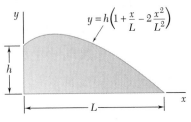

$$y = h\left(1 + \frac{x}{L} - 2\frac{x^2}{L^2}\right)$$

Fig. P5.42

$y = kx^2$

Fig. P5.43

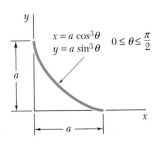

$x = ky^2$

Fig. P5.44

5.45 and 5.46 A homogeneous wire is bent into the shape shown. Determine by direct integration the x coordinate of its centroid.

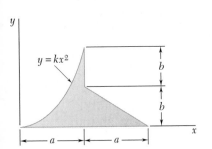

Fig. P5.45

$x = a \cos^3\theta$ $0 \le \theta \le \frac{\pi}{2}$
$y = a \sin^3\theta$

Fig. P5.46

*5.47 A homogeneous wire is bent into the shape shown. Determine by direct integration the x coordinate of its centroid. Express your answer in terms of a.

*5.48 and *5.49 Determine by direct integration the centroid of the area shown.

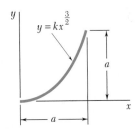

$y = kx^{\frac{3}{2}}$

Fig. P5.47

$y = a \sin\frac{\pi x}{L}$

Fig. P5.48

$r = a e^\theta$

Fig. P5.49

5.50 Determine the centroid of the area shown when $a = 2$ in.

5.51 Determine the value of a for which the ratio $\bar{x}/\bar{y}$ is 9.

5.52 Determine the volume and the surface area of the solid obtained by rotating the area of Prob. 5.1 about (a) the x axis, (b) the y axis.

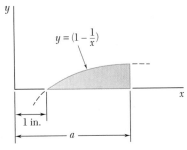

$y = \left(1 - \frac{1}{x}\right)$

Fig. P5.50 and P5.51

5.53 Determine the volume and the surface area of the solid obtained by rotating the area of Prob. 5.2 about (*a*) the line $y = 72$ mm, (*b*) the *x* axis.

5.54 Determine the volume and the surface area of the solid obtained by rotating the area of Prob. 5.8 about (*a*) the line $x = -60$ mm, (*b*) the line $y = 120$ mm.

5.55 Determine the volume of the solid generated by rotating the parabolic area shown about (*a*) the *x* axis, (*b*) the axis *AA'*.

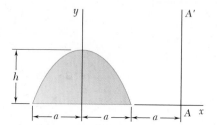

Fig. P5.55

5.56 Determine the volume and the surface area of the chain link shown, which is made from a 6-mm-diameter bar, if $R = 10$ mm and $L = 30$ mm.

Fig. P5.56

5.57 Verify that the expressions for the volumes of the first four shapes in Fig. 5.21 on page 260 are correct.

5.58 Determine the volume and weight of the solid brass knob shown, knowing that the specific weight of brass is 0.306 lb/in³.

5.59 Determine the total surface area of the solid brass knob shown.

1.25 in.

$r = 0.75$ in.

$r = 0.75$ in.

Fig. P5.58 and P5.59

5.60 The aluminum shade for the small high-intensity lamp shown has a uniform thickness of 1 mm. Knowing that the density of aluminum is 2800 kg/m³, determine the mass of the shade.

56 mm   32 mm   26 mm   66 mm

32 mm   28 mm

8 mm

Fig. P5.60

5.61 The escutcheon (a decorative plate placed on a pipe where the pipe exits from a wall) shown is cast from brass. Knowing that the density of brass is 8470 kg/m³, determine the mass of the escutcheon.

Fig. P5.61

5.62 A $\frac{3}{4}$-in.-diameter hole is drilled in a piece of 1-in.-thick steel; the hole is then countersunk as shown. Determine the volume of steel removed during the countersinking process.

Fig. P5.62

5.63 Knowing that two equal caps have been removed from a 10-in.-diameter wooden sphere, determine the total surface area of the remaining portion.

5.64 Determine the capacity, in liters, of the punch bowl shown if $R = 250$ mm.

Fig. P5.63

Fig. P5.64

*5.65 The shade for a wall-mounted light is formed from a thin sheet of translucent plastic. Determine the surface area of the outside of the shade, knowing that it has the parabolic cross section shown.

$y = kx^2$

Fig. P5.65

(a)

(b)

Fig. 5.17

*5.8 DISTRIBUTED LOADS ON BEAMS

The concept of the centroid of an area can be used to solve other problems besides those dealing with the weights of flat plates. Consider, for example, a beam supporting a *distributed load;* this load may consist of the weight of materials supported directly or indirectly by the beam, or it may be caused by wind or hydrostatic pressure. The distributed load can be represented by plotting the load w supported per unit length (Fig. 5.17); this load is expressed in N/m or in lb/ft. The magnitude of the force exerted on an element of beam of length dx is $dW = w\, dx$, and the total load supported by the beam is

$$W = \int_0^L w\, dx$$

We observe that the product $w\, dx$ is equal in magnitude to the element of area dA shown in Fig. 5.17a. The load W is thus equal in magnitude to the total area A under the load curve:

$$W = \int dA = A$$

We now determine where a *single concentrated load* $\mathbf{W}$, of the same magnitude W as the total distributed load, should be applied on the beam if it is to produce the same reactions at the supports (Fig. 5.17b). However, this concentrated load $\mathbf{W}$, which represents the resultant of the given distributed loading, is equivalent to the loading only when considering the free-body diagram of the entire beam. The point of application P of the equivalent concentrated load $\mathbf{W}$ is obtained by expressing that the moment of $\mathbf{W}$ about point O is equal to the sum of the moments of the elemental loads $d\mathbf{W}$ about O:

$$(OP)W = \int x\, dW$$

or, since $dW = w\, dx = dA$ and $W = A$,

$$(OP)A = \int_0^L x\, dA \tag{5.12}$$

Since the integral represents the first moment with respect to the w axis of the area under the load curve, it can be replaced by the product $\bar{x}A$. We therefore have $OP = \bar{x}$, where $\bar{x}$ is the distance from the w axis to the centroid C of the area A (this is *not* the centroid of the beam).

A *distributed load on a beam can thus be replaced by a concentrated load;* the magnitude of this single load is equal to the area under the load curve, and its line of action passes through the centroid of that area. It should be noted, however, that the concentrated load is equivalent to the given loading only as far as external forces are concerned. It can be used to determine reactions but should not be used to compute internal forces and deflections.

Photo 5.3 The roofs of the buildings shown must be able to support not only the total weight of the snow but also the nonsymmetric distributed loads resulting from drifting of the snow.

*5.9 FORCES ON SUBMERGED SURFACES

The approach used in the preceding section can be used to determine the resultant of the hydrostatic pressure forces exerted on a *rectangular surface* submerged in a liquid. Consider the rectangular plate shown in Fig. 5.18, which is of length L and width b, where b is measured perpendicular to the plane of the figure. As noted in Sec. 5.8, the load exerted on an element of the plate of length dx is $w\,dx$, where w is the load per unit length. However, this load can also be expressed as $p\,dA = pb\,dx$, where p is the gage pressure in the liquid† and b is the width of the plate; thus, $w = bp$. Since the gage pressure in a liquid is $p = \gamma h$, where γ is the specific weight of the liquid and h is the vertical distance from the free surface, it follows that

$$w = bp = b\gamma h \qquad (5.13)$$

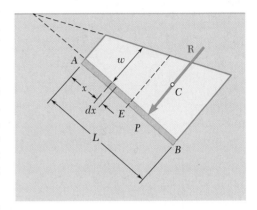

Fig. 5.18

which shows that the load per unit length w is proportional to h and, thus, varies linearly with x.

Recalling the results of Sec. 5.8, we observe that the resultant **R** of the hydrostatic forces exerted on one side of the plate is equal in magnitude to the trapezoidal area under the load curve and that its line of action passes through the centroid C of that area. The point P of the plate where **R** is applied is known as the *center of pressure*.‡

Next, we consider the forces exerted by a liquid on a curved surface of constant width (Fig. 5.19a). Since the determination of the resultant **R** of these forces by direct integration would not be easy, we consider the free body obtained by detaching the volume of liquid ABD bounded by the curved surface AB and by the two plane surfaces AD and DB shown in Fig. 5.19b. The forces acting on the free body ABD are the weight **W** of the detached volume of liquid, the resultant $\mathbf{R}_1$ of the forces exerted on AD, the resultant $\mathbf{R}_2$ of the forces exerted on BD, and the resultant $-\mathbf{R}$ of the forces exerted *by the curved surface on the liquid*. The resultant $-\mathbf{R}$ is equal and opposite to, and has the same line of action as, the resultant **R** of the forces exerted *by the liquid on the curved surface*. The forces **W**, $\mathbf{R}_1$, and $\mathbf{R}_2$ can be determined by standard methods; after their values have been found, the force $-\mathbf{R}$ is obtained by solving the equations of equilibrium for the free body of Fig. 5.19b. The resultant **R** of the hydrostatic forces exerted on the curved surface is then obtained by reversing the sense of $-\mathbf{R}$.

(a)

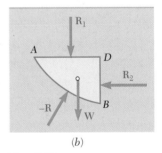

(b)

Fig. 5.19

The methods outlined in this section can be used to determine the resultant of the hydrostatic forces exerted on the surfaces of dams and rectangular gates and vanes. The resultants of forces on submerged surfaces of variable width will be determined in Chap. 9.

---

†The pressure p, which represents a load per unit area, is expressed in N/m² or in lb/ft². The derived SI unit N/m² is called a *pascal* (Pa).

‡Noting that the area under the load curve is equal to $w_E L$, where w_E is the load per unit length at the center E of the plate, and recalling Eq. (5.13), we can write

$$R = w_E L = (bp_E)L = p_E(bL) = p_E A$$

where A denotes the area of the *plate*. Thus, the magnitude of **R** can be obtained by multiplying the area of the plate by the pressure at its center E. The resultant **R**, however, *should be applied at P, not at E.*

$w_B = 4500$ N/m

$w_A = 1500$ N/m

A B

$L = 6$ m

SAMPLE PROBLEM 5.9

A beam supports a distributed load as shown. (*a*) Determine the equivalent concentrated load. (*b*) Determine the reactions at the supports.

$\bar{x} = 4$ m

II 4.5 kN/m

1.5 kN/m I

x

$\bar{x} = 2$ m

6 m

SOLUTION

a. Equivalent Concentrated Load. The magnitude of the resultant of the load is equal to the area under the load curve, and the line of action of the resultant passes through the centroid of the same area. We divide the area under the load curve into two triangles and construct the table below. To simplify the computations and tabulation, the given loads per unit length have been converted into kN/m.

Component	A, kN	$\bar{x}$, m	$\bar{x}A$, kN · m
Triangle I	4.5	2	9
Triangle II	13.5	4	54
	$\Sigma A = 18.0$		$\Sigma \bar{x}A = 63$

Thus, $\bar{X}\Sigma A = \Sigma \bar{x}A$: $\bar{X}(18$ kN$) = 63$ kN · m $\bar{X} = 3.5$ m

The equivalent concentrated load is

$$\mathbf{W} = 18 \text{ kN} \downarrow \quad \triangleleft$$

and its line of action is located at a distance

$$\bar{X} = 3.5 \text{ m to the right of } A \quad \triangleleft$$

18 kN

$\bar{X} = 3.5$ m

A B

b. Reactions. The reaction at A is vertical and is denoted by $\mathbf{A}$; the reaction at B is represented by its components $\mathbf{B}_x$ and $\mathbf{B}_y$. The given load can be considered to be the sum of two triangular loads as shown. The resultant of each triangular load is equal to the area of the triangle and acts at its centroid. We write the following equilibrium equations for the free body shown:

4.5 kN   13.5 kN

A

B_x

B_y

2 m

4 m

6 m

$\xrightarrow{+} \Sigma F_x = 0:$ $B_x = 0 \quad \triangleleft$

$+\uparrow \Sigma M_A = 0:$ $-(4.5$ kN$)(2$ m$) - (13.5$ kN$)(4$ m$) + B_y(6$ m$) = 0$

$$\mathbf{B}_y = 10.5 \text{ kN} \uparrow \quad \triangleleft$$

$+\uparrow \Sigma M_B = 0:$ $+(4.5$ kN$)(4$ m$) + (13.5$ kN$)(2$ m$) - A(6$ m$) = 0$

$$\mathbf{A} = 7.5 \text{ kN} \uparrow \quad \triangleleft$$

Alternative Solution. The given distributed load can be replaced by its resultant, which was found in part *a*. The reactions can be determined by writing the equilibrium equations $\Sigma F_x = 0$, $\Sigma M_A = 0$, and $\Sigma M_B = 0$. We again obtain

$$\mathbf{B}_x = 0 \quad \mathbf{B}_y = 10.5 \text{ kN} \uparrow \quad \mathbf{A} = 7.5 \text{ kN} \uparrow \quad \triangleleft$$

SAMPLE PROBLEM 5.10

The cross section of a concrete dam is as shown. Consider a 1-ft-thick section of the dam, and determine (a) the resultant of the reaction forces exerted by the ground on the base AB of the dam, (b) the resultant of the pressure forces exerted by the water on the face BC of the dam. The specific weights of concrete and water are 150 lb/ft³ and 62.4 lb/ft³, respectively.

SOLUTION

a. Ground Reaction. We choose as a free body the 1-ft-thick section *AEFCDB* of the dam and water. The reaction forces exerted by the ground on the base *AB* are represented by an equivalent force-couple system at *A*. Other forces acting on the free body are the weight of the dam, represented by the weights of its components $\mathbf{W}_1$, $\mathbf{W}_2$, and $\mathbf{W}_3$; the weight of the water $\mathbf{W}_4$; and the resultant $\mathbf{P}$ of the pressure forces exerted on section *BD* by the water to the right of section *BD*. We have

$$W_1 = \tfrac{1}{2}(9 \text{ ft})(22 \text{ ft})(1 \text{ ft})(150 \text{ lb/ft}^3) = 14{,}850 \text{ lb}$$
$$W_2 = (5 \text{ ft})(22 \text{ ft})(1 \text{ ft})(150 \text{ lb/ft}^3) = 16{,}500 \text{ lb}$$
$$W_3 = \tfrac{1}{3}(10 \text{ ft})(18 \text{ ft})(1 \text{ ft})(150 \text{ lb/ft}^3) = 9000 \text{ lb}$$
$$W_4 = \tfrac{2}{3}(10 \text{ ft})(18 \text{ ft})(1 \text{ ft})(62.4 \text{ lb/ft}^3) = 7488 \text{ lb}$$
$$P = \tfrac{1}{2}(18 \text{ ft})(1 \text{ ft})(18 \text{ ft})(62.4 \text{ lb/ft}^3) = 10{,}109 \text{ lb}$$

Equilibrium Equations

$$\xrightarrow{+}\Sigma F_x = 0: \qquad H - 10{,}109 \text{ lb} = 0 \qquad\qquad \mathbf{H} = 10{,}110 \text{ lb} \rightarrow \quad \blacktriangleleft$$

$$+\uparrow\Sigma F_y = 0: \qquad V - 14{,}850 \text{ lb} - 16{,}500 \text{ lb} - 9000 \text{ lb} - 7488 \text{ lb} = 0$$
$$\mathbf{V} = 47{,}840 \text{ lb} \uparrow \quad \blacktriangleleft$$

$$+\!\!\curvearrowleft \Sigma M_A = 0: \qquad -(14{,}850 \text{ lb})(6 \text{ ft}) - (16{,}500 \text{ lb})(11.5 \text{ ft})$$
$$- (9000 \text{ lb})(17 \text{ ft}) - (7488 \text{ lb})(20 \text{ ft}) + (10{,}109 \text{ lb})(6 \text{ ft}) + M = 0$$
$$\mathbf{M} = 520{,}960 \text{ lb} \cdot \text{ft} \curvearrowleft \quad \blacktriangleleft$$

We can replace the force-couple system obtained by a single force acting at a distance *d* to the right of *A*, where

$$d = \frac{520{,}960 \text{ lb} \cdot \text{ft}}{47{,}840 \text{ lb}} = 10.89 \text{ ft}$$

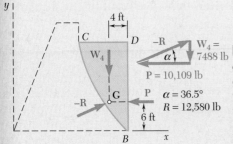

b. Resultant R of Water Forces. The parabolic section of water *BCD* is chosen as a free body. The forces involved are the resultant $-\mathbf{R}$ of the forces exerted by the dam on the water, the weight $\mathbf{W}_4$, and the force $\mathbf{P}$. Since these forces must be concurrent, $-\mathbf{R}$ passes through the point of intersection *G* of $\mathbf{W}_4$ and $\mathbf{P}$. A force triangle is drawn from which the magnitude and direction of $-\mathbf{R}$ are determined. The resultant $\mathbf{R}$ of the forces exerted by the water on the face *BC* is equal and opposite:

$$\mathbf{R} = 12{,}580 \text{ lb} \; \measuredangle\,36.5° \quad \blacktriangleleft$$

SOLVING PROBLEMS
ON YOUR OWN

The problems in this lesson involve two common and very important types of loading: distributed loads on beams and forces on submerged surfaces of constant width. As we discussed in Secs. 5.8 and 5.9 and illustrated in Sample Probs. 5.9 and 5.10, determining the single equivalent force for each of these loadings requires a knowledge of centroids.

1. Analyzing beams subjected to distributed loads. In Sec. 5.8, we showed that a distributed load on a beam can be replaced by a single equivalent force. The magnitude of this force is equal to the area under the distributed load curve and its line of action passes through the centroid of that area. Thus, you should begin your solution by replacing the various distributed loads on a given beam by their respective single equivalent forces. The reactions at the supports of the beam can then be determined by using the methods of Chap. 4.

When possible, complex distributed loads should be divided into the common-shape areas shown in Fig. 5.8A [Sample Prob. 5.9]. Each of these areas can then be replaced by a single equivalent force. If required, the system of equivalent forces can be reduced further to a single equivalent force. As you study Sample Prob. 5.9, note how we have used the analogy between force and area and the techniques for locating the centroid of a composite area to analyze a beam subjected to a distributed load.

2. Solving problems involving forces on submerged bodies. The following points and techniques should be remembered when solving problems of this type.

   a. The pressure p at a depth h below the free surface of a liquid is equal to γh or $\rho g h$, where γ and ρ are the specific weight and the density of the liquid, respectively. The load per unit length w acting on a submerged surface of constant width b is then

$$w = bp = b\gamma h = b\rho g h$$

   b. The line of action of the resultant force **R** acting on a submerged plane surface is perpendicular to the surface.

   c. For a vertical or inclined plane rectangular surface of width b, the loading on the surface can be represented by a linearly distributed load which is trapezoidal in shape (Fig. 5.18). Further, the magnitude of **R** is given by

$$R = \gamma h_E A$$

where h_E is the vertical distance to the center of the surface and A is the area of the surface.

d. The load curve will be triangular (rather than trapezoidal) when the top edge of a plane rectangular surface coincides with the free surface of the liquid, since the pressure of the liquid at the free surface is zero. For this case, the line of action of **R** is easily determined, for it passes through the centroid of a *triangular* distributed load.

e. For the general case, rather than analyzing a trapezoid, we suggest that you use the method indicated in part *b* of Sample Prob. 5.9. First divide the trapezoidal distributed load into two triangles, and then compute the magnitude of the resultant of each triangular load. (The magnitude is equal to the area of the triangle times the width of the plate.) Note that the line of action of each resultant force passes through the centroid of the corresponding triangle and that the sum of these forces is equivalent to **R**. Thus, rather than using **R**, you can use the two equivalent resultant forces, whose points of application are easily calculated. Of course, the equation given for R in paragraph *c* should be used when only the magnitude of **R** is needed.

f. When the submerged surface of constant width is curved, the resultant force acting on the surface is obtained by considering the equilibrium of the volume of liquid bounded by the curved surface and by horizontal and vertical planes (Fig. 5.19). Observe that the force $\mathbf{R_1}$ of Fig. 5.19 is equal to the weight of the liquid lying above the plane *AD*. The method of solution for problems involving curved surfaces is shown in part *b* of Sample Prob. 5.10.

In subsequent mechanics courses (in particular, mechanics of materials and fluid mechanics), you will have ample opportunity to use the ideas introduced in this lesson.

PROBLEMS

5.66 and 5.67 For the beam and loading shown, determine (*a*) the magnitude and location of the resultant of the distributed load, (*b*) the reactions at the beam supports.

Fig. P5.66

Fig. P5.67

5.68 through 5.73 Determine the reactions at the beam supports for the given loading.

Fig. P5.68

Fig. P5.69

Fig. *P5.70*

Fig. P5.71

Fig. P5.72

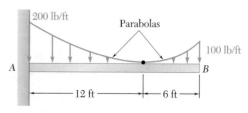

Fig. *P5.73*

5.74 Determine the reactions at the beam supports for the given loading when $w_0 = 400$ lb/ft.

Fig. P5.74 and P5.75

5.75 Determine (a) the distributed load w_0 at the end A of the beam ABC for which the reaction at C is zero, (b) the corresponding reaction at B.

5.76 Determine (a) the distance a so that the vertical reactions at supports A and B are equal, (b) the corresponding reactions at the supports.

5.77 Determine (a) the distance a so that the reaction at support B is minimum, (b) the corresponding reactions at the supports.

Fig. P5.76 and P5.77

5.78 A beam is subjected to a linearly distributed downward load and rests on two wide supports BC and DE, which exert uniformly distributed upward loads as shown. Determine the values of w_{BC} and w_{DE} corresponding to equilibrium when $w_A = 600$ N/m.

5.79 A beam is subjected to a linearly distributed downward load and rests on two wide supports BC and DE, which exert uniformly distributed upward loads as shown. Determine (a) the value of w_A so that $w_{BC} = w_{DE}$, (b) the corresponding values of w_{BC} and w_{DE}.

Fig. P5.78 and P5.79

In the following problems, use $\gamma = 62.4$ lb/ft^3 for the specific weight of fresh water and $\gamma_c = 150$ lb/ft^3 for the specific weight of concrete if U.S. customary units are used. With SI units, use $\rho = 10^3$ kg/m^3 for the density of fresh water and $\rho_c = 2.40 \times 10^3$ kg/m^3 for the density of concrete. (See the footnote on page 222 for how to determine the specific weight of a material given its density.)

5.80 and 5.81 The cross section of a concrete dam is as shown. For a 1-m-wide dam section determine (a) the resultant of the reaction forces exerted by the ground on the base AB of the dam, (b) the point of application of the resultant of part a, (c) the resultant of the pressure forces exerted by the water on the face BC of the dam.

Fig. P5.80

Fig. P5.81

Fig. P5.82 and P5.83

5.82 An automatic valve consists of a 9 × 9-in. square plate that is pivoted about a horizontal axis through *A* located at a distance *h* = 3.6 in. above the lower edge. Determine the depth of water *d* for which the valve will open.

5.83 An automatic valve consists of a 9 × 9-in. square plate that is pivoted about a horizontal axis through *A*. If the valve is to open when the depth of water is *d* = 18 in., determine the distance *h* from the bottom of the valve to the pivot *A*.

5.84 The 3 × 4-m side *AB* of a tank is hinged at its bottom *A* and is held in place by a thin rod *BC*. The maximum tensile force the rod can withstand without breaking is 200 kN, and the design specifications require the force in the rod not to exceed 20 percent of this value. If the tank is slowly filled with water, determine the maximum allowable depth of water *d* in the tank.

Fig. P5.84 and P5.85

5.85 The 3 × 4-m side of an open tank is hinged at its bottom *A* and is held in place by a thin rod *BC*. The tank is to be filled with glycerine, whose density is 1263 kg/m³. Determine the force **T** in the rod and the reactions at the hinge after the tank is filled to a depth of 2.9 m.

Fig. P5.86

5.86 The friction force between a 6 × 6-ft square sluice gate *AB* and its guides is equal to 10 percent of the resultant of the pressure forces exerted by the water on the face of the gate. Determine the initial force needed to lift the gate if it weighs 1000 lb.

5.87 A tank is divided into two sections by a 1 × 1-m square gate that is hinged at *A*. A couple of magnitude 490 N · m is required for the gate to rotate. If one side of the tank is filled with water at the rate of 0.1 m³/min and the other side is filled simultaneously with methyl alcohol (density ρ_{ma} = 789 kg/m³) at the rate of 0.2 m³/min, determine at what time and in which direction the gate will rotate.

Fig. P5.87

5.88 A prismatically shaped gate placed at the end of a freshwater channel is supported by a pin and bracket at A and rests on a frictionless support at B. The pin is located at a distance $h = 0.10$ m below the center of gravity C of the gate. Determine the depth of water d for which the gate will open.

5.89 A prismatically shaped gate placed at the end of a freshwater channel is supported by a pin and bracket at A and rests on a frictionless support at B. The pin is located at a distance h below the center of gravity C of the gate. Determine the distance h if the gate is to open when $d = 0.75$ m.

Fig. P5.88 and P5.89

5.90 The square gate AB is held in the position shown by hinges along its top edge A and by a shear pin at B. For a depth of water $d = 3.5$ ft, determine the force exerted on the gate by the shear pin.

5.91 A long trough is supported by a continuous hinge along its lower edge and by a series of horizontal cables attached to its upper edge. Determine the tension in each of the cables, at a time when the trough is completely full of water.

Fig. P5.90

Fig. P5.91

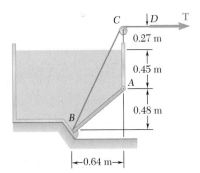

Fig. P5.92 and P5.93

5.92 A 0.5×0.8-m gate AB is located at the bottom of a tank filled with water. The gate is hinged along its top edge A and rests on a frictionless stop at B. Determine the reactions at A and B when cable BCD is slack.

5.93 A 0.5×0.8-m gate AB is located at the bottom of a tank filled with water. The gate is hinged along its top edge A and rests on a frictionless stop at B. Determine the minimum tension required in cable BCD to open the gate.

5.94 A 4×2-ft gate is hinged at A and is held in position by rod CD. End D rests against a spring whose constant is 828 lb/ft. The spring is undeformed when the gate is vertical. Assuming that the force exerted by rod CD on the gate remains horizontal, determine the minimum depth of water d for which the bottom B of the gate will move to the end of the cylindrical portion of the floor.

5.95 Solve Prob. 5.94 if the gate weighs 1000 lb.

Fig. P5.94

Photo 5.4 To predict the flight characteristics
of the modified Boeing 747 when used to
transport a space shuttle, the center of gravity of
each craft had to be determined.

VOLUMES

5.10 CENTER OF GRAVITY OF A THREE-DIMENSIONAL BODY. CENTROID OF A VOLUME

The *center of gravity* G of a three-dimensional body is obtained by
dividing the body into small elements and by then expressing that
the weight $\mathbf{W}$ of the body acting at G is equivalent to the system of
distributed forces $\Delta\mathbf{W}$ representing the weights of the small elements. Choosing the y axis to be vertical with positive sense upward
(Fig. 5.20) and denoting by $\bar{\mathbf{r}}$ the position vector of G, we write that

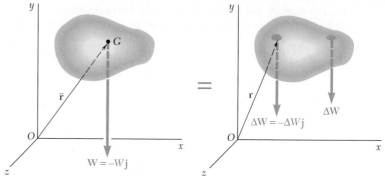

Fig. 5.20

$\mathbf{W}$ is equal to the sum of the elemental weights $\Delta\mathbf{W}$ and that its
moment about O is equal to the sum of the moments about O of
the elemental weights:

$$\Sigma\mathbf{F}: \qquad\qquad -W\mathbf{j} = \Sigma(-\Delta W\mathbf{j})$$
$$\Sigma\mathbf{M}_O: \qquad\qquad \bar{\mathbf{r}} \times (-W\mathbf{j}) = \Sigma[\mathbf{r} \times (-\Delta W\mathbf{j})] \qquad (5.14)$$

Rewriting the last equation in the form

$$\bar{\mathbf{r}}W \times (-\mathbf{j}) = (\Sigma\mathbf{r}\,\Delta W) \times (-\mathbf{j}) \qquad (5.15)$$

we observe that the weight $\mathbf{W}$ of the body is equivalent to the system
of the elemental weights $\Delta\mathbf{W}$ if the following conditions are satisfied:

$$W = \Sigma\,\Delta W \qquad \bar{\mathbf{r}}W = \Sigma\mathbf{r}\,\Delta W$$

Increasing the number of elements and simultaneously decreasing
the size of each element, we obtain in the limit

$$W = \int dW \qquad \bar{\mathbf{r}}W = \int \mathbf{r}\,dW \qquad (5.16)$$

We note that the relations obtained are independent of the orientation of the body. For example, if the body and the coordinate axes
were rotated so that the z axis pointed upward, the unit vector $-\mathbf{j}$
would be replaced by $-\mathbf{k}$ in Eqs. (5.14) and (5.15), but the relations
(5.16) would remain unchanged. Resolving the vectors $\bar{\mathbf{r}}$ and $\mathbf{r}$ into
rectangular components, we note that the second of the relations
(5.16) is equivalent to the three scalar equations

$$\bar{x}W = \int x\,dW \qquad \bar{y}W = \int y\,dW \qquad \bar{z}W = \int z\,dW \qquad (5.17)$$

If the body is made of a homogeneous material of specific weight γ, the magnitude dW of the weight of an infinitesimal element can be expressed in terms of the volume dV of the element, and the magnitude W of the total weight can be expressed in terms of the total volume V. We write

$$dW = \gamma \, dV \qquad W = \gamma V$$

Substituting for dW and W in the second of the relations (5.16), we write

$$\bar{\mathbf{r}}V = \int \mathbf{r} \, dV \tag{5.18}$$

or, in scalar form,

$$\bar{x}V = \int x \, dV \qquad \bar{y}V = \int y \, dV \qquad \bar{z}V = \int z \, dV \tag{5.19}$$

The point whose coordinates are $\bar{x}, \bar{y}, \bar{z}$ is also known as the *centroid C of the volume V* of the body. If the body is not homogeneous, Eqs. (5.19) cannot be used to determine the center of gravity of the body; however, Eqs. (5.19) still define the centroid of the volume.

The integral $\int x \, dV$ is known as the *first moment of the volume with respect to the yz plane*. Similarly, the integrals $\int y \, dV$ and $\int z \, dV$ define the first moments of the volume with respect to the zx plane and the xy plane, respectively. It is seen from Eqs. (5.19) that if the centroid of a volume is located in a coordinate plane, the first moment of the volume with respect to that plane is zero.

A volume is said to be symmetrical with respect to a given plane if for every point P of the volume there exists a point P' of the same volume, such that the line PP' is perpendicular to the given plane and is bisected by that plane. The plane is said to be a *plane of symmetry* for the given volume. When a volume V possesses a plane of symmetry, the first moment of V with respect to that plane is zero, and the centroid of the volume is located in the plane of symmetry. When a volume possesses two planes of symmetry, the centroid of the volume is located on the line of intersection of the two planes. Finally, when a volume possesses three planes of symmetry which intersect at a well-defined point (i.e., not along a common line), the point of intersection of the three planes coincides with the centroid of the volume. This property enables us to determine immediately the locations of the centroids of spheres, ellipsoids, cubes, rectangular parallelepipeds, etc.

The centroids of unsymmetrical volumes or of volumes possessing only one or two planes of symmetry should be determined by integration (Sec. 5.12). The centroids of several common volumes are shown in Fig. 5.21. It should be observed that in general the centroid of a volume of revolution *does not coincide* with the centroid of its cross section. Thus, the centroid of a hemisphere is different from that of a semicircular area, and the centroid of a cone is different from that of a triangle.

Shape		$\bar{x}$	Volume
Hemisphere		$\dfrac{3a}{8}$	$\dfrac{2}{3}\pi a^3$
Semiellipsoid of revolution		$\dfrac{3h}{8}$	$\dfrac{2}{3}\pi a^2 h$
Paraboloid of revolution		$\dfrac{h}{3}$	$\dfrac{1}{2}\pi a^2 h$
Cone		$\dfrac{h}{4}$	$\dfrac{1}{3}\pi a^2 h$
Pyramid		$\dfrac{h}{4}$	$\dfrac{1}{3}abh$

Fig. 5.21 Centroids of common shapes and volumes.

5.11 COMPOSITE BODIES

If a body can be divided into several of the common shapes shown in Fig. 5.21, its center of gravity G can be determined by expressing that the moment about O of its total weight is equal to the sum of the moments about O of the weights of the various component parts. Proceeding as in Sec. 5.10, we obtain the following equations defining the coordinates $\overline{X}, \overline{Y}, \overline{Z}$ of the center of gravity G.

$$\overline{X}\Sigma W = \Sigma \bar{x}W \quad \overline{Y}\Sigma W = \Sigma \bar{y}W \quad \overline{Z}\Sigma W = \Sigma \bar{z}W \qquad (5.20)$$

If the body is made of a homogeneous material, its center of gravity coincides with the centroid of its volume, and we obtain:

$$\overline{X}\Sigma V = \Sigma \bar{x}V \quad \overline{Y}\Sigma V = \Sigma \bar{y}V \quad \overline{Z}\Sigma V = \Sigma \bar{z}V \qquad (5.21)$$

5.12 DETERMINATION OF CENTROIDS OF VOLUMES BY INTEGRATION

The centroid of a volume bounded by analytical surfaces can be determined by evaluating the integrals given in Sec. 5.10:

$$\bar{x}V = \int x\,dV \quad \bar{y}V = \int y\,dV \quad \bar{z}V = \int z\,dV \qquad (5.22)$$

If the element of volume dV is chosen to be equal to a small cube of sides dx, dy, and dz, the evaluation of each of these integrals requires a *triple integration*. However, it is possible to determine the coordinates of the centroid of most volumes by *double integration* if dV is chosen to be equal to the volume of a thin filament (Fig. 5.22). The coordinates of the centroid of the volume are then obtained by rewriting Eqs. (5.22) as

$$\bar{x}V = \int \bar{x}_{el}\,dV \quad \bar{y}V = \int \bar{y}_{el}\,dV \quad \bar{z}V = \int \bar{z}_{el}\,dV \qquad (5.23)$$

and by then substituting the expressions given in Fig. 5.22 for the volume dV and the coordinates $\bar{x}_{el}, \bar{y}_{el}, \bar{z}_{el}$. By using the equation of the surface to express z in terms of x and y, the integration is reduced to a double integration in x and y.

If the volume under consideration possesses *two planes of symmetry*, its centroid must be located on the line of intersection of the two planes. Choosing the x axis to lie along this line, we have

$$\bar{y} = \bar{z} = 0$$

and the only coordinate to determine is $\bar{x}$. This can be done with a *single integration* by dividing the given volume into thin slabs parallel to the yz plane and expressing dV in terms of x and dx in the equation

$$\bar{x}V = \int \bar{x}_{el}\,dV \qquad (5.24)$$

For a body of revolution, the slabs are circular and their volume is given in Fig. 5.23.

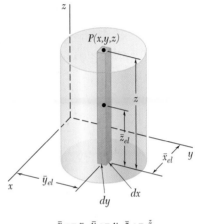

$\bar{x}_{el} = x, \; \bar{y}_{el} = y, \; \bar{z}_{el} = \frac{z}{2}$
$dV = z\,dx\,dy$

Fig. 5.22 Determination of the centroid of a volume by double integration.

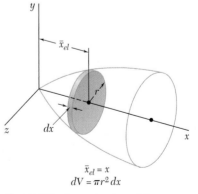

$\bar{x}_{el} = x$
$dV = \pi r^2\,dx$

Fig. 5.23 Determination of the centroid of a body of revolution.

SAMPLE PROBLEM 5.11

Determine the location of the center of gravity of the homogeneous body of revolution shown, which was obtained by joining a hemisphere and a cylinder and carving out a cone.

SOLUTION

Because of symmetry, the center of gravity lies on the x axis. As shown in the figure below, the body can be obtained by adding a hemisphere to a cylinder and then subtracting a cone. The volume and the abscissa of the centroid of each of these components are obtained from Fig. 5.21 and are entered in the table below. The total volume of the body and the first moment of its volume with respect to the yz plane are then determined.

Component	Volume, mm^3		$\bar{x}$, mm	$\bar{x}V$, mm^4
Hemisphere	$\dfrac{1}{2}\dfrac{4\pi}{3}(60)^3 =$	0.4524×10^6	-22.5	-10.18×10^6
Cylinder	$\pi(60)^2(100) =$	1.1310×10^6	$+50$	$+56.55 \times 10^6$
Cone	$-\dfrac{\pi}{3}(60)^2(100) =$	-0.3770×10^6	$+75$	-28.28×10^6
	$\Sigma V =$	1.206×10^6		$\Sigma\bar{x}V = +18.09 \times 10^6$

Thus,

$\overline{X}\Sigma V = \Sigma\bar{x}V$: $\qquad \overline{X}(1.206 \times 10^6 \text{ mm}^3) = 18.09 \times 10^6 \text{ mm}^4$

$$\overline{X} = 15 \text{ mm} \quad \blacktriangleleft$$

SAMPLE PROBLEM 5.12

Locate the center of gravity of the steel machine element shown. The diameter of each hole is 1 in.

SOLUTION

The machine element can be obtained by adding a rectangular parallelepiped (I) to a quarter cylinder (II) and then subtracting two 1-in.-diameter cylinders (III and IV). The volume and the coordinates of the centroid of each component are determined and are entered in the table below. Using the data in the table, we then determine the total volume and the moments of the volume with respect to each of the coordinate planes.

	V, in^3	$\bar{x}$, in.	$\bar{y}$, in.	$\bar{z}$, in.	$\bar{x}V$, in^4	$\bar{y}V$, in^4	$\bar{z}V$, in^4
I	$(4.5)(2)(0.5) = 4.5$	0.25	-1	2.25	1.125	-4.5	10.125
II	$\frac{1}{4}\pi(2)^2(0.5) = 1.571$	1.3488	-0.8488	0.25	2.119	-1.333	0.393
III	$-\pi(0.5)^2(0.5) = -0.3927$	0.25	-1	3.5	-0.098	0.393	-1.374
IV	$-\pi(0.5)^2(0.5) = -0.3927$	0.25	-1	1.5	-0.098	0.393	-0.589
	$\Sigma V = 5.286$				$\Sigma\bar{x}V = 3.048$	$\Sigma\bar{y}V = -5.047$	$\Sigma\bar{z}V = 8.555$

Thus,

$$\bar{X}\Sigma V = \Sigma\bar{x}V: \quad \bar{X}(5.286 \text{ in}^3) = 3.048 \text{ in}^4 \qquad \bar{X} = 0.577 \text{ in.} \blacktriangleleft$$

$$\bar{Y}\Sigma V = \Sigma\bar{y}V: \quad \bar{Y}(5.286 \text{ in}^3) = -5.047 \text{ in}^4 \qquad \bar{Y} = -0.955 \text{ in.} \blacktriangleleft$$

$$\bar{Z}\Sigma V = \Sigma\bar{z}V: \quad \bar{Z}(5.286 \text{ in}^3) = 8.555 \text{ in}^4 \qquad \bar{Z} = 1.618 \text{ in.} \blacktriangleleft$$

SAMPLE PROBLEM 5.13

Determine the location of the centroid of the half right circular cone shown.

SOLUTION

Since the xy plane is a plane of symmetry, the centroid lies in this plane and $\bar{z} = 0$. A slab of thickness dx is chosen as a differential element. The volume of this element is

$$dV = \tfrac{1}{2}\pi r^2\, dx$$

The coordinates $\bar{x}_{el}$ and $\bar{y}_{el}$ of the centroid of the element are obtained from Fig. 5.8 (semicircular area).

$$\bar{x}_{el} = x \qquad \bar{y}_{el} = \frac{4r}{3\pi}$$

We observe that r is proportional to x and write

$$\frac{r}{x} = \frac{a}{h} \qquad r = \frac{a}{h}x$$

The volume of the body is

$$V = \int dV = \int_0^h \tfrac{1}{2}\pi r^2\, dx = \int_0^h \tfrac{1}{2}\pi \left(\frac{a}{h}x\right)^2 dx = \frac{\pi a^2 h}{6}$$

The moment of the differential element with respect to the yz plane is $\bar{x}_{el}\, dV$; the total moment of the body with respect to this plane is

$$\int \bar{x}_{el}\, dV = \int_0^h x(\tfrac{1}{2}\pi r^2)\, dx = \int_0^h x(\tfrac{1}{2}\pi)\left(\frac{a}{h}x\right)^2 dx = \frac{\pi a^2 h^2}{8}$$

Thus,

$$\bar{x}V = \int \bar{x}_{el}\, dV \qquad \bar{x}\frac{\pi a^2 h}{6} = \frac{\pi a^2 h^2}{8} \qquad \bar{x} = \tfrac{3}{4}h \quad \blacktriangleleft$$

Likewise, the moment of the differential element with respect to the zx plane is $\bar{y}_{el}\, dV$; the total moment is

$$\int \bar{y}_{el}\, dV = \int_0^h \frac{4r}{3\pi}(\tfrac{1}{2}\pi r^2)\, dx = \frac{2}{3}\int_0^h \left(\frac{a}{h}x\right)^3 dx = \frac{a^3 h}{6}$$

Thus,

$$\bar{y}V = \int \bar{y}_{el}\, dV \qquad \bar{y}\frac{\pi a^2 h}{6} = \frac{a^3 h}{6} \qquad \bar{y} = \frac{a}{\pi} \quad \blacktriangleleft$$

SOLVING PROBLEMS ON YOUR OWN

In the problems for this lesson, you will be asked to locate the centers of gravity of three-dimensional bodies or the centroids of their volumes. All of the techniques we previously discussed for two-dimensional bodies—using symmetry, dividing the body into common shapes, choosing the most efficient differential element, etc.—may also be applied to the general three-dimensional case.

1. Locating the centers of gravity of composite bodies. In general, Eqs. (5.20) must be used:

$$\overline{X}\Sigma W = \Sigma\overline{x}W \qquad \overline{Y}\Sigma W = \Sigma\overline{y}W \qquad \overline{Z}\Sigma W = \Sigma\overline{z}W \qquad (5.20)$$

However, for the case of a *homogeneous body*, the center of gravity of the body coincides with the *centroid of its volume*. Therefore, for this special case, the center of gravity of the body can also be located using Eqs. (5.21):

$$\overline{X}\Sigma V = \Sigma\overline{x}V \qquad \overline{Y}\Sigma V = \Sigma\overline{y}V \qquad \overline{Z}\Sigma V = \Sigma\overline{z}V \qquad (5.21)$$

You should realize that these equations are simply an extension of the equations used for the two-dimensional problems considered earlier in the chapter. As the solutions of Sample Probs. 5.11 and 5.12 illustrate, the methods of solution for two- and three-dimensional problems are identical. Thus, we once again strongly encourage you to construct appropriate diagrams and tables when analyzing composite bodies. Also, as you study Sample Prob. 5.12, observe how the x and y coordinates of the centroid of the quarter cylinder were obtained using the equations for the centroid of a quarter circle.

We note that *two special cases* of interest occur when the given body consists of either uniform wires or uniform plates made of the same material.

    a. For a body made of *several wire elements* of the *same uniform cross section*, the cross-sectional area A of the wire elements will factor out of Eqs. (5.21) when V is replaced with the product AL, where L is the length of a given element. Equations (5.21) thus reduce in this case to

$$\overline{X}\Sigma L = \Sigma\overline{x}L \qquad \overline{Y}\Sigma L = \Sigma\overline{y}L \qquad \overline{Z}\Sigma L = \Sigma\overline{z}L$$

    b. For a body made of *several plates* of the *same uniform thickness*, the thickness t of the plates will factor out of Eqs. (5.21) when V is replaced with the product tA, where A is the area of a given plate. Equations (5.21) thus reduce in this case to

$$\overline{X}\Sigma A = \Sigma\overline{x}A \qquad \overline{Y}\Sigma A = \Sigma\overline{y}A \qquad \overline{Z}\Sigma A = \Sigma\overline{z}A$$

2. Locating the centroids of volumes by direct integration. As explained in Sec. 5.12, evaluating the integrals of Eqs. (5.22) can be simplified by choosing either a thin filament (Fig. 5.22) or a thin slab (Fig. 5.23) for the element of volume dV. Thus, you should begin your solution by identifying, if possible, the dV which produces the single or double integrals that are the easiest to compute. For bodies of revolution, this may be a thin slab (as in Sample Prob. 5.13) or a thin cylindrical shell. However, it is important to remember that the relationship that you establish among the variables (like the relationship between r and x in Sample Prob. 5.13) will directly affect the complexity of the integrals you will have to compute. Finally, we again remind you that $\overline{x}_{el}$, $\overline{y}_{el}$, and $\overline{z}_{el}$ in Eqs. (5.23) are the coordinates of the centroid of dV.

PROBLEMS

5.96 A hemisphere and a cone are attached as shown. Determine the location of the centroid of the composite body when (*a*) $h = 1.5a$, (*b*) $h = 2a$.

Fig. P5.96

5.97 Consider the composite body shown. Determine (*a*) the value of $\bar{x}$ when $h = L/2$, (*b*) the ratio h/L for which $\bar{x} = L$.

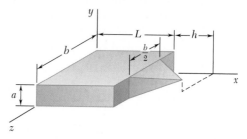

Fig. P5.97

5.98 Determine the *y* coordinate of the centroid of the body shown.

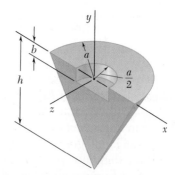

Fig. P5.98 and P5.99

5.99 Determine the *z* coordinate of the centroid of the body shown. (*Hint:* Use the result of Sample Prob. 5.13.)

5.100 and 5.101 For the machine element shown, locate the y coordinate of the center of gravity.

5.102 For the machine element shown, locate the x coordinate of the center of gravity.

5.103 For the machine element shown, locate the z coordinate of the center of gravity.

Fig. P5.100 and P5.103

Fig. P5.101 and *P5.102*

5.104 For the machine element shown, locate the x coordinate of the center of gravity.

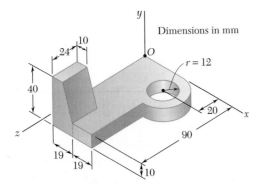

Fig. P5.104 and *P5.105*

5.105 For the machine element shown, locate the z coordinate of the center of gravity.

5.106 and 5.107   Locate the center of gravity of the sheet-metal form shown.

Fig. P5.106

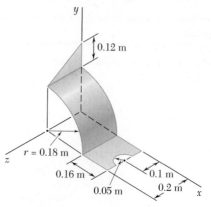

Fig. P5.107

5.108   A window awning is fabricated from sheet metal of uniform thickness. Locate the center of gravity of the awning.

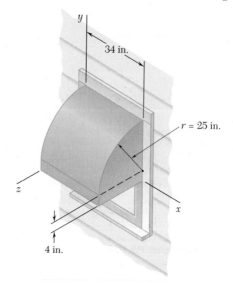

Fig. P5.108

5.109   A thin sheet of plastic of uniform thickness is bent to form a desk organizer. Locate the center of gravity of the organizer.

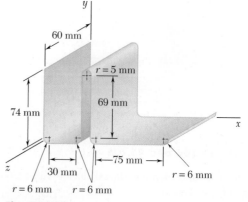

Fig. P5.109

5.110 A wastebasket, designed to fit in the corner of a room, is 16 in. high and has a base in the shape of a quarter circle of radius 10 in. Locate the center of gravity of the wastebasket, knowing that it is made of sheet metal of uniform thickness.

5.111 A mounting bracket for electronic components is formed from sheet metal of uniform thickness. Locate the center of gravity of the bracket.

Fig. P5.110

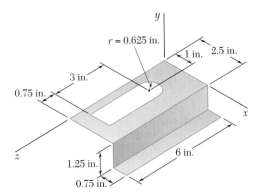

Fig. P5.111

5.112 An 8-in.-diameter cylindrical duct and a 4 × 8-in. rectangular duct are to be joined as indicated. Knowing that the ducts were fabricated from the same sheet metal, which is of uniform thickness, locate the center of gravity of the assembly.

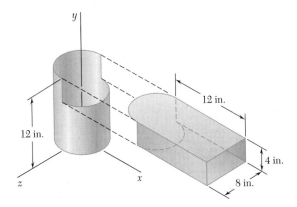

Fig. P5.112

5.113 An elbow for the duct of a ventilating system is made of sheet metal of uniform thickness. Locate the center of gravity of the elbow.

Fig. P5.113

5.114 and 5.115 Locate the center of gravity of the figure shown,
knowing that it is made of thin brass rods of uniform diameter.

Fig. P5.114

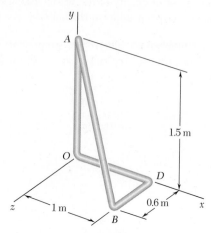

Fig. P5.115

5.116 A thin steel wire of uniform cross section is bent into the shape
shown. Locate its center of gravity.

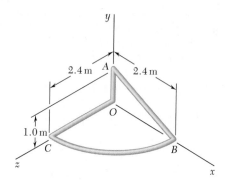

Fig. P5.116

5.117 The frame of a greenhouse is constructed from uniform aluminum
channels. Locate the center of gravity of the portion of the frame
shown.

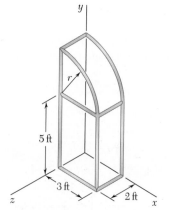

Fig. P5.117

5.118 Three brass plates are brazed to a steel pipe to form the flagpole base shown. Knowing that the pipe has a wall thickness of 8 mm and that each plate is 6 mm thick, determine the location of the center of gravity of the base. (Densities: brass = 8470 kg/m³; steel = 7860 kg/m³.)

5.119 A brass collar, of length 2.5 in., is mounted on an aluminum rod of length 4 in. Locate the center of gravity of the composite body. (Specific weights: brass = 0.306 lb/in³, aluminum = 0.101 lb/in³.)

Fig. P5.118

Fig. P5.119

5.120 A bronze bushing is mounted inside a steel sleeve. Knowing that the specific weight of bronze is 0.318 lb/in³ and of steel is 0.284 lb/in³, determine the location of the center of gravity of the assembly.

5.121 A scratch awl has a plastic handle and a steel blade and shank. Knowing that the density of plastic is 1030 kg/m³ and of steel is 7860 kg/m³, locate the center of gravity of the awl.

Fig. P5.120

Fig. P5.121

5.122 through 5.124 Determine by direct integration the values of $\bar{x}$ for the two volumes obtained by passing a vertical cutting plane through the given shape of Fig. 5.21. The cutting plane is parallel to the base of the given shape and divides the shape into two volumes of equal height.

    5.122 A hemisphere.
    5.123 A semiellipsoid of revolution.
    5.124 A paraboloid of revolution.

5.125 and 5.126 Locate the centroid of the volume obtained by rotating the shaded area about the x axis.

Fig. **P5.125**

Fig. **P5.126**

5.127 Locate the centroid of the volume obtained by rotating the shaded area about the line $x = h$.

Fig. **P5.127**

*5.128 Locate the centroid of the volume generated by revolving the portion of the sine curve shown about the x axis.

Fig. **P5.128 and P5.129**

*5.129 Locate the centroid of the volume generated by revolving the portion of the sine curve shown about the y axis. (*Hint:* Use a thin cylindrical shell of radius r and thickness dr as the element of volume.)

*5.130 Show that for a regular pyramid of height h and n sides ($n = 3$, 4, ...) the centroid of the volume of the pyramid is located at a distance $h/4$ above the base.

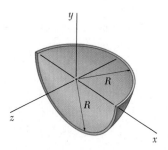

Fig. **P5.131**

5.131 Determine by direct integration the location of the centroid of one-half of a thin, uniform hemispherical shell of radius R.

5.132 The sides and the base of a punch bowl are of uniform thickness t. If $t \ll R$ and $R = 250$ mm, determine the location of the center of gravity of (a) the bowl, (b) the punch.

Fig. P5.132

5.133 Locate the centroid of the section shown, which was cut from a thin circular pipe by two oblique planes.

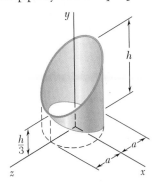

Fig. P5.133

*5.134 Locate the centroid of the section shown, which was cut from an elliptical cylinder by an oblique plane.

5.135 After grading a lot, a builder places four stakes to designate the corners of the slab for a house. To provide a firm, level base for the slab, the builder places a minimum of 3 in. of gravel beneath the slab. Determine the volume of gravel needed and the x coordinate of the centroid of the volume of the gravel. (*Hint:* The bottom surface of the gravel is an oblique plane, which can be represented by the equation $y = a + bx + cz$.)

Fig. P5.134

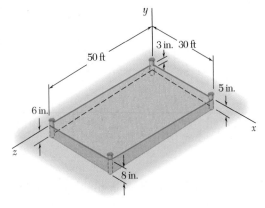

Fig. P5.135

5.136 Determine by direct integration the location of the centroid of the volume between the xz plane and the portion shown of the surface $y = 16h(ax - x^2)(bz - z^2)/a^2b^2$.

Fig. P5.136

This chapter was devoted chiefly to the determination of the *center of gravity* of a rigid body, i.e., to the determination of the point G where a single force $\mathbf{W}$, called the *weight* of the body, can be applied to represent the effect of the earth's attraction on the body.

Center of gravity of a two-dimensional body

In the first part of the chapter, we considered *two-dimensional bodies*, such as flat plates and wires contained in the xy plane. By adding force components in the vertical z direction and moments about the horizontal y and x axes [Sec. 5.2], we derived the relations

$$W = \int dW \qquad \bar{x}W = \int x\,dW \qquad \bar{y}W = \int y\,dW \qquad (5.2)$$

which define the weight of the body and the coordinates $\bar{x}$ and $\bar{y}$ of its center of gravity.

Centroid of an area or line

In the case of a *homogeneous flat plate of uniform thickness* [Sec. 5.3], the center of gravity G of the plate coincides with the *centroid C of the area A* of the plate, the coordinates of which are defined by the relations

$$\bar{x}A = \int x\,dA \qquad \bar{y}A = \int y\,dA \qquad (5.3)$$

Similarly, the determination of the center of gravity of a *homogeneous wire of uniform cross section* contained in a plane reduces to the determination of the *centroid C of the line L* representing the wire; we have

$$\bar{x}L = \int x\,dL \qquad \bar{y}L = \int y\,dL \qquad (5.4)$$

First moments

The integrals in Eqs. (5.3) are referred to as the *first moments* of the area A with respect to the y and x axes and are denoted by Q_y and Q_x, respectively [Sec. 5.4]. We have

$$Q_y = \bar{x}A \qquad Q_x = \bar{y}A \qquad (5.6)$$

The first moments of a line can be defined in a similar way.

Properties of symmetry

The determination of the centroid C of an area or line is simplified when the area or line possesses certain *properties of symmetry*. If the area or line is symmetric with respect to an axis, its centroid C

lies on that axis; if it is symmetric with respect to two axes, C is located at the intersection of the two axes; if it is symmetric with respect to a center O, C coincides with O.

The *areas and the centroids of various common shapes* are tabulated in Fig. 5.8. When a flat plate can be divided into several of these shapes, the coordinates $\overline{X}$ and $\overline{Y}$ of its center of gravity G can be determined from the coordinates $\overline{x}_1, \overline{x}_2, \ldots$ and $\overline{y}_1, \overline{y}_2, \ldots$ of the centers of gravity $G_1, G_2, \ldots$ of the various parts [Sec. 5.5]. Equating moments about the y and x axes, respectively (Fig. 5.24), we have

Center of gravity of a composite body

$$\overline{X}\Sigma W = \Sigma \overline{x}W \qquad \overline{Y}\Sigma W = \Sigma \overline{y}W \qquad (5.7)$$

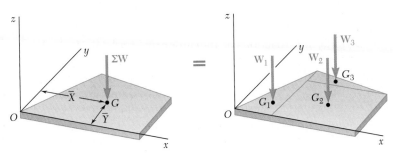

Fig. 5.24

If the plate is homogeneous and of uniform thickness, its center of gravity coincides with the centroid C of the area of the plate, and Eqs. (5.7) reduce to

$$Q_y = \overline{X}\Sigma A = \Sigma \overline{x}A \qquad Q_x = \overline{Y}\Sigma A = \Sigma \overline{y}A \qquad (5.8)$$

These equations yield the first moments of the composite area, or they can be solved for the coordinates $\overline{X}$ and $\overline{Y}$ of its centroid [Sample Prob. 5.1]. The determination of the center of gravity of a composite wire is carried out in a similar fashion [Sample Prob. 5.2].

When an area is bounded by analytical curves, the coordinates of its centroid can be determined by *integration* [Sec. 5.6]. This can be done by evaluating either the double integrals in Eqs. (5.3) or a *single integral* which uses one of the thin rectangular or pie-shaped elements of area shown in Fig. 5.12. Denoting by $\overline{x}_{el}$ and $\overline{y}_{el}$ the coordinates of the centroid of the element dA, we have

Determination of centroid by integration

$$Q_y = \overline{x}A = \int \overline{x}_{el}\, dA \qquad Q_x = \overline{y}A = \int \overline{y}_{el}\, dA \qquad (5.9)$$

It is advantageous to use the same element of area to compute both of the first moments Q_y and Q_x; the same element can also be used to determine the area A [Sample Prob. 5.4].

Theorems of Pappus-Guldinus

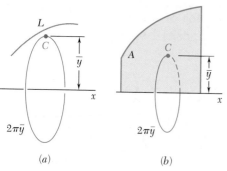

Fig. 5.25

The *theorems of Pappus-Guldinus* relate the determination of the area of a surface of revolution or the volume of a body of revolution to the determination of the centroid of the generating curve or area [Sec. 5.7]. The area A of the surface generated by rotating a curve of length L about a fixed axis (Fig. 5.25a) is

$$A = 2\pi\bar{y}L \qquad (5.10)$$

where $\bar{y}$ represents the distance from the centroid C of the curve to the fixed axis. Similarly, the volume V of the body generated by rotating an area A about a fixed axis (Fig. 5.25b) is

$$V = 2\pi\bar{y}A \qquad (5.11)$$

where $\bar{y}$ represents the distance from the centroid C of the area to the fixed axis.

Distributed loads

The concept of centroid of an area can also be used to solve problems other than those dealing with the weight of flat plates. For example, to determine the reactions at the supports of a beam [Sec. 5.8], we can replace a *distributed load* w by a concentrated load $\mathbf{W}$ equal in magnitude to the area A under the load curve and passing through the centroid C of that area (Fig. 5.26). The same approach can be used to determine the resultant of the hydrostatic forces exerted on a *rectangular plate submerged in a liquid* [Sec. 5.9].

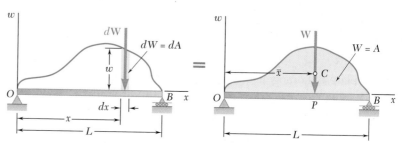

Fig. 5.26

Center of gravity of a three-dimensional body

The last part of the chapter was devoted to the determination of the *center of gravity* G of a three-dimensional body. The coordinates $\bar{x}$, $\bar{y}$, $\bar{z}$ of G were defined by the relations

$$\bar{x}W = \int x\, dW \qquad \bar{y}W = \int y\, dW \qquad \bar{z}W = \int z\, dW \qquad (5.17)$$

Centroid of a volume

In the case of a *homogeneous body*, the center of gravity G coincides with the *centroid C of the volume* V of the body; the coordinates of C are defined by the relations

$$\bar{x}V = \int x\, dV \qquad \bar{y}V = \int y\, dV \qquad \bar{z}V = \int z\, dV \qquad (5.19)$$

If the volume possesses a *plane of symmetry*, its centroid C will lie in that plane; if it possesses two planes of symmetry, C will be located on the line of intersection of the two planes; if it possesses three planes of symmetry which intersect at only one point, C will coincide with that point [Sec. 5.10].

The *volumes and centroids of various common three-dimensional shapes* are tabulated in Fig. 5.21. When a body can be divided into several of these shapes, the coordinates $\overline{X}, \overline{Y}, \overline{Z}$ of its center of gravity G can be determined from the corresponding coordinates of the centers of gravity of its various parts [Sec. 5.11]. We have

$$\overline{X}\Sigma W = \Sigma \overline{x}\, W \qquad \overline{Y}\Sigma W = \Sigma \overline{y}\, W \qquad \overline{Z}\Sigma W = \Sigma \overline{z}\, W \qquad (5.20)$$

If the body is made of a homogeneous material, its center of gravity coincides with the centroid C of its volume, and we write [Sample Probs. 5.11 and 5.12]

$$\overline{X}\Sigma V = \Sigma \overline{x}\, V \qquad \overline{Y}\Sigma V = \Sigma \overline{y}\, V \qquad \overline{Z}\Sigma V = \Sigma \overline{z}\, V \qquad (5.21)$$

When a volume is bounded by analytical surfaces, the coordinates of its centroid can be determined by *integration* [Sec. 5.12]. To avoid the computation of the triple integrals in Eqs. (5.19), we can use elements of volume in the shape of thin filaments, as shown in Fig. 5.27.

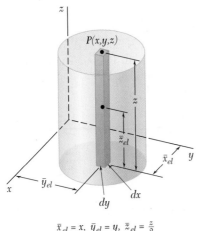

$$\overline{x}_{el} = x, \quad \overline{y}_{el} = y, \quad \overline{z}_{el} = \tfrac{z}{2}$$
$$dV = z\, dx\, dy$$

Fig. 5.27

Denoting by $\overline{x}_{el}$, $\overline{y}_{el}$, and $\overline{z}_{el}$ the coordinates of the centroid of the element dV, we rewrite Eqs. (5.19) as

$$\overline{x}V = \int \overline{x}_{el}\, dV \qquad \overline{y}V = \int \overline{y}_{el}\, dV \qquad \overline{z}V = \int \overline{z}_{el}\, dV \qquad (5.23)$$

which involve only double integrals. If the volume possesses *two planes of symmetry*, its centroid C is located on their line of intersection. Choosing the x axis to lie along that line and dividing the volume into thin slabs parallel to the yz plane, we can determine C from the relation

$$\overline{x}V = \int \overline{x}_{el}\, dV \qquad (5.24)$$

with a *single integration* [Sample Prob. 5.13]. For a body of revolution, these slabs are circular and their volume is given in Fig. 5.28.

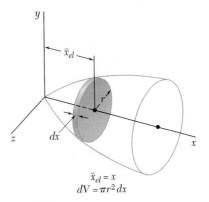

$$\overline{x}_{el} = x$$
$$dV = \pi r^2\, dx$$

Fig. 5.28

5.137 and 5.138 Locate the centroid of the plane area shown.

Fig. P5.137

Fig. P5.138

5.139 The frame for a sign is fabricated from thin, flat steel bar stock of mass per unit length 4.73 kg/m. The frame is supported by a pin at C and by a cable AB. Determine (*a*) the tension in the cable, (*b*) the reaction at C.

Fig. P5.139

5.140 Determine by direct integration the centroid of the area shown. Express your answer in terms of a and h.

5.141 Determine by direct integration the centroid of the area shown.

Fig. P5.140

Fig. P5.141

5.142 Three different drive belt profiles are to be studied. If at any given time each belt makes contact with one-half of the circumference of its pulley, determine the *contact area* between the belt and the pulley for each design.

(a)   (b)   (c)

Fig. P5.142

5.143 Determine the reactions at the beam supports for the given loading.

5.144 The beam *AB* supports two concentrated loads and rests on soil that exerts a linearly distributed upward load as shown. Determine the values of w_A and w_B corresponding to equilibrium.

5.145 The base of a dam for a lake is designed to resist up to 120 percent of the horizontal force of the water. After construction, it is found that silt (that is equivalent to a liquid of density $\rho_s = 1.76 \times 10^3$ kg/m³) is settling on the lake bottom at the rate of 12 mm/year. Considering a 1-m-wide section of dam, determine the number of years until the dam becomes unsafe.

Fig. P5.145

5.146 Determine the location of the centroid of the composite body shown when (a) $h = 2b$, (b) $h = 2.5b$.

5.147 Locate the center of gravity of the sheet-metal form shown.

5.148 Locate the centroid of the volume obtained by rotating the shaded area about the x axis.

Fig. P5.148

Fig. P5.143

Fig. P5.144

Fig. P5.146

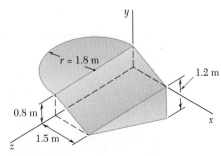

Fig. P5.147

COMPUTER PROBLEMS

5.C1 A beam is to carry a series of uniform and uniformly varying distributed loads as shown in part a of the figure. Divide the area under each portion of the load curve into two triangles (see Sample Prob. 5.9), and then write a computer program that can be used to calculate the reactions at A and B. Use this program to calculate the reactions at the supports for the beams shown in parts b and c of the figure.

(a)

(b)

(c)

Fig. P5.C1

5.C2 The three-dimensional structure shown is fabricated from five thin steel rods of equal diameter. Write a computer program that can be used to calculate the coordinates of the center of gravity of the structure. Use this program to locate the center of gravity when (a) $h = 12$ m, $R = 5$ m, $\alpha = 90°$; (b) $h = 570$ mm, $R = 760$ mm, $\alpha = 30°$; (c) $h = 21$ m, $R = 20$ m, $\alpha = 135°$.

Fig. P5.C2

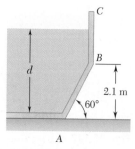

Fig. P5.C3

5.C3 An open tank is to be slowly filled with water. (The density of water is 10^3 kg/m^3.) Write a computer program that can be used to determine the resultant of the pressure forces exerted by the water on a 1-m-wide section of side ABC of the tank. Determine the resultant of the pressure forces for values of d from 0 to 3 m using 0.25-m increments.

5.C4 Approximate the curve shown using 10 straight-line segments, and then write a computer program that can be used to determine the location of the centroid of the curve. Use this program to determine the location of the centroid when (a) $a = 1$ in., $L = 11$ in., $h = 2$ in.; (b) $a = 2$ in., $L = 17$ in., $h = 4$ in.; (c) $a = 5$ in., $L = 12$ in., $h = 1$ in.

5.C5 Approximate the general spandrel shown using a series of n rectangles, each of width Δa and of the form $bcc'b'$, and then write a computer program that can be used to calculate the coordinates of the centroid of the area. Use this program to locate the centroid when (a) $m = 2$, $a = 80$ mm, $h = 80$ mm; (b) $m = 2$, $a = 80$ mm, $h = 500$ mm; (c) $m = 5$, $a = 80$ mm, $h = 80$ mm; (d) $m = 5$, $a = 80$ mm, $h = 500$ mm. In each case, compare the answers obtained to the exact values of $\bar{x}$ and $\bar{y}$ computed from the formulas given in Fig. 5.8A and determine the percentage error.

Fig. P5.C4

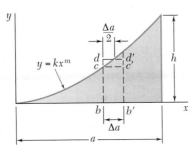

Fig. P5.C5

5.C6 Solve Prob. 5.C5, using rectangles of the form $bdd'b'$.

*__5.C7__ A farmer asks a group of engineering students to determine the volume of water in a small pond. Using cord, the students first establish a 2×2-ft grid across the pond and then record the depth of the water, in feet, at each intersection point of the grid (see the accompanying table). Write a computer program that can be used to determine (a) the volume of water in the pond, (b) the location of the center of gravity of the water. Approximate the depth of each 2×2-ft element of water using the average of the water depths at the four corners of the element.

		Cord								
	1	2	3	4	5	6	7	8	9	10
1	...	...	...	...	0	0	0	...	...	...
2	...	...	0	0	0	1	0	0	0	...
3	...	0	0	1	3	3	3	1	0	0
4	0	0	1	3	6	6	6	3	1	0
5	0	1	3	6	8	8	6	3	1	0
6	0	1	3	6	8	7	7	3	0	0
7	0	3	4	6	6	6	4	1	0	...
8	0	3	3	3	3	3	1	0	0	...
9	0	0	0	1	1	0	0	0	...	...
10	...	...	0	0	0	0	...	...	...	...

(Cord — left axis label for rows)

Trusses, such as this Pratt-style cantilever arch bridge in New York State, provide both a practical and an economical solution to many engineering problems.

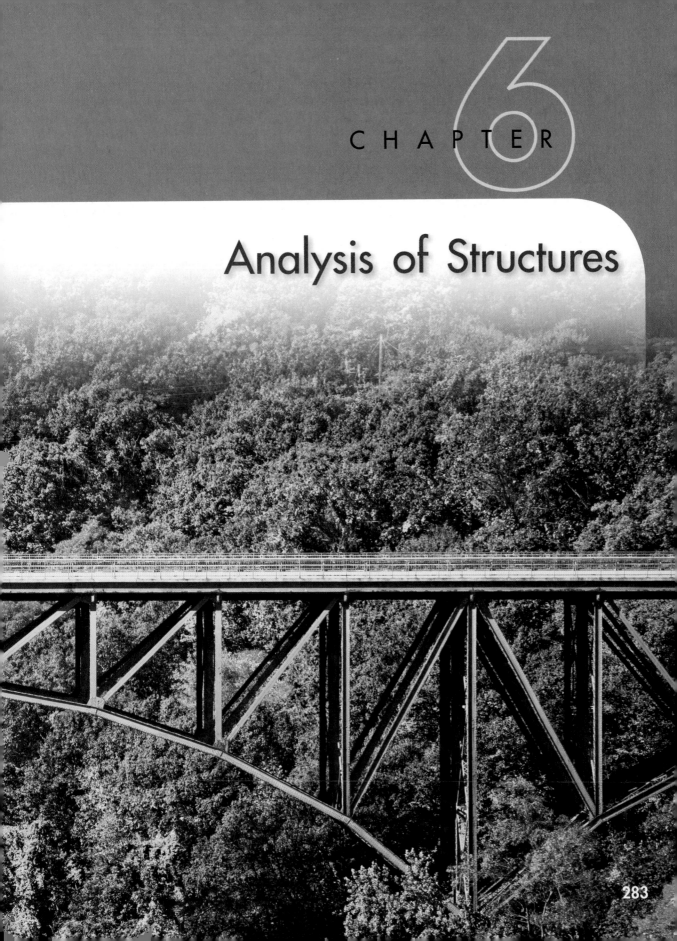

CHAPTER

6

Analysis of Structures

6.1　INTRODUCTION

The problems considered in the preceding chapters concerned the equilibrium of a single rigid body, and all forces involved were external to the rigid body. We now consider problems dealing with the equilibrium of structures made of several connected parts. These problems call for the determination not only of the external forces acting on the structure but also of the forces which hold together the various parts of the structure. From the point of view of the structure as a whole, these forces are *internal forces*.

Consider, for example, the crane shown in Fig. 6.1*a*, which carries a load W. The crane consists of three beams *AD*, *CF*, and *BE* connected by frictionless pins; it is supported by a pin at *A* and by a cable *DG*. The free-body diagram of the crane has been drawn in Fig. 6.1*b*. The external forces, which are shown in the diagram, include the weight **W**, the two components $\mathbf{A}_x$ and $\mathbf{A}_y$ of the reaction at *A*, and the force **T** exerted by the cable at *D*. The internal forces holding the various parts of the crane together do not appear in the diagram. If, however, the crane is dismembered and if a free-body diagram is drawn for each of its component parts, the forces holding the three beams together will also be represented, since these forces are external forces from the point of view of each component part (Fig. 6.1*c*).

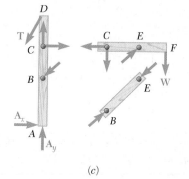

(a)　　　　(b)　　　　(c)

Fig. 6.1

It will be noted that the force exerted at *B* by member *BE* on member *AD* has been represented as equal and opposite to the force exerted at the same point by member *AD* on member *BE*; the force exerted at *E* by *BE* on *CF* is shown equal and opposite to the force exerted by *CF* on *BE*; and the components of the force exerted at *C* by *CF* on *AD* are shown equal and opposite to the components of the force exerted by *AD* on *CF*. This is in conformity with Newton's third law, which states that *the forces of action and reaction between bodies in contact have the same magnitude, same line of action, and opposite sense.* As pointed out in Chap. 1, this law, which is based on experimental evidence, is one of the six fundamental principles of elementary mechanics, and its application is essential to the solution of problems involving connected bodies.

In this chapter, three broad categories of engineering structures will be considered:

1. *Trusses,* which are designed to support loads and are usually stationary, fully constrained structures. Trusses consist exclusively of straight members connected at joints located at the ends of each member. Members of a truss, therefore, are *two-force members,* i.e., members acted upon by two equal and opposite forces directed along the member.

2. *Frames,* which are also designed to support loads and are also usually stationary, fully constrained structures. However, like the crane of Fig. 6.1, frames always contain at least one *multiforce member,* i.e., a member acted upon by three or more forces which, in general, are not directed along the member.

3. *Machines,* which are designed to transmit and modify forces and are structures containing moving parts. Machines, like frames, always contain at least one multiforce member.

Photo 6.1 Shown is a pin-jointed connection on the approach span to the San Francisco–Oakland Bay Bridge.

TRUSSES

6.2 DEFINITION OF A TRUSS

The truss is one of the major types of engineering structures. It provides both a practical and an economical solution to many engineering situations, especially in the design of bridges and buildings. A typical truss is shown in Fig. 6.2a. A truss consists of straight members connected at joints. Truss members are connected at their extremities only; thus no member is continuous through a joint. In Fig. 6.2a, for example, there is no member AB; there are instead two distinct members AD and DB. Most actual structures are made of several trusses joined together to form a space framework. Each truss is designed to carry those loads which act in its plane and thus may be treated as a two-dimensional structure.

In general, the members of a truss are slender and can support little lateral load; all loads, therefore, must be applied to the various joints, and not to the members themselves. When a concentrated load is to be applied between two joints, or when a distributed load is to be supported by the truss, as in the case of a bridge truss, a floor system must be provided which, through the use of stringers and floor beams, transmits the load to the joints (Fig. 6.3).

The weights of the members of the truss are also assumed to be applied to the joints, half of the weight of each member being applied to each of the two joints the member connects. Although the members are actually joined together by means of welded, bolted, or riveted connections, it is customary to assume that the members are pinned together; therefore, the forces acting at each end of a member reduce to a single force and no couple. Thus, the only forces assumed to be applied to a truss member are a single

Fig. 6.2

Fig. 6.3

(a)　　　(b)

Fig. 6.4

force at each end of the member. Each member can then be treated as a two-force member, and the entire truss can be considered as a group of pins and two-force members (Fig. 6.2b). An individual member can be acted upon as shown in either of the two sketches of Fig. 6.4. In Fig. 6.4a, the forces tend to pull the member apart, and the member is in tension; in Fig. 6.4b, the forces tend to compress the member, and the member is in compression. A number of typical trusses are shown in Fig. 6.5.

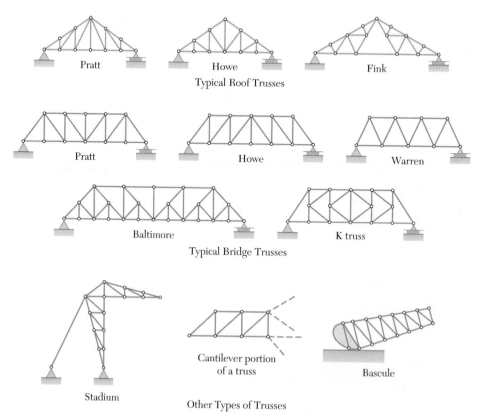

Pratt　　　Howe　　　Fink

Typical Roof Trusses

Pratt　　　Howe　　　Warren

Baltimore　　　K truss

Typical Bridge Trusses

Stadium

Cantilever portion
of a truss

Bascule

Other Types of Trusses

Fig. 6.5

6.3 SIMPLE TRUSSES

Consider the truss of Fig. 6.6*a*, which is made of four members connected by pins at *A*, *B*, *C*, and *D*. If a load is applied at *B*, the truss will greatly deform, completely losing its original shape. In contrast, the truss of Fig. 6.6*b*, which is made of three members connected by pins at *A*, *B*, and *C*, will deform only slightly under a load applied at *B*. The only possible deformation for this truss is one involving small changes in the length of its members. The truss of Fig. 6.6*b* is said to be a *rigid truss*, the term rigid being used here to indicate that the truss *will not collapse*.

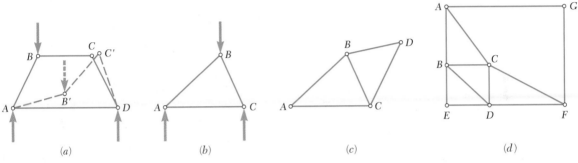

(a)   (b)   (c)   (d)

Fig. 6.6

As shown in Fig. 6.6*c*, a larger rigid truss can be obtained by adding two members *BD* and *CD* to the basic triangular truss of Fig. 6.6*b*. This procedure can be repeated as many times as desired, and the resulting truss will be rigid if each time two new members are added, they are attached to two existing joints and connected at a new joint.† A truss which can be constructed in this manner is called a *simple truss*.

It should be noted that a simple truss is not necessarily made only of triangles. The truss of Fig. 6.6*d*, for example, is a simple truss which was constructed from triangle *ABC* by adding successively the joints *D*, *E*, *F*, and *G*. On the other hand, rigid trusses are not always simple trusses, even when they appear to be made of triangles. The Fink and Baltimore trusses shown in Fig. 6.5, for instance, are not simple trusses, since they cannot be constructed from a single triangle in the manner described above. All the other trusses shown in Fig. 6.5 are simple trusses, as may be easily checked. (For the K truss, start with one of the central triangles.)

Returning to Fig. 6.6, we note that the basic triangular truss of Fig. 6.6*b* has three members and three joints. The truss of Fig. 6.6*c* has two more members and one more joint, i.e., five members and four joints altogether. Observing that every time two new members are added, the number of joints is increased by one, we find that in a simple truss the total number of members is $m = 2n - 3$, where n is the total number of joints.

Photo 6.2 Two K trusses were used as the main components of the movable bridge shown which moved above a large stockpile of ore. The bucket below the trusses picked up ore and redeposited it until the ore was thoroughly mixed. The ore was then sent to the mill for processing into steel.

†The three joints must not be in a straight line.

(a)

(b)

Fig. 6.7

Photo 6.3 Because roof trusses, such as those shown, require support only at their ends, it is possible to construct buildings with large, unobstructed floor areas.

6.4 ANALYSIS OF TRUSSES BY THE METHOD OF JOINTS

We saw in Sec. 6.2 that a truss can be considered as a group of pins and two-force members. The truss of Fig. 6.2, whose free-body diagram is shown in Fig. 6.7a, can thus be dismembered, and a free-body diagram can be drawn for each pin and each member (Fig. 6.7b). Each member is acted upon by two forces, one at each end; these forces have the same magnitude, same line of action, and opposite sense (Sec. 4.6). Furthermore, Newton's third law indicates that the forces of action and reaction between a member and a pin are equal and opposite. Therefore, the forces exerted by a member on the two pins it connects must be directed along that member and be equal and opposite. The common magnitude of the forces exerted by a member on the two pins it connects is commonly referred to as the *force in the member* considered, even though this quantity is actually a scalar. Since the lines of action of all the internal forces in a truss are known, the analysis of a truss reduces to computing the forces in its various members and to determining whether each of its members is in tension or in compression.

Since the entire truss is in equilibrium, each pin must be in equilibrium. The fact that a pin is in equilibrium can be expressed by drawing its free-body diagram and writing two equilibrium equations (Sec. 2.9). If the truss contains n pins, there will, therefore, be $2n$ equations available, which can be solved for $2n$ unknowns. In the case of a simple truss, we have $m = 2n - 3$, that is, $2n = m + 3$, and the number of unknowns which can be determined from the free-body diagrams of the pins is thus $m + 3$. This means that the forces in all the members, the two components of the reaction $\mathbf{R}_A$, and the reaction $\mathbf{R}_B$ can be found by considering the free-body diagrams of the pins.

The fact that the entire truss is a rigid body in equilibrium can be used to write three more equations involving the forces shown in the free-body diagram of Fig. 6.7a. Since they do not contain any new information, these equations are not independent of the equations associated with the free-body diagrams of the pins. Nevertheless, they can be used to determine the components of the reactions at the supports. The arrangement of pins and members in a simple truss is such that it will then always be possible to find a joint involving only two unknown forces. These forces can be determined by the methods of Sec. 2.11 and their values transferred to the adjacent joints and treated as known quantities at these joints. This procedure can be repeated until all unknown forces have been determined.

As an example, the truss of Fig. 6.7 will be analyzed by considering the equilibrium of each pin successively, starting with a joint at which only two forces are unknown. In the truss considered, all pins are subjected to at least three unknown forces. Therefore, the reactions at the supports must first be determined by considering the entire truss as a free body and using the equations of equilibrium of a rigid body. We find in this way that $\mathbf{R}_A$ is vertical and determine the magnitudes of $\mathbf{R}_A$ and $\mathbf{R}_B$.

The number of unknown forces at joint A is thus reduced to two, and these forces can be determined by considering the equilibrium of pin A. The reaction $\mathbf{R}_A$ and the forces $\mathbf{F}_{AC}$ and $\mathbf{F}_{AD}$ exerted on pin A by members AC and AD, respectively, must form a force triangle. First we draw $\mathbf{R}_A$ (Fig. 6.8); noting that $\mathbf{F}_{AC}$ and $\mathbf{F}_{AD}$ are directed along AC and AD, respectively, we complete the triangle and determine the magnitude and sense of $\mathbf{F}_{AC}$ and $\mathbf{F}_{AD}$. The magnitudes F_{AC} and F_{AD} represent the forces in members AC and AD. Since $\mathbf{F}_{AC}$ is directed down and to the left, that is, *toward* joint A, member AC pushes on pin A and is in compression. Since $\mathbf{F}_{AD}$ is directed *away* from joint A, member AD pulls on pin A and is in tension.

	Free-body diagram	Force polygon
Joint A		
Joint D		
Joint C		
Joint B		

Fig. 6.8

We can now proceed to joint D, where only two forces, $\mathbf{F}_{DC}$ and $\mathbf{F}_{DB}$, are still unknown. The other forces are the load $\mathbf{P}$, which is given, and the force $\mathbf{F}_{DA}$ exerted on the pin by member AD. As indicated above, this force is equal and opposite to the force $\mathbf{F}_{AD}$ exerted by the same member on pin A. We can draw the force polygon corresponding to joint D, as shown in Fig. 6.8, and determine the forces

$\mathbf{F}_{DC}$ and $\mathbf{F}_{DB}$ from that polygon. However, when more than three forces are involved, it is usually more convenient to solve the equations of equilibrium $\Sigma F_x = 0$ and $\Sigma F_y = 0$ for the two unknown forces. Since both of these forces are found to be directed away from joint D, members DC and DB pull on the pin and are in tension.

Next, joint C is considered; its free-body diagram is shown in Fig. 6.8. It is noted that both $\mathbf{F}_{CD}$ and $\mathbf{F}_{CA}$ are known from the analysis of the preceding joints and that only $\mathbf{F}_{CB}$ is unknown. Since the equilibrium of each pin provides sufficient information to determine two unknowns, a check of our analysis is obtained at this joint. The force triangle is drawn, and the magnitude and sense of $\mathbf{F}_{CB}$ are determined. Since $\mathbf{F}_{CB}$ is directed toward joint C, member CB pushes on pin C and is in compression. The check is obtained by verifying that the force $\mathbf{F}_{CB}$ and member CB are parallel.

At joint B, all of the forces are known. Since the corresponding pin is in equilibrium, the force triangle must close and an additional check of the analysis is obtained.

It should be noted that the force polygons shown in Fig. 6.8 are not unique. Each of them could be replaced by an alternative configuration. For example, the force triangle corresponding to joint A could be drawn as shown in Fig. 6.9. The triangle actually shown in Fig. 6.8 was obtained by drawing the three forces $\mathbf{R}_A$, $\mathbf{F}_{AC}$, and $\mathbf{F}_{AD}$ in tip-to-tail fashion in the order in which their lines of action are encountered when moving clockwise around joint A. The other force polygons in Fig. 6.8, having been drawn in the same way, can be made to fit into a single diagram, as shown in Fig. 6.10. Such a diagram, known as *Maxwell's diagram*, greatly facilitates the *graphical analysis* of truss problems.

Fig. 6.9

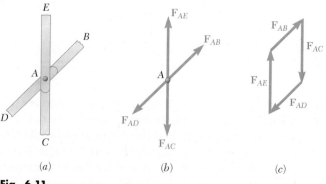

Fig. 6.10

*6.5 JOINTS UNDER SPECIAL LOADING CONDITIONS

Consider Fig. 6.11a, in which the joint shown connects four members lying in two intersecting straight lines. The free-body diagram of Fig. 6.11b shows that pin A is subjected to two pairs of directly opposite forces. The corresponding force polygon, therefore, must be a parallelogram (Fig. 6.11c), and *the forces in opposite members must be equal*.

(a) (b) (c)

Fig. 6.11

Consider next Fig. 6.12*a*, in which the joint shown connects three members and supports a load **P**. Two of the members lie in the same line, and the load **P** acts along the third member. The free-body diagram of pin *A* and the corresponding force polygon will be as shown in Fig. 6.11*b* and *c*, with **F**$_{AE}$ replaced by the load **P**. Thus, *the forces in the two opposite members must be equal, and the force in the other member must equal P*. A particular case of special interest is shown in Fig. 6.12*b*. Since, in this case, no external load is applied to the joint, we have *P* = 0, and the force in member *AC* is zero. Member *AC* is said to be a *zero-force member*.

Consider now a joint connecting two members only. From Sec. 2.9, we know that a particle which is acted upon by two forces will be in equilibrium if the two forces have the same magnitude, same line of action, and opposite sense. In the case of the joint of Fig. 6.13*a*, which connects two members *AB* and *AD* lying in the same line, *the forces in the two members must be equal* for pin *A* to be in equilibrium. In the case of the joint of Fig. 6.13*b*, pin *A* cannot be in equilibrium unless the forces in both members are zero. Members connected as shown in Fig. 6.13*b*, therefore, must be *zero-force members*.

Spotting the joints which are under the special loading conditions listed above will expedite the analysis of a truss. Consider, for example, a Howe truss loaded as shown in Fig. 6.14. All of the members represented by green lines will be recognized as zero-force members. Joint *C* connects three members, two of which lie in the same line, and is not subjected to any external load; member *BC* is thus a zero-force member. Applying the same reasoning to joint *K*, we find that member *JK* is also a zero-force member. But joint *J* is now in the same situation as joints *C* and *K*, and member *IJ* must be a zero-force member. The examination of joints *C*, *J*, and *K* also shows that the forces in members *AC* and *CE* are equal, that the forces in members *HJ* and *JL* are equal, and that the forces in members *IK* and *KL* are equal. Turning our attention to joint *I*, where the 20-kN load and member *HI* are collinear, we note that the force in member *HI* is 20 kN (tension) and that the forces in members *GI* and *IK* are equal. Hence, the forces in members *GI*, *IK*, and *KL* are equal.

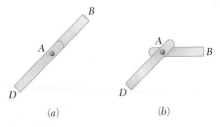

Fig. 6.12

(a)   (b)

Fig. 6.13

(a)   (b)

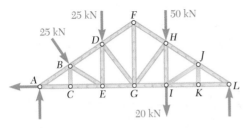

Fig. 6.14

Note that the conditions described above do not apply to joints *B* and *D* in Fig. 6.14, and it would be wrong to assume that the force in member *DE* is 25 kN or that the forces in members *AB* and *BD* are equal. The forces in these members and in all remaining members should be found by carrying out the analysis of joints *A*, *B*, *D*, *E*, *F*, *G*, *H*, and *L* in the usual manner. Thus, until you have become thoroughly familiar with the conditions under which the rules established in this

Photo 6.4 Three-dimensional or space trusses are used for broadcast and power transmission line towers, roof framing, and spacecraft applications, such as components of the *International Space Station*.

section can be applied, you should draw the free-body diagrams of all pins and write the corresponding equilibrium equations (or draw the corresponding force polygons) whether or not the joints being considered are under one of the special loading conditions described above.

A final remark concerning zero-force members: These members are not useless. For example, although the zero-force members of Fig. 6.14 do not carry any loads under the loading conditions shown, the same members would probably carry loads if the loading conditions were changed. Besides, even in the case considered, these members are needed to support the weight of the truss and to maintain the truss in the desired shape.

*6.6 SPACE TRUSSES

When several straight members are joined together at their extremities to form a three-dimensional configuration, the structure obtained is called a *space truss*.

We recall from Sec. 6.3 that the most elementary two-dimensional rigid truss consisted of three members joined at their extremities to form the sides of a triangle; by adding two members at a time to this basic configuration, and connecting them at a new joint, it was possible to obtain a larger rigid structure which was defined as a simple truss. Similarly, the most elementary rigid space truss consists of six members joined at their extremities to form the edges of a tetrahedron *ABCD* (Fig. 6.15*a*). By adding three members at a time to this basic configuration, such as *AE*, *BE*, and *CE*, attaching them to three existing joints, and connecting them at a new joint,† we can obtain a larger rigid structure which is defined as a *simple space truss* (Fig. 6.15*b*). Observing that the basic tetrahedron has six members and four joints and that every time three members are added, the number of joints is increased by one, we conclude that in a simple space truss the total number of members is $m = 3n - 6$, where n is the total number of joints.

If a space truss is to be completely constrained and if the reactions at its supports are to be statically determinate, the supports should consist of a combination of balls, rollers, and balls and sockets which provides six unknown reactions (see Sec. 4.9). These unknown reactions may be readily determined by solving the six equations expressing that the three-dimensional truss is in equilibrium.

Although the members of a space truss are actually joined together by means of bolted or welded connections, it is assumed that each joint consists of a ball-and-socket connection. Thus, no couple will be applied to the members of the truss, and each member can be treated as a two-force member. The conditions of equilibrium for each joint will be expressed by the three equations $\Sigma F_x = 0$, $\Sigma F_y = 0$, and $\Sigma F_z = 0$. In the case of a simple space truss containing n joints, writing the conditions of equilibrium for each joint will thus yield $3n$ equations. Since $m = 3n - 6$, these equations suffice to determine all unknown forces (forces in m members and six reactions at the supports). However, to avoid the necessity of solving simultaneous equations, care should be taken to select joints in such an order that no selected joint will involve more than three unknown forces.

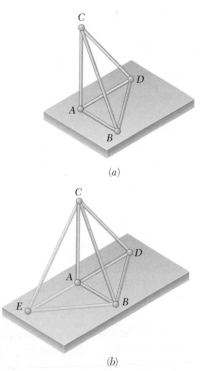

(a)

(b)

Fig. 6.15

†The four joints must not lie in a plane.

2000 lb   1000 lb
|←12 ft→|←12 ft→|
A   B   C
                           8 ft
D   E
|← 6 ft →|← 12 ft →|← 6 ft →|

SAMPLE PROBLEM 6.1

Using the method of joints, determine the force in each member of the truss shown.

SOLUTION

Free-Body: Entire Truss. A free-body diagram of the entire truss is drawn; external forces acting on this free body consist of the applied loads and the reactions at C and E. We write the following equilibrium equations.

$$+\circlearrowleft \Sigma M_C = 0: \qquad (2000 \text{ lb})(24 \text{ ft}) + (1000 \text{ lb})(12 \text{ ft}) - E(6 \text{ ft}) = 0$$
$$E = +10{,}000 \text{ lb} \qquad\qquad \mathbf{E} = 10{,}000 \text{ lb} \uparrow$$

$$\xrightarrow{+} \Sigma F_x = 0: \qquad\qquad\qquad\qquad\qquad\qquad\qquad \mathbf{C}_x = 0$$

$$+\uparrow \Sigma F_y = 0: \qquad -2000 \text{ lb} - 1000 \text{ lb} + 10{,}000 \text{ lb} + C_y = 0$$
$$C_y = -7000 \text{ lb} \qquad\qquad \mathbf{C}_y = 7000 \text{ lb} \downarrow$$

Free-Body: Joint A. This joint is subjected to only two unknown forces, namely, the forces exerted by members AB and AD. A force triangle is used to determine $\mathbf{F}_{AB}$ and $\mathbf{F}_{AD}$. We note that member AB pulls on the joint and thus is in tension and that member AD pushes on the joint and thus is in compression. The magnitudes of the two forces are obtained from the proportion

$$\frac{2000 \text{ lb}}{4} = \frac{F_{AB}}{3} = \frac{F_{AD}}{5}$$

$$F_{AB} = 1500 \text{ lb } T \blacktriangleleft$$
$$F_{AD} = 2500 \text{ lb } C \blacktriangleleft$$

Free-Body: Joint D. Since the force exerted by member AD has been determined, only two unknown forces are now involved at this joint. Again, a force triangle is used to determine the unknown forces in members DB and DE.

$$F_{DB} = F_{DA} \qquad\qquad F_{DB} = 2500 \text{ lb } T \blacktriangleleft$$
$$F_{DE} = 2(\tfrac{3}{5})F_{DA} \qquad\qquad F_{DE} = 3000 \text{ lb } C \blacktriangleleft$$

Free-Body: Joint B. Since more than three forces act at this joint, we determine the two unknown forces $\mathbf{F}_{BC}$ and $\mathbf{F}_{BE}$ by solving the equilibrium equations $\Sigma F_x = 0$ and $\Sigma F_y = 0$. We arbitrarily assume that both unknown forces act away from the joint, i.e., that the members are in tension. The positive value obtained for F_{BC} indicates that our assumption was correct; member BC is in tension. The negative value of F_{BE} indicates that our assumption was wrong; member BE is in compression.

$$+\uparrow\Sigma F_y = 0: \qquad -1000 - \tfrac{4}{5}(2500) - \tfrac{4}{5}F_{BE} = 0$$
$$F_{BE} = -3750 \text{ lb} \qquad F_{BE} = 3750 \text{ lb } C \quad \blacktriangleleft$$

$$\xrightarrow{+}\Sigma F_x = 0: \qquad F_{BC} - 1500 - \tfrac{3}{5}(2500) - \tfrac{3}{5}(3750) = 0$$
$$F_{BC} = +5250 \text{ lb} \qquad F_{BC} = 5250 \text{ lb } T \quad \blacktriangleleft$$

Free-Body: Joint E. The unknown force $\mathbf{F}_{EC}$ is assumed to act away from the joint. Summing x components, we write

$$\xrightarrow{+}\Sigma F_x = 0: \qquad \tfrac{3}{5}F_{EC} + 3000 + \tfrac{3}{5}(3750) = 0$$
$$F_{EC} = -8750 \text{ lb} \qquad F_{EC} = 8750 \text{ lb } C \quad \blacktriangleleft$$

Summing y components, we obtain a check of our computations:

$$+\uparrow\Sigma F_y = 10{,}000 - \tfrac{4}{5}(3750) - \tfrac{4}{5}(8750)$$
$$= 10{,}000 - 3000 - 7000 = 0 \qquad \text{(checks)}$$

Free-Body: Joint C. Using the computed values of $\mathbf{F}_{CB}$ and $\mathbf{F}_{CE}$, we can determine the reactions $\mathbf{C}_x$ and $\mathbf{C}_y$ by considering the equilibrium of this joint. Since these reactions have already been determined from the equilibrium of the entire truss, we will obtain two checks of our computations. We can also simply use the computed values of all forces acting on the joint (forces in members and reactions) and check that the joint is in equilibrium:

$$\xrightarrow{+}\Sigma F_x = -5250 + \tfrac{3}{5}(8750) = -5250 + 5250 = 0 \qquad \text{(checks)}$$
$$+\uparrow\Sigma F_y = -7000 + \tfrac{4}{5}(8750) = -7000 + 7000 = 0 \qquad \text{(checks)}$$

SOLVING PROBLEMS ON YOUR OWN

In this lesson you learned to use the *method of joints* to determine the forces in the members of a *simple truss*, that is, a truss that can be constructed from a basic triangular truss by adding to it two new members at a time and connecting them at a new joint.

Your solution will consist of the following steps:

1. Draw a free-body diagram of the entire truss, and use this diagram to determine the reactions at the supports.

2. Locate a joint connecting only two members, and draw the free-body diagram of its pin. Use this free-body diagram to determine the unknown force in each of the two members. If only three forces are involved (the two unknown forces and a known one), you will probably find it more convenient to draw and solve the corresponding force triangle. If more than three forces are involved, you should write and solve the equilibrium equations for the pin, $\Sigma F_x = 0$ and $\Sigma F_y = 0$, assuming that the members are in tension. A positive answer means that the member is in tension, a negative answer that the member is in compression. Once the forces have been found, enter their values on a sketch of the truss, with T for tension and C for compression.

3. Next, locate a joint where the forces in only two of the connected members are still unknown. Draw the free-body diagram of the pin and use it as indicated above to determine the two unknown forces.

4. Repeat this procedure until the forces in all the members of the truss have been found. Since you previously used the three equilibrium equations associated with the free-body diagram of the entire truss to determine the reactions at the supports, you will end up with three extra equations. These equations can be used to check your computations.

5. Note that the choice of the first joint is not unique. Once you have determined the reactions at the supports of the truss, you can choose either of two joints as a starting point for your analysis. In Sample Prob. 6.1, we started at joint A and proceeded through joints D, B, E, and C, but we could also have started at joint C and proceeded through joints E, B, D, and A. On the other hand, having selected a first joint, you may in some cases reach a point in your analysis beyond which you cannot proceed. You must then start again from another joint to complete your solution.

Keep in mind that the analysis of a *simple truss* can always be carried out by the method of joints. Also remember that it is helpful to outline your solution *before* starting any computations.

PROBLEMS

6.1 through 6.8   Using the method of joints, determine the force in each member of the truss shown. State whether each member is in tension or compression.

Fig. P6.1

Fig. P6.2

Fig. P6.3

Fig. P6.4

Fig. P6.5

Fig. P6.6

Fig. P6.7

Fig. P6.8

6.9 Determine the force in each member of the Gambrel roof truss shown. State whether each member is in tension or compression.

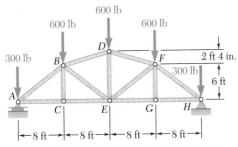

Fig. P6.9

6.10 Determine the force in each member of the Howe roof truss shown. State whether each member is in tension or compression.

6.11 Determine the force in each member of the Pratt roof truss shown. State whether each member is in tension or compression.

Fig. P6.10

Fig. P6.11

6.12 Determine the force in each member of the Fink roof truss shown. State whether each member is in tension or compression.

6.13 Determine the force in each member of the double-pitch roof truss shown. State whether each member is in tension or compression.

Fig. P6.12

Fig. P6.13

6.14 The truss shown is one of several supporting an advertising panel. Determine the force in each member of the truss for a wind load equivalent to the two forces shown. State whether each member is in tension or compression.

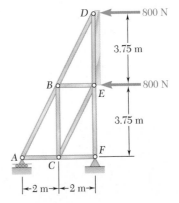

Fig. P6.14

6.15 Determine the force in each of the members located to the left of line *FGH* for the studio roof truss shown. State whether each member is in tension or compression.

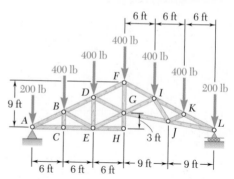

Fig. P6.15 and P6.16

6.16 Determine the force in member *FG* and in each of the members located to the right of *FG* for the studio roof truss shown. State whether each member is in tension or compression.

6.17 Determine the force in each of the members located to the left of *FG* for the scissors roof truss shown. State whether each member is in tension or compression.

6.18 Determine the force in member *FG* and in each of the members located to the right of *FG* for the scissors roof truss shown. State whether each member is in tension or compression.

6.19 Determine the force in each member of the Warren bridge truss shown. State whether each member is in tension or compression.

6.20 Solve Prob. 6.19 assuming that the load applied at *E* has been removed.

6.21 Determine the force in each member of the Pratt bridge truss shown. State whether each member is in tension or compression.

Fig. P6.17 and P6.18

Fig. P6.19

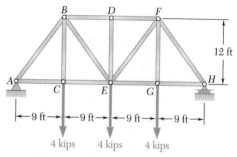

Fig. P6.21

6.22 Solve Prob. 6.21 assuming that the load applied at *G* has been removed.

6.23 The portion of truss shown represents the upper part of a power transmission line tower. For the given loading, determine the force in each of the members located above *HJ*. State whether each member is in tension or compression.

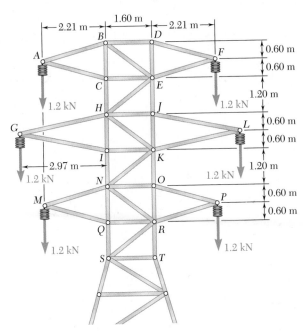

Fig. P6.23

6.24 For the tower and loading of Prob. 6.23 and knowing that $F_{CH} = F_{EJ} = 1.2$ kN C and $F_{EH} = 0$, determine the force in member *HJ* and in each of the members located between *HJ* and *NO*. State whether each member is in tension or compression.

6.25 Solve Prob. 6.23 assuming that the cables hanging from the right side of the tower have fallen to the ground.

6.26 Determine the force in each of the members connecting joints *A* through *F* of the vaulted roof truss shown. State whether each member is in tension or compression.

6.27 Determine the force in each member of the truss shown. State whether each member is in tension or compression.

Fig. P6.26

Fig. P6.27

Fig. P6.28

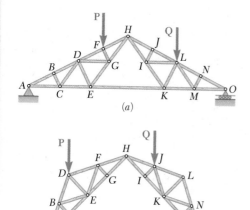

(a)

(b)

Fig. P6.32

6.28 Determine the force in each member of the truss shown. State whether each member is in tension or compression.

6.29 Determine whether the trusses of Probs. 6.31a, 6.32a, and 6.33a are simple trusses.

6.30 Determine whether the trusses of Probs. 6.31b, 6.32b, and 6.33b are simple trusses.

6.31 For the given loading, determine the zero-force members in each of the two trusses shown.

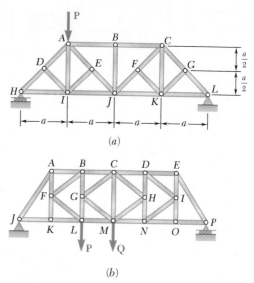

(a)

(b)

Fig. P6.31

6.32 For the given loading, determine the zero-force members in each of the two trusses shown.

6.33 For the given loading, determine the zero-force members in each of the two trusses shown.

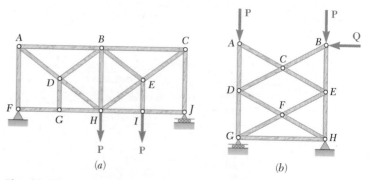

(a)

(b)

Fig. P6.33

6.34 Determine the zero-force members in the truss of (a) Prob. 6.26, (b) Prob. 6.28.

*6.35 The truss shown consists of six members and is supported by a short link at A, two short links at B, and a ball and socket at D. Determine the force in each of the members for the given loading.

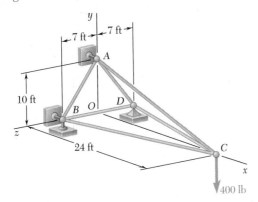

Fig. P6.35

*6.36 The truss shown consists of six members and is supported by a ball and socket at B, a short link at C, and two short links at D. Determine the force in each of the members for $\mathbf{P} = (-2184 \text{ N})\mathbf{j}$ and $\mathbf{Q} = 0$.

*6.37 The truss shown consists of six members and is supported by a ball and socket at B, a short link at C, and two short links at D. Determine the force in each of the members for $\mathbf{P} = 0$ and $\mathbf{Q} = (2968 \text{ N})\mathbf{i}$.

*6.38 The truss shown consists of nine members and is supported by a ball and socket at A, two short links at B, and a short link at C. Determine the force in each of the members for the given loading.

Fig. P6.36 and P6.37

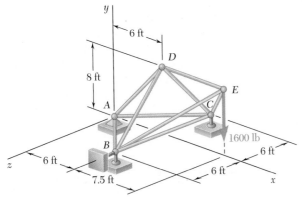

Fig. P6.38

*6.39 The truss shown consists of nine members and is supported by a ball and socket at B, a short link at C, and two short links at D. (a) Check that this truss is a simple truss, that it is completely constrained, and that the reactions at its supports are statically determinate. (b) Determine the force in each member for $\mathbf{P} = (-1200 \text{ N})\mathbf{j}$ and $\mathbf{Q} = 0$.

*6.40 Solve Prob. 6.39 for $\mathbf{P} = 0$ and $\mathbf{Q} = (-900 \text{ N})\mathbf{k}$.

Fig. P6.39

Fig. P6.41 and P6.42

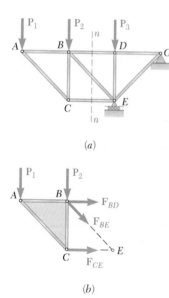

Fig. 6.16

*6.41 The truss shown consists of 18 members and is supported by a ball and socket at A, two short links at B, and one short link at G. (*a*) Check that this truss is a simple truss, that it is completely constrained, and that the reactions at its supports are statically determinate. (*b*) For the given loading, determine the force in each of the six members joined at E.

*6.42 The truss shown consists of 18 members and is supported by a ball and socket at A, two short links at B, and one short link at G. (*a*) Check that this truss is a simple truss, that it is completely constrained, and that the reactions at its supports are statically determinate. (*b*) For the given loading, determine the force in each of the six members joined at G.

6.7 ANALYSIS OF TRUSSES BY THE METHOD OF SECTIONS

The method of joints is most effective when the forces in all the members of a truss are to be determined. If, however, the force in only one member or the forces in a very few members are desired, another method, the method of sections, is more efficient.

Assume, for example, that we want to determine the force in member BD of the truss shown in Fig. 6.16*a*. To do this, we must determine the force with which member BD acts on either joint B or joint D. If we were to use the method of joints, we would choose either joint B or joint D as a free body. However, we can also choose as a free body a larger portion of the truss, composed of several joints and members, provided that the desired force is one of the external forces acting on that portion. If, in addition, the portion of the truss is chosen so that there is a total of only three unknown forces acting upon it, the desired force can be obtained by solving the equations of equilibrium for this portion of the truss. In practice, the portion of the truss to be utilized is obtained by *passing a section* through three members of the truss, one of which is the desired member, i.e., by drawing a line which divides the truss into two completely separate parts but does not intersect more than three members. Either of the two portions of the truss obtained after the intersected members have been removed can then be used as a free body.†

In Fig. 6.16*a*, the section *nn* has been passed through members BD, BE, and CE, and the portion ABC of the truss is chosen as the free body (Fig. 6.16*b*). The forces acting on the free body are the loads $\mathbf{P}_1$ and $\mathbf{P}_2$ at points A and B and the three unknown forces $\mathbf{F}_{BD}$, $\mathbf{F}_{BE}$, and $\mathbf{F}_{CE}$. Since it is not known whether the members removed were in tension or compression, the three forces have been arbitrarily drawn away from the free body as if the members were in tension.

---

†In the analysis of certain trusses, sections are passed which intersect more than three members; the forces in one, or possibly two, of the intersected members may be obtained if equilibrium equations can be found, each of which involves only one unknown (see Probs. 6.61 through 6.64).

The fact that the rigid body ABC is in equilibrium can be expressed by writing three equations which can be solved for the three unknown forces. If only the force $\mathbf{F}_{BD}$ is desired, we need write only one equation, provided that the equation does not contain the other unknowns. Thus the equation $\Sigma M_E = 0$ yields the value of the magnitude F_{BD} of the force $\mathbf{F}_{BD}$ (Fig. 6.16b). A positive sign in the answer will indicate that our original assumption regarding the sense of $\mathbf{F}_{BD}$ was correct and that member BD is in tension; a negative sign will indicate that our assumption was incorrect and that BD is in compression.

On the other hand, if only the force $\mathbf{F}_{CE}$ is desired, an equation which does not involve $\mathbf{F}_{BD}$ or $\mathbf{F}_{BE}$ should be written; the appropriate equation is $\Sigma M_B = 0$. Again a positive sign for the magnitude F_{CE} of the desired force indicates a correct assumption, that is, tension; and a negative sign indicates an incorrect assumption, that is, compression.

If only the force $\mathbf{F}_{BE}$ is desired, the appropriate equation is $\Sigma F_y = 0$. Whether the member is in tension or compression is again determined from the sign of the answer.

When the force in only one member is determined, no independent check of the computation is available. However, when all the unknown forces acting on the free body are determined, the computations can be checked by writing an additional equation. For instance, if $\mathbf{F}_{BD}$, $\mathbf{F}_{BE}$, and $\mathbf{F}_{CE}$ are determined as indicated above, the computation can be checked by verifying that $\Sigma F_x = 0$.

*6.8 TRUSSES MADE OF SEVERAL SIMPLE TRUSSES

Consider two simple trusses ABC and DEF. If they are connected by three bars BD, BE, and CE as shown in Fig. 6.17a, they will form together a rigid truss $ABDF$. The trusses ABC and DEF can also be combined into a single rigid truss by joining joints B and D into a single joint B and by connecting joints C and E by a bar CE (Fig. 6.17b). The truss thus obtained is known as a *Fink truss*. It should be noted that the trusses of Fig. 6.17a and b are *not* simple trusses; they cannot be constructed from a triangular truss by adding successive pairs of members as prescribed in Sec. 6.3. They are rigid trusses, however, as we can check by comparing the systems of connections used to hold the simple trusses ABC and DEF together (three bars in Fig. 6.17a, one pin and one bar in Fig. 6.17b) with the systems of supports discussed in Secs. 4.4 and 4.5. Trusses made of several simple trusses rigidly connected are known as *compound trusses*.

(a)

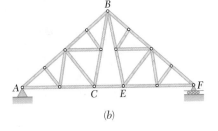

(b)

Fig. 6.17

In a compound truss the number of members m and the number of joints n are still related by the formula $m = 2n - 3$. This can be verified by observing that, if a compound truss is supported by a frictionless pin and a roller (involving three unknown reactions), the total number of unknowns is $m + 3$, and this number must be equal to the number $2n$ of equations obtained by expressing that the n pins are in equilibrium; it follows that $m = 2n - 3$. Compound trusses supported by a pin and a roller, or by an equivalent system of supports, are *statically determinate, rigid,* and *completely constrained.* This means that all of the unknown reactions and the forces in all the members can be determined by the methods of statics, and that the truss will neither collapse nor move. The forces in the members, however, cannot all be determined by the method of joints, except by solving a large number of simultaneous equations. In the case of the compound truss of Fig. 6.17*a*, for example, it is more efficient to pass a section through members *BD*, *BE*, and *CE* to determine the forces in these members.

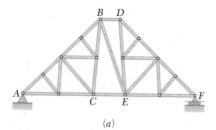

Fig. 6.17 (repeated)

Suppose, now, that the simple trusses *ABC* and *DEF* are connected by *four* bars *BD*, *BE*, *CD*, or *CE* (Fig. 6.18). The number of members m is now larger than $2n - 3$; the truss obtained is *overrigid,* and one of the four members *BD*, *BE*, *CD*, or *CE* is said to be *redundant.* If the truss is supported by a pin at *A* and a roller at *F*, the total number of unknowns is $m + 3$. Since $m > 2n - 3$, the number $m + 3$ of unknowns is now larger than the number $2n$ of available independent equations; the truss is *statically indeterminate.*

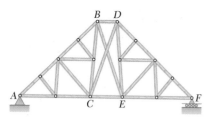

Fig. 6.18

Finally, let us assume that the two simple trusses *ABC* and *DEF* are joined by a pin as shown in Fig. 6.19*a*. The number of members m is smaller than $2n - 3$. If the truss is supported by a pin at *A* and a roller at *F*, the total number of unknowns is $m + 3$. Since $m < 2n - 3$, the number $m + 3$ of unknowns is now smaller than the number $2n$ of equilibrium equations which should be satisfied; the truss is *nonrigid* and will collapse under its own weight. However, if two pins are used to support it, the truss becomes *rigid* and will not collapse (Fig. 6.19*b*). We note that the total number of unknowns is now $m + 4$ and is equal to the number $2n$ of equations. More generally, if the reactions at the supports involve r unknowns, the condition for a compound truss to be statically determinate, rigid, and completely constrained is $m + r = 2n$. However, while necessary this condition is not sufficient for the equilibrium of a structure which ceases to be rigid when detached from its supports (see Sec. 6.11).

(*a*)

(*b*)

Fig. 6.19

28 kips   28 kips

A   C   E   G   I   K   16 kips

10 ft

B

D   F   H   J

8 ft   8 ft   8 ft   8 ft   8 ft

SAMPLE PROBLEM 6.2

Determine the force in members EF and GI of the truss shown.

SOLUTION

Free-Body: Entire Truss. A free-body diagram of the entire truss is drawn; external forces acting on this free body consist of the applied loads and the reactions at B and J. We write the following equilibrium equations.

$+\gamma\Sigma M_B = 0$:

$$-(28 \text{ kips})(8 \text{ ft}) - (28 \text{ kips})(24 \text{ ft}) - (16 \text{ kips})(10 \text{ ft}) + J(32 \text{ ft}) = 0$$
$$J = +33 \text{ kips} \qquad \mathbf{J} = 33 \text{ kips}\uparrow$$

$\xrightarrow{+}\Sigma F_x = 0$: $B_x + 16 \text{ kips} = 0$

$$B_x = -16 \text{ kips} \qquad \mathbf{B}_x = 16 \text{ kips}\leftarrow$$

$+\gamma\Sigma M_J = 0$:

$$(28 \text{ kips})(24 \text{ ft}) + (28 \text{ kips})(8 \text{ ft}) - (16 \text{ kips})(10 \text{ ft}) - B_y(32 \text{ ft}) = 0$$
$$B_y = +23 \text{ kips} \qquad \mathbf{B}_y = 23 \text{ kips}\uparrow$$

Force in Member EF. Section nn is passed through the truss so that it intersects member EF and only two additional members. After the intersected members have been removed, the left-hand portion of the truss is chosen as a free body. Three unknowns are involved; to eliminate the two horizontal forces, we write

$+\uparrow\Sigma F_y = 0$: $+23 \text{ kips} - 28 \text{ kips} - F_{EF} = 0$
$$F_{EF} = -5 \text{ kips}$$

The sense of $\mathbf{F}_{EF}$ was chosen assuming member EF to be in tension; the negative sign obtained indicates that the member is in compression.

$$F_{EF} = 5 \text{ kips } C \quad \blacktriangleleft$$

Force in Member GI. Section mm is passed through the truss so that it intersects member GI and only two additional members. After the intersected members have been removed, we choose the right-hand portion of the truss as a free body. Three unknown forces are again involved; to eliminate the two forces passing through point H, we write

$+\gamma\Sigma M_H = 0$: $(33 \text{ kips})(8 \text{ ft}) - (16 \text{ kips})(10 \text{ ft}) + F_{GI}(10 \text{ ft}) = 0$
$$F_{GI} = -10.4 \text{ kips} \qquad F_{GI} = 10.4 \text{ kips } C \quad \blacktriangleleft$$

305

SAMPLE PROBLEM 6.3

Determine the force in members FH, GH, and GI of the roof truss shown.

SOLUTION

Free Body: Entire Truss. From the free-body diagram of the entire truss, we find the reactions at A and L:

$$\mathbf{A} = 12.50 \text{ kN}\uparrow \qquad \mathbf{L} = 7.50 \text{ kN}\uparrow$$

We note that

$$\tan \alpha = \frac{FG}{GL} = \frac{8 \text{ m}}{15 \text{ m}} = 0.5333 \quad \alpha = 28.07°$$

Force in Member GI. Section nn is passed through the truss as shown. Using the portion HLI of the truss as a free body, the value of F_{GI} is obtained by writing

$$+\uparrow\Sigma M_H = 0: \qquad (7.50 \text{ kN})(10 \text{ m}) - (1 \text{ kN})(5 \text{ m}) - F_{GI}(5.33 \text{ m}) = 0$$
$$F_{GI} = +13.13 \text{ kN} \qquad F_{GI} = 13.13 \text{ kN } T \quad \blacktriangleleft$$

Force in Member FH. The value of F_{FH} is obtained from the equation $\Sigma M_G = 0$. We move $\mathbf{F}_{FH}$ along its line of action until it acts at point F, where it is resolved into its x and y components. The moment of $\mathbf{F}_{FH}$ with respect to point G is now equal to $(F_{FH} \cos \alpha)(8 \text{ m})$.

$$+\uparrow\Sigma M_G = 0:$$
$$(7.50 \text{ kN})(15 \text{ m}) - (1 \text{ kN})(10 \text{ m}) - (1 \text{ kN})(5 \text{ m}) + (F_{FH} \cos \alpha)(8 \text{ m}) = 0$$
$$F_{FH} = -13.81 \text{ kN} \qquad F_{FH} = 13.81 \text{ kN } C \quad \blacktriangleleft$$

Force in Member GH. We first note that

$$\tan \beta = \frac{GI}{HI} = \frac{5 \text{ m}}{\frac{2}{3}(8 \text{ m})} = 0.9375 \quad \beta = 43.15°$$

The value of F_{GH} is then determined by resolving the force $\mathbf{F}_{GH}$ into x and y components at point G and solving the equation $\Sigma M_L = 0$.

$$+\uparrow\Sigma M_L = 0: \qquad (1 \text{ kN})(10 \text{ m}) + (1 \text{ kN})(5 \text{ m}) + (F_{GH} \cos \beta)(15 \text{ m}) = 0$$
$$F_{GH} = -1.371 \text{ kN} \qquad F_{GH} = 1.371 \text{ kN } C \quad \blacktriangleleft$$

SOLVING PROBLEMS
ON YOUR OWN

The *method of joints* that you studied earlier is usually the best method to use when the forces *in all the members* of a simple truss are to be found. However, the method of sections, which was covered in this lesson, is more effective when the force *in only one member* or the forces *in a very few members* of a simple truss are desired. The method of sections must also be used when the truss *is not a simple truss*.

A. To determine the force in a given truss member by the method of sections, you should follow these steps:

1. Draw a free-body diagram of the entire truss, and use this diagram to determine the reactions at the supports.

2. Pass a section through three members of the truss, one of which is the desired member. After you have removed these members, you will obtain two separate portions of truss.

3. Select one of the two portions of truss you have obtained, and draw its free-body diagram. This diagram should include the external forces applied to the selected portion as well as the forces exerted on it by the intersected members before these members were removed.

4. You can now write three equilibrium equations which can be solved for the forces in the three intersected members.

5. An alternative approach is to write a single equation, which can be solved for the force in the desired member. To do so, first observe whether the forces exerted by the other two members on the free body are parallel or whether their lines of action intersect.

    a. If these forces are parallel, they can be eliminated by writing an equilibrium equation involving *components in a direction perpendicular* to these two forces.

    b. If their lines of action intersect at a point H, they can be eliminated by writing an equilibrium equation involving *moments about H*.

6. Keep in mind that the section you use must intersect three members only. This is because the equilibrium equations in step 4 can be solved for three unknowns only. However, you can pass a section through more than three members to find the force in one of those members if you can write an equilibrium equation containing only that force as an unknown. Such special situations are found in Probs. 6.61 through 6.64.

(continued)

B. About completely constrained and determinate trusses:

1. First note that any simple truss which is simply supported is a completely constrained and determinate truss.

2. To determine whether any other truss is or is not completely constrained and determinate, you first count the number m of its members, the number n of its joints, and the number r of the reaction components at its supports. You then compare the sum $m + r$ representing the number of unknowns and the product $2n$ representing the number of available independent equilibrium equations.

    a. If $m + r < 2n$, there are fewer unknowns than equations. Thus, some of the equations cannot be satisfied; the truss is only *partially constrained*.

    b. If $m + r > 2n$, there are more unknowns than equations. Thus, some of the unknowns cannot be determined; the truss is *indeterminate*.

    c. If $m + r = 2n$, there are as many unknowns as there are equations. This, however, does not mean that all the unknowns can be determined and that all the equations can be satisfied. To find out whether the truss is *completely* or *improperly constrained*, you should try to determine the reactions at its supports and the forces in its members. If all can be found, the truss is *completely constrained and determinate*.

6.43 Determine the force in members *CD* and *DF* of the truss shown.

Fig. P6.43 and P6.44

6.44 Determine the force in members *FG* and *FH* of the truss shown.

6.45 A Warren bridge truss is loaded as shown. Determine the force in members *CE*, *DE*, and *DF*.

6.46 A Warren bridge truss is loaded as shown. Determine the force in members *EG*, *FG*, and *FH*.

6.47 Determine the force in members *DF*, *EF*, and *EG* of the truss shown.

Fig. P6.45 and P6.46

Fig. P6.47 and P6.48

6.48 Determine the force in members *GI*, *GJ*, and *HI* of the truss shown.

6.49 Determine the force in members *AD*, *CD*, and *CE* of the truss shown.

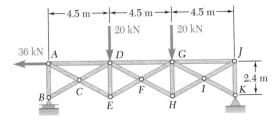

Fig. P6.49 and P6.50

6.50 Determine the force in members *DG*, *FG*, and *FH* of the truss shown.

6.51 A stadium roof truss is loaded as shown. Determine the force in members *AB*, *AG*, and *FG*.

Fig. P6.51 and P6.52

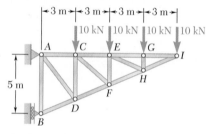

Fig. P6.53 and P6.54

6.52 A stadium roof truss is loaded as shown. Determine the force in members *AE*, *EF*, and *FJ*.

6.53 Determine the force in members *CD* and *DF* of the truss shown.

6.54 Determine the force in members *CE* and *EF* of the truss shown.

6.55 The truss shown was designed to support the roof of a food market. For the given loading, determine the force in members *FG*, *EG*, and *EH*.

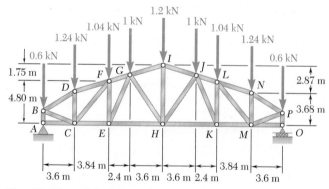

Fig. P6.55 and P6.56

6.56 The truss shown was designed to support the roof of a food market. For the given loading, determine the force in members *KM*, *LM*, and *LN*.

6.57 A Polynesian, or duopitch, roof truss is loaded as shown. Determine the force in members *DF*, *EF*, and *EG*.

Fig. P6.57 and P6.58

6.58 A Polynesian, or duopitch, roof truss is loaded as shown. Determine the force in members *HI*, *GI*, and *GJ*.

6.59 Determine the force in members *DE* and *DF* of the truss shown when $P = 20$ kips.

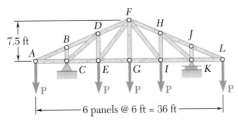

Fig. P6.59 and P6.60

6.60 Determine the force in members *EG* and *EF* of the truss shown when $P = 20$ kips.

6.61 Determine the force in members *EH* and *GI* of the truss shown. (*Hint:* Use section *aa*.)

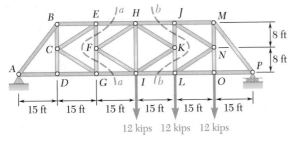

Fig. P6.61 and P6.62

6.62 Determine the force in members *HJ* and *IL* of the truss shown. (*Hint:* Use section *bb*.)

6.63 Determine the force in members *DG* and *FI* of the truss shown. (*Hint:* Use section *aa*.)

6.64 Determine the force in members *GJ* and *IK* of the truss shown. (*Hint:* Use section *bb*.)

Fig. P6.63 and P6.64

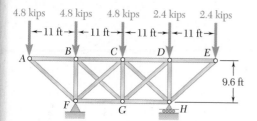

4.8 kips 4.8 kips 4.8 kips 2.4 kips 2.4 kips

← 11 ft →← 11 ft →← 11 ft →← 11 ft →

9.6 ft

Fig. P6.65

6.65 and 6.66 The diagonal members in the center panels of the truss shown are very slender and can act only in tension; such members are known as *counters*. Determine the forces in the counters that are acting under the given loading.

6.67 and 6.68 The diagonal members in the center panels of the power transmission line tower shown are very slender and can act only in tension; such members are known as *counters*. For the given loading, determine (*a*) which of the two counters listed below is acting, (*b*) the force in that counter.

     6.67 Counters *CJ* and *HE*.
     6.68 Counters *IO* and *KN*.

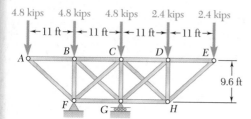

4.8 kips 4.8 kips 4.8 kips 2.4 kips 2.4 kips

← 11 ft →← 11 ft →← 11 ft →← 11 ft →

9.6 ft

Fig. P6.66

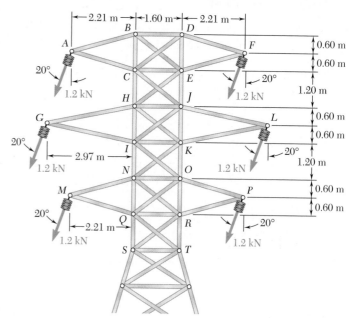

Fig. P6.67 and P6.68

6.69 Classify each of the structures shown as completely, partially, or improperly constrained; if completely constrained, further classify as determinate or indeterminate. (All members can act both in tension and in compression.)

(*a*) (*b*) (*c*)

Fig. P6.69

6.70 through 6.74 Classify each of the structures shown as completely, partially, or improperly constrained; if completely constrained, further classify as determinate or indeterminate. (All members can act both in tension and in compression.)

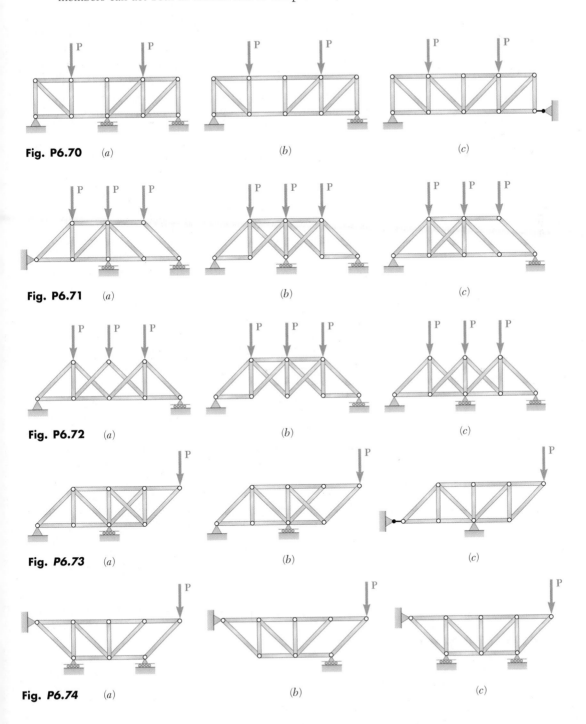

Fig. P6.70 (a) (b) (c)

Fig. P6.71 (a) (b) (c)

Fig. P6.72 (a) (b) (c)

Fig. P6.73 (a) (b) (c)

Fig. P6.74 (a) (b) (c)

6.9 STRUCTURES CONTAINING MULTIFORCE MEMBERS

Under trusses, we have considered structures consisting entirely of pins and straight two-force members. The forces acting on the two-force members were known to be directed along the members themselves. We now consider structures in which at least one of the members is a *multiforce* member, i.e., a member acted upon by three or more forces. These forces will generally not be directed along the members on which they act; their direction is unknown, and they should be represented therefore by two unknown components.

Frames and machines are structures containing multiforce members. *Frames* are designed to support loads and are usually stationary, fully constrained structures. *Machines* are designed to transmit and modify forces; they may or may not be stationary and will always contain moving parts.

6.10 ANALYSIS OF A FRAME

As a first example of analysis of a frame, the crane described in Sec. 6.1, which carries a given load W (Fig. 6.20a), will again be considered. The free-body diagram of the entire frame is shown in Fig. 6.20b. This diagram can be used to determine the external forces acting on the frame. Summing moments about A, we first determine the force $\mathbf{T}$ exerted by the cable; summing x and y components, we then determine the components $\mathbf{A}_x$ and $\mathbf{A}_y$ of the reaction at the pin A.

In order to determine the internal forces holding the various parts of a frame together, we must dismember the frame and draw a free-body diagram for each of its component parts (Fig. 6.20c). First, the two-force members should be considered. In this frame, member BE is the only two-force member. The forces acting at each end of this member must have the same magnitude, same line of action, and opposite sense (Sec. 4.6). They are therefore directed along BE and will be denoted, respectively, by $\mathbf{F}_{BE}$ and $-\mathbf{F}_{BE}$. Their sense will be arbitrarily assumed as shown in Fig. 6.20c; later the sign obtained for the common magnitude F_{BE} of the two forces will confirm or deny this assumption.

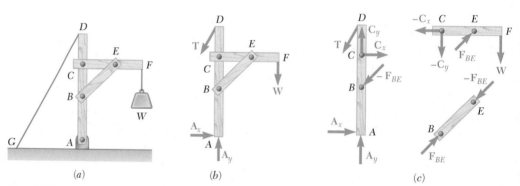

(a)   *(b)*   *(c)*

Fig. 6.20

Next, we consider the multiforce members, i.e., the members which are acted upon by three or more forces. According to Newton's third law, the force exerted at B by member BE on member AD must be equal and opposite to the force $\mathbf{F}_{BE}$ exerted by AD on BE. Similarly, the force exerted at E by member BE on member CF must be equal and opposite to the force $-\mathbf{F}_{BE}$ exerted by CF on BE. Thus the forces that the two-force member BE exerts on AD and CF are, respectively, equal to $-\mathbf{F}_{BE}$ and $\mathbf{F}_{BE}$; they have the same magnitude F_{BE} and opposite sense, and should be directed as shown in Fig. 6.20c.

At C two multiforce members are connected. Since neither the direction nor the magnitude of the forces acting at C is known, these forces will be represented by their x and y components. The components $\mathbf{C}_x$ and $\mathbf{C}_y$ of the force acting on member AD will be arbitrarily directed to the right and upward. Since, according to Newton's third law, the forces exerted by member CF on AD and by member AD on CF are equal and opposite, the components of the force acting on member CF *must* be directed to the left and downward; they will be denoted, respectively, by $-\mathbf{C}_x$ and $-\mathbf{C}_y$. Whether the force $\mathbf{C}_x$ is actually directed to the right and the force $-\mathbf{C}_x$ is actually directed to the left will be determined later from the sign of their common magnitude C_x, a plus sign indicating that the assumption made was correct, and a minus sign that it was wrong. The free-body diagrams of the multiforce members are completed by showing the external forces acting at A, D, and F.†

The internal forces can now be determined by considering the free-body diagram of either of the two multiforce members. Choosing the free-body diagram of CF, for example, we write the equations $\Sigma M_C = 0$, $\Sigma M_E = 0$, and $\Sigma F_x = 0$, which yield the values of the magnitudes F_{BE}, C_y, and C_x, respectively. These values can be checked by verifying that member AD is also in equilibrium.

It should be noted that the pins in Fig. 6.20 were assumed to form an integral part of one of the two members they connected and so it was not necessary to show their free-body diagram. This assumption can always be used to simplify the analysis of frames and machines. When a pin connects three or more members, however, or when a pin connects a support and two or more members, or when a load is applied to a pin, a clear decision must be made in choosing the member to which the pin will be assumed to belong. (If multiforce members are involved, the pin should be attached to one of these members.) The various forces exerted on the pin should then be clearly identified. This is illustrated in Sample Prob. 6.6.

---

†It is not strictly necessary to use a minus sign to distinguish the force exerted by one member on another from the equal and opposite force exerted by the second member on the first, since the two forces belong to different free-body diagrams and thus cannot easily be confused. In the Sample Problems, the same symbol is used to represent equal and opposite forces which are applied to different free bodies. It should be noted that, under these conditions, the sign obtained for a given force component will not directly relate the sense of that component to the sense of the corresponding coordinate axis. Rather, a positive sign will indicate that *the sense assumed for that component in the free-body diagram* is correct, and a negative sign will indicate that it is wrong.

6.11 FRAMES WHICH CEASE TO BE RIGID WHEN DETACHED FROM THEIR SUPPORTS

The crane analyzed in Sec. 6.10 was so constructed that it could keep the same shape without the help of its supports; it was therefore considered as a rigid body. Many frames, however, will collapse if detached from their supports; such frames cannot be considered as rigid bodies. Consider, for example, the frame shown in Fig. 6.21*a*, which consists of two members *AC* and *CB* carrying loads **P** and **Q** at their midpoints; the members are supported by pins at *A* and *B* and are connected by a pin at *C*. If detached from its supports, this frame will not maintain its shape; it should therefore be considered as made of *two distinct rigid parts AC and CB*.

The equations $\Sigma F_x = 0$, $\Sigma F_y = 0$, $\Sigma M = 0$ (about any given point) express the conditions for the *equilibrium of a rigid body* (Chap. 4); we should use them, therefore, in connection with the free-body diagrams of rigid bodies, namely, the free-body diagrams of members *AC* and *CB* (Fig. 6.21*b*). Since these members are multiforce members, and since pins are used at the supports and at the connection, the reactions at *A* and *B* and the forces at *C* will each be represented by two components. In accordance with Newton's third law, the components of the force exerted by *CB* on *AC* and the components of the force exerted by *AC* on *CB* will be represented by vectors of the same magnitude and opposite sense; thus, if the first pair of components consists of $\mathbf{C}_x$ and $\mathbf{C}_y$, the second pair will be represented by $-\mathbf{C}_x$ and $-\mathbf{C}_y$. We note that four unknown force components act on free body *AC*, while only three independent equations can be used to express that the body is in equilibrium; similarly, four unknowns, but only three equations, are associated with *CB*. However, only six different unknowns are involved in the analysis of the two members, and altogether six equations are available to express that the members are in equilibrium. Writing $\Sigma M_A = 0$ for free body *AC* and $\Sigma M_B = 0$ for *CB*, we obtain two simultaneous equations which may be solved for the common magnitude C_x of the components $\mathbf{C}_x$ and $-\mathbf{C}_x$, and for the common magnitude C_y of the components $\mathbf{C}_y$ and $-\mathbf{C}_y$. We then write $\Sigma F_x = 0$ and $\Sigma F_y = 0$ for each of the two free bodies, obtaining, successively, the magnitudes A_x, A_y, B_x, and B_y.

(a)

(b)

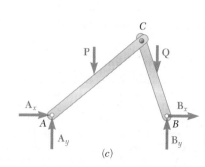

(c)

Fig. 6.21

It can now be observed that since the equations of equilibrium $\Sigma F_x = 0$, $\Sigma F_y = 0$, and $\Sigma M = 0$ (about any given point) are satisfied by the forces acting on free body AC, and since they are also satisfied by the forces acting on free body CB, they must be satisfied when the forces acting on the two free bodies are considered simultaneously. Since the internal forces at C cancel each other, we find that the equations of equilibrium must be satisfied by the external forces shown on the free-body diagram of the frame ACB itself (Fig. 6.21c), although the frame is not a rigid body. These equations can be used to determine some of the components of the reactions at A and B. We will also find, however, that *the reactions cannot be completely determined from the free-body diagram of the whole frame.* It is thus necessary to dismember the frame and to consider the free-body diagrams of its component parts (Fig. 6.21b), even when we are interested in determining external reactions only. This is because the equilibrium equations obtained for free body ACB are *necessary conditions* for the equilibrium of a nonrigid structure, *but are not sufficient conditions*.

The method of solution outlined in the second paragraph of this section involved simultaneous equations. A more efficient method is now presented, which utilizes the free body ACB as well as the free bodies AC and CB. Writing $\Sigma M_A = 0$ and $\Sigma M_B = 0$ for free body ACB, we obtain B_y and A_y. Writing $\Sigma M_C = 0$, $\Sigma F_x = 0$, and $\Sigma F_y = 0$ for free body AC, we obtain, successively, A_x, C_x, and C_y. Finally, writing $\Sigma F_x = 0$ for ACB, we obtain B_x.

We noted above that the analysis of the frame of Fig. 6.21 involves six unknown force components and six independent equilibrium equations. (The equilibrium equations for the whole frame were obtained from the original six equations and, therefore, are not independent.) Moreover, we checked that all unknowns could be actually determined and that all equations could be satisfied. The frame considered is *statically determinate and rigid.†* In general, to determine whether a structure is statically determinate and rigid, we should draw a free-body diagram for each of its component parts and count the reactions and internal forces involved. We should also determine the number of independent equilibrium equations (excluding equations expressing the equilibrium of the whole structure or of groups of component parts already analyzed). If there are more unknowns than equations, the structure is *statically indeterminate.* If there are fewer unknowns than equations, the structure is *nonrigid.* If there are as many unknowns as equations, *and if all unknowns can be determined and all equations satisfied* under general loading conditions, the structure is *statically determinate and rigid.* If, however, due to an *improper arrangement* of members and supports, all unknowns cannot be determined and all equations cannot be satisfied, the structure is *statically indeterminate and nonrigid.*

---

†The word "rigid" is used here to indicate that the frame will maintain its shape as long as it remains attached to its supports.

SAMPLE PROBLEM 6.4

In the frame shown, members *ACE* and *BCD* are connected by a pin at *C* and by the link *DE*. For the loading shown, determine the force in link *DE* and the components of the force exerted at *C* on member *BCD*.

SOLUTION

Free Body: Entire Frame. Since the external reactions involve only three unknowns, we compute the reactions by considering the free-body diagram of the entire frame.

$+\uparrow\Sigma F_y = 0$: $A_y - 480\text{ N} = 0$ $A_y = +480\text{ N}$ $\mathbf{A}_y = 480\text{ N}\uparrow$
$+\curvearrowleft\Sigma M_A = 0$: $-(480\text{ N})(100\text{ mm}) + B(160\text{ mm}) = 0$
                                           $B = +300\text{ N}$ $\mathbf{B} = 300\text{ N}\rightarrow$

$\xrightarrow{+}\Sigma F_x = 0$: $B + A_x = 0$
                      $300\text{ N} + A_x = 0$ $A_x = -300\text{ N}$ $\mathbf{A}_x = 300\text{ N}\leftarrow$

Members. We now dismember the frame. Since only two members are connected at *C*, the components of the unknown forces acting on *ACE* and *BCD* are, respectively, equal and opposite and are assumed directed as shown. We assume that link *DE* is in tension and exerts equal and opposite forces at *D* and *E*, directed as shown.

Free Body: Member BCD. Using the free body *BCD*, we write

$+\curvearrowleft\Sigma M_C = 0$:
        $(F_{DE}\sin\alpha)(250\text{ mm}) + (300\text{ N})(80\text{ mm}) + (480\text{ N})(100\text{ mm}) = 0$
        $F_{DE} = -561\text{ N}$ $F_{DE} = 561\text{ N } C$ ◄
$\xrightarrow{+}\Sigma F_x = 0$: $C_x - F_{DE}\cos\alpha + 300\text{ N} = 0$
        $C_x - (-561\text{ N})\cos 28.07° + 300\text{ N} = 0$ $C_x = -795\text{ N}$
$+\uparrow\Sigma F_y = 0$: $C_y - F_{DE}\sin\alpha - 480\text{ N} = 0$
        $C_y - (-561\text{ N})\sin 28.07° - 480\text{ N} = 0$ $C_y = +216\text{ N}$

From the signs obtained for C_x and C_y we conclude that the force components $\mathbf{C}_x$ and $\mathbf{C}_y$ exerted on member *BCD* are directed, respectively, to the left and up. We have

$$\mathbf{C}_x = 795\text{ N}\leftarrow, \mathbf{C}_y = 216\text{ N}\uparrow \quad ◄$$

Free Body: Member ACE (Check). The computations are checked by considering the free body *ACE*. For example,

$+\curvearrowleft\Sigma M_A = (F_{DE}\cos\alpha)(300\text{ mm}) + (F_{DE}\sin\alpha)(100\text{ mm}) - C_x(220\text{ mm})$
$= (-561\cos\alpha)(300) + (-561\sin\alpha)(100) - (-795)(220) = 0$

SAMPLE PROBLEM 6.5

Determine the components of the forces acting on each member of the frame shown.

SOLUTION

Free Body: Entire Frame. Since the external reactions involve only three unknowns, we compute the reactions by considering the free-body diagram of the entire frame.

$$+\uparrow\Sigma M_E = 0: \quad -(2400 \text{ N})(3.6 \text{ m}) + F(4.8 \text{ m}) = 0$$
$$F = +1800 \text{ N} \qquad\qquad \mathbf{F} = 1800 \text{ N}\uparrow \quad \blacktriangleleft$$
$$+\uparrow\Sigma F_y = 0: \quad -2400 \text{ N} + 1800 \text{ N} + E_y = 0$$
$$E_y = +600 \text{ N} \qquad\qquad \mathbf{E}_y = 600 \text{ N}\uparrow \quad \blacktriangleleft$$
$$\xrightarrow{+}\Sigma F_x = 0: \qquad\qquad\qquad\qquad \mathbf{E}_x = 0 \quad \blacktriangleleft$$

Members. The frame is now dismembered; since only two members are connected at each joint, equal and opposite components are shown on each member at each joint.

Free Body: Member BCD

$$+\uparrow\Sigma M_B = 0: \quad -(2400 \text{ N})(3.6 \text{ m}) + C_y(2.4 \text{ m}) = 0 \quad C_y = +3600 \text{ N} \quad \blacktriangleleft$$
$$+\uparrow\Sigma M_C = 0: \quad -(2400 \text{ N})(1.2 \text{ m}) + B_y(2.4 \text{ m}) = 0 \quad B_y = +1200 \text{ N} \quad \blacktriangleleft$$
$$\xrightarrow{+}\Sigma F_x = 0: \quad -B_x + C_x = 0$$

We note that neither B_x nor C_x can be obtained by considering only member BCD. The positive values obtained for B_y and C_y indicate that the force components $\mathbf{B}_y$ and $\mathbf{C}_y$ are directed as assumed.

Free Body: Member ABE

$$+\uparrow\Sigma M_A = 0: \quad B_x(2.7 \text{ m}) = 0 \qquad\qquad\qquad B_x = 0 \quad \blacktriangleleft$$
$$\xrightarrow{+}\Sigma F_x = 0: \quad +B_x - A_x = 0 \qquad\qquad\qquad A_x = 0 \quad \blacktriangleleft$$
$$+\uparrow\Sigma F_y = 0: \quad -A_y + B_y + 600 \text{ N} = 0$$
$$-A_y + 1200 \text{ N} + 600 \text{ N} = 0 \qquad A_y = +1800 \text{ N} \quad \blacktriangleleft$$

Free Body: Member BCD. Returning now to member BCD, we write

$$\xrightarrow{+}\Sigma F_x = 0: \quad -B_x + C_x = 0 \qquad 0 + C_x = 0 \qquad C_x = 0 \quad \blacktriangleleft$$

Free Body: Member ACF (Check). All unknown components have now been found; to check the results, we verify that member ACF is in equilibrium.

$$+\uparrow\Sigma M_C = (1800 \text{ N})(2.4 \text{ m}) - A_y(2.4 \text{ m}) - A_x(2.7 \text{ m})$$
$$= (1800 \text{ N})(2.4 \text{ m}) - (1800 \text{ N})(2.4 \text{ m}) - 0 = 0 \quad \text{(checks)}$$

SAMPLE PROBLEM 6.6

A 600-lb horizontal force is applied to pin A of the frame shown. Determine the forces acting on the two vertical members of the frame.

SOLUTION

Free Body: Entire Frame. The entire frame is chosen as a free body; although the reactions involve four unknowns, $\mathbf{E}_y$ and $\mathbf{F}_y$ may be determined by writing

$+\uparrow\!\!\downarrow\Sigma M_E = 0:$ $\quad -(600\text{ lb})(10\text{ ft}) + F_y(6\text{ ft}) = 0$
$\qquad\qquad\qquad F_y = +1000\text{ lb}$ $\qquad\qquad \mathbf{F}_y = 1000\text{ lb}\uparrow$ ◄

$+\uparrow\Sigma F_y = 0:$ $\quad E_y + F_y = 0$
$\qquad\qquad\qquad E_y = -1000\text{ lb}$ $\qquad\qquad \mathbf{E}_y = 1000\text{ lb}\downarrow$ ◄

Members. The equations of equilibrium of the entire frame are not sufficient to determine $\mathbf{E}_x$ and $\mathbf{F}_x$. The free-body diagrams of the various members must now be considered in order to proceed with the solution. In dismembering the frame we will assume that pin A is attached to the multiforce member ACE and, thus, that the 600-lb force is applied to that member. We also note that AB and CD are two-force members.

Free Body: Member ACE

$+\uparrow\Sigma F_y = 0:$ $\quad -\frac{5}{13}F_{AB} + \frac{5}{13}F_{CD} - 1000\text{ lb} = 0$
$+\uparrow\!\!\downarrow\Sigma M_E = 0:$ $\quad -(600\text{ lb})(10\text{ ft}) - (\frac{12}{13}F_{AB})(10\text{ ft}) - (\frac{12}{13}F_{CD})(2.5\text{ ft}) = 0$

Solving these equations simultaneously, we find

$$F_{AB} = -1040\text{ lb} \qquad F_{CD} = +1560\text{ lb} \quad ◄$$

The signs obtained indicate that the sense assumed for F_{CD} was correct and the sense for F_{AB} incorrect. Summing now x components,

$\overset{+}{\rightarrow}\Sigma F_x = 0:$ $\quad 600\text{ lb} + \frac{12}{13}(-1040\text{ lb}) + \frac{12}{13}(+1560\text{ lb}) + E_x = 0$
$\qquad\qquad\qquad E_x = -1080\text{ lb}$ $\qquad\qquad \mathbf{E}_x = 1080\text{ lb}\leftarrow$ ◄

Free Body: Entire Frame. Since $\mathbf{E}_x$ has been determined, we can return to the free-body diagram of the entire frame and write

$\overset{+}{\rightarrow}\Sigma F_x = 0:$ $\quad 600\text{ lb} - 1080\text{ lb} + F_x = 0$
$\qquad\qquad\qquad F_x = +480\text{ lb}$ $\qquad\qquad \mathbf{F}_x = 480\text{ lb}\rightarrow$ ◄

Free Body: Member BDF (Check). We can check our computations by verifying that the equation $\Sigma M_B = 0$ is satisfied by the forces acting on member BDF.

$+\uparrow\!\!\downarrow\Sigma M_B = -\left(\frac{12}{13}F_{CD}\right)(2.5\text{ ft}) + (F_x)(7.5\text{ ft})$
$\qquad\qquad = -\frac{12}{13}(1560\text{ lb})(2.5\text{ ft}) + (480\text{ lb})(7.5\text{ ft})$
$\qquad\qquad = -3600\text{ lb}\cdot\text{ft} + 3600\text{ lb}\cdot\text{ft} = 0 \quad \text{(checks)}$

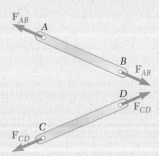

SOLVING PROBLEMS ON YOUR OWN

In this lesson you learned to analyze *frames containing one or more multiforce members*. In the problems that follow you will be asked to determine the external reactions exerted on the frame and the internal forces that hold together the members of the frame.

In solving problems involving frames containing one or more multiforce members, follow these steps:

1. Draw a free-body diagram of the entire frame. Use this free-body diagram to calculate, to the extent possible, the reactions at the supports. (In Sample Prob. 6.6 only two of the four reaction components could be found from the free body of the entire frame.)

2. Dismember the frame, and draw a free-body diagram of each member.

3. Considering first the two-force members, apply equal and opposite forces to each two-force member at the points where it is connected to another member. If the two-force member is a straight member, these forces will be directed along the axis of the member. If you cannot tell at this point whether the member is in tension or compression, just *assume* that the member is in tension and *direct both of the forces away from the member*. Since these forces have the same unknown magnitude, give them both the *same name* and, to avoid any confusion later, *do not use a plus sign or a minus sign.*

4. Next, consider the multiforce members. For each of these members, show all the forces acting on the member, including *applied loads, reactions, and internal forces at connections*. The magnitude and direction of any reaction or reaction component found earlier from the free-body diagram of the entire frame should be clearly indicated.

    a. Where a multiforce member is connected to a two-force member, apply to the multiforce member a force *equal and opposite* to the force drawn on the free-body diagram of the two-force member, *giving it the same name.*

    b. Where a multiforce member is connected to another multiforce member, use *horizontal and vertical components* to represent the internal forces at that point, since neither the direction nor the magnitude of these forces is known. The direction you choose for each of the two force components exerted on the first multiforce member is arbitrary, but *you must apply equal and opposite force components of the same name* to the other multiforce member. Again, *do not use a plus sign or a minus sign.*

(continued)

5. The internal forces may now be determined, as well as any *reactions* that you have not already found.

    a. The free-body diagram of each of the multiforce members can provide you with *three equilibrium equations.*

    b. To simplify your solution, you should seek a way to write an equation involving a single unknown. If you can locate *a point where all but one of the unknown force components intersect,* you will obtain an equation in a single unknown by summing moments about that point. *If all unknown forces except one are parallel,* you will obtain an equation in a single unknown by summing force components in a direction perpendicular to the parallel forces.

    c. Since you arbitrarily chose the direction of each of the unknown forces, you cannot determine until the solution is completed whether your guess was correct. To do that, consider the *sign* of the value found for each of the unknowns: a *positive* sign means that the direction you selected was *correct;* a *negative* sign means that the direction is *opposite* to the direction you assumed.

6. To be more effective and efficient as you proceed through your solution, observe the following rules:

    a. If an equation involving only one unknown can be found, write that equation and *solve it for that unknown.* Immediately *replace* that unknown wherever it appears on other free-body diagrams *by the value you have found.* Repeat this process by seeking equilibrium equations involving only one unknown until you have found all of the internal forces and unknown reactions.

    b. If an equation involving only one unknown cannot be found, you may have to *solve a pair of simultaneous equations.* Before doing so, check that you have shown the values of all of the reactions that were obtained from the free-body diagram of the entire frame.

    c. The total number of equations of equilibrium for the entire frame and for the individual members *will be larger than the number of unknown forces and reactions.* After you have found all the reactions and all the internal forces, you can use the remaining equations to check the accuracy of your computations.

PROBLEMS

FREE BODY PRACTICE PROBLEMS

6.F1 For the frame and loading shown, draw the free-body diagram(s) needed to determine the forces acting on member ABC at B and C.

Fig. P6.F1

Dimensions in mm

Fig. P6.F2

6.F2 For the frame and loading shown, draw the free-body diagram(s) needed to determine all forces acting on member $GBEH$.

6.F3 For the frame and loading shown, draw the free-body diagram(s) needed to determine the reactions at B and F.

Fig. P6.F3

6.F4 Knowing that the surfaces at A and D are frictionless, draw the free-body diagram(s) needed to determine the forces exerted at B and C on member BCE.

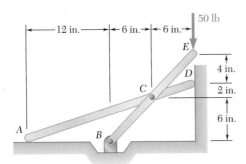

Fig. P6.F4

6.75 and 6.76 Determine the force in member *BD* and the component of the reaction at *C*.

Fig. P6.75

Fig. P6.76

6.77 Determine the components of all forces acting on member *ABCD* of the assembly shown.

Fig. P6.77

6.78 Determine the components of all forces acting on member *ABD* of the frame shown.

6.79 For the frame and loading shown, determine the components of all forces acting on member *ABC*.

6.80 Solve Prob. 6.79 assuming that the 20-kip load is replaced by a clockwise couple of magnitude 100 kip · ft applied to member *EDC* at point *D*.

6.81 Determine the components of all forces acting on member *ABCD* when $\theta = 0$.

Fig. P6.78

Fig. P6.79

Fig. P6.81 and P6.82

6.82 Determine the components of all forces acting on member *ABCD* when $\theta = 90°$.

6.83 and 6.84 Determine the components of the reactions at A and E if a 750-N force directed vertically downward is applied (*a*) at B, (*b*) at D.

6.85 and 6.86 Determine the components of the reactions at A and E if the frame is loaded by a clockwise couple of magnitude $36 \text{ N} \cdot \text{m}$ applied (*a*) at B, (*b*) at D.

6.87 Determine all the forces exerted on member AI if the frame is loaded by a clockwise couple of magnitude $1200 \text{ lb} \cdot \text{in.}$ applied (*a*) at point D, (*b*) at point E.

Fig. P6.83 and P6.85

Fig. P6.84 and P6.86

Fig. P6.87 and P6.88

6.88 Determine all the forces exerted on member AI if the frame is loaded by a 40-lb force directed horizontally to the right and applied (*a*) at point D, (*b*) at point E.

6.89 Determine the components of the reactions at A and B, (*a*) if the 100-lb load is applied as shown, (*b*) if the 100-lb load is moved along its line of action and is applied at point F.

6.90 (*a*) Show that when a frame supports a pulley at A, an equivalent loading of the frame and of each of its component parts can be obtained by removing the pulley and applying at A two forces equal and parallel to the forces that the cable exerted on the pulley. (*b*) Show that if one end of the cable is attached to the frame at a point B, a force of magnitude equal to the tension in the cable should also be applied at B.

Fig. P6.89

Fig. P6.90

6.91 A 3-ft-diameter pipe is supported every 16 ft by a small frame like that shown. Knowing that the combined weight of the pipe and its contents is 500 lb/ft and assuming frictionless surfaces, determine the components (*a*) of the reaction at E, (*b*) of the force exerted at C on member CDE.

6.92 Solve Prob. 6.91 for a frame where $h = 6$ ft.

Fig. P6.91

6.93 Knowing that the pulley has a radius of 0.5 m, determine the components of the reactions at A and E.

Fig. P6.93

Fig. P6.94

6.94 Knowing that the pulley has a radius of 50 mm, determine the components of the reactions at B and E.

6.95 A trailer weighing 2400 lb is attached to a 2900-lb pickup truck by a ball-and-socket truck hitch at D. Determine (*a*) the reactions at each of the six wheels when the truck and trailer are at rest, (*b*) the additional load on each of the truck wheels due to the trailer.

Fig. P6.95

Fig. P6.96

6.96 In order to obtain a better weight distribution over the four wheels of the pickup truck of Prob. 6.95, a compensating hitch of the type shown is used to attach the trailer to the truck. The hitch consists of two bar springs (only one is shown in the figure) that fit into bearings inside a support rigidly attached to the truck. The springs are also connected by chains to the trailer frame, and specially designed hooks make it possible to place both chains in tension. (*a*) Determine the tension T required in each of the two chains if the additional load due to the trailer is to be evenly distributed over the four wheels of the truck. (*b*) What are the resulting reactions at each of the six wheels of the trailer-truck combination?

6.97 The cab and motor units of the front-end loader shown are connected by a vertical pin located 2 m behind the cab wheels. The distance from C to D is 1 m. The center of gravity of the 300-kN motor unit is located at G_m, while the centers of gravity of the 100-kN cab and 75-kN load are located, respectively, at G_c and G_l. Knowing that the machine is at rest with its brakes released, determine (a) the reactions at each of the four wheels, (b) the forces exerted on the motor unit at C and D.

Fig. P6.97

Fig. P6.99

6.98 Solve Prob. 6.97 assuming that the 75-kN load has been removed.

6.99 and 6.100 For the frame and loading shown, determine the components of all forces acting on member ABE.

6.101 For the frame and loading shown, determine the components of all forces acting on member ABD.

Fig. P6.100

Fig. P6.101

6.102 Solve Prob. 6.101 assuming that the 360-lb load has been removed.

6.103 For the frame and loading shown, determine the components of the forces acting on member CDE at C and D.

Fig. P6.103

40 lb

Fig. P6.104

450 lb

Fig. P6.107

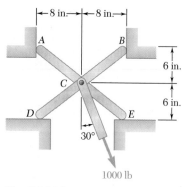

1000 lb

Fig. P6.108

6.104 For the frame and loading shown, determine the components of the forces acting on member *CFE* at *C* and *F*.

6.105 For the frame and loading shown, determine the components of all forces acting on member *ABD*.

Dimensions in mm

Fig. P6.105

6.106 Solve Prob. 6.105 assuming that the 3-kN load has been removed.

6.107 Determine the reaction at *F* and the force in members *AE* and *BD*.

6.108 For the frame and loading shown, determine the reactions at *A*, *B*, *D*, and *E*. Assume that the surface at each support is frictionless.

6.109 The axis of the three-hinge arch *ABC* is a parabola with vertex at *B*. Knowing that $P = 112$ kN and $Q = 140$ kN, determine (*a*) the components of the reaction at *A*, (*b*) the components of the force exerted at *B* on segment *AB*.

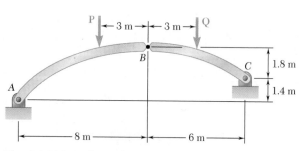

Fig. P6.109 and P6.110

6.110 The axis of the three-hinge arch *ABC* is a parabola with vertex at *B*. Knowing that $P = 140$ kN and $Q = 112$ kN, determine (*a*) the components of the reaction at *A*, (*b*) the components of the force exerted at *B* on segment *AB*.

6.111, 6.112, and 6.113 Members *ABC* and *CDE* are pin-connected at *C* and supported by four links. For the loading shown, determine the force in each link.

Fig. P6.111

Fig. P6.112

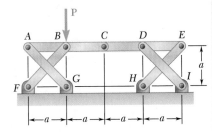

Fig. P6.113

6.114 Members *ABC* and *CDE* are pin-connected at *C* and supported by the four links *AF, BG, DG,* and *EH*. For the loading shown, determine the force in each link.

6.115 Solve Prob. 6.112 assuming that the force **P** is replaced by a clockwise couple of moment **M₀** applied to member *CDE* at *D*.

6.116 Solve Prob. 6.114 assuming that the force **P** is replaced by a clockwise couple of moment **M₀** applied at the same point.

6.117 Four beams, each of length 3*a*, are held together by single nails at *A, B, C,* and *D*. Each beam is attached to a support located at a distance *a* from an end of the beam as shown. Assuming that only vertical forces are exerted at the connections, determine the vertical reactions at *E, F, G,* and *H*.

Fig. P6.114

Fig. P6.117

6.118 Four beams, each of length 2*a*, are nailed together at their midpoints to form the support system shown. Assuming that only vertical forces are exerted at the connections, determine the vertical reactions at *A, D, E,* and *H*.

Fig. P6.118

6.119 through 6.121 Each of the frames shown consists of two L-shaped members connected by two rigid links. For each frame, determine the reactions at the supports and indicate whether the frame is rigid.

(a)

(b)

(c)

Fig. P6.119

(a)

(b)

(c)

Fig. P6.120

(a)

(b)

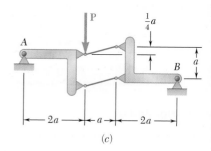

(c)

Fig. P6.121

6.12 MACHINES

Machines are structures designed to transmit and modify forces. Whether they are simple tools or include complicated mechanisms, their main purpose is to transform *input forces* into *output forces*. Consider, for example, a pair of cutting pliers used to cut a wire (Fig. 6.22a). If we apply two equal and opposite forces **P** and **−P** on their handles, they will exert two equal and opposite forces **Q** and **−Q** on the wire (Fig. 6.22b).

Fig. 6.22

Photo 6.5 The lamp shown can be placed in many positions. By considering various free bodies, the force in the springs and the internal forces at the joints can be determined.

To determine the magnitude Q of the output forces when the magnitude P of the input forces is known (or, conversely, to determine P when Q is known), we draw a free-body diagram of the pliers *alone,* showing the input forces **P** and $-$**P** and the *reactions* $-$**Q** and **Q** that the wire exerts on the pliers (Fig. 6.23). However, since a pair of pliers forms a nonrigid structure, we must use one of the component parts as a free body in order to determine the unknown forces. Considering Fig. 6.24a, for example, and taking moments about A, we obtain the relation $Pa = Qb$, which defines the magnitude Q in terms of P or P in terms of Q. The same free-body diagram can be used to determine the components of the internal force at A; we find $A_x = 0$ and $A_y = P + Q$.

In the case of more complicated machines, it generally will be necessary to use several free-body diagrams and, possibly, to solve simultaneous equations involving various internal forces. The free bodies should be chosen to include the input forces and the reactions to the output forces, and the total number of unknown force components involved should not exceed the number of available independent equations. It is advisable, before attempting to solve a problem, to determine whether the structure considered is determinate. There is no point, however, in discussing the rigidity of a machine, since a machine includes moving parts and thus *must* be nonrigid.

Fig. 6.23

Fig. 6.24

SAMPLE PROBLEM 6.7

A hydraulic-lift table is used to raise a 1000-kg crate. It consists of a platform and two identical linkages on which hydraulic cylinders exert equal forces. (Only one linkage and one cylinder are shown.) Members EDB and CG are each of length $2a$, and member AD is pinned to the midpoint of EDB. If the crate is placed on the table, so that half of its weight is supported by the system shown, determine the force exerted by each cylinder in raising the crate for $\theta = 60°$, $a = 0.70$ m, and $L = 3.20$ m. Show that the result obtained is independent of the distance d.

SOLUTION

The machine considered consists of the platform and of the linkage. Its free-body diagram includes an input force $\mathbf{F}_{DH}$ exerted by the cylinder, the weight $\frac{1}{2}\mathbf{W}$, equal and opposite to the output force, and reactions at E and G that we assume to be directed as shown. Since more than three unknowns are involved, this diagram will not be used. The mechanism is dismembered and a free-body diagram is drawn for each of its component parts. We note that AD, BC, and CG are two-force members. We already assumed member CG to be in compression; we now assume that AD and BC are in tension and direct as shown the forces exerted on them. Equal and opposite vectors will be used to represent the forces exerted by the two-force members on the platform, on member BDE, and on roller C.

332

Free Body: Platform ABC.

$$\xrightarrow{+}\Sigma F_x = 0: \qquad F_{AD}\cos\theta = 0 \qquad F_{AD} = 0$$
$$+\uparrow\Sigma F_y = 0: \qquad B + C - \tfrac{1}{2}W = 0 \qquad B + C = \tfrac{1}{2}W \qquad (1)$$

Free Body: Roller C.   We draw a force triangle and obtain $F_{BC} = C\cot\theta$.

Free Body: Member BDE.   Recalling that $F_{AD} = 0$,

$$+\gamma\Sigma M_E = 0: \quad F_{DH}\cos(\phi - 90°)a - B(2a\cos\theta) - F_{BC}(2a\sin\theta) = 0$$
$$F_{DH}a\sin\phi - B(2a\cos\theta) - (C\cot\theta)(2a\sin\theta) = 0$$
$$F_{DH}\sin\phi - 2(B + C)\cos\theta = 0$$

Recalling Eq. (1), we have

$$F_{DH} = W\frac{\cos\theta}{\sin\phi} \qquad (2)$$

and we observe that *the result obtained is independent of d.*   ◄

Applying first the law of sines to triangle *EDH*, we write

$$\frac{\sin\phi}{EH} = \frac{\sin\theta}{DH} \qquad \sin\phi = \frac{EH}{DH}\sin\theta \qquad (3)$$

Using now the law of cosines, we have

$$(DH)^2 = a^2 + L^2 - 2aL\cos\theta$$
$$= (0.70)^2 + (3.20)^2 - 2(0.70)(3.20)\cos 60°$$
$$(DH)^2 = 8.49 \qquad DH = 2.91\text{ m}$$

We also note that

$$W = mg = (1000\text{ kg})(9.81\text{ m/s}^2) = 9810\text{ N} = 9.81\text{ kN}$$

Substituting for $\sin\phi$ from (3) into (2) and using the numerical data, we write

$$F_{DH} = W\frac{DH}{EH}\cot\theta = (9.81\text{ kN})\frac{2.91\text{ m}}{3.20\text{ m}}\cot 60°$$
$$F_{DH} = 5.15\text{ kN} \quad ◄$$

SOLVING PROBLEMS
ON YOUR OWN

This lesson was devoted to the analysis of *machines*. Since machines are designed to transmit or modify forces, they always contain moving parts. However, the machines considered here will always be at rest, and you will be working with the set of *forces required to maintain the equilibrium of the machine.*

Known forces that act on a machine are called *input forces. A machine transforms the input forces into output forces,* such as the cutting forces applied by the pliers of Fig. 6.22. You will determine the output forces by finding the forces equal and opposite to the output forces that should be applied to the machine to maintain its equilibrium.

In the preceding lesson you analyzed frames; you will now use almost the same procedure to analyze machines:

1. Draw a free-body diagram of the whole machine, and use it to determine as many as possible of the unknown forces exerted on the machine.

2. Dismember the machine, and draw a free-body diagram of each member.

3. Considering first the two-force members, apply equal and opposite forces to each two-force member at the points where it is connected to another member. If you cannot tell at this point whether the member is in tension or in compression just *assume* that the member is in tension and *direct both of the forces away from the member.* Since these forces have the same unknown magnitude, *give them both the same name.*

4. Next consider the multiforce members. For each of these members, show all the forces acting on the member, including applied loads and forces, reactions, and internal forces at connections.

    a. Where a multiforce member is connected to a two-force member, apply to the multiforce member a force *equal and opposite* to the force drawn on the free-body diagram of the two-force member, *giving it the same name.*

    b. Where a multiforce member is connected to another multiforce member, use *horizontal and vertical components* to represent the internal forces at that point. The directions you choose for each of the two force components exerted on the first multiforce member are arbitrary, but *you must apply equal and opposite force components of the same name* to the other multiforce member.

5. Equilibrium equations can be written after you have completed the various free-body diagrams.

    a. To simplify your solution, you should, whenever possible, write and solve equilibrium equations involving single unknowns.

    b. Since you arbitrarily chose the direction of each of the unknown forces, you must determine at the end of the solution whether your guess was correct. To that effect, *consider the sign* of the value found for each of the unknowns. A *positive* sign indicates that your guess was correct, and a *negative* sign indicates that it was not.

6. Finally, you should check your solution by substituting the results obtained into an equilibrium equation that you have not previously used.

PROBLEMS

FREE BODY PRACTICE PROBLEMS

6.F5 The position of member *ABC* is controlled by the hydraulic cylinder *CD*. Knowing that θ = 30°, draw the free-body diagram(s) needed to determine the force exerted by the hydraulic cylinder on pin *C*, and the reaction at *B*.

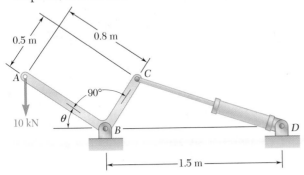

Fig. P6.F5

6.F6 Arm *ABC* is connected by pins to a collar at *B* and to crank *CD* at *C*. Neglecting the effect of friction, draw the free-body diagram(s) needed to determine the couple **M** to hold the system in equilibrium when θ = 30°.

Fig. P6.F6

6.F7 Since the brace shown must remain in position even when the magnitude of **P** is very small, a single safety spring is attached at *D* and *E*. The spring *DE* has a constant of 50 lb/in. and an unstretched length of 7 in. Knowing that *l* = 10 in. and that the magnitude of **P** is 800 lb, draw the free-body diagram(s) needed to determine the force **Q** required to release the brace.

Fig. P6.F7

6.F8 A log weighing 800 lb is lifted by a pair of tongs as shown. Draw the free-body diagram(s) needed to determine the forces exerted at *E* and *F* on tong *DEF*.

Fig. P6.F8

335

Fig. P6.122

END-OF-SECTION PROBLEMS

6.122 The shear shown is used to cut and trim electronic-circuit-board laminates. For the position shown, determine (*a*) the vertical component of the force exerted on the shearing blade at *D*, (*b*) the reaction at *C*.

6.123 The press shown is used to emboss a small seal at *E*. Knowing that *P* = 250 N, determine (*a*) the vertical component of the force exerted on the seal, (*b*) the reaction at *A*.

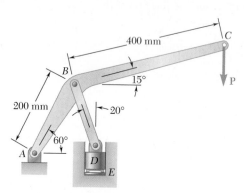

Fig. P6.123 and P6.124

6.124 The press shown is used to emboss a small seal at *E*. Knowing that the vertical component of the force exerted on the seal must be 900 N, determine (*a*) the required vertical force **P**, (*b*) the corresponding reaction at *A*.

6.125 Water pressure in the supply system exerts a downward force of 135 N on the vertical plug at *A*. Determine the tension in the fusible link *DE* and the force exerted on member *BCE* at *B*.

Fig. P6.126

Fig. P6.125

6.126 An 84-lb force is applied to the toggle vise at *C*. Knowing that θ = 90°, determine (*a*) the vertical force exerted on the block at *D*, (*b*) the force exerted on member *ABC* at *B*.

6.127 Solve Prob. 6.126 when θ = 0.

6.128 For the system and loading shown, determine (*a*) the force **P** required for equilibrium, (*b*) the corresponding force in member *BD*, (*c*) the corresponding reaction at *C*.

6.129 The Whitworth mechanism shown is used to produce a quick-return motion of point *D*. The block at *B* is pinned to the crank *AB* and is free to slide in a slot cut in member *CD*. Determine the couple **M** that must be applied to the crank *AB* to hold the mechanism in equilibrium when (*a*) $\alpha = 0$, (*b*) $\alpha = 30°$.

Fig. P6.128

Fig. P6.129

6.130 Solve Prob. 6.129 when (*a*) $\alpha = 60°$, (*b*) $\alpha = 90°$.

6.131 A couple **M** of magnitude 1.5 kN · m is applied to the crank of the engine system shown. For each of the two positions shown, determine the force **P** required to hold the system in equilibrium.

Fig. P6.131 and P6.132

6.132 A force **P** of magnitude 16 kN is applied to the piston of the engine system shown. For each of the two positions shown, determine the couple **M** required to hold the system in equilibrium.

6.133 The pin at *B* is attached to member *ABC* and can slide freely along the slot cut in the fixed plate. Neglecting the effect of friction, determine the couple **M** required to hold the system in equilibrium when $\theta = 30°$.

6.134 The pin at *B* is attached to member *ABC* and can slide freely along the slot cut in the fixed plate. Neglecting the effect of friction, determine the couple **M** required to hold the system in equilibrium when $\theta = 60°$.

Fig. P6.133 and P6.134

Fig. P6.135

6.135 and 6.136 Rod CD is attached to the collar D and passes through a collar welded to end B of lever AB. Neglecting the effect of friction, determine the couple **M** required to hold the system in equilibrium when $\theta = 30°$.

Fig. P6.136

6.137 and 6.138 Two rods are connected by a frictionless collar B. Knowing that the magnitude of the couple $\mathbf{M}_A$ is 500 lb · in., determine (a) the couple $\mathbf{M}_C$ required for equilibrium, (b) the corresponding components of the reaction at C.

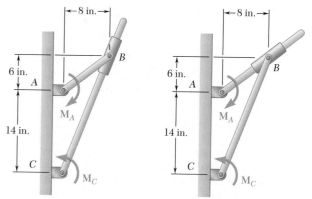

Fig. P6.137   **Fig. P6.138**

6.139 Two hydraulic cylinders control the position of the robotic arm ABC. Knowing that in the position shown the cylinders are parallel, determine the force exerted by each cylinder when $P = 160$ N and $Q = 80$ N.

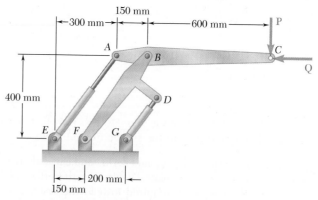

Fig. P6.139 and P6.140

6.140 Two hydraulic cylinders control the position of the robotic arm ABC. In the position shown, the cylinders are parallel and both are in tension. Knowing that $F_{AE} = 600$ N and $F_{DG} = 50$ N, determine the forces **P** and **Q** applied at C to arm ABC.

6.141 The tongs shown are used to apply a total upward force of 45 kN on a pipe cap. Determine the forces exerted at D and F on tong ADF.

Fig. P6.141

Fig. P6.142

6.142 If the toggle shown is added to the tongs of Prob. 6.141 and a single vertical force is applied at G, determine the forces exerted at D and F on tong ADF.

6.143 A small barrel weighing 60 lb is lifted by a pair of tongs as shown. Knowing that $a = 5$ in., determine the forces exerted at B and D on tong ABD.

6.144 A 39-ft length of railroad rail of weight 44 lb/ft is lifted by the tongs shown. Determine the forces exerted at D and F on tong BDF.

Fig. P6.143

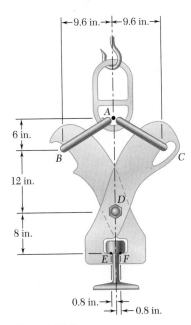

Fig. P6.144

6.145 Determine the magnitude of the gripping forces produced when two 300-N forces are applied as shown.

Fig. P6.145

6.146 The compound-lever pruning shears shown can be adjusted by placing pin A at various ratchet positions on blade ACE. Knowing that 300-lb vertical forces are required to complete the pruning of a small branch, determine the magnitude P of the forces that must be applied to the handles when the shears are adjusted as shown.

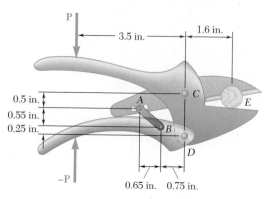

Fig. P6.146

6.147 The pliers shown are used to grip a 0.3-in.-diameter rod. Knowing that two 60-lb forces are applied to the handles, determine (a) the magnitude of the forces exerted on the rod, (b) the force exerted by the pin at A on portion AB of the pliers.

6.148 In using the bolt cutter shown, a worker applies two 300-N forces to the handles. Determine the magnitude of the forces exerted by the cutter on the bolt.

6.149 The specialized plumbing wrench shown is used in confined areas (e.g., under a basin or sink). It consists essentially of a jaw BC pinned at B to a long rod. Knowing that the forces exerted on the nut are equivalent to a clockwise (when viewed from above) couple of magnitude 135 lb · in., determine (a) the magnitude of the force exerted by pin B on jaw BC, (b) the couple $\mathbf{M}_0$ that is applied to the wrench.

6.150 and 6.151 Determine the force $\mathbf{P}$ that must be applied to the toggle CDE to maintain bracket ABC in the position shown.

Fig. P6.147

Fig. P6.148

Fig. P6.149

Fig. P6.150

Fig. P6.151

6.152 A 45-lb shelf is held horizontally by a self-locking brace that consists of two parts *EDC* and *CDB* hinged at *C* and bearing against each other at *D*. Determine the force **P** required to release the brace.

Fig. P6.152

6.153 The telescoping arm *ABC* is used to provide an elevated platform for construction workers. The workers and the platform together have a mass of 200 kg and have a combined center of gravity located directly above *C*. For the position when $\theta = 20°$, determine (*a*) the force exerted at *B* by the single hydraulic cylinder *BD*, (*b*) the force exerted on the supporting carriage at *A*.

6.154 The telescoping arm *ABC* of Prob. 6.153 can be lowered until end *C* is close to the ground, so that workers can easily board the platform. For the position when $\theta = -20°$, determine (*a*) the force exerted at *B* by the single hydraulic cylinder *BD*, (*b*) the force exerted on the supporting carriage at *A*.

6.155 The bucket of the front-end loader shown carries a 3200-lb load. The motion of the bucket is controlled by two identical mechanisms, only one of which is shown. Knowing that the mechanism shown supports one-half of the 3200-lb load, determine the force exerted (*a*) by cylinder *CD*, (*b*) by cylinder *FH*.

Fig. P6.153

Dimensions in inches

Fig. P6.155

6.156 The motion of the bucket of the front-end loader shown is controlled by two arms and a linkage that are pin-connected at *D*. The arms are located symmetrically with respect to the central, vertical, and longitudinal plane of the loader; one arm *AFJ* and its control cylinder *EF* are shown. The single linkage *GHDB* and its control cylinder *BC* are located in the plane of symmetry. For the position and loading shown, determine the force exerted (*a*) by cylinder *BC*, (*b*) by cylinder *EF*.

Fig. P6.156

6.157 The motion of the backhoe bucket shown is controlled by the hydraulic cylinders *AD*, *CG*, and *EF*. As a result of an attempt to dislodge a portion of a slab, a 2-kip force **P** is exerted on the bucket teeth at *J*. Knowing that $\theta = 45°$, determine the force exerted by each cylinder.

Fig. P6.157

6.158 Solve Prob. 6.157 assuming that the 2-kip force **P** acts horizontally to the right ($\theta = 0$).

6.159 In the planetary gear system shown, the radius of the central gear *A* is $a = 18$ mm, the radius of each planetary gear is *b*, and the radius of the outer gear *E* is $(a + 2b)$. A clockwise couple of magnitude $M_A = 10$ N · m is applied to the central gear *A* and a counterclockwise couple of magnitude $M_S = 50$ N · m is applied to the spider *BCD*. If the system is to be in equilibrium, determine (*a*) the required radius *b* of the planetary gears, (*b*) the magnitude M_E of the couple that must be applied to the outer gear *E*.

Fig. P6.159

6.160 The gears D and G are rigidly attached to shafts that are held by frictionless bearings. If $r_D = 90$ mm and $r_G = 30$ mm, determine (a) the couple $\mathbf{M}_0$ that must be applied for equilibrium, (b) the reactions at A and B.

Fig. P6.160

*6.161 Two shafts AC and CF, which lie in the vertical xy plane, are connected by a universal joint at C. The bearings at B and D do not exert any axial force. A couple of magnitude 500 lb · in. (clockwise when viewed from the positive x axis) is applied to shaft CF at F. At a time when the arm of the crosspiece attached to shaft CF is horizontal, determine (a) the magnitude of the couple that must be applied to shaft AC at A to maintain equilibrium, (b) the reactions at B, D, and E. (*Hint:* The sum of the couples exerted on the crosspiece must be zero.)

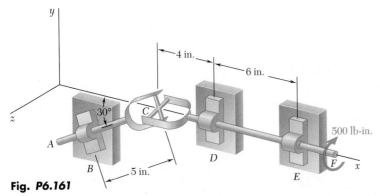

Fig. P6.161

*6.162 Solve Prob. 6.161 assuming that the arm of the crosspiece attached to shaft CF is vertical.

*6.163 The large mechanical tongs shown are used to grab and lift a thick 7500-kg steel slab HJ. Knowing that slipping does not occur between the tong grips and the slab at H and J, determine the components of all forces acting on member EFH. (*Hint:* Consider the symmetry of the tongs to establish relationships between the components of the force acting at E on EFH and the components of the force acting at D on DGJ.)

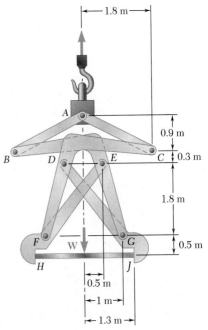

Fig. P6.163

In this chapter you learned to determine the *internal forces* holding together the various parts of a structure.

Analysis of trusses

The first half of the chapter was devoted to the analysis of *trusses,* i.e., to the analysis of structures consisting of *straight members connected at their extremities only.* The members being slender and unable to support lateral loads, all the loads must be applied at the joints; a truss may thus be assumed to consist of *pins and two-force members* [Sec. 6.2].

Simple trusses

A truss is said to be *rigid* if it is designed in such a way that it will not greatly deform or collapse under a small load. A triangular truss consisting of three members connected at three joints is clearly a rigid truss (Fig. 6.25a) and so will be the truss obtained by adding two new members to the first one and connecting them at a new joint (Fig. 6.25b). Trusses obtained by repeating this procedure are called *simple trusses.* We may check that in a simple truss the total number of members is $m = 2n - 3$, where n is the total number of joints [Sec. 6.3].

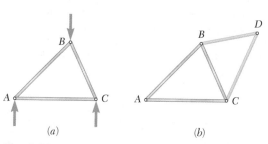

Fig. 6.25

Method of joints

The forces in the various members of a simple truss can be determined by the *method of joints* [Sec. 6.4]. First, the reactions at the supports can be obtained by considering the entire truss as a free body. The free-body diagram of each pin is then drawn, showing the forces exerted on the pin by the members or supports it connects. Since the members are straight two-force members, the force exerted by a member on the pin is directed along that member, and only the magnitude of the force is unknown. It is always possible in the case of a simple truss to draw the free-body diagrams of the pins in such an order that only two unknown forces are included in each diagram. These forces can be obtained from the corresponding two equilibrium equations or—if only three forces are involved—from the corresponding force triangle. If the force exerted by a member on a pin is directed toward that pin, the member is in *compression;*

if it is directed away from the pin, the member is in *tension* [Sample Prob. 6.1]. The analysis of a truss is sometimes expedited by first recognizing *joints under special loading conditions* [Sec. 6.5]. The method of joints can also be extended to the analysis of three-dimensional or *space trusses* [Sec. 6.6].

Method of sections

The *method of sections* is usually preferred to the method of joints when the force in only one member—or very few members—of a truss is desired [Sec. 6.7]. To determine the force in member *BD* of the truss of Fig. 6.26*a*, for example, we *pass a section* through members *BD*, *BE*, and *CE*, remove these members, and use the portion *ABC* of the truss as a free body (Fig. 6.26*b*). Writing $\Sigma M_E = 0$, we determine the magnitude of the force $\mathbf{F}_{BD}$, which represents the force in member *BD*. A positive sign indicates that the member is in *tension;* a negative sign indicates that it is in *compression* [Sample Probs. 6.2 and 6.3].

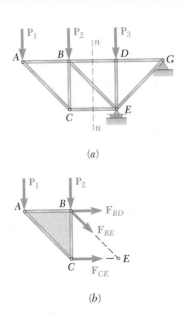

(a)

(b)

Fig. 6.26

Compound trusses

The method of sections is particularly useful in the analysis of *compound trusses*, i.e., trusses which cannot be constructed from the basic triangular truss of Fig. 6.25*a* but which can be obtained by rigidly connecting several simple trusses [Sec. 6.8]. If the component trusses have been properly connected (e.g., one pin and one link, or three nonconcurrent and nonparallel links) and if the resulting structure is properly supported (e.g., one pin and one roller), the compound truss is *statically determinate, rigid, and completely constrained*. The following necessary—but not sufficient—condition is then satisfied: $m + r = 2n$, where m is the number of members, r is the number of unknowns representing the reactions at the supports, and n is the number of joints.

Frames and machines

The second part of the chapter was devoted to the analysis of *frames and machines*. Frames and machines are structures which contain *multiforce members*, i.e., members acted upon by three or more forces. Frames are designed to support loads and are usually stationary, fully constrained structures. Machines are designed to transmit or modify forces and always contain moving parts [Sec. 6.9].

Analysis of a frame

To *analyze a frame,* we first consider the *entire frame as a free body* and write three equilibrium equations [Sec. 6.10]. If the frame remains rigid when detached from its supports, the reactions involve only three unknowns and may be determined from these equations [Sample Probs. 6.4 and 6.5]. On the other hand, if the frame ceases to be rigid when detached from its supports, the reactions involve more than three unknowns and cannot be completely determined from the equilibrium equations of the frame [Sec. 6.11; Sample Prob. 6.6].

Multiforce members

We then *dismember the frame* and identify the various members as either two-force members or multiforce members; pins are assumed to form an integral part of one of the members they connect. We draw the free-body diagram of each of the multiforce members, noting that when two multiforce members are connected to the same two-force member, they are acted upon by that member with *equal and opposite forces of unknown magnitude but known direction*. When two multiforce members are connected by a pin, they exert on each other *equal and opposite forces of unknown direction,* which should be represented by *two unknown components.* The equilibrium equations obtained from the free-body diagrams of the multiforce members can then be solved for the various internal forces [Sample Probs. 6.4 and 6.5]. The equilibrium equations can also be used to complete the determination of the reactions at the supports [Sample Prob. 6.6]. Actually, if the frame is *statically determinate and rigid,* the free-body diagrams of the multiforce members could provide as many equations as there are unknown forces (including the reactions) [Sec. 6.11]. However, as suggested above, it is advisable to first consider the free-body diagram of the entire frame to minimize the number of equations that must be solved simultaneously.

Analysis of a machine

To *analyze a machine,* we dismember it and, following the same procedure as for a frame, draw the free-body diagram of each of the multiforce members. The corresponding equilibrium equations yield the *output forces* exerted by the machine in terms of the *input forces* applied to it, as well as the *internal forces* at the various connections [Sec. 6.12; Sample Prob. 6.7].

REVIEW PROBLEMS

6.164 Using the method of joints, determine the force in each member of the truss shown. State whether each member is in tension or compression.

6.165 Using the method of joints, determine the force in each member of the roof truss shown. State whether each member is in tension or compression.

Fig. P6.164

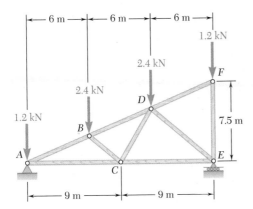

Fig. P6.165

6.166 A Howe scissors roof truss is loaded as shown. Determine the force in members *DF*, *DG*, and *EG*.

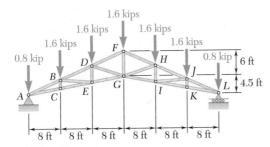

Fig. P6.166 and P6.167

6.167 A Howe scissors roof truss is loaded as shown. Determine the force in members *GI*, *HI*, and *HJ*.

6.168 Rod *CD* is fitted with a collar at *D* that can be moved along rod *AB*, which is bent in the shape of an arc of circle. For the position when $\theta = 30°$, determine (*a*) the force in rod *CD*, (*b*) the reaction at *B*.

Fig. P6.168

347

Fig. P6.169

6.169 For the frame and loading shown, determine the components of all forces acting on member *ABC*.

6.170 Knowing that each pulley has a radius of 250 mm, determine the components of the reactions at *D* and *E*.

Fig. P6.170

6.171 For the frame and loading shown, determine the components of the forces acting on member *DABC* at *B* and *D*.

Fig. P6.171

Fig. P6.172

6.172 For the frame and loading shown, determine (*a*) the reaction at *C*, (*b*) the force in member *AD*.

6.173 The control rod *CE* passes through a horizontal hole in the body of the toggle system shown. Knowing that link *BD* is 250 mm long, determine the force **Q** required to hold the system in equilibrium when $\beta = 20°$.

Fig. P6.173

6.174 Determine the magnitude of the gripping forces exerted along line *aa* on the nut when two 50-lb forces are applied to the handles as shown. Assume that pins *A* and *D* slide freely in slots cut in the jaws.

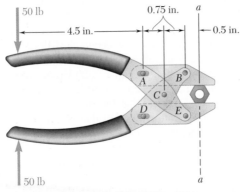

Fig. P6.174

6.175 Knowing that the frame shown has a sag at *B* of *a* = 1 in., determine the force **P** required to maintain equilibrium in the position shown.

Fig. P6.175

COMPUTER PROBLEMS

Fig. P6.C1

6.C1 A Pratt steel truss is to be designed to support three 10-kip loads as shown. The length of the truss is to be 40 ft. The height of the truss and thus the angle θ, as well as the cross-sectional areas of the various members, are to be selected to obtain the most economical design. Specifically, the cross-sectional area of each member is to be chosen so that the stress (force divided by area) in that member is equal to 20 kips/in², the allowable stress for the steel used; the total weight of the steel, and thus its cost, must be as small as possible. (*a*) Knowing that the specific weight of the steel used is 0.284 lb/in³, write a computer program that can be used to calculate the weight of the truss and the cross-sectional area of each load-bearing member located to the left of *DE* for values of θ from 20° to 80° using 5° increments. (*b*) Using appropriate smaller increments, determine the optimum value of θ and the corresponding values of the weight of the truss and of the cross-sectional areas of the various members. Ignore the weight of any zero-force member in your computations.

6.C2 The floor of a bridge will rest on stringers that will be simply supported by transverse floor beams, as in Fig. 6.3. The ends of the beams will be connected to the upper joints of two trusses, one of which is shown in Fig. P6.C2. As part of the design of the bridge, it is desired to simulate the effect on this truss of driving a 12-kN truck over the bridge. Knowing that the distance between the truck's axles is $b = 2.25$ m and assuming that the weight of the truck is equally distributed over its four wheels, write a computer program that can be used to calculate the forces created by the truck in members *BH* and *GH* for values of *x* from 0 to 17.25 m using 0.75-m increments. From the results obtained, determine (*a*) the maximum tensile force in *BH*, (*b*) the maximum compressive force in *BH*, (*c*) the maximum tensile force in *GH*. Indicate in each case the corresponding value of *x*. (*Note:* The increments have been selected so that the desired values are among those that will be tabulated.)

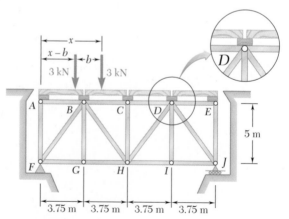

Fig. P6.C2

6.C3 In the mechanism shown the position of boom *AC* is controlled by arm *BD*. For the loading shown, write a computer program and use it to determine the couple **M** required to hold the system in equilibrium for values of θ from $-30°$ to $90°$ using $10°$ increments. Also, for the same values of θ, determine the reaction at *A*. As a part of the design process of the mechanism, use appropriate smaller increments and determine (*a*) the value of θ for which *M* is maximum and the corresponding value of *M*, (*b*) the value of θ for which the reaction at *A* is maximum and the corresponding magnitude of this reaction.

6.C4 The design of a robotic system calls for the two-rod mechanism shown. Rods *AC* and *BD* are connected by a slider block *D* as shown. Neglecting the effect of friction, write a computer program and use it to determine the couple $\mathbf{M}_A$ required to hold the rods in equilibrium for values of θ from 0 to $120°$ using $10°$ increments. For the same values of θ, determine the magnitude of the force **F** exerted by rod *AC* on the slider block.

6.C5 The compound-lever pruning shears shown can be adjusted by placing pin *A* at various ratchet positions on blade *ACE*. Knowing that the length *AB* is 0.85 in., write a computer program and use it to determine the magnitude of the vertical forces applied to the small branch for values of *d* from 0.4 in. to 0.6 in. using 0.025-in. increments. As a part of the design of the shears, use appropriate smaller increments and determine the smallest allowable value of *d* if the force in link *AB* is not to exceed 500 lb.

Fig. P6.C3

Fig. P6.C4

Fig. P6.C5

6.C6 Rod *CD* is attached to collar *D* and passes through a collar welded to end *B* of lever *AB*. As an initial step in the design of lever *AB*, write a computer program and use it to calculate the magnitude *M* of the couple required to hold the system in equilibrium for values of θ from $15°$ to $90°$ using $5°$ increments. Using appropriate smaller increments, determine the value of θ for which *M* is minimum and the corresponding value of *M*.

Fig. P6.C6

The tractive force that a railroad locomotive can develop depends upon the frictional resistance between the drive wheels and the rails. When the potential exists for wheel slip to occur, such as when a train travels upgrade over wet rails, sand is deposited on top of the railhead to increase this friction.

CHAPTER 8

Friction

411

8.1 INTRODUCTION

In the preceding chapters, it was assumed that surfaces in contact were either *frictionless* or *rough*. If they were frictionless, the force each surface exerted on the other was normal to the surfaces and the two surfaces could move freely with respect to each other. If they were rough, it was assumed that tangential forces could develop to prevent the motion of one surface with respect to the other.

This view was a simplified one. Actually, no perfectly frictionless surface exists. When two surfaces are in contact, tangential forces, called *friction forces,* will always develop if one attempts to move one surface with respect to the other. On the other hand, these friction forces are limited in magnitude and will not prevent motion if sufficiently large forces are applied. The distinction between frictionless and rough surfaces is thus a matter of degree. This will be seen more clearly in the present chapter, which is devoted to the study of friction and of its applications to common engineering situations.

There are two types of friction: *dry friction,* sometimes called *Coulomb friction,* and *fluid friction.* Fluid friction develops between layers of fluid moving at different velocities. Fluid friction is of great importance in problems involving the flow of fluids through pipes and orifices or dealing with bodies immersed in moving fluids. It is also basic in the analysis of the motion of *lubricated mechanisms.* Such problems are considered in texts on fluid mechanics. The present study is limited to dry friction, i.e., to problems involving rigid bodies which are in contact along *nonlubricated* surfaces.

In the first part of this chapter, the equilibrium of various rigid bodies and structures, assuming dry friction at the surfaces of contact, is analyzed. Later a number of specific engineering applications where dry friction plays an important role are considered: wedges, square-threaded screws, journal bearings, thrust bearings, rolling resistance, and belt friction.

8.2 THE LAWS OF DRY FRICTION. COEFFICIENTS OF FRICTION

The laws of dry friction are exemplified by the following experiment. A block of weight W is placed on a horizontal plane surface (Fig. 8.1a). The forces acting on the block are its weight W and the reaction of the surface. Since the weight has no horizontal component, the reaction of the surface also has no horizontal component; the reaction is therefore *normal* to the surface and is represented by N in Fig. 8.1a. Suppose, now, that a horizontal force P is applied to the block (Fig. 8.1b). If P is small, the block will not move; some other horizontal force must therefore exist, which balances P. This other force is the *static-friction force* F, which is actually the resultant of a great number of forces acting over the entire surface of contact between the block and the plane. The nature of these forces is not known exactly, but it is generally assumed that these forces are due to the irregularities of the surfaces in contact and, to a certain extent, to molecular attraction.

If the force **P** is increased, the friction force **F** also increases, continuing to oppose **P**, until its magnitude reaches a certain *maximum value* F_m (Fig. 8.1c). If **P** is further increased, the friction force

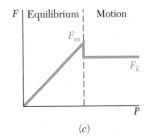

(a) (b) (c)

Fig. 8.1

cannot balance it any more and the block starts sliding.† As soon as the block has been set in motion, the magnitude of **F** drops from F_m to a lower value F_k. This is because there is less interpenetration between the irregularities of the surfaces in contact when these surfaces move with respect to each other. From then on, the block keeps sliding with increasing velocity while the friction force, denoted by $\mathbf{F}_k$ and called the *kinetic-friction force*, remains approximately constant.

Experimental evidence shows that the maximum value F_m of the static-friction force is proportional to the normal component N of the reaction of the surface. We have

$$F_m = \mu_s N \tag{8.1}$$

where μ_s is a constant called the *coefficient of static friction*. Similarly, the magnitude F_k of the kinetic-friction force may be put in the form

$$F_k = \mu_k N \tag{8.2}$$

where μ_k is a constant called the *coefficient of kinetic friction*. The coefficients of friction μ_s and μ_k do not depend upon the area of

†It should be noted that, as the magnitude F of the friction force increases from 0 to F_m, the point of application A of the resultant **N** of the normal forces of contact moves to the right, so that the couples formed, respectively, by **P** and **F** and by **W** and **N** remain balanced. If **N** reaches B before F reaches its maximum value F_m, the block will tip about B before it can start sliding (see Probs. 8.15 through 8.18).

the surfaces in contact. Both coefficients, however, depend strongly on the *nature* of the surfaces in contact. Since they also depend upon the exact condition of the surfaces, their value is seldom known with an accuracy greater than 5 percent. Approximate values of coefficients of static friction for various dry surfaces are given in Table 8.1. The corresponding values of the coefficient of kinetic friction would be about 25 percent smaller. Since coefficients of friction are dimensionless quantities, the values given in Table 8.1 can be used with both SI units and U.S. customary units.

TABLE 8.1 Approximate Values of Coefficient of Static Friction for Dry Surfaces

Metal on metal	0.15–0.60
Metal on wood	0.20–0.60
Metal on stone	0.30–0.70
Metal on leather	0.30–0.60
Wood on wood	0.25–0.50
Wood on leather	0.25–0.50
Stone on stone	0.40–0.70
Earth on earth	0.20–1.00
Rubber on concrete	0.60–0.90

From the description given above, it appears that four different situations can occur when a rigid body is in contact with a horizontal surface:

1. The forces applied to the body do not tend to move it along the surface of contact; there is no friction force (Fig. 8.2*a*).

2. The applied forces tend to move the body along the surface of contact but are not large enough to set it in motion. The friction force **F** which has developed can be found by solving the equations of equilibrium for the body. Since there is no evidence that **F** has reached its maximum value, the equation $F_m = \mu_s N$ *cannot be used* to determine the friction force (Fig. 8.2*b*).

3. The applied forces are such that the body is just about to slide. We say that *motion is impending*. The friction force **F** has reached its maximum value F_m and, together with the normal force **N**, balances the applied forces. Both the equations of equilibrium and the equation $F_m = \mu_s N$ *can be used*. We also note that the friction force has a sense opposite to the sense of impending motion (Fig. 8.2*c*).

4. The body is sliding under the action of the applied forces, and the equations of equilibrium do not apply any more. However, **F** is now equal to F_k and the equation $F_k = \mu_k N$ may be used. The sense of $\mathbf{F}_k$ is opposite to the sense of motion (Fig. 8.2*d*).

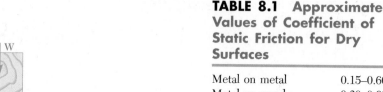

(*a*) No friction ($P_x = 0$)

$F = 0$
$N = P + W$

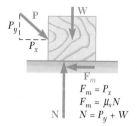

(*b*) No motion ($P_x < F_m$)

$F = P_x$
$F < \mu_s N$
$N = P_y + W$

(*c*) Motion impending $\longrightarrow$ ($P_x = F_m$)

$F_m = P_x$
$F_m = \mu_s N$
$N = P_y + W$

(*d*) Motion $\longrightarrow$ ($P_x > F_m$)

$F_k < P_x$
$F_k = \mu_k N$
$N = P_y + W$

Fig. 8.2

8.3 ANGLES OF FRICTION

It is sometimes convenient to replace the normal force **N** and the friction force **F** by their resultant **R**. Let us consider again a block of weight **W** resting on a horizontal plane surface. If no horizontal force is applied to the block, the resultant **R** reduces to the normal force **N** (Fig. 8.3a). However, if the applied force **P** has a horizontal component $\mathbf{P}_x$ which tends to move the block, the force **R** will have a horizontal component **F** and, thus, will form an angle ϕ with the normal to the surface (Fig. 8.3b). If $\mathbf{P}_x$ is increased until motion becomes impending, the angle between **R** and the vertical grows and reaches a maximum value (Fig. 8.3c). This value is called the *angle of static friction* and is denoted by ϕ_s. From the geometry of Fig. 8.3c, we note that

$$\tan \phi_s = \frac{F_m}{N} = \frac{\mu_s N}{N}$$

$$\tan \phi_s = \mu_s \tag{8.3}$$

If motion actually takes place, the magnitude of the friction force drops to F_k; similarly, the angle ϕ between **R** and **N** drops to a lower value ϕ_k, called the *angle of kinetic friction* (Fig. 8.3d). From the geometry of Fig. 8.3d, we write

$$\tan \phi_k = \frac{F_k}{N} = \frac{\mu_k N}{N}$$

$$\tan \phi_k = \mu_k \tag{8.4}$$

Another example will show how the angle of friction can be used to advantage in the analysis of certain types of problems. Consider a block resting on a board and subjected to no other force than its weight **W** and the reaction **R** of the board. The board can be given any desired inclination. If the board is horizontal, the force **R** exerted by the board on the block is perpendicular to the board and balances the weight **W** (Fig. 8.4a). If the board is given a small angle of inclination θ, the force **R** will deviate from the perpendicular to the board by the angle θ and will keep balancing **W** (Fig. 8.4b); it will then have a normal component **N** of magnitude $N = W \cos \theta$ and a tangential component **F** of magnitude $F = W \sin \theta$.

If we keep increasing the angle of inclination, motion will soon become impending. At that time, the angle between **R** and the normal will have reached its maximum value ϕ_s (Fig. 8.4c). The value of the angle of inclination corresponding to impending motion is called the *angle of repose*. Clearly, the angle of repose is equal to the angle of static friction ϕ_s. If the angle of inclination θ is further increased, motion starts and the angle between **R** and the normal drops to the lower value ϕ_k (Fig. 8.4d). The reaction **R** is not vertical any more, and the forces acting on the block are unbalanced.

(a) No friction

(b) No motion

(c) Motion impending ⟶

(d) Motion ⟶

Fig. 8.3

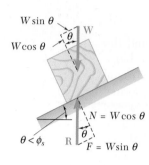

$\theta = 0$

R

(*a*) No friction

$W \cos \theta$

$W \sin \theta$

$N = W \cos \theta$

$\theta < \phi_s$ R $F = W \sin \theta$

(*b*) No motion

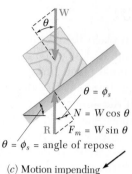

$\theta = \phi_s$

$N = W \cos \theta$

R $F_m = W \sin \theta$

$\theta = \phi_s$ = angle of repose

(*c*) Motion impending

$N = W \cos \theta$

ϕ_k

$\theta > \phi_s$ R $F_k < W \sin \theta$

(*d*) Motion

Fig. 8.4

Photo 8.1 The coefficient of static friction between a package and the inclined conveyer belt must be sufficiently large to enable the package to be transported without slipping.

8.4 PROBLEMS INVOLVING DRY FRICTION

Problems involving dry friction are found in many engineering applications. Some deal with simple situations such as the block sliding on a plane described in the preceding sections. Others involve more complicated situations as in Sample Prob. 8.3; many deal with the stability of rigid bodies in accelerated motion and will be studied in dynamics. Also, a number of common machines and mechanisms can be analyzed by applying the laws of dry friction. These include wedges, screws, journal and thrust bearings, and belt transmissions. They will be studied in the following sections.

The *methods* which should be used to solve problems involving dry friction are the same that were used in the preceding chapters. If a problem involves only a motion of translation, with no possible rotation, the body under consideration can usually be treated as a particle, and the methods of Chap. 2 used. If the problem involves a possible rotation, the body must be considered as a rigid body, and the methods of Chap. 4 should be used. If the structure considered is made of several parts, the principle of action and reaction must be used as was done in Chap. 6.

If the body considered is acted upon by more than three forces (including the reactions at the surfaces of contact), the reaction at each surface will be represented by its components **N** and **F** and the problem will be solved from the equations of equilibrium. If only three forces act on the body under consideration, it may be more convenient to represent each reaction by the single force **R** and to solve the problem by drawing a force triangle.

Most problems involving friction fall into one of the following *three groups:* In the *first group* of problems, all applied forces are given and the coefficients of friction are known; we are to determine whether the body considered will remain at rest or slide. The friction force **F** *required to maintain equilibrium* is unknown (its magnitude is *not* equal to $\mu_s N$) and should be determined, together with the normal force **N**, by drawing a free-body diagram and *solving the equations of equilibrium* (Fig. 8.5*a*). The value found for the magnitude F of the friction force is then compared with the maximum value $F_m = \mu_s N$. If F is smaller than or equal to F_m, the body remains at rest. If the value found for F is larger than F_m, equilibrium cannot be maintained and motion takes place; the actual magnitude of the friction force is then $F_k = \mu_k N$.

In problems of the *second group*, all applied forces are given and the motion is known to be impending; we are to determine the value of the coefficient of static friction. Here again, we determine the friction force and the normal force by drawing a free-body diagram and solving the equations of equilibrium (Fig. 8.5b). Since we know that the value found for F is the maximum value F_m, the coefficient of friction may be found by writing and solving the equation $F_m = \mu_s N$.

In problems of the *third group*, the coefficient of static friction is given, and it is known that the motion is impending in a given direction; we are to determine the magnitude or the direction of one of the applied forces. The friction force should be shown in the free-body diagram with a *sense opposite to that of the impending motion* and with a magnitude $F_m = \mu_s N$ (Fig. 8.5c). The equations of equilibrium can then be written, and the desired force determined.

As noted above, when only three forces are involved it may be more convenient to represent the reaction of the surface by a single force **R** and to solve the problem by drawing a force triangle. Such a solution is used in Sample Prob. 8.2.

When two bodies A and B are in contact (Fig. 8.6a), the forces of friction exerted, respectively, by A on B and by B on A are equal and opposite (Newton's third law). In drawing the free-body diagram of one of the bodies, it is important to include the appropriate friction force with its correct sense. The following rule should then be observed: *The sense of the friction force acting on A is opposite to that of the motion (or impending motion) of A as observed from B* (Fig. 8.6b).† The sense of the friction force acting on B is determined in a similar way (Fig. 8.6c). Note that the motion of A as observed from B is a *relative* motion. For example, if body A is fixed and body B moves, body A will have a relative motion with respect to B. Also, if both B and A are moving down but B is moving faster than A, body A will be observed, from B, to be moving up.

(a)

(b)

(c)

Fig. 8.5

---

†It is therefore *the same as that of the motion of B as observed from A*.

(a)

(b)

(c)

Fig. 8.6

SAMPLE PROBLEM 8.1

A 100-lb force acts as shown on a 300-lb block placed on an inclined plane. The coefficients of friction between the block and the plane are $\mu_s = 0.25$ and $\mu_k = 0.20$. Determine whether the block is in equilibrium, and find the value of the friction force.

SOLUTION

Force Required for Equilibrium. We first determine the value of the friction force *required to maintain equilibrium*. Assuming that **F** is directed down and to the left, we draw the free-body diagram of the block and write

$$+\nearrow \Sigma F_x = 0: \qquad 100 \text{ lb} - \tfrac{3}{5}(300 \text{ lb}) - F = 0$$
$$F = -80 \text{ lb} \qquad \mathbf{F} = 80 \text{ lb} \nearrow$$

$$+\nwarrow \Sigma F_y = 0: \qquad N - \tfrac{4}{5}(300 \text{ lb}) = 0$$
$$N = +240 \text{ lb} \qquad \mathbf{N} = 240 \text{ lb} \nwarrow$$

The force **F** required to maintain equilibrium is an 80-lb force directed up and to the right; the tendency of the block is thus to move down the plane.

Maximum Friction Force. The magnitude of the maximum friction force which may be developed is

$$F_m = \mu_s N \qquad F_m = 0.25(240 \text{ lb}) = 60 \text{ lb}$$

Since the value of the force required to maintain equilibrium (80 lb) is larger than the maximum value which may be obtained (60 lb), equilibrium will not be maintained and *the block will slide down the plane.*

Actual Value of Friction Force. The magnitude of the actual friction force is obtained as follows:

$$F_{\text{actual}} = F_k = \mu_k N$$
$$= 0.20(240 \text{ lb}) = 48 \text{ lb}$$

The sense of this force is opposite to the sense of motion; the force is thus directed up and to the right:

$$\mathbf{F}_{\text{actual}} = 48 \text{ lb} \nearrow \qquad \blacktriangleleft$$

It should be noted that the forces acting on the block are not balanced; the resultant is

$$\tfrac{3}{5}(300 \text{ lb}) - 100 \text{ lb} - 48 \text{ lb} = 32 \text{ lb} \swarrow$$

25°

P

800 N

SAMPLE PROBLEM 8.2

A support block is acted upon by two forces as shown. Knowing that the coefficients of friction between the block and the incline are $\mu_s = 0.35$ and $\mu_k = 0.25$, determine the force **P** required (*a*) to start the block moving up the incline, (*b*) to keep it moving up, (*c*) to prevent it from sliding down.

SOLUTION

Free-Body Diagram. For each part of the problem we draw a free-body diagram of the block and a force triangle including the 800-N vertical force, the horizontal force **P**, and the force **R** exerted on the block by the incline. The direction of **R** must be determined in each separate case. We note that since **P** is perpendicular to the 800-N force, the force triangle is a right triangle, which can easily be solved for **P**. In most other problems, however, the force triangle will be an oblique triangle and should be solved by applying the law of sines.

a. Force *P* to Start Block Moving Up

$$\tan \phi_s = \mu_s$$
$$= 0.35$$
$$\phi_s = 19.29°$$
$$25° + 19.29° = 44.29°$$

$$P = (800 \text{ N}) \tan 44.29°$$

$$P = 780 \text{ N} \leftarrow \quad \blacktriangleleft$$

b. Force *P* to Keep Block Moving Up

$$\tan \phi_k = \mu_k$$
$$= 0.25$$
$$\phi_k = 14.04°$$
$$25° + 14.04° = 39.04°$$

$$P = (800 \text{ N}) \tan 39.04°$$

$$P = 649 \text{ N} \leftarrow \quad \blacktriangleleft$$

c. Force *P* to Prevent Block from Sliding Down

$$\phi_s = 19.29°$$
$$25° - 19.29° = 5.71°$$

$$P = (800 \text{ N}) \tan 5.71°$$

$$P = 80.0 \text{ N} \leftarrow \quad \blacktriangleleft$$

SAMPLE PROBLEM 8.3

The movable bracket shown may be placed at any height on the 3-in.-diameter pipe. If the coefficient of static friction between the pipe and bracket is 0.25, determine the minimum distance x at which the load **W** can be supported. Neglect the weight of the bracket.

SOLUTION

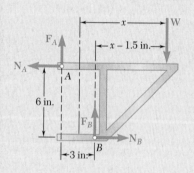

Free-Body Diagram. We draw the free-body diagram of the bracket. When **W** is placed at the minimum distance x from the axis of the pipe, the bracket is just about to slip, and the forces of friction at A and B have reached their maximum values:

$$F_A = \mu_s N_A = 0.25 \, N_A$$
$$F_B = \mu_s N_B = 0.25 \, N_B$$

Equilibrium Equations

$\xrightarrow{+} \Sigma F_x = 0:$ $N_B - N_A = 0$
$N_B = N_A$

$+\uparrow \Sigma F_y = 0:$ $F_A + F_B - W = 0$
$0.25 N_A + 0.25 N_B = W$

And, since N_B has been found equal to N_A,

$$0.50 N_A = W$$
$$N_A = 2W$$

$+\!\!\uparrow \Sigma M_B = 0:$ $N_A(6 \text{ in.}) - F_A(3 \text{ in.}) - W(x - 1.5 \text{ in.}) = 0$
$6N_A - 3(0.25 N_A) - Wx + 1.5W = 0$
$6(2W) - 0.75(2W) - Wx + 1.5W = 0$

Dividing through by W and solving for x,

$x = 12 \text{ in.}$ ◀

SOLVING PROBLEMS
ON YOUR OWN

In this lesson you studied and applied the *laws of dry friction*. Previously you had encountered only (*a*) frictionless surfaces that could move freely with respect to each other, (*b*) rough surfaces that allowed no motion relative to each other.

A. In solving problems involving dry friction, you should keep the following in mind.

1. The reaction R exerted by a surface on a free body can be resolved into a component **N** and a tangential component **F**. The tangential component is known as the *friction force*. When a body is in contact with a fixed surface the direction of the friction force **F** is opposite to that of the actual or impending motion of the body.

   a. No motion will occur as long as F does not exceed the maximum value $F_m = \mu_s N$, where μ_s is the *coefficient of static friction*.

   b. Motion will occur if a value of F larger than F_m is required to maintain equilibrium. As motion takes place, the actual value of F drops to $F_k = \mu_k N$, where μ_k is the *coefficient of kinetic friction* [Sample Prob. 8.1].

2. When only three forces are involved an alternative approach to the analysis of friction may be preferred [Sample Prob. 8.2]. The reaction **R** is defined by its magnitude R and the angle ϕ it forms with the normal to the surface. No motion will occur as long as ϕ does not exceed the maximum value ϕ_s, where $\tan \phi_s = \mu_s$. Motion will occur if a value of ϕ larger than ϕ_s is required to maintain equilibrium, and the actual value of ϕ will drop to ϕ_k, where $\tan \phi_k = \mu_k$.

3. When two bodies are in contact the sense of the actual or impending relative motion at the point of contact must be determined. On each of the two bodies a friction force **F** should be shown in a direction opposite to that of the actual or impending motion of the body as seen from the other body.

(*continued*)

B. Methods of solution. The first step in your solution is to *draw a free-body diagram* of the body under consideration, resolving the force exerted on each surface where friction exists into a normal component **N** and a friction force **F**. If several bodies are involved, draw a free-body diagram of each of them, labeling and directing the forces at each surface of contact as you learned to do when analyzing frames in Chap. 6.

The problem you have to solve may fall in one of the following three categories:

1. All the applied forces and the coefficients of friction are known, and you must determine whether equilibrium is maintained. Note that in this situation the friction force is unknown and *cannot be assumed to be equal* to $\mu_s N$.

a. Write the equations of equilibrium to determine N and F.

b. Calculate the maximum allowable friction force, $F_m = \mu_s N$. If $F \leq F_m$, equilibrium is maintained. If $F > F_m$, motion occurs, and the magnitude of the friction force is $F_k = \mu_k N$ [Sample Prob. 8.1].

2. All the applied forces are known, and you must find the smallest allowable value of μ_s for which equilibrium is maintained. You will assume that motion is impending and determine the corresponding value of μ_s.

a. Write the equations of equilibrium to determine N and F.

b. Since motion is impending, $F = F_m$. Substitute the values found for N and F into the equation $F_m = \mu_s N$ and solve for μ_s.

3. The motion of the body is impending and μ_s is known; you must find some unknown quantity, such as a distance, an angle, the magnitude of a force, or the direction of a force.

a. Assume a possible motion of the body and, on the free-body diagram, draw the friction force in a direction opposite to that of the assumed motion.

b. Since motion is impending, $F = F_m = \mu_s N$. Substituting for μ_s its known value, you can express F in terms of N on the free-body diagram, thus eliminating one unknown.

c. Write and solve the equilibrium equations for the unknown you seek [Sample Prob. 8.3].

PROBLEMS

FREE BODY PRACTICE PROBLEMS

8.F1 Draw the free-body diagram needed to determine the smallest force **P** for which equilibrium of the 7.5-kg block is maintained.

8.F2 Two blocks A and B are connected by a cable as shown. Knowing that the coefficient of static friction at all surfaces of contact is 0.30 and neglecting the friction of the pulleys, draw the free-body diagrams needed to determine the smallest force **P** required to move the blocks.

$$\mu_s = 0.45$$
$$\mu_k = 0.35$$

7.5 kg

40°

P

Fig. P8.F1

P

A
60 lb

B
40 lb

Fig. P8.F2

8.F3 The cylinder shown is of weight W and radius r, and the coefficient of static friction μ_s is the same at A and B. Draw the free-body diagram needed to determine the largest couple **M** that can be applied to the cylinder if it is not to rotate.

A

M

B

Fig. P8.F3

8.F4 A uniform crate of mass 30 kg must be moved up along the 15° incline without tipping. Knowing that the force **P** is horizontal, draw the free-body diagram needed to determine the largest allowable coefficient of static friction between the crate and the incline, and the corresponding force **P**.

L

P
A

B

L

C

D
15°

Fig. P8.F4

END-OF-SECTION PROBLEMS

8.1 Determine whether the block shown is in equilibrium and find the magnitude and direction of the friction force when $\theta = 25°$ and $P = 750$ N.

Fig. P8.1 and P8.2

8.2 Determine whether the block shown is in equilibrium and find the magnitude and direction of the friction force when $\theta = 30°$ and $P = 150$ N.

8.3 Determine whether the block shown is in equilibrium and find the magnitude and direction of the friction force when $P = 100$ lb.

8.4 Determine whether the block shown is in equilibrium and find the magnitude and direction of the friction force when $P = 60$ lb.

8.5 Determine the smallest value of P required to (*a*) start the block up the incline, (*b*) keep it moving up, (*c*) prevent it from moving down.

Fig. P8.3, P8.4, and P8.5

8.6 Knowing that the coefficient of friction between the 25-kg block and the incline is $\mu_s = 0.25$, determine (*a*) the smallest value of P required to start the block moving up the incline, (*b*) the corresponding value of β.

8.7 The 80-lb block is attached to link AB and rests on a moving belt. Knowing that $\mu_s = 0.25$ and $\mu_k = 0.20$, determine the magnitude of the horizontal force **P** that should be applied to the belt to maintain its motion (*a*) to the right, (*b*) to the left.

Fig. P8.6

Fig. P8.7

8.8 The coefficients of friction between the block and the rail are $\mu_s = 0.30$ and $\mu_k = 0.25$. Knowing that $\theta = 65°$, determine the smallest value of P required (*a*) to start the block moving up the rail, (*b*) to keep it from moving down.

Fig. P8.8

8.9 Considering only values of θ less than 90°, determine the smallest value of θ required to start the block moving to the right when (a) W = 75 lb, (b) W = 100 lb.

8.10 Determine the range of values of P for which equilibrium of the block shown is maintained.

$\mu_s = 0.25$
$\mu_k = 0.20$

Fig. P8.9

$\mu_s = 0.25$
$\mu_k = 0.20$
30°
P
500 N

Fig. P8.10

8.11 The 20-lb block A and the 30-lb block B are supported by an incline that is held in the position shown. Knowing that the coefficient of static friction is 0.15 between the two blocks and zero between block B and the incline, determine the value of θ for which motion is impending.

8.12 The 20-lb block A and the 30-lb block B are supported by an incline that is held in the position shown. Knowing that the coefficient of static friction is 0.15 between all surfaces of contact, determine the value of θ for which motion is impending.

Fig. P8.11 and P8.12

8.13 and 8.14 The coefficients of friction are $\mu_s = 0.40$ and $\mu_k = 0.30$ between all surfaces of contact. Determine the smallest force P required to start the 30-kg block moving if cable AB (a) is attached as shown, (b) is removed.

20 kg A
P
30 kg B

Fig. P8.13

8.15 A 40-kg packing crate must be moved to the left along the floor without tipping. Knowing that the coefficient of static friction between the crate and the floor is 0.35, determine (a) the largest allowable value of α, (b) the corresponding magnitude of the force **P**.

20 kg A B
P
30 kg

Fig. P8.14

P
α
A
B
0.5 m
C
D
0.8 m

Fig. P8.15 and P8.16

8.16 A 40-kg packing crate is pulled by a rope as shown. The coefficient of static friction between the crate and the floor is 0.35. If α = 40°, determine (a) the magnitude of the force **P** required to move the crate, (b) whether the crate will slide or tip.

Fig. P8.17 and P8.18

Fig. P8.19

Fig. P8.21 and P8.22

8.17 A 120-lb cabinet is mounted on casters that can be locked to prevent their rotation. The coefficient of static friction between the floor and each caster is 0.30. If $h = 32$ in., determine the magnitude of the force **P** required to move the cabinet to the right (a) if all casters are locked, (b) if the casters at B are locked and the casters at A are free to rotate, (c) if the casters at A are locked and the casters at B are free to rotate.

8.18 A 120-lb cabinet is mounted on casters that can be locked to prevent their rotation. The coefficient of static friction between the floor and each caster is 0.30. Assuming that the casters at both A and B are locked, determine (a) the force **P** required to move the cabinet to the right, (b) the largest allowable value of h if the cabinet is not to tip over.

8.19 Wire is being drawn at a constant rate from a spool by applying a vertical force **P** to the wire as shown. The spool and the wire wrapped on the spool have a combined weight of 20 lb. Knowing that the coefficients of friction at both A and B are $\mu_s = 0.40$ and $\mu_k = 0.30$, determine the required magnitude of the force **P**.

8.20 Solve Prob. 8.19 assuming that the coefficients of friction at B are zero.

8.21 The hydraulic cylinder shown exerts a force of 3 kN directed to the right on point B and to the left on point E. Determine the magnitude of the couple **M** required to rotate the drum clockwise at a constant speed.

8.22 A couple **M** of magnitude 100 N · m is applied to the drum as shown. Determine the smallest force that must be exerted by the hydraulic cylinder on joints B and E if the drum is not to rotate.

8.23 A slender rod of length L is lodged between peg C and the vertical wall, and supports a load **P** at end A. Knowing that the coefficient of static friction between the peg and the rod is 0.15 and neglecting friction at the roller, determine the range of values of the ratio L/a for which equilibrium is maintained.

8.24 Solve Prob. 8.23 assuming that the coefficient of static friction between the peg and the rod is 0.60.

Fig. P8.23

8.25 A 6.5-m ladder *AB* leans against a wall as shown. Assuming that the coefficient of static friction μ_s is zero at *B*, determine the smallest value of μ_s at *A* for which equilibrium is maintained.

8.26 A 6.5-m ladder *AB* leans against a wall as shown. Assuming that the coefficient of static friction μ_s is the same at *A* and *B*, determine the smallest value of μ_s for which equilibrium is maintained.

8.27 The press shown is used to emboss a small seal at *E*. Knowing that the coefficient of static friction between the vertical guide and the embossing die *D* is 0.30, determine the force exerted by the die on the seal.

Fig. P8.25 and P8.26

Fig. P8.27

8.28 The machine base shown has a mass of 75 kg and is fitted with skids at *A* and *B*. The coefficient of static friction between the skids and the floor is 0.30. If a force **P** of magnitude 500 N is applied at corner *C*, determine the range of values of θ for which the base will not move.

8.29 The 50-lb plate *ABCD* is attached at *A* and *D* to collars that can slide on the vertical rod. Knowing that the coefficient of static friction is 0.40 between both collars and the rod, determine whether the plate is in equilibrium in the position shown when the magnitude of the vertical force applied at *E* is (*a*) *P* = 0, (*b*) *P* = 20 lb.

Fig. P8.28

Fig. P8.29

8.30 In Prob. 8.29, determine the range of values of the magnitude *P* of the vertical force applied at *E* for which the plate will move downward.

8.31 A rod *DE* and a small cylinder are placed between two guides as shown. The rod is not to slip downward, however large the force **P** may be; i.e., the arrangement is said to be self-locking. Neglecting the weight of the cylinder, determine the minimum allowable coefficients of static friction at *A*, *B*, and *C*.

Fig. P8.31

8.32 A 500-N concrete block is to be lifted by the pair of tongs shown. Determine the smallest allowable value of the coefficient of static friction between the block and the tongs at *F* and *G*.

8.33 The 100-mm-radius cam shown is used to control the motion of the plate *CD*. Knowing that the coefficient of static friction between the cam and the plate is 0.45 and neglecting friction at the roller supports, determine (*a*) the force **P** required to maintain the motion of the plate, knowing that the plate is 20 mm thick, (*b*) the largest thickness of the plate for which the mechanism is self-locking (i.e., for which the plate cannot be moved however large the force **P** may be).

Fig. P8.32

Fig. P8.33

8.34 A safety device used by workers climbing ladders fixed to high structures consists of a rail attached to the ladder and a sleeve that can slide on the flange of the rail. A chain connects the worker's belt to the end of an eccentric cam that can be rotated about an axle attached to the sleeve at *C*. Determine the smallest allowable common value of the coefficient of static friction between the flange of the rail, the pins at *A* and *B*, and the eccentric cam if the sleeve is not to slide down when the chain is pulled vertically downward.

Fig. P8.34

8.35 To be of practical use, the safety sleeve described in Prob. 8.34 must be free to slide along the rail when pulled upward. Determine the largest allowable value of the coefficient of static friction between the flange of the rail and the pins at A and B if the sleeve is to be free to slide when pulled as shown in the figure, assuming (a) $\theta = 60°$, (b) $\theta = 50°$, (c) $\theta = 40°$.

8.36 Two 10-lb blocks A and B are connected by a slender rod of negligible weight. The coefficient of static friction is 0.30 between all surfaces of contact, and the rod forms an angle $\theta = 30°$ with the vertical. (a) Show that the system is in equilibrium when $P = 0$. (b) Determine the largest value of P for which equilibrium is maintained.

Fig. P8.35

Fig. P8.36

8.37 Bar AB is attached to collars that can slide on the inclined rods shown. A force $\mathbf{P}$ is applied at point D located at a distance a from end A. Knowing that the coefficient of static friction μ_s between each collar and the rod upon which it slides is 0.30 and neglecting the weights of the bar and of the collars, determine the smallest value of the ratio a/L for which equilibrium is maintained.

Fig. P8.37

8.38 Two identical uniform boards, each of weight 40 lb, are temporarily leaned against each other as shown. Knowing that the coefficient of static friction between all surfaces is 0.40, determine (a) the largest magnitude of the force $\mathbf{P}$ for which equilibrium will be maintained, (b) the surface at which motion will impend.

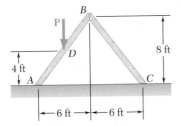

Fig. P8.38

8.39 Knowing that the coefficient of static friction between the collar and the rod is 0.35, determine the range of values of P for which equilibrium is maintained when $\theta = 50°$ and $M = 20$ N · m.

8.40 Knowing that the coefficient of static friction between the collar and the rod is 0.40, determine the range of values of M for which equilibrium is maintained when $\theta = 60°$ and $P = 200$ N.

Fig. P8.39 and P8.40

Fig. P8.41

Fig. P8.43

Fig. P8.46 and P8.47

8.41 A 10-ft beam, weighing 1200 lb, is to be moved to the left onto the platform. A horizontal force **P** is applied to the dolly, which is mounted on frictionless wheels. The coefficients of friction between all surfaces are $\mu_s = 0.30$ and $\mu_k = 0.25$, and initially $x = 2$ ft. Knowing that the top surface of the dolly is slightly higher than the platform, determine the force **P** required to start moving the beam. (*Hint:* The beam is supported at A and D.)

8.42 (*a*) Show that the beam of Prob. 8.41 *cannot* be moved if the top surface of the dolly is slightly *lower* than the platform. (*b*) Show that the beam *can* be moved if two 175-lb workers stand on the beam at B and determine how far to the left the beam can be moved.

8.43 Two 8-kg blocks A and B resting on shelves are connected by a rod of negligible mass. Knowing that the magnitude of a horizontal force **P** applied at C is slowly increased from zero, determine the value of P for which motion occurs, and what that motion is, when the coefficient of static friction between all surfaces is (*a*) $\mu_s = 0.40$, (*b*) $\mu_s = 0.50$.

8.44 A slender steel rod of length 225 mm is placed inside a pipe as shown. Knowing that the coefficient of static friction between the rod and the pipe is 0.20, determine the largest value of θ for which the rod will not fall into the pipe.

Fig. P8.44

8.45 In Prob. 8.44, determine the smallest value of θ for which the rod will not fall out of the pipe.

8.46 Two slender rods of negligible weight are pin-connected at C and attached to blocks A and B, each of weight W. Knowing that $\theta = 80°$ and that the coefficient of static friction between the blocks and the horizontal surface is 0.30, determine the largest value of P for which equilibrium is maintained.

8.47 Two slender rods of negligible weight are pin-connected at C and attached to blocks A and B, each of weight W. Knowing that $P = 1.260W$ and that the coefficient of static friction between the blocks and the horizontal surface is 0.30, determine the range of values of θ, between 0 and 180°, for which equilibrium is maintained.

8.5 WEDGES

Wedges are simple machines used to raise large stone blocks and other heavy loads. These loads can be raised by applying to the wedge a force usually considerably smaller than the weight of the load. In addition, because of the friction between the surfaces in contact, a properly shaped wedge will remain in place after being forced under the load. Wedges can thus be used advantageously to make small adjustments in the position of heavy pieces of machinery.

Consider the block A shown in Fig. 8.7a. This block rests against a vertical wall B and is to be raised slightly by forcing a wedge C between block A and a second wedge D. We want to find the minimum value of the force **P** which must be applied to the wedge C to move the block. It will be assumed that the weight **W** of the block is known, either given in pounds or determined in newtons from the mass of the block expressed in kilograms.

The free-body diagrams of block A and of wedge C have been drawn in Fig. 8.7b and c. The forces acting on the block include its weight and the normal and friction forces at the surfaces of contact with wall B and wedge C. The magnitudes of the friction forces F_1 and F_2 are equal, respectively, to $\mu_s N_1$ and $\mu_s N_2$ since the motion of the block must be started. It is important to show the friction forces with their correct sense. Since the block will move upward, the force F_1 exerted by the wall on the block must be directed downward. On the other hand, since the wedge C moves to the right, the relative motion of A with respect to C is to the left and the force F_2 exerted by C on A must be directed to the right.

Considering now the free body C in Fig. 8.7c, we note that the forces acting on C include the applied force **P** and the normal and friction forces at the surfaces of contact with A and D. The weight of the wedge is small compared with the other forces involved and can be neglected. The forces exerted by A on C are equal and opposite to the forces N_2 and F_2 exerted by C on A and are denoted, respectively, by $-N_2$ and $-F_2$; the friction force $-F_2$ must therefore be directed to the left. We check that the force F_3 exerted by D is also directed to the left.

The total number of unknowns involved in the two free-body diagrams can be reduced to four if the friction forces are expressed in terms of the normal forces. Expressing that block A and wedge C are in equilibrium will provide four equations which can be solved to obtain the magnitude of **P**. It should be noted that in the example considered here, it will be more convenient to replace each pair of normal and friction forces by their resultant. Each free body is then subjected to only three forces, and the problem can be solved by drawing the corresponding force triangles (see Sample Prob. 8.4).

8.6 SQUARE-THREADED SCREWS

Square-threaded screws are frequently used in jacks, presses, and other mechanisms. Their analysis is similar to the analysis of a block sliding along an inclined plane.

Consider the jack shown in Fig. 8.8. The screw carries a load **W** and is supported by the base of the jack. Contact between screw and base takes place along a portion of their threads. By applying a force **P** on the handle, the screw can be made to turn and to raise the load **W**.

(a)

(b)

(c)

Fig. 8.7

Fig. 8.8

Photo 8.2 Wedges are used as shown to split tree trunks because the normal forces exerted by the wedges on the wood are much larger than the forces required to insert the wedges.

The thread of the base has been unwrapped and shown as a straight line in Fig. 8.9a. The correct slope was obtained by plotting horizontally the product $2\pi r$, where r is the mean radius of the thread, and vertically the *lead L* of the screw, i.e., the distance through which the screw advances in one turn. The angle θ this line forms with the horizontal is the *lead angle*. Since the force of friction between two surfaces in contact does not depend upon the area of contact, a much smaller than actual area of contact between the two threads can be assumed, and the screw can be represented by the block shown in Fig. 8.9a. It should be noted, however, that in this analysis of the jack, the friction between cap and screw is neglected.

The free-body diagram of the block should include the load **W**, the reaction **R** of the base thread, and a horizontal force **Q** having the same effect as the force **P** exerted on the handle. The force **Q** should have the same moment as **P** about the axis of the screw and its magnitude should thus be $Q = Pa/r$. The force **Q**, and thus the force **P** required to raise the load **W**, can be obtained from the free-body diagram shown in Fig. 8.9a. The friction angle is taken equal to ϕ_s since the load will presumably be raised through a succession of short strokes. In mechanisms providing for the continuous rotation of a screw, it may be desirable to distinguish between the force required to start motion (using ϕ_s) and that required to maintain motion (using ϕ_k).

(*a*) Impending motion upward

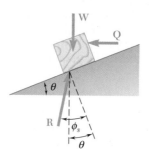

(*b*) Impending motion downward with $\phi_s > \theta$

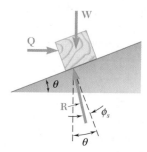

(*c*) Impending motion downward with $\phi_s < \theta$

Fig. 8.9 Block-and-incline analysis of a screw.

If the friction angle ϕ_s is larger than the lead angle θ, the screw is said to be *self-locking;* it will remain in place under the load. To lower the load, we must then apply the force shown in Fig. 8.9b. If ϕ_s is smaller than θ, the screw will unwind under the load; it is then necessary to apply the force shown in Fig. 8.9c to maintain equilibrium.

The lead of a screw should not be confused with its *pitch*. The lead was defined as the distance through which the screw advances in one turn; the pitch is the distance measured between two consecutive threads. While lead and pitch are equal in the case of *single-threaded* screws, they are different in the case of *multiple-threaded* screws, i.e., screws having several independent threads. It is easily verified that for double-threaded screws, the lead is twice as large as the pitch; for triple-threaded screws, it is three times as large as the pitch; etc.

SAMPLE PROBLEM 8.4

The position of the machine block B is adjusted by moving the wedge A. Knowing that the coefficient of static friction is 0.35 between all surfaces of contact, determine the force $\mathbf{P}$ required (a) to raise block B, (b) to lower block B.

SOLUTION

For each part, the free-body diagrams of block B and wedge A are drawn, together with the corresponding force triangles, and the law of sines is used to find the desired forces. We note that since $\mu_s = 0.35$, the angle of friction is

$$\phi_s = \tan^{-1} 0.35 = 19.3°$$

a. Force P to Raise Block

Free Body: Block B

$$\frac{R_1}{\sin 109.3°} = \frac{400\ \text{lb}}{\sin 43.4°}$$
$$R_1 = 549\ \text{lb}$$

Free Body: Wedge A

$$\frac{P}{\sin 46.6°} = \frac{549\ \text{lb}}{\sin 70.7°}$$
$$P = 423\ \text{lb} \qquad \mathbf{P} = 423\ \text{lb} \leftarrow$$

b. Force P to Lower Block

Free Body: Block B

$$\frac{R_1}{\sin 70.7°} = \frac{400\ \text{lb}}{\sin 98.0°}$$
$$R_1 = 381\ \text{lb}$$

Free Body: Wedge A

$$\frac{P}{\sin 30.6°} = \frac{381\ \text{lb}}{\sin 70.7°}$$
$$P = 206\ \text{lb} \qquad \mathbf{P} = 206\ \text{lb} \rightarrow$$

SAMPLE PROBLEM 8.5

A clamp is used to hold two pieces of wood together as shown. The clamp has a double square thread of mean diameter equal to 10 mm with a pitch of 2 mm. The coefficient of friction between threads is $\mu_s = 0.30$. If a maximum couple of 40 N · m is applied in tightening the clamp, determine (a) the force exerted on the pieces of wood, (b) the couple required to loosen the clamp.

SOLUTION

a. Force Exerted by Clamp. The mean radius of the screw is $r = 5$ mm. Since the screw is double-threaded, the lead L is equal to twice the pitch: $L = 2(2$ mm$) = 4$ mm. The lead angle θ and the friction angle ϕ_s are obtained by writing

$$\tan \theta = \frac{L}{2\pi r} = \frac{4\,\text{mm}}{10\pi\,\text{mm}} = 0.1273 \qquad \theta = 7.3°$$

$$\tan \phi_s = \mu_s = 0.30 \qquad\qquad \phi_s = 16.7°$$

The force **Q** which should be applied to the block representing the screw is obtained by expressing that its moment Qr about the axis of the screw is equal to the applied couple.

$$Q(5\,\text{mm}) = 40\ \text{N} \cdot \text{m}$$

$$Q = \frac{40\ \text{N} \cdot \text{m}}{5\ \text{mm}} = \frac{40\ \text{N} \cdot \text{m}}{5 \times 10^{-3}\,\text{m}} = 8000\ \text{N} = 8\ \text{kN}$$

The free-body diagram and the corresponding force triangle can now be drawn for the block; the magnitude of the force **W** exerted on the pieces of wood is obtained by solving the triangle.

$$W = \frac{Q}{\tan(\theta + \phi_s)} = \frac{8\ \text{kN}}{\tan 24.0°}$$

$$W = 17.97\ \text{kN} \quad \blacktriangleleft$$

b. Couple Required to Loosen Clamp. The force **Q** required to loosen the clamp and the corresponding couple are obtained from the free-body diagram and force triangle shown.

$$Q = W \tan(\phi_s - \theta) = (17.97\ \text{kN}) \tan 9.4°$$
$$= 2.975\ \text{kN}$$

$$\text{Couple} = Qr = (2.975\ \text{kN})(5\ \text{mm})$$

$$= (2.975 \times 10^3\ \text{N})(5 \times 10^{-3}\ \text{m}) = 14.87\ \text{N} \cdot \text{m}$$

$$\text{Couple} = 14.87\ \text{N} \cdot \text{m} \quad \blacktriangleleft$$

SOLVING PROBLEMS
ON YOUR OWN

In this lesson you learned to apply the laws of friction to the solution of problems involving *wedges* and *square-threaded screws*.

1. Wedges. Keep the following in mind when solving a problem involving a wedge:

a. First draw a free-body diagram of the wedge and of all the other bodies involved. Carefully note the sense of the relative motion of all surfaces of contact and show each friction force acting in *a direction opposite* to the direction of that relative motion.

b. Show the maximum static friction force F_m at each surface if the wedge is to be inserted or removed, *since motion will be impending in each of these cases*.

c. The reaction R and the angle of friction, rather than the normal force and the friction force, can be used in many applications. You can then draw one or more force triangles and determine the unknown quantities either graphically or by trigonometry [Sample Prob. 8.4].

2. Square-Threaded Screws. The analysis of a square-threaded screw is equivalent to the analysis of a block sliding on an incline. To draw the appropriate incline, you should unwrap the thread of the screw and represent it by a straight line [Sample Prob. 8.5]. When solving a problem involving a square-threaded screw, keep the following in mind:

a. Do not confuse the pitch of a screw with the lead of a screw. The *pitch* of a screw is the distance between two consecutive threads, while the *lead* of a screw is the distance the screw advances in one full turn. The lead and the pitch are equal only in single-threaded screws. In a double-threaded screw, the lead is twice the pitch.

b. The couple required to tighten a screw is different from the couple required to loosen it. Also, screws used in jacks and clamps are usually *self-locking;* that is, the screw will remain stationary as long as no couple is applied to it, and a couple must be applied to the screw to loosen it [Sample Prob. 8.5].

PROBLEMS

Fig. P8.48

8.48 The machine part ABC is supported by a frictionless hinge at B and a 10° wedge at C. Knowing that the coefficient of static friction at both surfaces of the wedge is 0.20, determine (*a*) the force $\mathbf{P}$ required to move the wedge, (*b*) the components of the corresponding reaction at B.

8.49 Solve Prob. 8.48 assuming that the force $\mathbf{P}$ is directed to the right.

8.50 and 8.51 The elevation of the end of the steel beam supported by a concrete floor is adjusted by means of the steel wedges E and F. The base plate CD has been welded to the lower flange of the beam, and the end reaction of the beam is known to be 100 kN. The coefficient of static friction is 0.30 between two steel surfaces and 0.60 between steel and concrete. If the horizontal motion of the beam is prevented by the force $\mathbf{Q}$, determine (*a*) the force $\mathbf{P}$ required to raise the beam, (*b*) the corresponding force $\mathbf{Q}$.

Fig. P8.50

8.52 and 8.53 Two 10° wedges of negligible weight are used to move and position the 400-lb block. Knowing that the coefficient of static friction is 0.25 at all surfaces of contact, determine the smallest force $\mathbf{P}$ that should be applied as shown to one of the wedges.

Fig. P8.51

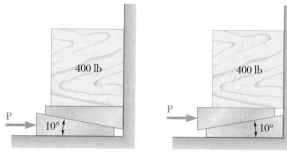

Fig. P8.52   **Fig. P8.53**

8.54 Block A supports a pipe column and rests as shown on wedge B. Knowing that the coefficient of static friction at all surfaces of contact is 0.25 and that $\theta = 45°$, determine the smallest force $\mathbf{P}$ required to raise block A.

8.55 Block A supports a pipe column and rests as shown on wedge B. Knowing that the coefficient of static friction at all surfaces of contact is 0.25 and that $\theta = 45°$, determine the smallest force $\mathbf{P}$ for which equilibrium is maintained.

Fig. P8.54, P8.55, and P8.56

8.56 Block A supports a pipe column and rests as shown on wedge B. The coefficient of static friction at all surfaces of contact is 0.25. If $\mathbf{P} = 0$, determine (*a*) the angle θ for which sliding is impending, (*b*) the corresponding force exerted on the block by the vertical wall.

8.57 A wedge A of negligible weight is to be driven between two 100-lb plates B and C. The coefficient of static friction between all surfaces of contact is 0.35. Determine the magnitude of the force **P** required to start moving the wedge (a) if the plates are equally free to move, (b) if plate C is securely bolted to the surface.

Fig. P8.57

8.58 A 10° wedge is used to split a section of a log. The coefficient of static friction between the wedge and the log is 0.35. Knowing that a force **P** of magnitude 600 lb was required to insert the wedge, determine the magnitude of the forces exerted on the wood by the wedge after insertion.

Fig. P8.58

8.59 A 10° wedge is to be forced under end B of the 5-kg rod AB. Knowing that the coefficient of static friction is 0.40 between the wedge and the rod and 0.20 between the wedge and the floor, determine the smallest force **P** required to raise end B of the rod.

8.60 The spring of the door latch has a constant of 1.8 lb/in. and in the position shown exerts a 0.6-lb force on the bolt. The coefficient of static friction between the bolt and the strike plate is 0.40; all other surfaces are well lubricated and may be assumed frictionless. Determine the magnitude of the force **P** required to start closing the door.

Fig. P8.59

Fig. P8.60

8.61 In Prob. 8.60, determine the angle that the face of the bolt should form with the line BC if the force **P** required to close the door is to be the same for both the position shown and the position when B is almost at the strike plate.

8.62 A 5° wedge is to be forced under a 1400-lb machine base at A. Knowing that the coefficient of static friction at all surfaces is 0.20, (a) determine the force **P** required to move the wedge, (b) indicate whether the machine base will move.

8.63 Solve Prob. 8.62 assuming that the wedge is to be forced under the machine base at B instead of A.

Fig. P8.62

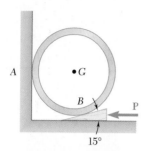

Fig. P8.64 and P8.65

8.64 A 15° wedge is forced under a 50-kg pipe as shown. The coefficient of static friction at all surfaces is 0.20. (a) Show that slipping will occur between the pipe and the vertical wall. (b) Determine the force **P** required to move the wedge.

8.65 A 15° wedge is forced under a 50-kg pipe as shown. Knowing that the coefficient of static friction at both surfaces of the wedge is 0.20, determine the largest coefficient of static friction between the pipe and the vertical wall for which slipping will occur at A.

*8.66 A 200-N block rests as shown on a wedge of negligible weight. The coefficient of static friction μ_s is the same at both surfaces of the wedge, and friction between the block and the vertical wall may be neglected. For $P = 100$ N, determine the value of μ_s for which motion is impending. (*Hint:* Solve the equation obtained by trial and error.)

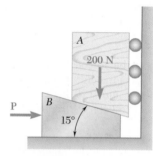

Fig. P8.66

*8.67 Solve Prob. 8.66 assuming that the rollers are removed and that μ_s is the coefficient of friction at all surfaces of contact.

8.68 Derive the following formulas relating the load **W** and the force **P** exerted on the handle of the jack discussed in Sec. 8.6. (a) $P = (Wr/a)\tan(\theta + \phi_s)$, to raise the load; (b) $P = (Wr/a)\tan(\phi_s - \theta)$, to lower the load if the screw is self-locking; (c) $P = (Wr/a)\tan(\theta - \phi_s)$, to hold the load if the screw is not self-locking.

Fig. P8.69

8.69 The square-threaded worm gear shown has a mean radius of 2 in. and a lead of 0.5 in. The large gear is subjected to a constant clockwise couple of 9.6 kip · in. Knowing that the coefficient of static friction between the two gears is 0.12, determine the couple that must be applied to shaft AB in order to rotate the large gear counterclockwise. Neglect friction in the bearings at A, B, and C.

8.70 In Prob. 8.69, determine the couple that must be applied to shaft AB in order to rotate the large gear clockwise.

8.71 High-strength bolts are used in the construction of many steel structures. For a 24-mm-nominal-diameter bolt, the required minimum bolt tension is 210 kN. Assuming the coefficient of friction to be 0.40, determine the required couple that should be applied to the bolt and nut. The mean diameter of the thread is 22.6 mm, and the lead is 3 mm. Neglect friction between the nut and washer, and assume the bolt to be square-threaded.

Fig. P8.71

8.72 The position of the automobile jack shown is controlled by a screw *ABC* that is single-threaded at each end (right-handed thread at *A*, left-handed thread at *C*). Each thread has a pitch of 0.1 in. and a mean diameter of 0.375 in. If the coefficient of static friction is 0.15, determine the magnitude of the couple **M** that must be applied to raise the automobile.

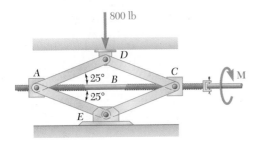

Fig. P8.72

8.73 For the jack of Prob. 8.72, determine the magnitude of the couple **M** that must be applied to lower the automobile.

8.74 In the gear-pulling assembly shown, the square-threaded screw *AB* has a mean radius of 15 mm and a lead of 4 mm. Knowing that the coefficient of static friction is 0.10, determine the couple that must be applied to the screw in order to produce a force of 3 kN on the gear. Neglect friction at end *A* of the screw.

Fig. P8.74

8.75 The ends of two fixed rods *A* and *B* are each made in the form of a single-threaded screw of mean radius 6 mm and pitch 2 mm. Rod *A* has a right-handed thread and rod *B* has a left-handed thread. The coefficient of static friction between the rods and the threaded sleeve is 0.12. Determine the magnitude of the couple that must be applied to the sleeve in order to draw the rods closer together.

Fig. P8.75

8.76 Assuming that in Prob. 8.75 a right-handed thread is used on *both* rods *A* and *B*, determine the magnitude of the couple that must be applied to the sleeve in order to rotate it.

*8.7 JOURNAL BEARINGS. AXLE FRICTION

Journal bearings are used to provide lateral support to rotating shafts and axles. Thrust bearings, which will be studied in the next section, are used to provide axial support to shafts and axles. If the journal bearing is fully lubricated, the frictional resistance depends upon the speed of rotation, the clearance between axle and bearing, and the viscosity of the lubricant. As indicated in Sec. 8.1, such problems are studied in fluid mechanics. The methods of this chapter, however, can be applied to the study of axle friction when the bearing is not lubricated or only partially lubricated. It can then be assumed that the axle and the bearing are in direct contact along a single straight line.

Fig. 8.10

Consider two wheels, each of weight **W**, rigidly mounted on an axle supported symmetrically by two journal bearings (Fig. 8.10a). If the wheels rotate, we find that to keep them rotating at constant speed, it is necessary to apply to each of them a couple **M**. The free-body diagram in Fig. 8.10c represents one of the wheels and the corresponding half axle in projection on a plane perpendicular to the axle. The forces acting on the free body include the weight **W** of the wheel, the couple **M** required to maintain its motion, and a force **R** representing the reaction of the bearing. This force is vertical, equal, and opposite to **W** but does not pass through the center O of the axle; **R** is located to the right of O at a distance such that its moment about O balances the moment **M** of the couple. Therefore, contact between the axle and bearing does not take place at the lowest point A when the axle rotates. It takes place at point B (Fig. 8.10b) or, rather, along a straight line intersecting the plane of the figure at B. Physically, this is explained by the fact that when the wheels are set in motion, the axle "climbs" in the bearings until slippage occurs. After sliding back slightly, the axle settles more or less in the position shown. This position is such that the angle between the reaction **R** and the normal to the surface of the bearing is equal to the angle of kinetic friction ϕ_k. The distance from O to the line of action of **R** is thus $r \sin \phi_k$, where r is the radius of the axle. Writing that $\Sigma M_O = 0$ for the forces acting on the free body considered, we obtain the magnitude of the couple **M** required to overcome the frictional resistance of one of the bearings:

$$M = Rr \sin \phi_k \qquad (8.5)$$

Observing that, for small values of the angle of friction, $\sin \phi_k$ can be replaced by $\tan \phi_k$, that is, by μ_k, we write the approximate formula

$$M \approx Rr\mu_k \tag{8.6}$$

In the solution of certain problems, it may be more convenient to let the line of action of **R** pass through O, as it does when the axle does not rotate. A couple $-\mathbf{M}$ of the same magnitude as the couple **M** but of opposite sense must then be added to the reaction **R** (Fig. 8.10d). This couple represents the frictional resistance of the bearing.

In case a graphical solution is preferred, the line of action of **R** can be readily drawn (Fig. 8.10e) if we note that it must be tangent to a circle centered at O and of radius

$$r_f = r \sin \phi_k \approx r\mu_k \tag{8.7}$$

This circle is called the *circle of friction* of the axle and bearing and is independent of the loading conditions of the axle.

*8.8 THRUST BEARINGS. DISK FRICTION

Two types of thrust bearings are used to provide axial support to rotating shafts and axles: (1) *end bearings* and (2) *collar bearings* (Fig. 8.11). In the case of collar bearings, friction forces develop between the two ring-shaped areas which are in contact. In the case of end bearings, friction takes place over full circular areas, or over ring-shaped areas when the end of the shaft is hollow. Friction between circular areas, called *disk friction,* also occurs in other mechanisms, such as *disk clutches*.

(a) End bearing   (b) Collar bearing

Fig. 8.11 Thrust bearings.

To obtain a formula which is valid in the most general case of disk friction, let us consider a rotating hollow shaft. A couple **M** keeps the shaft rotating at constant speed while a force **P** maintains it in contact with a fixed bearing (Fig. 8.12). Contact between the shaft and

Fig. 8.12

the bearing takes place over a ring-shaped area of inner radius R_1 and outer radius R_2. Assuming that the pressure between the two surfaces in contact is uniform, we find that the magnitude of the normal force $\Delta\mathbf{N}$ exerted on an element of area ΔA is $\Delta N = P\,\Delta A/A$, where $A = \pi(R_2^2 - R_1^2)$, and that the magnitude of the friction force $\Delta\mathbf{F}$ acting on ΔA is $\Delta F = \mu_k\,\Delta N$. Denoting by r the distance from the axis of the shaft to the element of area ΔA, we express the magnitude ΔM of the moment of $\Delta\mathbf{F}$ about the axis of the shaft as follows:

$$\Delta M = r\,\Delta F = \frac{r\mu_k P\,\Delta A}{\pi(R_2^2 - R_1^2)}$$

The equilibrium of the shaft requires that the moment $\mathbf{M}$ of the couple applied to the shaft be equal in magnitude to the sum of the moments of the friction forces $\Delta\mathbf{F}$. Replacing ΔA by the infinitesimal element $dA = r\,d\theta\,dr$ used with polar coordinates, and integrating over the area of contact, we thus obtain the following expression for the magnitude of the couple $\mathbf{M}$ required to overcome the frictional resistance of the bearing:

$$M = \frac{\mu_k P}{\pi(R_2^2 - R_1^2)} \int_0^{2\pi} \int_{R_1}^{R_2} r^2\,dr\,d\theta$$

$$= \frac{\mu_k P}{\pi(R_2^2 - R_1^2)} \int_0^{2\pi} \tfrac{1}{3}(R_2^3 - R_1^3)\,d\theta$$

$$M = \tfrac{2}{3}\mu_k P \frac{R_2^3 - R_1^3}{R_2^2 - R_1^2} \tag{8.8}$$

When contact takes place over a full circle of radius R, formula (8.8) reduces to

$$M = \tfrac{2}{3}\mu_k PR \tag{8.9}$$

The value of M is then the same as would be obtained if contact between shaft and bearing took place at a single point located at a distance $2R/3$ from the axis of the shaft.

The largest couple which can be transmitted by a disk clutch without causing slippage is given by a formula similar to (8.9), where μ_k has been replaced by the coefficient of static friction μ_s.

*8.9 WHEEL FRICTION. ROLLING RESISTANCE

The wheel is one of the most important inventions of our civilization. Its use makes it possible to move heavy loads with relatively little effort. Because the point of the wheel in contact with the ground at any given instant has no relative motion with respect to the ground, the wheel eliminates the large friction forces which would arise if the load were in direct contact with the ground. However, some resistance to the wheel's motion exists. This resistance has two distinct causes. It is due (1) to a combined effect of axle friction and friction at the rim and (2) to the fact that the wheel and the ground deform, with the result that contact between wheel and ground takes place over a certain area, rather than at a single point.

To understand better the first cause of resistance to the motion of a wheel, let us consider a railroad car supported by eight wheels mounted on axles and bearings. The car is assumed to be moving to the right at constant speed along a straight horizontal track. The free-body diagram of one of the wheels is shown in Fig. 8.13*a*. The forces acting on the free body include the load **W** supported by the wheel and the normal reaction **N** of the track. Since **W** is drawn through the center *O* of the axle, the frictional resistance of the bearing should be represented by a counterclockwise couple **M** (see Sec. 8.7). To keep the free body in equilibrium, we must add two equal and opposite forces **P** and **F**, forming a clockwise couple of moment −**M**. The force **F** is the friction force exerted by the track on the wheel, and **P** represents the force which should be applied to the wheel to keep it rolling at constant speed. Note that the forces **P** and **F** would not exist if there were no friction between wheel and track. The couple **M** representing the axle friction would then be zero; the wheel would slide on the track without turning in its bearing.

The couple **M** and the forces **P** and **F** also reduce to zero when there is no axle friction. For example, a wheel which is not held in bearings and rolls freely and at constant speed on horizontal ground (Fig. 8.13*b*) will be subjected to only two forces: its own weight **W** and the normal reaction **N** of the ground. Regardless of the value of the coefficient of friction between wheel and ground no friction force will act on the wheel. A wheel rolling freely on horizontal ground should thus keep rolling indefinitely.

Experience, however, indicates that the wheel will slow down and eventually come to rest. This is due to the second type of resistance mentioned at the beginning of this section, known as the *rolling resistance*. Under the load **W**, both the wheel and the ground deform slightly, causing the contact between wheel and ground to take place over a certain area. Experimental evidence shows that the resultant of the forces exerted by the ground on the wheel over this area is a force **R** applied at a point *B*, which is not located directly under the center *O* of the wheel, but slightly in front of it (Fig. 8.13*c*). To balance the moment of **W** about *B* and to keep the wheel rolling at constant speed, it is necessary to apply a horizontal force **P** at the center of the wheel. Writing $\Sigma M_B = 0$, we obtain

$$Pr = Wb \qquad (8.10)$$

where r = radius of wheel
b = horizontal distance between *O* and *B*

The distance b is commonly called the *coefficient of rolling resistance*. It should be noted that b is not a dimensionless coefficient since it represents a length; b is usually expressed in inches or in millimeters. The value of b depends upon several parameters in a manner which has not yet been clearly established. Values of the coefficient of rolling resistance vary from about 0.01 in. or 0.25 mm for a steel wheel on a steel rail to 5.0 in. or 125 mm for the same wheel on soft ground.

(*a*) Effect of axle friction

(*b*) Free wheel

(*c*) Rolling resistance

Fig. 8.13

A pulley of diameter 4 in. can rotate about a fixed shaft of diameter 2 in. The coefficient of static friction between the pulley and shaft is 0.20. Determine (*a*) the smallest vertical force **P** required to start raising a 500-lb load, (*b*) the smallest vertical force **P** required to hold the load, (*c*) the smallest horizontal force **P** required to start raising the same load.

SOLUTION

a. Vertical Force P Required to Start Raising the Load. When the forces in both parts of the rope are equal, contact between the pulley and shaft takes place at *A*. When **P** is increased, the pulley rolls around the shaft slightly and contact takes place at *B*. The free-body diagram of the pulley when motion is impending is drawn. The perpendicular distance from the center *O* of the pulley to the line of action of **R** is

$$r_f = r \sin \phi_s \approx r\mu_s \qquad r_f \approx (1 \text{ in.})0.20 = 0.20 \text{ in.}$$

Summing moments about *B*, we write

$$+\gamma \ \Sigma M_B = 0: \qquad (2.20 \text{ in.})(500 \text{ lb}) - (1.80 \text{ in.})P = 0$$
$$P = 611 \text{ lb} \qquad\qquad\qquad \mathbf{P} = 611 \text{ lb} \downarrow \ \blacktriangleleft$$

b. Vertical Force P to Hold the Load. As the force **P** is decreased, the pulley rolls around the shaft and contact takes place at *C*. Considering the pulley as a free body and summing moments about *C*, we write

$$+\gamma \ \Sigma M_C = 0: \qquad (1.80 \text{ in.})(500 \text{ lb}) - (2.20 \text{ in.})P = 0$$
$$P = 409 \text{ lb} \qquad\qquad\qquad \mathbf{P} = 409 \text{ lb} \downarrow \ \blacktriangleleft$$

c. Horizontal Force P to Start Raising the Load. Since the three forces **W**, **P**, and **R** are not parallel, they must be concurrent. The direction of **R** is thus determined from the fact that its line of action must pass through the point of intersection *D* of **W** and **P**, and must be tangent to the circle of friction. Recalling that the radius of the circle of friction is $r_f = 0.20$ in., we write

$$\sin \theta = \frac{OE}{OD} = \frac{0.20 \text{ in.}}{(2 \text{ in.})\sqrt{2}} = 0.0707 \qquad \theta = 4.1°$$

From the force triangle, we obtain

$$P = W \cot (45° - \theta) = (500 \text{ lb}) \cot 40.9°$$
$$= 577 \text{ lb} \qquad\qquad\qquad \mathbf{P} = 577 \text{ lb} \rightarrow \ \blacktriangleleft$$

SOLVING PROBLEMS
ON YOUR OWN

In this lesson you learned about several additional engineering applications of the laws of friction.

1. Journal bearings and axle friction. In journal bearings, the *reaction does not pass through the center of the shaft or axle* which is being supported. The distance from the center of the shaft or axle to the line of action of the reaction (Fig. 8.10) is defined by the equation.

$$r_f = r \sin \phi_k \approx r\mu_k$$

if motion is actually taking place, and by the equation

$$r_f = r \sin \phi_s \approx r\mu_s$$

if the motion is impending.

Once you have determined the line of action of the reaction, you can draw a *free-body diagram* and use the corresponding equations of equilibrium to complete your solution [Sample Prob. 8.6]. In some problems, it is useful to observe that the line of action of the reaction must be tangent to a circle of radius $r_f \approx r\mu_k$, or $r_f \approx r\mu_s$, known as the *circle of friction* [Sample Prob. 8.6, part *c*].

2. Thrust bearings and disk friction. In a *thrust bearing* the magnitude of the couple required to overcome frictional resistance is equal to the sum of the moments of the *kinetic friction forces* exerted on the elements of the end of the shaft [Eqs. (8.8) and (8.9)].

An example of disk friction is the *disk clutch*. It is analyzed in the same way as a thrust bearing, except that to determine the largest couple that can be transmitted, you must compute the sum of the moments of the *maximum static friction forces* exerted on the disk.

3. Wheel friction and rolling resistance. You saw that the rolling resistance of a wheel is caused by deformations of both the wheel and the ground. The line of action of the reaction **R** of the ground on the wheel intersects the ground at a horizontal distance b from the center of the wheel. The distance b is known as the *coefficient of rolling resistance* and is expressed in inches or millimeters.

4. In problems involving both rolling resistance and axle friction, your free-body diagram should show that the line of action of the reaction **R** of the ground on the wheel is tangent to the friction circle of the axle and intersects the ground at a horizontal distance from the center of the wheel equal to the coefficient of rolling resistance.

PROBLEMS

8.77 A lever of negligible weight is loosely fitted onto a 30-mm-radius fixed shaft as shown. Knowing that a force **P** of magnitude 275 N will just start the lever rotating clockwise, determine (a) the coefficient of static friction between the shaft and the lever, (b) the smallest force **P** for which the lever does not start rotating counterclockwise.

Fig. P8.77

8.78 A hot-metal ladle and its contents weigh 130 kips. Knowing that the coefficient of static friction between the hooks and the pinion is 0.30, determine the tension in cable *AB* required to start tipping the ladle.

Fig. P8.78

8.79 and 8.80 The double pulley shown is attached to a 10-mm-radius shaft that fits loosely in a fixed bearing. Knowing that the coefficient of static friction between the shaft and the poorly lubricated bearing is 0.40, determine the magnitude of the force **P** required to start raising the load.

Fig. P8.79 and P8.81

Fig. P8.80 and P8.82

8.81 and 8.82 The double pulley shown is attached to a 10-mm-radius shaft that fits loosely in a fixed bearing. Knowing that the coefficient of static friction between the shaft and the poorly lubricated bearing is 0.40, determine the magnitude of the smallest force **P** required to maintain equilibrium.

446

8.83 The block and tackle shown are used to raise a 150-lb load. Each of the 3-in.-diameter pulleys rotates on a 0.5-in.-diameter axle. Knowing that the coefficient of static friction is 0.20, determine the tension in each portion of the rope as the load is slowly raised.

8.84 The block and tackle shown are used to lower a 150-lb load. Each of the 3-in.-diameter pulleys rotates on a 0.5-in.-diameter axle. Knowing that the coefficient of static friction is 0.20, determine the tension in each portion of the rope as the load is slowly lowered.

8.85 A scooter is to be designed to roll down a 2 percent slope at a constant speed. Assuming that the coefficient of kinetic friction between the 25-mm-diameter axles and the bearings is 0.10, determine the required diameter of the wheels. Neglect the rolling resistance between the wheels and the ground.

8.86 The link arrangement shown is frequently used in highway bridge construction to allow for expansion due to changes in temperature. At each of the 60-mm-diameter pins A and B the coefficient of static friction is 0.20. Knowing that the vertical component of the force exerted by BC on the link is 200 kN, determine (a) the horizontal force that should be exerted on beam BC to just move the link, (b) the angle that the resulting force exerted by beam BC on the link will form with the vertical.

8.87 and 8.88 A lever AB of negligible weight is loosely fitted onto a 2.5-in.-diameter fixed shaft. Knowing that the coefficient of static friction between the fixed shaft and the lever is 0.15, determine the force **P** required to start the lever rotating counterclockwise.

Fig. *P8.83* and **P8.84**

Fig. P8.86

Fig. *P8.87* and P8.89

Fig. P8.88 and P8.90

8.89 and 8.90 A lever AB of negligible weight is loosely fitted onto a 2.5-in.-diameter fixed shaft. Knowing that the coefficient of static friction between the fixed shaft and the lever is 0.15, determine the force **P** required to start the lever rotating clockwise.

8.91 A loaded railroad car has a mass of 30 Mg and is supported by eight 800-mm-diameter wheels with 125-mm-diameter axles. Knowing that the coefficients of friction are $\mu_s = 0.020$ and $\mu_k = 0.015$, determine the horizontal force required (a) to start the car moving, (b) to keep the car moving at a constant speed. Neglect rolling resistance between the wheels and the rails.

4 kN

M

50 mm

120 mm

Fig. P8.92

8.92 Knowing that a couple of magnitude 30 N · m is required to start the vertical shaft rotating, determine the coefficient of static friction between the annular surfaces of contact.

8.93 A 50-lb electric floor polisher is operated on a surface for which the coefficient of kinetic friction is 0.25. Assuming that the normal force per unit area between the disk and the floor is uniformly distributed, determine the magnitude Q of the horizontal forces required to prevent motion of the machine.

−Q

20 in.

Q

18 in.

Fig. P8.93

*8.94 The frictional resistance of a thrust bearing decreases as the shaft and bearing surfaces wear out. It is generally assumed that the wear is directly proportional to the distance traveled by any given point of the shaft and thus to the distance r from the point to the axis of the shaft. Assuming, then, that the normal force per unit area is inversely proportional to r, show that the magnitude M of the couple required to overcome the frictional resistance of a worn-out end bearing (with contact over the full circular area) is equal to 75 percent of the value given by Eq. (8.9) for a new bearing.

*8.95 Assuming that bearings wear out as indicated in Prob. 8.94, show that the magnitude M of the couple required to overcome the frictional resistance of a worn-out collar bearing is

$$M = \tfrac{1}{2}\mu_k P(R_1 + R_2)$$

where P = magnitude of the total axial force
R_1, R_2 = inner and outer radii of the collar

*8.96 Assuming that the pressure between the surfaces of contact is uniform, show that the magnitude M of the couple required to overcome frictional resistance for the conical bearing shown is

$$M = \frac{2}{3}\frac{\mu_k P}{\sin \theta}\frac{R_2^3 - R_1^3}{R_2^2 - R_1^2}$$

P

M

θ θ

R_1

R_2

Fig. P8.96

8.97 Solve Prob. 8.93 assuming that the normal force per unit area between the disk and the floor varies linearly from a maximum at the center to zero at the circumference of the disk.

8.98 Determine the horizontal force required to move a 2500-lb automobile with 23-in.-diameter tires along a horizontal road at a constant speed. Neglect all forms of friction except rolling resistance, and assume the coefficient of rolling resistance to be 0.05 in.

8.99 Knowing that a 6-in.-diameter disk rolls at a constant velocity down a 2 percent incline, determine the coefficient of rolling resistance between the disk and the incline.

8.100 A 900-kg machine base is rolled along a concrete floor using a series of steel pipes with outside diameters of 100 mm. Knowing that the coefficient of rolling resistance is 0.5 mm between the pipes and the base and 1.25 mm between the pipes and the concrete floor, determine the magnitude of the force **P** required to slowly move the base along the floor.

Fig. P8.100

8.101 Solve Prob. 8.85 including the effect of a coefficient of rolling resistance of 1.75 mm.

8.102 Solve Prob. 8.91 including the effect of a coefficient of rolling resistance of 0.5 mm.

8.10 BELT FRICTION

Consider a flat belt passing over a fixed cylindrical drum (Fig. 8.14a). We propose to determine the relation existing between the values T_1 and T_2 of the tension in the two parts of the belt when the belt is just about to slide toward the right.

Let us detach from the belt a small element PP' subtending an angle $\Delta\theta$. Denoting by T the tension at P and by $T + \Delta T$ the tension at P', we draw the free-body diagram of the element of the belt (Fig. 8.14b). Besides the two forces of tension, the forces acting on the free body are the normal component $\Delta\mathbf{N}$ of the reaction of the drum and the friction force $\Delta\mathbf{F}$. Since motion is assumed to be impending, we have $\Delta F = \mu_s \Delta N$. It should be noted that if $\Delta\theta$ is made to approach zero, the magnitudes ΔN and ΔF, and the *difference* ΔT between the tension at P and the tension at P', will also approach zero; the value T of the tension at P, however, will remain unchanged. This observation helps in understanding our choice of notations.

Choosing the coordinate axes shown in Fig. 8.14b, we write the equations of equilibrium for the element PP':

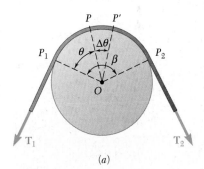

(a)

$$\Sigma F_x = 0: \quad (T + \Delta T) \cos\frac{\Delta\theta}{2} - T \cos\frac{\Delta\theta}{2} - \mu_s \Delta N = 0 \quad (8.11)$$

$$\Sigma F_y = 0: \quad \Delta N - (T + \Delta T) \sin\frac{\Delta\theta}{2} - T \sin\frac{\Delta\theta}{2} = 0 \quad (8.12)$$

Solving Eq. (8.12) for ΔN and substituting into (8.11), we obtain after reductions

$$\Delta T \cos\frac{\Delta\theta}{2} - \mu_s(2T + \Delta T) \sin\frac{\Delta\theta}{2} = 0$$

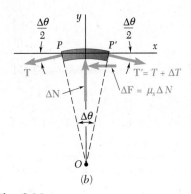

(b)

Both terms are now divided by $\Delta\theta$. For the first term, this is done simply by dividing ΔT by $\Delta\theta$. The division of the second term is

Fig. 8.14

carried out by dividing the terms in the parentheses by 2 and the sine by $\Delta\theta/2$. We write

$$\frac{\Delta T}{\Delta\theta}\cos\frac{\Delta\theta}{2} - \mu_s\left(T + \frac{\Delta T}{2}\right)\frac{\sin(\Delta\theta/2)}{\Delta\theta/2} = 0$$

If we now let $\Delta\theta$ approach 0, the cosine approaches 1 and $\Delta T/2$ approaches zero, as noted above. The quotient of sin $(\Delta\theta/2)$ over $\Delta\theta/2$ approaches 1, according to a lemma derived in all calculus textbooks. Since the limit of $\Delta T/\Delta\theta$ is by definition equal to the derivative $dT/d\theta$, we write

$$\frac{dT}{d\theta} - \mu_s T = 0 \qquad \frac{dT}{T} = \mu_s d\theta$$

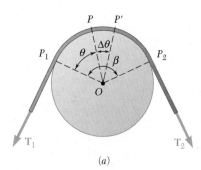

Both members of the last equation (Fig. 8.14a) will now be integrated from P_1 to P_2. At P_1, we have $\theta = 0$ and $T = T_1$; at P_2, we have $\theta = \beta$ and $T = T_2$. Integrating between these limits, we write

$$\int_{T_1}^{T_2}\frac{dT}{T} = \int_0^\beta \mu_s\,d\theta$$

$$\ln T_2 - \ln T_1 = \mu_s\beta$$

Fig. 8.14a (repeated)

or, noting that the left-hand member is equal to the natural logarithm of the quotient of T_2 and T_1,

$$\ln\frac{T_2}{T_1} = \mu_s\beta \tag{8.13}$$

This relation can also be written in the form

$$\frac{T_2}{T_1} = e^{\mu_s\beta} \tag{8.14}$$

Photo 8.3 By wrapping the rope around the bollard, the force exerted by the worker to control the rope is much smaller than the tension in the taut portion of the rope.

The formulas we have derived apply equally well to problems involving flat belts passing over fixed cylindrical drums and to problems involving ropes wrapped around a post or capstan. They can also be used to solve problems involving band brakes. In such problems, it is the drum which is about to rotate, while the band remains fixed. The formulas can also be applied to problems involving belt drives. In these problems, both the pulley and the belt rotate; our concern is then to find whether the belt will slip, i.e., whether it will move *with respect* to the pulley.

Formulas (8.13) and (8.14) should be used only if the belt, rope, or brake is *about to slip*. Formula (8.14) will be used if T_1 or T_2 is desired; formula (8.13) will be preferred if either μ_s or the angle of contact β is desired. We should note that T_2 is always larger than T_1; T_2 therefore represents the tension in that part of the belt or rope which *pulls*, while T_1 is the tension in the part which *resists*. We should also observe that the angle of contact β must be expressed in *radians*. The angle β may be larger than 2π; for example, if a rope is wrapped n times around a post, β is equal to $2\pi n$.

If the belt, rope, or brake is actually slipping, formulas similar to (8.13) and (8.14), but involving the coefficient of kinetic friction μ_k, should be used. If the belt, rope, or brake is not slipping and is not about to slip, none of these formulas can be used.

The belts used in belt drives are often V-shaped. In the V belt shown in Fig. 8.15a contact between belt and pulley takes place

(a)

(b)

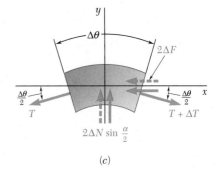
(c)

Fig. 8.15

along the sides of the groove. The relation existing between the values T_1 and T_2 of the tension in the two parts of the belt when the belt is just about to slip can again be obtained by drawing the free-body diagram of an element of belt (Fig. 8.15b and c). Equations similar to (8.11) and (8.12) are derived, but the magnitude of the total friction force acting on the element is now $2\,\Delta F$, and the sum of the y components of the normal forces is $2\,\Delta N \sin(\alpha/2)$. Proceeding as above, we obtain

$$\ln \frac{T_2}{T_1} = \frac{\mu_s \beta}{\sin(\alpha/2)} \tag{8.15}$$

or,

$$\frac{T_2}{T_1} = e^{\mu_s \beta / \sin(\alpha/2)} \tag{8.16}$$

150 N   7500 N

SAMPLE PROBLEM 8.7

A hawser thrown from a ship to a pier is wrapped two full turns around a bollard. The tension in the hawser is 7500 N; by exerting a force of 150 N on its free end, a dockworker can just keep the hawser from slipping. (*a*) Determine the coefficient of friction between the hawser and the bollard. (*b*) Determine the tension in the hawser that could be resisted by the 150-N force if the hawser were wrapped three full turns around the bollard.

SOLUTION

a. Coefficient of Friction. Since slipping of the hawser is impending, we use Eq. (8.13):

$$\ln \frac{T_2}{T_1} = \mu_s \beta$$

Since the hawser is wrapped two full turns around the bollard, we have

$$\beta = 2(2\pi \text{ rad}) = 12.57 \text{ rad}$$
$$T_1 = 150 \text{ N} \qquad T_2 = 7500 \text{ N}$$

Therefore,

$$\mu_s \beta = \ln \frac{T_2}{T_1}$$
$$\mu_s (12.57 \text{ rad}) = \ln \frac{7500 \text{ N}}{150 \text{ N}} = \ln 50 = 3.91$$
$$\mu_s = 0.311 \qquad\qquad \mu_s = 0.311 \blacktriangleleft$$

b. Hawser Wrapped Three Turns Around Bollard. Using the value of μ_s obtained in part *a*, we now have

$$\beta = 3(2\pi \text{ rad}) = 18.85 \text{ rad}$$
$$T_1 = 150 \text{ N} \qquad \mu_s = 0.311$$

Substituting these values into Eq. (8.14), we obtain

$$\frac{T_2}{T_1} = e^{\mu_s \beta}$$
$$\frac{T_2}{150 \text{ N}} = e^{(0.311)(18.85)} = e^{5.862} = 351.5$$
$$T_2 = 52\ 725 \text{ N}$$
$$T_2 = 52.7 \text{ kN} \blacktriangleleft$$

$T_1 = 150$ N T_2

SAMPLE PROBLEM 8.8

A flat belt connects pulley A, which drives a machine tool, to pulley B, which is attached to the shaft of an electric motor. The coefficients of friction are $\mu_s = 0.25$ and $\mu_k = 0.20$ between both pulleys and the belt. Knowing that the maximum allowable tension in the belt is 600 lb, determine the largest torque which can be exerted by the belt on pulley A.

SOLUTION

Since the resistance to slippage depends upon the angle of contact β between pulley and belt, as well as upon the coefficient of static friction μ_s, and since μ_s is the same for both pulleys, slippage will occur first on pulley B, for which β is smaller.

Pulley B. Using Eq. (8.14) with $T_2 = 600$ lb, $\mu_s = 0.25$, and $\beta = 120° = 2\pi/3$ rad, we write

$$\frac{T_2}{T_1} = e^{\mu_s \beta} \qquad \frac{600 \text{ lb}}{T_1} = e^{0.25(2\pi/3)} = 1.688$$

$$T_1 = \frac{600 \text{ lb}}{1.688} = 355.4 \text{ lb}$$

Pulley A. We draw the free-body diagram of pulley A. The couple $\mathbf{M}_A$ is applied to the pulley by the machine tool to which it is attached and is equal and opposite to the torque exerted by the belt. We write

$+\uparrow \Sigma M_A = 0: \qquad M_A - (600 \text{ lb})(8 \text{ in.}) + (355.4 \text{ lb})(8 \text{ in.}) = 0$

$M_A = 1957 \text{ lb} \cdot \text{in.} \qquad\qquad M_A = 163.1 \text{ lb} \cdot \text{ft} \ \blacktriangleleft$

Note. We may check that the belt does not slip on pulley A by computing the value of μ_s required to prevent slipping at A and verifying that it is smaller than the actual value of μ_s. From Eq. (8.13) we have

$$\mu_s \beta = \ln \frac{T_2}{T_1} = \ln \frac{600 \text{ lb}}{355.4 \text{ lb}} = 0.524$$

and, since $\beta = 240° = 4\pi/3$ rad,

$$\frac{4\pi}{3}\mu_s = 0.524 \qquad \mu_s = 0.125 < 0.25$$

SOLVING PROBLEMS
ON YOUR OWN

In the preceding section you learned about *belt friction*. The problems you will solve include belts passing over fixed drums, band brakes in which the drum rotates while the band remains fixed, and belt drives.

1. Problems involving belt friction fall into one of the following two categories:

a. Problems in which slipping is impending. One of the following formulas, involving the *coefficient of static friction* μ_s, may then be used,

$$\ln \frac{T_2}{T_1} = \mu_s \beta \tag{8.13}$$

or

$$\frac{T_2}{T_1} = e^{\mu_s \beta} \tag{8.14}$$

b. Problems in which slipping is occurring. The formulas to be used can be obtained from Eqs. (8.13) and (8.14) by replacing μ_s with the *coefficient of kinetic friction* μ_k.

2. As you start solving a belt-friction problem, be sure to remember the following:

a. The angle β must be expressed in radians. In a belt-and-drum problem, this is the angle subtending the arc of the drum on which the belt is wrapped.

b. The larger tension is always denoted by T_2 and the *smaller tension is denoted by T_1.*

c. The larger tension occurs at the end of the belt which is in the direction of the motion, or impending motion, of the belt relative to the drum.

3. In each of the problems you will be asked to solve, three of the four quantities T_1, T_2, β, and μ_s (or μ_k) will either be given or readily found, and you will then solve the appropriate equation for the fourth quantity. Here are two kinds of problems that you will encounter:

a. Find μ_s between belt and drum, knowing that slipping is impending. From the given data, determine T_1, T_2, and β; substitute these values into Eq. (8.13) and solve for μ_s [Sample Prob. 8.7, part *a*]. Follow the same procedure to find the *smallest value* of μ_s for which slipping will not occur.

b. Find the magnitude of a force or couple applied to the belt or drum, knowing that slipping is impending. The given data should include μ_s and β. If it also includes T_1 or T_2, use Eq. (8.14) to find the other tension. If neither T_1 nor T_2 is known but some other data is given, use the free-body diagram of the belt-drum system to write an equilibrium equation that you will solve simultaneously with Eq. (8.14) for T_1 and T_2. You will then be able to find the magnitude of the specified force or couple from the free-body diagram of the system. Follow the same procedure to determine the *largest value* of a force or couple which can be applied to the belt or drum if no slipping is to occur [Sample Prob. 8.8].

PROBLEMS

8.103 A 300-lb block is supported by a rope that is wrapped $1\frac{1}{2}$ times around a horizontal rod. Knowing that the coefficient of static friction between the rope and the rod is 0.15, determine the range of values of P for which equilibrium is maintained.

8.104 A hawser is wrapped two full turns around a bollard. By exerting an 80-lb force on the free end of the hawser, a dockworker can resist a force of 5000 lb on the other end of the hawser. Determine (a) the coefficient of static friction between the hawser and the bollard, (b) the number of times the hawser should be wrapped around the bollard if a 20,000-lb force is to be resisted by the same 80-lb force.

Fig. P8.103

8.105 A rope *ABCD* is looped over two pipes as shown. Knowing that the coefficient of static friction is 0.25, determine (a) the smallest value of the mass *m* for which equilibrium is possible, (b) the corresponding tension in portion *BC* of the rope.

8.106 A rope *ABCD* is looped over two pipes as shown. Knowing that the coefficient of static friction is 0.25, determine (a) the largest value of the mass *m* for which equilibrium is possible, (b) the corresponding tension in portion *BC* of the rope.

Fig. P8.105 and P8.106

8.107 Knowing that the coefficient of static friction is 0.25 between the rope and the horizontal pipe and 0.20 between the rope and the vertical pipe, determine the range of values of P for which equilibrium is maintained.

Fig. *P8.107* and *P8.108*

8.108 Knowing that the coefficient of static friction is 0.30 between the rope and the horizontal pipe and that the smallest value of P for which equilibrium is maintained is 80 N, determine (a) the largest value of P for which equilibrium is maintained, (b) the coefficient of static friction between the rope and the vertical pipe.

8.109 A band brake is used to control the speed of a flywheel as shown. The coefficients of friction are $\mu_s = 0.30$ and $\mu_k = 0.25$. Determine the magnitude of the couple being applied to the flywheel, knowing that $P = 45$ N and that the flywheel is rotating counterclockwise at a constant speed.

Fig. P8.109

455

←18.75 in.→

Fig. P8.110 and P8.111

8.110 The setup shown is used to measure the output of a small turbine. When the flywheel is at rest, the reading of each spring scale is 14 lb. If a 105-lb · in. couple must be applied to the flywheel to keep it rotating clockwise at a constant speed, determine (*a*) the reading of each scale at that time, (*b*) the coefficient of kinetic friction. Assume that the length of the belt does not change.

8.111 The setup shown is used to measure the output of a small turbine. The coefficient of kinetic friction is 0.20 and the reading of each spring scale is 16 lb when the flywheel is at rest. Determine (*a*) the reading of each scale when the flywheel is rotating clockwise at a constant speed, (*b*) the couple that must be applied to the flywheel. Assume that the length of the belt does not change.

8.112 A flat belt is used to transmit a couple from drum *B* to drum *A*. Knowing that the coefficient of static friction is 0.40 and that the allowable belt tension is 450 N, determine the largest couple that can be exerted on drum *A*.

$r_A = 120$ mm

A

15°   15°

B

$r_B = 50$ mm

Fig. P8.112

8.113 A flat belt is used to transmit a couple from pulley *A* to pulley *B*. The radius of each pulley is 60 mm, and a force of magnitude $P = 900$ N is applied as shown to the axle of pulley *A*. Knowing that the coefficient of static friction is 0.35, determine (*a*) the largest couple that can be transmitted, (*b*) the corresponding maximum value of the tension in the belt.

P

A   B

←——— 240 mm ———→

Fig. P8.113

8.114 Solve Prob. 8.113 assuming that the belt is looped around the pulleys in a figure eight.

8.115 The speed of the brake drum shown is controlled by a belt attached to the control bar AD. A force **P** of magnitude 25 lb is applied to the control bar at A. Determine the magnitude of the couple being applied to the drum, knowing that the coefficient of kinetic friction between the belt and the drum is 0.25, that $a = 4$ in., and that the drum is rotating at a constant speed (a) counterclockwise, (b) clockwise.

8.116 The speed of the brake drum shown is controlled by a belt attached to the control bar AD. Knowing that $a = 4$ in., determine the maximum value of the coefficient of static friction for which the brake is not self-locking when the drum rotates counterclockwise.

8.117 The speed of the brake drum shown is controlled by a belt attached to the control bar AD. Knowing that the coefficient of static friction is 0.30 and that the brake drum is rotating counterclockwise, determine the minimum value of a for which the brake is not self-locking.

Fig. P8.115, P8.116, and P8.117

8.118 Bucket A and block C are connected by a cable that passes over drum B. Knowing that drum B rotates slowly counterclockwise and that the coefficients of friction at all surfaces are $\mu_s = 0.35$ and $\mu_k = 0.25$, determine the smallest combined mass m of the bucket and its contents for which block C will (a) remain at rest, (b) start moving up the incline, (c) continue moving up the incline at a constant speed.

Fig. P8.118

8.119 Solve Prob. 8.118 assuming that drum B is frozen and cannot rotate.

8.120 and 8.122 A cable is placed around three parallel pipes. Knowing that the coefficients of friction are $\mu_s = 0.25$ and $\mu_k = 0.20$, determine (a) the smallest weight W for which equilibrium is maintained, (b) the largest weight W that can be raised if pipe B is slowly rotated counterclockwise while pipes A and C remain fixed.

Fig. P8.120 and P8.121

Fig. P8.122 and P8.123

8.121 and 8.123 A cable is placed around three parallel pipes. Two of the pipes are fixed and do not rotate; the third pipe is slowly rotated. Knowing that the coefficients of friction are $\mu_s = 0.25$ and $\mu_k = 0.20$, determine the largest weight W that can be raised (a) if only pipe A is rotated counterclockwise, (b) if only pipe C is rotated clockwise.

8.124 A recording tape passes over the 20-mm-radius drive drum B and under the idler drum C. Knowing that the coefficients of friction between the tape and the drums are $\mu_s = 0.40$ and $\mu_k = 0.30$ and that drum C is free to rotate, determine the smallest allowable value of P if slipping of the tape on drum B is not to occur.

Fig. P8.124

8.125 Solve Prob. 8.124 assuming that the idler drum C is frozen and cannot rotate.

8.126 The strap wrench shown is used to grip the pipe firmly without marring the external surface of the pipe. Knowing that the coefficient of static friction is the same for all surfaces of contact, determine the smallest value of μ_s for which the wrench will be self-locking when $a = 200$ mm, $r = 30$ mm, and $\theta = 65°$.

Fig. P8.126

8.127 Solve Prob. 8.126 assuming that $\theta = 75°$.

8.128 The 10-lb bar AE is suspended by a cable that passes over a 5-in.-radius drum. Vertical motion of end E of the bar is prevented by the two stops shown. Knowing that $\mu_s = 0.30$ between the cable and the drum, determine (a) the largest counterclockwise couple M_0 that can be applied to the drum if slipping is not to occur, (b) the corresponding force exerted on end E of the bar.

Fig. P8.128

8.129 Solve Prob. 8.128 assuming that a clockwise couple $\mathbf{M}_0$ is applied to the drum.

8.130 Prove that Eqs. (8.13) and (8.14) are valid for any shape of surface provided that the coefficient of friction is the same at all points of contact.

Fig. P8.130

8.131 Complete the derivation of Eq. (8.15), which relates the tension in both parts of a V belt.

8.132 Solve Prob. 8.112 assuming that the flat belt and drums are replaced by a V belt and V pulleys with $\alpha = 36°$. (The angle α is as shown in Fig. 8.15a.)

8.133 Solve Prob. 8.113 assuming that the flat belt and pulleys are replaced by a V belt and V pulleys with $\alpha = 36°$. (The angle α is as shown in Fig. 8.15a.)

This chapter was devoted to the study of *dry friction*, i.e., to problems involving rigid bodies which are in contact along *nonlubricated surfaces.*

Fig. 8.16

Static and kinetic friction   Applying a horizontal force **P** to a block resting on a horizontal surface [Sec. 8.2], we note that the block at first does not move. This shows that a *friction force* **F** must have developed to balance **P** (Fig. 8.16). As the magnitude of **P** is increased, the magnitude of **F** also increases until it reaches a maximum value F_m. If **P** is further increased, the block starts sliding and the magnitude of **F** drops from F_m to a lower value F_k. Experimental evidence shows that F_m and F_k are proportional to the normal component N of the reaction of the surface. We have

$$F_m = \mu_s N \qquad F_k = \mu_k N \qquad (8.1, 8.2)$$

where μ_s and μ_k are called, respectively, the *coefficient of static friction* and the *coefficient of kinetic friction*. These coefficients depend on the nature and the condition of the surfaces in contact. Approximate values of the coefficients of static friction were given in Table 8.1.

Angles of friction

Fig. 8.17

It is sometimes convenient to replace the normal force **N** and the friction force **F** by their resultant **R** (Fig. 8.17). As the friction force increases and reaches its maximum value $F_m = \mu_s N$, the angle ϕ that **R** forms with the normal to the surface increases and reaches a maximum value ϕ_s, called the *angle of static friction*. If motion actually takes place, the magnitude of **F** drops to F_k; similarly the angle ϕ drops to a lower value ϕ_k, called the *angle of kinetic friction*. As shown in Sec. 8.3, we have

$$\tan \phi_s = \mu_s \qquad \tan \phi_k = \mu_k \qquad (8.3, 8.4)$$

When solving equilibrium problems involving friction, we should keep in mind that the magnitude F of the friction force is equal to $F_m = \mu_s N$ *only if the body is about to slide* [Sec. 8.4]. *If motion is not impending,* F and N should be considered as *independent unknowns* to be determined from the equilibrium equations (Fig. 8.18a). We

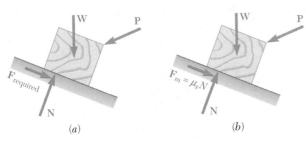

Fig. 8.18

should also check that the value of F required to maintain equilibrium is not larger than F_m; if it were, the body would move and the magnitude of the friction force would be $F_k = \mu_k N$ [Sample Prob. 8.1]. On the other hand, *if motion is known to be impending,* F has reached its maximum value $F_m = \mu_s N$ (Fig. 8.18b), and this expression may be substituted for F in the equilibrium equations [Sample Prob. 8.3]. When only three forces are involved in a free-body diagram, including the reaction **R** of the surface in contact with the body, it is usually more convenient to solve the problem by drawing a force triangle [Sample Prob. 8.2].

When a problem involves the analysis of the forces exerted on each other by *two bodies A and B*, it is important to show the friction forces with their correct sense. The correct sense for the friction force exerted by B on A, for instance, is opposite to that of the *relative motion* (or impending motion) of A with respect to B [Fig. 8.6].

In the second part of the chapter we considered a number of specific engineering applications where dry friction plays an important role. In the case of *wedges*, which are simple machines used to raise heavy loads [Sec. 8.5], two or more free-body diagrams were drawn and care was taken to show each friction force with its correct sense [Sample Prob. 8.4]. The analysis of *square-threaded screws*, which are frequently used in jacks, presses, and other mechanisms, was reduced to the analysis of a block sliding on an incline by unwrapping the thread of the screw and showing it as a straight line [Sec. 8.6]. This is done again in Fig. 8.19, where r denotes the *mean radius* of the thread, L is the *lead* of the screw, i.e., the distance through which the screw advances in one turn, **W** is the load, and Qr is equal to the couple exerted on the screw. It was noted that in the case of multiple-threaded screws the lead L of the screw is *not* equal to its pitch, which is the distance measured between two consecutive threads.

Fig. 8.19

Other engineering applications considered in this chapter were *journal bearings* and *axle friction* [Sec. 8.7], *thrust bearings* and *disk friction* [Sec. 8.8], *wheel friction* and *rolling resistance* [Sec. 8.9], and *belt friction* [Sec. 8.10].

Belt friction   In solving a problem involving a *flat belt* passing over a fixed cylinder, it is important to first determine the direction in which the belt slips or is about to slip. If the drum is rotating, the motion or impending motion of the belt should be determined *relative* to the rotating drum. For instance, if the belt shown in Fig. 8.20 is about to slip to

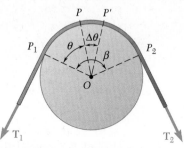

Fig. 8.20

the right relative to the drum, the friction forces exerted by the drum on the belt will be directed to the left and the tension will be larger in the right-hand portion of the belt than in the left-hand portion. Denoting the larger tension by T_2, the smaller tension by T_1, the coefficient of static friction by μ_s, and the angle (in radians) subtended by the belt by β, we derived in Sec. 8.10 the formulas

$$\ln\frac{T_2}{T_1} = \mu_s\beta \qquad (8.13)$$

$$\frac{T_2}{T_1} = e^{\mu_s\beta} \qquad (8.14)$$

which were used in solving Sample Probs. 8.7 and 8.8. If the belt actually slips on the drum, the coefficient of static friction μ_s should be replaced by the coefficient of kinetic friction μ_k in both of these formulas.

REVIEW PROBLEMS

8.134 Determine whether the block shown is in equilibrium and find the magnitude and direction of the friction force when $\theta = 35°$ and $P = 200$ N.

Fig. P8.134

8.135 Three 4-kg packages A, B, and C are placed on a conveyor belt that is at rest. Between the belt and both packages A and C the coefficients of friction are $\mu_s = 0.30$ and $\mu_k = 0.20$; between package B and the belt the coefficients are $\mu_s = 0.10$ and $\mu_k = 0.08$. The packages are placed on the belt so that they are in contact with each other and at rest. Determine which, if any, of the packages will move and the friction force acting on each package.

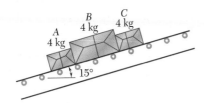

Fig. P8.135

8.136 The cylinder shown is of weight W and radius r. Express in terms W and r the magnitude of the largest couple **M** that can be applied to the cylinder if it is not to rotate, assuming the coefficient of static friction to be (a) zero at A and 0.30 at B, (b) 0.25 at A and 0.30 at B.

Fig. P8.136

8.137 End A of a slender, uniform rod of length L and weight W bears on a surface as shown, while end B is supported by a cord BC. Knowing that the coefficients of friction are $\mu_s = 0.40$ and $\mu_k = 0.30$, determine (a) the largest value of θ for which motion is impending, (b) the corresponding value of the tension in the cord.

Fig. P8.137

A ⟶ 1.2 m ⟶ B

0.9 m

C   D

E

a

Fig. P8.138

8.138 A worker slowly moves a 50-kg crate to the left along a loading dock by applying a force **P** at corner B as shown. Knowing that the crate starts to tip about the edge E of the loading dock when $a = 200$ mm, determine (a) the coefficient of kinetic friction between the crate and the loading dock, (b) the corresponding magnitude P of the force.

8.139 A window sash weighing 10 lb is normally supported by two 5-lb sash weights. Knowing that the window remains open after one sash cord has broken, determine the smallest possible value of the coefficient of static friction. (Assume that the sash is slightly smaller than the frame and will bind only at points A and D.)

Fig. P8.139

Fig. P8.140

8.140 The slender rod AB of length $l = 600$ mm is attached to a collar at B and rests on a small wheel located at a horizontal distance $a = 80$ mm from the vertical rod on which the collar slides. Knowing that the coefficient of static friction between the collar and the vertical rod is 0.25 and neglecting the radius of the wheel, determine the range of values of P for which equilibrium is maintained when $Q = 100$ N and $\theta = 30°$.

8.141 The machine part ABC is supported by a frictionless hinge at B and a 10° wedge at C. Knowing that the coefficient of static friction is 0.20 at both surfaces of the wedge, determine (a) the force **P** required to move the wedge to the left, (b) the components of the corresponding reaction at B.

Fig. P8.141

8.142 A conical wedge is placed between two horizontal plates that are then slowly moved toward each other. Indicate what will happen to the wedge (a) if $\mu_s = 0.20$, (b) if $\mu_s = 0.30$.

Fig. P8.142

8.143 In the machinist's vise shown, the movable jaw D is rigidly attached to the tongue AB that fits loosely into the fixed body of the vise. The screw is single-threaded into the fixed base and has a mean diameter of 0.75 in. and a pitch of 0.25 in. The coefficient of static friction is 0.25 between the threads and also between the tongue and the body. Neglecting bearing friction between the screw and the movable head, determine the couple that must be applied to the handle in order to produce a clamping force of 1 kip.

Fig. P8.143

8.144 A lever of negligible weight is loosely fitted onto a 75-mm-diameter fixed shaft. It is observed that the lever will just start rotating if a 3-kg mass is added at C. Determine the coefficient of static friction between the shaft and the lever.

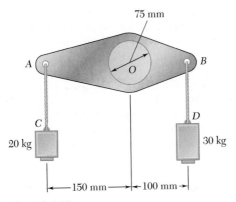

Fig. P8.144

8.145 In the pivoted motor mount shown, the weight **W** of the 175-lb motor is used to maintain tension in the drive belt. Knowing that the coefficient of static friction between the flat belt and drums A and B is 0.40, and neglecting the weight of platform CD, determine the largest couple that can be transmitted to drum B when the drive drum A is rotating clockwise.

Fig. P8.145

COMPUTER PROBLEMS

Fig. P8.C1

8.C1 The position of the 10-kg rod AB is controlled by the 2-kg block shown, which is slowly moved to the left by the force $\mathbf{P}$. Knowing that the coefficient of kinetic friction between all surfaces of contact is 0.25, write a computer program and use it to calculate the magnitude P of the force for values of x from 900 to 100 mm, using 50-mm decrements. Using appropriate smaller decrements, determine the maximum value of P and the corresponding value of x.

8.C2 Blocks A and B are supported by an incline that is held in the position shown. Knowing that block A weighs 20 lb and that the coefficient of static friction between all surfaces of contact is 0.15, write a computer program and use it to calculate the value of θ for which motion is impending for weights of block B from 0 to 100 lb, using 10-lb increments.

Fig. P8.C2

8.C3 A 300-g cylinder C rests on cylinder D as shown. Knowing that the coefficient of static friction μ_s is the same at A and B, write a computer program and use it to determine, for values of μ_s from 0 to 0.40 and using 0.05 increments, the largest counterclockwise couple $\mathbf{M}$ that can be applied to cylinder D if it is not to rotate.

Fig. P8.C3

8.C4 Two rods are connected by a slider block D and are held in equilibrium by the couple $\mathbf{M}_A$ as shown. Knowing that the coefficient of static friction between rod AC and the slider block is 0.40, write a computer program and use it to determine, for values of θ from 0 to 120° and using 10° increments, the range of values of M_A for which equilibrium is maintained.

Fig. P8.C4

8.C5 The 10-lb block A is slowly moved up the circular cylindrical surface by a cable that passes over a small fixed cylindrical drum at B. The coefficient of kinetic friction is known to be 0.30 between the block and the surface and between the cable and the drum. Write a computer program and use it to calculate the force $\mathbf{P}$ required to maintain the motion for values of θ from 0 to 90°, using 10° increments. For the same values of θ calculate the magnitude of the reaction between the block and the surface. [Note that the angle of contact between the cable and the fixed drum is $\beta = \pi - (\theta/2)$.]

8.C6 A flat belt is used to transmit a couple from drum A to drum B. The radius of each drum is 80 mm, and the system is fitted with an idler wheel C that is used to increase the contact between the belt and the drums. The allowable belt tension is 200 N, and the coefficient of static friction between the belt and the drums is 0.30. Write a computer program and use it to calculate the largest couple that can be transmitted for values of θ from 0 to 30°, using 5° increments.

Fig. P8.C5

Fig. P8.C6

8.C7 Two collars A and B that slide on vertical rods with negligible friction are connected by a 30-in. cord that passes over a fixed shaft at C. The coefficient of static friction between the cord and the fixed shaft is 0.30. Knowing that the weight of collar B is 8 lb, write a computer program and use it to determine, for values of θ from 0 to 60° and using 10° increments, the largest and smallest weight of collar A for which equilibrium is maintained.

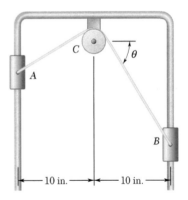

Fig. P8.C7

8.C8 The end B of a uniform beam of length L is being pulled by a stationary crane. Initially the beam lies on the ground with end A directly below pulley C. As the cable is slowly pulled in, the beam first slides to the left with $\theta = 0$ until it has moved through a distance x_0. In a second phase, end B is raised, while end A keeps sliding to the left until x reaches its maximum value x_m and θ the corresponding value θ_1. The beam then rotates about A' while θ keeps increasing. As θ reaches the value θ_2, end A starts sliding to the right and keeps sliding in an irregular manner until B reaches C. Knowing that the coefficients of friction between the beam and the ground are $\mu_s = 0.50$ and $\mu_k = 0.40$, (a) write a program to compute x for any value of θ while the beam is sliding to the left and use this program to determine x_0, x_m, and θ_1, (b) modify the program to compute for any θ the value of x for which sliding would be impending to the right and use this new program to determine the value θ_2 of θ corresponding to $x = x_m$.

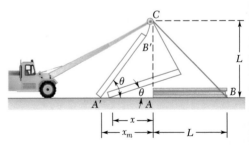

Fig. P8.C8

Appendix

Fundamentals of Engineering Examination

Engineers are required to be licensed when their work directly affects the public health, safety, and welfare. The intent is to ensure that engineers have met minimum qualifications involving competence, ability, experience, and character. The licensing process involves an initial exam, called the *Fundamentals of Engineering Examination;* professional experience; and a second exam, called the *Principles and Practice of Engineering.* Those who successfully complete these requirements are licensed as a *Professional Engineer.* The exams are developed under the auspices of the *National Council of Examiners for Engineering and Surveying.*

The first exam, the *Fundamentals of Engineering Examination,* can be taken just before or after graduation from a four-year accredited engineering program. The exam stresses subject material in a typical undergraduate engineering program, including statics. The topics included in the exam cover much of the material in this book. The following is a list of the main topic areas, with references to the appropriate sections in this book. Also included are problems that can be solved to review this material.

Concurrent Force Systems (2.2–2.9; 2.12–2.14)
Problems: 2.33, 2.35, 2.36, 2.37, 2.75, 2.84, 2.92, 2.93, 2.97

Vector Forces (3.4–3.11)
Problems: 3.17, 3.18, 3.24, 3.33, 3.37, 3.39

Equilibrium in Two Dimensions (2.11; 4.1–4.7)
Problems: 4.1, 4.9, 4.10, 4.17, 4.29, 4.32, 4.67, 4.81

Equilibrium in Three Dimensions (2.15; 4.8–4.9)
Problems: 4.97, 4.99, 4.100, 4.105, 4.113, 4.115, 4.128, 4.129, 4.140

Centroid of an Area (5.2–5.7)
Problems: 5.9, 5.17, 5.28, 5.36, 5.41, 5.56, 5.62, 5.97, 5.100, 5.103, 5.126

Analysis of Trusses (6.2–6.7)
Problems; 6.2, 6.5, 6.33, 6.45, 6.46, 6.50

Equilibrium of Two-Dimensional Frames (6.9–6.11)
Problems: 6.76, 6.82, 6.89, 6.93, 6.94

Shear and Bending Moment (7.3–7.6)
Problems: 7.22, 7.25, 7.31, 7.36, 7.45, 7.49, 7.70, 7.83

Friction (8.2–8.5; 8.10)
Problems: 8.11, 8.15, 8.21, 8.30, 8.50, 8.53, 8.101, 8.104, 8.105

Moments of Inertia (9.2–9.10)
Problems: 9.5, 9.31, 9.32, 9.33, 9.77, 9.78, 9.84, 9.89, 9.101, 9.103

Photo Credits

CHAPTER 1

Opener (crane): © Tom Paiva/Getty Images; (Manhattan Bridge): © Getty Images RF; (x-lift): © Tom Brakefield/SuperStock; (tugboats pushing tanker): © Daniel Sheehan; (communication tower): © Alfredo Maiquez/Getty Images; (construction worker): © Lester Lefkowitz/Getty Images; (Newton): © Lebrecht Music and Arts Photo Library/Alamy; **Photo 1.1:** © PhotoLink/Getty Images RF.

CHAPTER 2

Opener: © Tom Paiva/Getty Images; **Photo 2.1:** © H. David Seawell/Corbis; **Photo 2.2:** © WIN-Initiative/Getty Images.

CHAPTER 3

Opener: © Daniel Sheehan; **Photo 3.1:** © McGraw-Hill/Photo by Lucinda Dowell; **Photo 3.2:** © Steve Hix; **Photo 3.3:** © Jose Luis Pelaez/Getty Images; **Photo 3.4:** © Images-USA/Alamy RF; **Photo 3.5:** © Dana White/Photo Edit.

CHAPTER 4

Opener: © Alfredo Maiquez/Getty Images; **Photo 4.1, Photo 4.2, Photo 4.3:** © The McGraw-Hill Companies, Inc./Photo by Lucinda Dowell; **Photo 4.4, Photo 4.5:** Courtesy National Information Service for Earthquake Engineering, University of California, Berkeley; **Photo 4.6:** © McGraw-Hill/Photo by Lucinda Dowell; **Photo 4.7:** Courtesy of SKF, Limited.

CHAPTER 5

Opener: © Christopher Morris/Corbis; **Photo 5.1:** © Christies Images/SuperStock; **Photo 5.2:** Value RF/© Kevin Burke/Corbis;

Photo 5.3: © Ghislain & Marie David de Lossy/Getty Images; **Photo 5.4:** NASA.

CHAPTER 6

Opener: © Alan Schein Photography/Corbis; **Photo 6.1:** Courtesy National Information Service for Earthquake Engineering, University of California, Berkeley; **Photo 6.2:** Courtesy of Ferdinand Beer; **Photo 6.3:** © The McGraw-Hill Companies, Inc./Photo by Sabina Dowell; **Photo 6.4:** © EyeWire Collection/Getty Images RF; **Photo 6.5:** © Mouse in the House/Alamy.

CHAPTER 7

Opener: © Getty Images RF; **Photo 7.1:** © The McGraw-Hill Companies, Inc./Photo by Sabina Dowell; **Photo 7.2:** © Alan Thornton/Getty Images; **Photo 7.3:** © Michael S. Yamashita/Corbis; **Photo 7.4:** © Steve Kahn.

CHAPTER 8

Opener: © Bicot (Marc Caya); **Photo 8.1:** © Chuck Savage/Corbis; **Photo 8.2:** © Ted Spiegel/Corbis; **Photo 8.3:** © Adam Woolfitt/Corbis.

CHAPTER 9

Opener: © Lester Lefkowitz/Getty Images; **Photo 9.1:** © Ed Eckstein/Corbis; **Photo 9.2:** Reprinted Courtesy of Caterpillar Inc.

CHAPTER 10

Opener: © Tom Brakefield/SuperStock; **Photo 10.1:** Courtesy of Altec Industries; **Photo 10.2:** Courtesy of DE-STA-CO.

Index

Answers to Problems

Answers to problems with a number set in straight type are given on this and the following pages. Answers to problems set in italic are not listed.

CHAPTER 2

2.1 3.30 kN ⦨ 66.6°.
2.2 139.1 lb ⦨ 67.0°.
2.4 8.03 kips ⦨ 3.8°.
2.5 (a) 101.4 N.
     (b) 196.6 N.
2.6 (a) 3660 N.
     (b) 3730 N.
2.7 2600 N ⦨ 53.5°.
2.8 (a) 853 lb.
     (b) 567 lb.
2.10 (a) 37.1°.
     (b) 73.2 N.
2.11 (a) 392 lb. (b) 346 lb.
2.13 (a) 368 lb →. (b) 213 lb.
2.14 (a) 21.1 N ↓. (b) 45.3 N.
2.15 139.1 lb ⦨ 67.0°.
2.16 8.03 kips ⦨ 3.8°.
2.18 100.3 N ⦨ 21.2°.
2.19 104.4 N ⦨ 86.7°.
2.21 (80 N) 61.3 N, 51.4 N; (120 N) 41.0 N, 112.8 N; (150 N)
     −122.9 N, 86.0 N.
2.22 (40 lb) 20.0 lb, −34.6 lb; (50 lb) −38.3 lb, −32.1 lb; (60 lb)
     54.4 lb, 25.4 lb.
2.24 (102 lb) −48.0 lb, 90.0 lb; (106 lb) 56.0 lb, 90.0 lb; (200 lb)
     −160.0 lb, −120.0 lb.
2.25 (a) 2190 N. (b) 2060 N.
2.26 (a) 610 lb. (b) 500 lb.
2.28 (a) 373 lb. (b) 286 lb.
2.30 (a) 621 N. (b) 160.8 N.
2.31 654 N ⦨ 21.5°.
2.32 251 N ⦨ 85.3°.
2.33 54.9 lb ⦨ 48.9°.
2.35 309 N ⦨ 86.6°.
2.36 474 N ⦨ 32.5°.
2.37 203 lb ⦨ 8.46°.
2.39 (a) 21.7°. (b) 229 N.
2.40 (a) 26.5 N. (b) 623 N.
2.42 (a) 29.4°. (b) 371 lb.
2.43 (a) 6.37 kN. (b) 12.47 kN.
2.45 (a) 1244 lb. (b) 115.4 lb.
2.46 (a) 172.7 lb. (b) 231 lb.
2.48 (a) 305 N. (b) 514 N.
2.49 T_c = 5.87 kips; T_D = 9.14 kips.
2.51 (a) 312 N. (b) 144 N.
2.52 0 < P < 514 N.
2.53 (a) 1213 N. (b) 166.3 N
2.54 (a) 863 N. (b) 1216 N
2.55 F_A = 1303 lb; F_B = 420 lb.
2.57 (a) 1081 N. (b) 82.5°.
2.58 (a) 1294 N. (b) 62.5°.

2.59 (a) 5.00° ⦨. (b) 104.6 lb.
2.61 (a) 784 N. (b) 71.0°.
2.62 1.250 m.
2.63 (a) 10.98 lb. (b) 30.0 lb.
2.65 27.4° < α < 222.6°.
2.67 (a) 300 lb. (b) 300 lb. (c) 200 lb. (d) 200 lb. (e) 150.0 lb.
2.68 (b) 200 lb. (d) 150.0 lb.
2.69 (a) 1293 N. (b) 2220 N.
2.71 (a) −130.1 N; +816 N; +357 N. (b) 98.3°; 25.0°; 66.6°.
2.72 (a) +390 N; +614 N; +181.8 N. (b) 58.7°; 35.0°; 76.0°.
2.73 (a) −175.8 N; −257 N; +251 N. (b) 116.1°; 130.0°; 51.1°.
2.74 (a) +350 N; −169.0 N; +93.8 N. (b) 28.9°; 115.0°; 76.4°.
2.75 (a) −1861 lb; +3360 lb; +677 lb. (b) 118.5°; 30.5°; 80.0°.
2.77 (a) +56.4 lb; −103.9 lb; −20.5 lb. (b) 62.0°; 150.0°; 99.8°.
2.79 950 N; 43.4°; 71.6°; 127.6°.
2.81 (a) 43.9°. (b) F_x = +107.7 lb; F_z = 267 lb; F = 416 lb.
2.82 (a) 114.4°. (b) F_y = +694 N; F_z = +855 N; F = 1209.1 N.
2.83 (a) 194.0 N; 108.0 N. (b) 105.1°; 62.0°.
2.85 −1.260 kips; +1.213 kips; +0.970 kips.
2.86 −0.820 kips; +0.978 kips; −0.789 kips.
2.87 −1125 N; 750 N; 450 N.
2.89 240 N; −255 N; 160.0 N.
2.91 940 N; 65.7°; 28.2°; 76.4°.
2.92 940 N; 63.4°; 27.2°; 84.5°.
2.94 913 lb; 50.6°; 117.6°; 51.8°.
2.95 748 N; 120.1°; 52.5°; 128.0°.
2.96 3120 N; 37.4°; 122.0°; 72.6°.
2.97 130.0 lb.
2.99 13.98 kN.
2.101 926 N ↑.
2.103 2100 lb.
2.104 1868 lb.
2.106 T_{AB} = 571 lb; T_{AC} = 830 lb; T_{AD} = 528 lb.
2.107 960 N.
2.108 0 ≤ Q < 300 N.
2.109 845 N.
2.110 768 N.
2.112 3090 lb.
2.113 T_{AB} = 31.7 lb; T_{AC} = 64.3 lb.
2.115 T_{AB} = 510 N; T_{AC} = 56.2 N; T_{AD} = 536 N.
2.116 T_{AB} = 1340 N; T_{AC} = 1025 N; T_{AD} = 915 N.
2.117 T_{AB} = 1431 N; T_{AC} = 1560 N; T_{AD} = 183.0 N.
2.118 T_{AB} = 1249 N; T_{AC} = 490 N; T_{AD} = 1647 N.
2.119 T_{AB} = 842 lb; T_{AC} = 624 lb; T_{AD} = 1088 lb.
2.121 T_{BAC} = 76.7 lb; T_{AD} = 26.9 lb; T_{AE} = 49.2 lb.
2.122 P = 305 lb; T_{BAC} = 117.0 lb; T_{AD} = 40.9 lb.
2.123 P = 131.2 N; Q = 29.6 N.
2.125 (a) 1155 N. (b) 1012 N.
2.127 21.8 kN ⦨ 73.4°.
2.128 (a) 523 lb. (b) 428 lb.
2.129 (a) 95.1 lb. (b) 95.0 lb.

3.121 $\mathbf{R} = -(420 \text{ N})\mathbf{j} - (50.0 \text{ N})\mathbf{j} - (250 \text{ N})\mathbf{k}$;
$\mathbf{M} = (30.8 \text{ N} \cdot \text{m})\mathbf{j} - (22.0 \text{ N} \cdot \text{m})\mathbf{k}$.

3.122 (a) $\mathbf{B} = (2.50 \text{ lb})\mathbf{i}$, $\mathbf{C} = (0.1000 \text{ lb})\mathbf{i} - (2.47 \text{ lb})\mathbf{j} - (0.700 \text{ lb})\mathbf{k}$.
(b) $R_y = -2.47 \text{ lb}$; $M_x = 1.360 \text{ lb} \cdot \text{ft}$.

3.123 (a) $\mathbf{F}_B = -(80.0 \text{ N})\mathbf{k}$, $\mathbf{F}_C = -(30.0 \text{ N})\mathbf{i} + (40.0 \text{ N})\mathbf{k}$.
(b) $R_y = 0$, $R_z = 40.0 \text{ N}$. (c) When the slot in vertical

3.124 (a) $60.0°$. (b) $(20.0 \text{ lb})\mathbf{i} - (34.6 \text{ lb})\mathbf{j}$; $(520 \text{ lb} \cdot \text{in.})\mathbf{i}$.

3.127 1035 N; 2.57 m from OG and 3.05 m from OE.

3.128 2.32 m from OG and 1.165 m from OE.

3.129 405 lb; 12.60 ft to the right of AB and 2.94 ft below BC.

3.130 $a = 0.722 \text{ ft}$; $b = 20.6 \text{ ft}$.

3.133 (a) P, $\theta_x = 90.0°$; $\theta_y = 90.0°$, $\theta_z = 0$. (b) $5a/2$. (c) Axis of the wrench is parallel to the z axis at $x = a$, $y = -a$.

3.134 (a) $P\sqrt{3}$; $\theta_x = \theta_y = \theta_z = 54.7°$. (b) $-a$.
(c) Axis of the wrench is diagonal OA.

3.135 (a) $-(21.0 \text{ lb})\mathbf{j}$. (b) 0.571 in. (c) Axis of wrench is parallel to the y axis at $x = 0$; $z = 1.667$ in.

3.137 (a) $-(84.0 \text{ N})\mathbf{j} - (80.0 \text{ N})\mathbf{k}$. (b) 0.477 m.
(c) $x = 0.526 \text{ m}$, $y = 0$, $z = -0.1857 \text{ m}$.

3.139 (a) $3P(2\mathbf{i} - 20\mathbf{j} - \mathbf{k})/25$. (b) $-0.0988\,a$.
(c) $x = 2.00\,a$, $z = -1.990\,a$.

3.142 $\mathbf{R} = (20.0 \text{ N})\mathbf{i} + (30.0 \text{ N})\mathbf{j} - (10.00 \text{ N})\mathbf{k}$; $y = -0.540 \text{ m}$, $z = -0.420 \text{ m}$.

3.143 $\mathbf{F}_A = (M/b)\mathbf{i} + \text{R}[1+(a/b)]\mathbf{k}$; $\mathbf{F}_B = -(M/b)\mathbf{i} - (aR/b)\mathbf{k}$.

3.147 41.7 N · m ↖. (b) 147.4 N ∠ 45.0°.

3.148 116.2 lb · ft ↖.

3.150 27.4°.

3.151 1.252 m.

3.153 (a) $\mathbf{F} = 560 \text{ lb}$ ↘ 20.0°; $\mathbf{M} = 7720 \text{ lb} \cdot \text{ft}$ ↓.
(b) $\mathbf{F} = 560 \text{ lb}$ ↘ 20.0°; $\mathbf{M} = 4290 \text{ lb} \cdot \text{ft}$ ↓.

3.154 $(0.227 \text{ lb})\mathbf{i} + (0.1057 \text{ lb})\mathbf{k}$; 63.6 in. to the right of B.

3.156 (a) 6.91 m. (b) 458 N; 3.16 m to the right of A.

3.158 $\mathbf{F}_B = 35.0 \text{ kips}$ ↓; $\mathbf{F}_F = 25.0 \text{ kips}$ ↓.

3.C3 *4 sides:* $\beta = 10°$, $\alpha = 44.1°$;
$\beta = 20°$, $\alpha = 41.6°$;
$\beta = 30°$, $\alpha = 37.8°$.

3.C4 $\theta = 0$ *rev:* $M = 97.0 \text{ N} \cdot \text{m}$;
$\theta = 6$ *rev:* $M = 63.3 \text{ N} \cdot \text{m}$;
$\theta = 12$ *rev:* $M = 9.17 \text{ N} \cdot \text{m}$.

3.C6 $d_{AB} = 36.0 \text{ in.}$; $d_{CD} = 9.00 \text{ in.}$; $d_{\min} = 58.3 \text{ in.}$

CHAPTER 4

4.1 (a) 6.07 kN ↑. (b) 4.23 kN ↑.

4.2 (a) 4.89 kN ↑. (b) 3.69 kN ↑.

4.3 (a) $\mathbf{A} = 20.0 \text{ lb}$ ↓; $\mathbf{B} = 150.0 \text{ lb}$ ↑.
(b) $\mathbf{A} = 10.00 \text{ lb}$ ↓; $\mathbf{B} = 140.0 \text{ lb}$ ↑.

4.5 (a) 37.9 N ↑. (b) 373 N ↑.

4.6 (a) 2.76 N ↑. (b) 391 N ↑.

4.8 (a) 245 lb ↑. (b) 140.0 lb ↑.

4.9 2.00 in. ≤ a ≤ 10.00 in.

4.10 150.0 mm ≤ d ≤ 400 mm.

4.11 0.500 kN ≤ Q ≤ 11.00 kN.

4.14 6.00 kips ≤ P ≤ 42.0 kips.

4.15 (a) 2.00 kN. (b) 2.32 kN ∠ 46.4°.

4.17 (a) 150.0 lb. (b) 225 lb ⬈ 32.3°.

4.18 111.2 lb →.

4.19 (a) 600 N. (b) 1253 N ∠ 69.8°.

4.21 (a) $\mathbf{A} = 225 \text{ N}$ ↑; $\mathbf{C} = 641 \text{ N}$ ⬈ 20.6°.
(b) $\mathbf{A} = 365 \text{ N}$ ∠ 60.0°; $\mathbf{C} = 844 \text{ N}$ ⬈ 22.0°.

4.23 (a) $\mathbf{A} = 150.0 \text{ N}$ ∠ 30.0°; $\mathbf{B} = 150.0 \text{ N}$ ↘ 30.0°.
(b) $\mathbf{A} = 433 \text{ N}$ ↖ 12.55°; $\mathbf{B} = 488 \text{ N}$ ↘ 30.0°.

4.25 (a) $\mathbf{A} = 44.7$ ↖ 26.6°; $\mathbf{B} = 30.0 \text{ lb}$ ↑.
(b) $\mathbf{A} = 30.2 \text{ lb}$ ↖ 41.4°; $\mathbf{B} = 34.6 \text{ lb}$ ↘ 60.0°.

4.26 (a) $\mathbf{A} = 20.0 \text{ lb}$ ↑; $\mathbf{B} = 50.0 \text{ lb}$ ↘ 36.9°.
(b) $\mathbf{A} = 23.1 \text{ lb}$ ∠ 60.0°; $\mathbf{B} = 59.6 \text{ lb}$ ↘ 30.2°.

4.27 (a) 190.9 N. (b) 142.3 N ∠ 18.43°.

4.28 (a) 324 N. (b) 270 N →.

4.29 (a) 117.0 lb. (b) 129.8 lb ↖ 56.3°.

4.30 (a) 195.0 lb. (b) 255 lb ↖ 45.0°.

4.31 $T = 80.0 \text{ N}$; $\mathbf{C} = 89.4 \text{ N}$ ∠ 26.6°.

4.32 (a) 130.0 N. (b) 224 N ⬊ 2.05°.

4.35 (a) 600 N. (b) $\mathbf{A} = 4.00 \text{ kN}$ ←; $\mathbf{B} = 4.00 \text{ kN}$ →.

4.36 (a) 105.1 N. (b) $\mathbf{A} = 147.2 \text{ N}$ ↑; $\mathbf{B} = 105.1 \text{ N}$ ←.

4.37 $T_{BE} = 50.0 \text{ lb}$; $\mathbf{A} = 18.75 \text{ lb}$ →; $\mathbf{D} = 18.75 \text{ lb}$ ←.

4.38 $\mathbf{A} = 69.3 \text{ lb}$ →; $\mathbf{B} = 34.6 \text{ lb}$ ↖ 60.0°; $\mathbf{C} = 173.2 \text{ lb}$ ↘ 60.0°.

4.39 $T = 80.0 \text{ N}$; $\mathbf{A} = 160.0 \text{ N}$ ↖ 30.0°; $\mathbf{C} = 160.0 \text{ N}$ ↘ 30.0°.

4.40 $T = 69.3 \text{ N}$; $\mathbf{A} = 140.0 \text{ N}$ ↖ 30.0°; $\mathbf{C} = 180.0 \text{ N}$ ↘ 30.0°.

4.43 (a) $\mathbf{D} = 20.0 \text{ lb}$ ↓; $\mathbf{M}_D = 20.0 \text{ lb} \cdot \text{ft}$ ↖.
(b) $\mathbf{D} = 10.00 \text{ lb}$ ↓; $\mathbf{M}_D = 30.0 \text{ lb} \cdot \text{ft}$ ↓.

4.45 (a) $\mathbf{A} = 78.5 \text{ N}$ ↑; $\mathbf{M}_A = 125.6 \text{ N} \cdot \text{m}$ ↖.
(b) $\mathbf{A} = 111.0 \text{ N}$ ∠ 45.0°; $\mathbf{M}_A = 125.6 \text{ N} \cdot \text{m}$ ↖.
(c) $\mathbf{A} = 157.0 \text{ N}$ ↑; $\mathbf{M}_A = 251 \text{ N} \cdot \text{m}$.

4.46 $\mathbf{C} = 28.3 \text{ N}$ ↘ 45.0°; $\mathbf{M}_C = 4.30 \text{ N} \cdot \text{m}$ ↓.

4.47 $\mathbf{C} = 28.3 \text{ N}$ ↘ 45.0°; $\mathbf{M}_C = 4.50 \text{ N} \cdot \text{m}$ ↓.

4.48 (a) $\mathbf{E} = 8.80 \text{ kips}$ ↑; $\mathbf{M}_E = 36.0 \text{ kip} \cdot \text{ft}$ ↓.
(b) $\mathbf{E} = 4.80 \text{ kips}$ ↑; $\mathbf{M}_E = 51.0 \text{ kip} \cdot \text{ft}$ ↓.

4.50 $\mathbf{A} = 1848 \text{ N}$ ∠ 82.6°; $\mathbf{M}_A = 1431 \text{ N} \cdot \text{m}$ ↓.

4.51 (a) $\theta = 2 \cos^{-1}\left[\frac{1}{4}\left(\frac{W}{P} \pm \sqrt{\frac{W^2}{P^2} + 8}\right)\right]$. (b) $\theta = 65.1°$.

4.52 (a) $\theta = 2 \sin^{-1}(W/2P)$. (b) $\theta = 29.0°$.

4.53 (a) $T = \frac{1}{2}W(1 - \tan\theta)$. (b) $\theta = 39.8°$.

4.54 (a) $\sin\theta + \cos\theta = M/pl$. (b) 17.11° and 72.9°.

4.55 141.1°.

4.56 (a) $(1 - \cos\theta)\tan\theta = W/2kl$. (b) 49.7°.

4.59 (1) completely constrained; determinate; $\mathbf{A} = \mathbf{C} = 196.2 \text{ N}$ ↑.
(2) completely constrained; determinate; $\mathbf{B} = 0$, $\mathbf{C} = \mathbf{D} = 196.2 \text{ N}$ ↑.
(3) completely constrained; indeterminate; $\mathbf{A}_x = 294 \text{ N}$ →; $\mathbf{D}_x = 294 \text{ N}$ ←.
(4) improperly constrained; indeterminate; no equilibrium.
(5) partially constrained; determinate; equilibrium; $\mathbf{C} = \mathbf{D} = 196.2 \text{ N}$ ↑.
(6) completely constrained; determinate; $\mathbf{B} = 294 \text{ N}$ →, $\mathbf{D} = 491 \text{ N}$ ↘ 53.1°.
(7) partially constrained; no equilibrium.
(8) completely constrained; indeterminate; $\mathbf{B} = 196.2 \text{ N}$ ↑, $\mathbf{D}_y = 196.2 \text{ N}$ ↑.

4.61 $\mathbf{A} = 680 \text{ N}$ ∠ 28.1°; $\mathbf{B} = 600 \text{ N}$ ←.

4.62 200 mm.

4.64 $T = 289 \text{ lb}$; $\mathbf{A} = 577 \text{ lb}$ ∠ 60.0°.

4.65 $\mathbf{A} = 63.6 \text{ lb}$ ↖ 45.0°; $\mathbf{C} = 87.5 \text{ lb}$ ↘ 59.0°.

4.67 $\mathbf{B} = 888 \text{ N}$ ↖ 41.3°; $\mathbf{D} = 943 \text{ N}$ ↘ 45.0°.

4.68 $\mathbf{B} = 1001 \text{ N}$ ↘ 48.2°; $\mathbf{D} = 943 \text{ N}$ ↖ 45.0°.

4.69 $\mathbf{A} = 778 \text{ N}$ ↓; $\mathbf{C} = 1012 \text{ N}$ ↘ 77.9°.

4.71 (a) 24.9 lb ⬈ 30.0°. (b) 15.34 lb ∠ 30.0°.

4.72 $\mathbf{A} = 37.1 \text{ lb}$ ∠ 62.4°; $T = 18.57 \text{ lb}$.

4.73 (a) 499 N. (b) 457 N ↘ 26.6°.

4.75 $\mathbf{A} = 163.1 \text{ N}$ ↖ 74.1°; $\mathbf{B} = 258 \text{ N}$ ↘ 65.0°.

4.77 (a) $2P$ ↘ 60.0°. (b) $1.239P$ ↖ 36.2°.

4.78 (a) $1.155P$ ↘ 30.0°. (b) $1.086P$ ∠ 22.9°.

4.79 (a) $\mathbf{A} = 150.0 \text{ N}$ ∠ 30.0°; $\mathbf{B} = 150.0 \text{ N}$ ↘ 30.0°.
(b) $\mathbf{A} = 433 \text{ N}$ ↖ 12.55°; $\mathbf{B} = 488 \text{ N}$ ↘ 30.0°.

4.80 (a) 119.3 lb. (b) 178.7 lb ↘ 60.5°.

4.81 $T = 100.0$ lb; $\mathbf{B} = 111.1$ lb $\searrow 30.3°$.

4.83 (a) 225 mm. (b) 23.1 N. (c) 12.21 N $\rightarrow$.

4.84 32.5°.

4.87 (a) 59.4°. (b) $\mathbf{A} = 8.45$ lb $\rightarrow$; 13.09 lb $\searrow 49.8°$.

4.88 60.0 mm.

4.89 $\tan\theta = 2\tan\beta$.

4.90 (a) 49.1°. (b) $\mathbf{A} = 45.3$ N $\leftarrow$; $\mathbf{B} = 90.6$ N $\measuredangle 60.0°$.

4.91 (a) 1200 N. (b) $\mathbf{C} = (400$ N$)\mathbf{i} + (1200$ N$)\mathbf{j}$; $\mathbf{D} = -(1600$ N$)\mathbf{i} - (480$ N$)\mathbf{j}$.

4.93 $\mathbf{A} = (24.0$ lb$)\mathbf{j} - (2.31$ lb$)\mathbf{k}$; $\mathbf{B} = (16.00$ lb$)\mathbf{j} - (9.24$ lb$)\mathbf{k}$; $\mathbf{C} = (11.55$ lb$)\mathbf{k}$.

4.94 $\mathbf{A} = (14.00$ lb$)\mathbf{j} + (4.50$ lb$)\mathbf{k}$; $\mathbf{D} = (6.00$ lb$)\mathbf{j} + (10.50$ lb$)\mathbf{k}$.

4.95 $\mathbf{A} = (120.0$ N$)\mathbf{j} + (133.3$ N$)\mathbf{k}$; $\mathbf{D} = (60.0$ N$)\mathbf{j} + (166.7$ N$)\mathbf{k}$.

4.97 $T_A = 23.5$ N; $T_C = 11.77$ N; $T_D = 105.9$ N.

4.98 (a) 0.480 m. (b) $T_A = 23.5$ N; $T_C = 0$; $T_D = 117.7$ N.

4.99 $T_A = 5.63$ lb; $T_B = 16.88$ lb; $T_C = 22.5$ lb.

4.101 (a) 121.9 N. (b) -46.2 N. (c) 100.9 N.

4.102 (a) 95.6 N. (b) -7.36 N. (c) 88.3 N.

4.103 $T_A = 30.0$ lb; $T_B = 10.00$ lb; $T_C = 40.0$ lb.

4.105 $T_{AD} = 2.60$ kN; $T_{AE} = 2.80$ kN; $\mathbf{C} = (1.800$ kN$)\mathbf{j} + (4.80$ kN$)\mathbf{k}$.

4.106 $T_{AD} = 5.20$ kN; $T_{AE} = 5.60$ kN; $\mathbf{C} = (9.60$ kN$)\mathbf{k}$.

4.107 $T_{BD} = T_{BE} = 1100$ lb; $\mathbf{A} = (1200$ lb$)\mathbf{i} - (560$ lb$)\mathbf{j}$.

4.108 $T_{BE} = T_{BF} = 17.50$ kN; $\mathbf{A} = -(7.00$ kN$)\mathbf{i} + (22.4$ kN$)\mathbf{j}$.

4.109 $T_{BE} = 6.62$ kN; $T_{BF} = 25.1$ kN; $\mathbf{A} = -(6.34$ kN$)\mathbf{i} + (20.3$ kN$)\mathbf{j} + (2.96$ kN$)\mathbf{k}$.

4.112 $T_{DE} = T_{DF} = 262$ lb; $\mathbf{A} = -(801$ lb$)\mathbf{i} + (1544$ lb$)\mathbf{j}$.

4.113 (a) 345 N. (b) $\mathbf{A} = (114.5$ N$)\mathbf{i} + (377$ N$)\mathbf{j} + (144.5$ N$)\mathbf{k}$; $\mathbf{B} = (113.2$ N$)\mathbf{j} + (185.5$ N$)\mathbf{k}$.

4.115 (a) 49.5 lb. (b) $\mathbf{A} = -(12.00)\mathbf{i} + (22.5$ lb$)\mathbf{j} - (4.00$ lb$)\mathbf{k}$; $\mathbf{B} = (15.00$ lb$)\mathbf{j} + (34.0$ lb$)\mathbf{k}$.

4.116 (a) 118.8 lb. (b) $\mathbf{A} = (93.8$ lb$)\mathbf{i} + (22.5$ lb$)\mathbf{j} + (70.8$ lb$)\mathbf{k}$; $\mathbf{B} = (15.00$ lb$)\mathbf{j} - (8.33$ lb$)\mathbf{k}$.

4.117 (a) 101.6 N. (b) $\mathbf{A} = -(26.3$ N$)\mathbf{i}$; $\mathbf{B} = (98.1$ N$)\mathbf{j}$.

4.119 (a) 49.5 lb. (b) $\mathbf{A} = -(12.00$ lb$)\mathbf{i} + (37.5$ lb$)\mathbf{j} + (30.0$ lb$)\mathbf{k}$; $\mathbf{M}_A = -(1020$ lb $\cdot$ in.$)\mathbf{j} + (450$ lb $\cdot$ in.$)\mathbf{k}$.

4.120 (a) 462 N. (b) $\mathbf{C} = (169.1$ N$)\mathbf{j} + (400$ N$)\mathbf{k}$; $\mathbf{M}_C = (20.0$ N $\cdot$ m$)\mathbf{j} + (151.5$ N $\cdot$ m$)\mathbf{k}$.

4.121 $T_{CF} = 200$ N; $T_{DE} = 450$ N; $\mathbf{A} = (160.0$ N$)\mathbf{i} + (270$ N$)\mathbf{k}$; $\mathbf{M}_A = -(16.20$ N $\cdot$ m$)\mathbf{i}$.

4.122 (a) 5.00 lb. (b) $\mathbf{C} = -(5.00$ lb$)\mathbf{i} + (6.00$ lb$)\mathbf{j} - (5.00$ lb$)\mathbf{k}$; $\mathbf{M}_C = (8.00$ lb $\cdot$ in.$)\mathbf{j} - (12.00$ lb $\cdot$ in.$)\mathbf{k}$.

4.125 $T_{BD} = 2.18$ kN; $T_{BE} = 3.96$ kN; $T_{CD} = 1.500$ kN.

4.126 $T_{BD} = 0$; $T_{BE} = 3.96$ kN; $T_{CO} = 3.00$ kN.

4.127 (a) $T_B = -0.366P$; $T_C = 1.219P$; $T_D = -0.853P$. (b) $\mathbf{F} = -0.345P\mathbf{i} + P\mathbf{j} - 0.862\,P\mathbf{k}$.

4.129 $\mathbf{A} = (120.0$ lb$)\mathbf{j} - (150.0$ lb$)\mathbf{k}$; $\mathbf{B} = (180.0$ lb$)\mathbf{i} + (150.0$ lb$)\mathbf{k}$; $\mathbf{C} = -(180.0$ lb$)\mathbf{i} + (120.0$ lb$)\mathbf{j}$.

4.130 $\mathbf{A} = (20.0$ lb$)\mathbf{j} + (25.0$ lb$)\mathbf{k}$; $\mathbf{B} = (30.0$ lb$)\mathbf{i} - (25.0$ lb$)\mathbf{k}$; $\mathbf{C} = -(30.0$ lb$)\mathbf{i} - (20.0$ lb$)\mathbf{j}$.

4.131 $\mathbf{B} = (60.0$ N$)\mathbf{k}$; $\mathbf{C} = (30.0$ N$)\mathbf{j} - (16.00$ N$)\mathbf{k}$; $\mathbf{D} = -(30.0$ N$)\mathbf{j} + (4.00$ N$)\mathbf{k}$.

4.133 373 N.

4.135 $(45.0$ lb$)\mathbf{j}$.

4.136 (a) $x = 4.00$ ft; $y = 8.00$ ft; (b) 10.73 lb.

4.137 (a) $x = 0$ ft; $y = 16.00$ ft. (b) 11.31 lb.

4.138 360 N.

4.140 85.3 lb.

4.141 181.7 lb.

4.142 42.0 N $\uparrow$.

4.143 (a) 80.8 lb $\downarrow$. (b) 216 lb $\measuredangle 22.0°$.

4.145 (a) 875 lb. (b) 1584 lb $\searrow 45.0°$.

4.147 $\mathbf{C} = 1951$ N $\searrow 88.5°$; $\mathbf{M}_C = 75.0$ N $\cdot$ m $\downarrow$.

4.149 $\mathbf{A} = 170.0$ N $\searrow 33.9°$. $\mathbf{C} = 160.0$ N $\measuredangle 28.1°$.

4.150 (a) $T_A = 6.00$ lb; $T_B = T_C = 9.00$ lb. (b) 15.00 in.

4.151 $T_{BE} = 975$ N; $T_{CF} = 600$ N; $T_{DG} = 625$ N; $\mathbf{A} = (2100$ N$)\mathbf{i} + (175.0$ N$)\mathbf{j} - (375$ N$)\mathbf{k}$.

4.153 (a) $\mathbf{A} = 0.745P \measuredangle 63.4°$; $\mathbf{C} = 0.471P \searrow 45.0°$.
(b) $\mathbf{A} = 0.812P \measuredangle 60.0°$; $\mathbf{C} = 0.503P \nearrow 36.2°$.
(c) $\mathbf{A} = 0.448P \searrow 60.0°$; $\mathbf{C} = 0.652P \measuredangle 69.9°$.
(d) improperly constrained: no equilibrium.

4.C1 $\theta = 20°$; $T = 114.8$ lb; $\theta = 70°$; $T = 127.7$ lb; $T_{max} = 132.2$ lb at $\theta = 50.4°$.

4.C2 $x = 600$ mm: $P = 31.4$ N; $x = 150$ mm: $P = 37.7$ N; $P_{max} = 47.2$ N at $x = 283$ mm.

4.C3 $\theta = 30°$: $W = 9.66$ lb; $\theta = 60°$; $W = 36.6$ lb; $W = 5$ lb at $\theta = 22.9°$ [Also at $\theta = 175.7°$].

4.C4 $\theta = 30°$: $W = 0.80$ lb; $\theta = 60°$: $W = 4.57$ lb; $W = 5$ lb at $\theta = 62.6°$ [Also at $\theta = 159.6°$].

4.C5 $\theta = 30°$: $m = 7.09$ kg; $\theta = 60°$: $m = 11.02$ kg. When $m = 10$ kg, $\theta = 51.0°$.

4.C6 $\theta = 15°$: $T_{BD} = 10.30$ kN, $T_{BE} = 21.7$ kN; $\theta = 30°$: $T_{BD} = 5.69$ kN, $T_{BE} = 24.4$ kN; $T_{max} = 26.5$ kN at $\theta = 36.9°$.

CHAPTER 5

5.1 $\bar{X} = 1.045$ in., $\bar{Y} = 3.59$ in.

5.2 $\bar{X} = 36.0$ mm, $\bar{Y} = 48.0$ mm.

5.3 $\bar{X} = 19.27$ mm, $\bar{Y} = 26.6$ mm.

5.4 $\bar{X} = 5.67$ in., $\bar{Y} = 5.17$ in.

5.6 $\bar{X} = 7.22$ in., $\bar{Y} = 9.56$ in.

5.8 $\bar{X} = -10.00$ mm, $\bar{Y} = 87.5$ mm.

5.9 $\bar{X} = 92.0$ mm, $\bar{Y} = 23.3$ mm.

5.10 $\bar{X} = 0$, $\bar{Y} = 6.45$ in.

5.11 $\bar{X} = 0$, $\bar{Y} = 1.372$ in.

5.13 $\bar{X} = 50.5$ mm, $\bar{Y} = 19.34$ mm.

5.14 $\bar{X} = 3.20$ in. $\bar{Y} = 2.00$ in.

5.17 $a/r = 0.508$.

5.18 $\bar{Y} = \dfrac{2}{3}\left(\dfrac{r_2^3 - r_1^3}{r_2^2 - r_1^2}\right)\left(\dfrac{2\cos\alpha}{\pi - 2\alpha}\right)$.

5.19 $\bar{Y} = \left(\dfrac{r_1 + r_2}{\pi - 2\alpha}\right)\cos\alpha$.

5.20 0.235 in^3 for A, -0.235 in^3 for A_2.

5.22 459 N.

5.23 (a) $b(c^2 - y^2)/2$. (b) $y = 0$, $Q_x = bc^2/2$.

5.24 $\bar{X} = 36.6$ mm, $\bar{Y} = 47.6$ mm.

5.26 $\bar{X} = 5.52$ in., $\bar{Y} = 5.16$ in.

5.28 120.0 mm.

5.29 99.5 mm.

5.31 (a) 5.09 lb. (b) 9.48 lb $\searrow 57.5°$.

5.32 (a) 0.513 a. (b) 0.691 a.

5.34 $\bar{x} = a/3$, $\bar{y} = 2h/3$.

5.36 $\bar{x} = a/2$, $\bar{y} = 2h/5$.

5.37 $\bar{y} = \bar{x} = 9a/20$.

5.38 $\bar{x} = 2a/3(4 - \pi)$, $\bar{y} = 2b/3(4 - \pi)$.

5.40 $\bar{x} = 5a/8$, $\bar{y} = b/3$.

5.41 $\bar{x} = 3a/8$, $\bar{y} = b$.

5.43 $\bar{x} = a.$, $\bar{y} = 17b/35$.

5.44 $\bar{x} = 17a/130$, $\bar{y} = 11b/26$.

5.45 $-2\sqrt{2}r/3\pi$.

5.46 $2a/5$.

5.48 $\bar{x} = L/\pi$, $\bar{y} = \pi a/8$.

5.49 $\bar{x} = -9.27a$, $\bar{y} = 3.09a$.

5.50 $\bar{x} = 1.629$ in., $\bar{y} = 0.1853$ in.

5.51 $a = 1.901$ in. or 3.74 in.

5.52 (a) Volume = 248 in^3, Area = 547 in^2.
(b) Volume = 72.3 in^3, Area = 169.6 in^2.

5.53 (a) Volume = 423×10^3 mm^3, Area = 37.2×10^3 mm^2.
(b) Volume = 847×10^3 mm^3, Area = 72.5×10^3 mm^2.

5.54 (a) Volume = 2.26×10^6 mm^3, Area = 116.3×10^3 mm^2.
(b) Volume = 1.471×10^6 mm^3, Area = 116.3×10^3 mm^2.

5.56 $V = 3470$ mm^3; $A = 2320$ mm^2.

5.58 $V = 3.96$ in^3; $W = 1.211$ lb.

5.60 0.0305 kg.

5.62 0.0900 in^3.

5.63 308 in^2.

5.64 31.9 liters.

5.66 (a) $\mathbf{R} = 7.60$ kN $\downarrow$, $\bar{x} = 2.57$ m, (b) $\mathbf{A} = 4.35$ kN $\uparrow$;
$\mathbf{B} = 3.25$ kN $\uparrow$.

5.67 (a) $\mathbf{R} = 1215$ lb $\downarrow$, $\bar{x} = 4.33$ ft. (b) $\mathbf{A} = 630$ lb $\uparrow$;
$\mathbf{B} = 585$ lb $\uparrow$.

5.68 $\mathbf{A} = 105.0$ N $\uparrow$; $\mathbf{B} = 270$ N $\uparrow$.

5.69 $\mathbf{A} = 2860$ lb $\uparrow$; $\mathbf{B} = 740$ lb $\uparrow$.

5.71 $\mathbf{A} = 32.0$ kN $\uparrow$; $M_A = 124.0$ kN $\cdot$ m $\uparrow$.

5.72 $\mathbf{A} = 3.00$ kN $\uparrow$; $M_A = 12.60$ kN $\cdot$ m $\uparrow$.

5.74 $\mathbf{B} = 3770$ lb $\uparrow$; $\mathbf{C} = 429$ lb $\uparrow$.

5.75 (a) 900 lb/ft. (b) 7200 lb $\uparrow$.

5.76 (a) 0.536 m. (b) $\mathbf{A} = \mathbf{B} = 761$ N $\uparrow$.

5.78 $w_{BC} = 2810$ N/m; $w_{DE} = 3150$ N/m.

5.80 (a) $\mathbf{H} = 44.1$ kN $\rightarrow$; $\mathbf{V} = 228$ kN $\uparrow$. (b) 1.159 m to the right of A. (c) $\mathbf{R} = 59.1$ kN $\nearrow$ 41.6°.

5.81 (a) $\mathbf{H} = 254$ kN $\rightarrow$; $\mathbf{V} = 831$ kN $\uparrow$. (b) 3.25 m to the right of A (c) $\mathbf{R} = 268$ kN $\nearrow$ 18.43°.

5.82 12.00 in.

5.83 4.00 in.

5.84 $\mathbf{T} = 67.2$ kN $\leftarrow$; $\mathbf{A} = 141.2$ kN $\leftarrow$.

5.86 3.70 kips $\uparrow$.

5.87 $t = 35.7$ $\uparrow$; gate rotates clockwise.

5.88 0.683 m.

5.89 0.0711 m.

5.91 208 lb.

5.92 $\mathbf{A} = 1197$ N $\searrow$ 53.1°; $\mathbf{B} = 1511$ N $\searrow$ 53.1°.

5.93 3570 N.

5.94 6.00 ft.

5.96 (a) 0.0536 a below base of cone.
(b) 0.0625 a above base of cone.

5.97 (a) 0.548 L. (b) $2\sqrt{3}$.

5.98 $-(2h^2 - 3b^2)/2(4h - 3b)$.

5.99 $-a(4h - 2b)/\pi(4h - 3b)$.

5.100 -0.1403 in.

5.101 19.13 mm.

5.103. 3.47 in.

5.104 18.28 in.

5.106 $\bar{X} = 45.0$ mm; $\bar{Z} = -20.2$ mm.

5.107 $\bar{X} = 0.1402$ m; $\bar{Y} = 0.0944$ m; $\bar{Z} = 0.0959$ m.

5.108 $\bar{X} = 17.00$ in.; $\bar{Y} = 15.68$ in.; $\bar{Z} = 14.16$ in.

5.109 $\bar{X} = 46.5$ mm; $\bar{Y} = 27.2$ mm; $\bar{Z} = 30.0$ mm.

5.110 $\bar{X} = \bar{Z} = 4.21$ in.; $\bar{Y} = 7.03$ in.

5.113 $\bar{X} = 180.2$ mm; $\bar{Y} = 38.0$ mm; $\bar{Z} = 193.5$ mm.

5.114 $\bar{X} = 0$; $\bar{Y} = 10.05$ in.; $\bar{Z} = 5.15$ in.

5.115 $\bar{X} = 0.410$ m; $\bar{Y} = 0.510$ m; $\bar{Z} = 0.1500$ m.

5.116 $\bar{X} = 0.909$ m; $\bar{Y} = 0.1842$ m; $\bar{Z} = 0.884$ m.

5.118 $\bar{X} = \bar{Z} = 0$; $\bar{Y} = 83.3$ mm above the base.

5.120 $\bar{Y} = 0.526$ in. above the base.

5.121 $\bar{X} = 61.1$ mm from the end of the handle.

5.122 $(\bar{x}_1) = 21a/88$; $(\bar{x}_2) = 27a/40$.

5.123 $(\bar{x}_1) = 21h/88$; $(\bar{x}_2) = 27h/40$.

5.124 $(\bar{x}_1) = 2h/9$; $(\bar{x}_2) = 2h/3$.

5.126 $\bar{x} = 2.34$ m; $\bar{y} = \bar{z} = 0$.

5.128 $\bar{x} = 1.297$ a; $\bar{y} = \bar{z} = 0$.

5.129 $\bar{x} = \bar{z} = 0$; $\bar{y} = 0.374$ b.

5.132 (a) $\bar{x} = \bar{z} = 0$; $\bar{y} = -121.9$ mm. (b) $\bar{x} = \bar{z} = 0$;
$\bar{y} = -90.2$ mm.

5.134 $\bar{x} = 0$; $\bar{y} = 5h/16$; $\bar{z} = -b/4$.

5.135 $V = 688$ ft^3; $\bar{x} = 15.91$ ft.

5.136 $\bar{x} = a/2$; $y = 8h/25$; $\bar{z} = b/2$.

5.137 $\bar{x} = 1.643$ in.; $\bar{y} = 17.46$ in.

5.138 $\bar{x} = 30.0$ mm; $\bar{y} = 64.8$ mm.

5.140 $\bar{x} = 2a/5$; $\bar{y} = 4h/7$.

5.141 $\bar{x} = 5L/4$; $\bar{y} = 33a/40$.

5.143 $\mathbf{B} = 1360$ lb $\uparrow$; $\mathbf{C} = 2360$ lb $\uparrow$.

5.144 $w_A = 10.00$ kN/m; $w_B = 50.0$ kN/m.

5.146 (a) $b/10$ to the left of base of cone
(b) 0.01136b to the right of base of cone.

5.147 $\bar{X} = 0.295$ m; $\bar{Y} = 0.423$ m; $\bar{Z} = 1.703$ m.

5.C1 (b) $\mathbf{A} = 1220$ lb $\uparrow$; $\mathbf{B} = 1830$ lb $\uparrow$.
(c) $\mathbf{A} = 1265$ lb $\uparrow$; $\mathbf{B} = 1601$ lb $\uparrow$.

5.C2 (a) $\bar{X} = 0$, $\bar{Y} = 0.278$ m. $\bar{Z} = 0.0878$ m.
(b) $\bar{X} = 0.0487$ mm, $\bar{Y} = 0.1265$ mm, $\bar{Z} = 0.0997$ mm.
(c) $\bar{X} = -0.0372$ m, $\bar{Y} = 0.1659$ m, $\bar{Z} = 0.1043$ m.

5.C3 $d = 1.00$ m: $\mathbf{F} = 5.66$ kN $\searrow$ 30°;
$d = 3.00$ m: $\mathbf{F} = 49.9$ kN $\searrow$ 27.7°.

5.C4 (a) $\bar{X} = 5.80$ in., $\bar{Y} = 1.492$ in. (b) $\bar{X} = 9.11$ in., $\bar{Y} = 2.78$ in.
(c) $\bar{X} = 8.49$ in., $\bar{Y} = 0.375$ in.

5.C5 With $n = 40$: (a) $\bar{X} = 60.2$ mm, $\bar{Y} = 23.4$ mm.
(b) $\bar{X} = 60.2$ mm, $\bar{Y} = 146.2$ mm.
(c) $\bar{X} = 68.7$ mm. $\bar{Y} = 20.4$ mm.
(d) $\bar{X} = 68.7$ mm, $\bar{Y} = 127.8$ mm.

5.C6 With $n = 40$: (a) $\bar{X} = 60.0$ mm, $\bar{Y} = 24.0$ mm.
(b) $\bar{X} = 60.0$ mm, $\bar{Y} = 150.0$ mm.
(c) $\bar{X} = 68.6$ mm, $\bar{Y} = 21.8$ mm.
(d) $\bar{X} = 68.6$ mm, $\bar{Y} = 136.1$ mm.

5.C7 (a) $V = 628$ ft^3.
(b) $\bar{X} = 8.65$ ft, $\bar{Y} = -4.53$ ft, $\bar{Z} = 9.27$ ft.

CHAPTER 6

6.1 $F_{AB} = 180.0$ kN T; $F_{AC} = 156.0$ kN C; $F_{BC} = 144.0$ kN T.

6.2 $F_{AB} = 720$ lb T; $F_{AC} = 1200$ lb C; $F_{BC} = 780$ lb C.

6.3 $F_{AB} = 52.0$ kN T; $F_{AC} = 64.0$ kN T; $F_{BC} = 80.0$ kN C.

6.5 $F_{AB} = F_{BC} = 0$; $F_{AD} = F_{CF} = 1.000$ kip C; $F_{BD} = F_{CF} = 6.80$ kips C; $F_{BE} = 2.40$ kips T; $F_{DE} = F_{EF} = 6.00$ kips T.

6.7 $F_{AB} = 20.0$ kN T; $F_{AD} = 20.6$ kN C; $F_{BC} = 30.0$ kN T;
$F_{BD} = 30.0$ kN T; $F_{CD} = 10.00$ kN T.

6.8 $F_{AB} = 4.00$ kN T; $F_{AD} = 15.00$ kN T; $F_{BD} = 9.00$ kN C;
$F_{BE} = 5.00$ kN T; $F_{CD} = 16.00$ kN C; $F_{DE} = 4.00$ kN C.

6.9 $F_{AB} = F_{FH} = 1500$ lb C; $F_{AC} = F_{CE} = F_{EG} = F_{GH} = 1200$ lb T; $F_{BC} = F_{FG} = 0$; $F_{BD} = F_{DF} = 1200$ lb C;
$F_{BE} = F_{EF} = 60.0$ lb C; $F_{DE} = 72.0$ lb T.

6.10 $F_{AB} = F_{FH} = 1500$ lb C; $F_{AC} = F_{CE} = F_{EG} = F_{GH} = 1200$ lb T; $F_{BC} = F_{FG} = 0$; $F_{BD} = F_{DF} = 1000$ lb C;
$F_{BE} = F_{EF} = 500$ lb C; $F_{DE} = 600$ lb T.

6.11 $F_{AB} = 47.2$ kN C; $F_{AC} = 44.6$ kN T; $F_{BC} = 10.50$ kN C;
$F_{BD} = 47.2$ kN C; $F_{CD} = 17.50$ kN C; $F_{CE} = 30.6$ kN T;
$F_{DE} = 0$.

6.13 F_{AB} = 7.83 kN C; F_{AC} = 7.00 kN T; F_{BC} = 1.886 kN C;
F_{BD} = 6.34 kN C; F_{CD} = 1.491 kN T; F_{CE} = 5.00 kN T;
F_{DE} = 2.83 kN C; F_{DF} = 3.35 kN C; F_{EF} = 2.75 kN T;
F_{EG} = 1.061 kN C; F_{EH} = 3.75 kN T; F_{FG} = 4.24 kN C;
F_{GH} = 5.30 kN C.

6.15 F_{AB} = 2240 lb C; F_{AC} = F_{CE} = 2000 lb T; F_{BC} = F_{EH} = 0;
F_{BD} = 1789 lb C; F_{BE} = 447 lb C; F_{DE} = 600 lb C;
F_{DF} = 2010 lb C; F_{DG} = 224 lb T; F_{EG} = 1789 lb T.

6.17 F_{AB} = 9.90 kN C; F_{AC} = 7.83 kN T; F_{BC} = 0; F_{BD} = 7.07 kN
C; F_{BE} = 2.00 kN C; F_{CE} = 7.83 kN T; F_{DE} = 1.000 kN T;
F_{DF} = 5.03 kN C; F_{DG} = 0.559 kN C; F_{EG} = 5.59 kN T.

6.18 F_{FG} = 3.50 kN T; F_{FH} = 5.03 kN C; F_{GH} = 1.677 kN T;
F_{GI} = F_{IK} = F_{KL} = 3.35 kN T; F_{HI} = F_{IJ} = F_{JK} = 0;
F_{HJ} = F_{JL} = 4.24 kN C.

6.19 F_{AB} = F_{FG} = 7.50 kips C; F_{AC} = F_{EG} = 4.50 kips T;
F_{BC} = F_{EF} = 7.50 kips T; F_{BD} = F_{DF} = 9.00 kips C;
F_{CD} = F_{DE} = 0; F_{CE} = 9.00 kips T.

6.21 F_{AB} = F_{FH} = 7.50 kips C; F_{AC} = F_{GH} = 4.50 kips T;
F_{BC} = F_{FG} = 4.00 kips T; F_{BD} = F_{DF} = 6.00 kips C;
F_{BE} = F_{EF} = 2.50 kips T; F_{CE} = F_{EG} = 4.50 kips T; F_{DE} = 0.

6.22 F_{AB} = 6.25 kips C; F_{AC} = 3.75 kips T; F_{BC} = 4.00 kips T;
F_{BD} = F_{DF} = 4.50 kips C; F_{BE} = 1.250 kips T; F_{CE} =
3.75 kips T; F_{DE} = F_{FG} = 0; F_{EF} = 3.75 kips T; F_{EG} =
F_{GH} = 2.25 kips T; F_{FH} = 3.75 kips T.

6.23 F_{AB} = F_{DF} = 2.29 kN T; F_{AC} = F_{EF} = 2.29 kN C; F_{BC} =
F_{DE} = 0.600 kN C; F_{BD} = 2.21 kN T; F_{BE} = F_{EH} = 0; F_{CE} =
2.21 kN C; F_{CH} = F_{EJ} = 1.200 kN C.

6.26 F_{AB} = 9.39 kN C; F_{AC} = 8.40 kN T; F_{BC} = 2.26 kN C;
F_{BD} = 7.60 kN C; F_{CD} = 0.128 kN C; F_{CE} = 7.07 kN T;
F_{DE} = 2.14 kN C; F_{DF} = 6.10 kN C; F_{EF} = 2.23 kN T.

6.27 F_{AB} = 31.0 kips C; F_{AC} = 28.3 kips C; F_{AD} = 15.09 kips T;
F_{AE} = 9.50 kips T; F_{BD} = 21.5 kips T; F_{BF} = 28.0 kips C;
F_{CE} = 41.0 kips T; F_{CG} = 42.0 kips C; F_{DE} = 22.0 kips T;
F_{DF} = 33.5 kips T; F_{EG} = 0.

6.28 F_{AB} = F_{BC} = F_{CD} = 36.0 kips T; F_{AE} = 57.6 kips T;
F_{AF} = 45.0 kips C; F_{BF} = F_{BG} = F_{CG} = F_{CH} = 0; F_{DH} =
F_{FG} = F_{GH} = 39.0 kips C; F_{EF} = 36.0 kips C.

6.29 Truss of prob. 6.33a is the only simple truss.

6.30 Trusses of prob 6.31b and prob 6.33b are simple trusses.

6.31 (a) AI, BJ, CK, DI, EI, FK, GK. (b) FK, IO.

6.34 (a) GH, GJ, IJ. (b) BF, BG, CG, CH.

6.35 F_{AB} = F_{AD} = 244 lb C; F_{AC} = 1040 lb T; F_{BC} = F_{CD} =
500 lb T; F_{BD} = 280 lb T.

6.36 F_{AB} = F_{AD} = 861 N C; F_{AC} = 676 N C; F_{BC} = F_{CD} =
162.5 N T; F_{BD} = 244 N T.

6.37 F_{AB} = F_{AD} = 2810 N T; F_{AC} = 5510 N C; F_{BC} = F_{CD} =
1325 N T; F_{BD} = 1908 N C.

6.38 F_{AB} = F_{AC} = 1061 lb C; F_{AD} = 2500 lb T; F_{BC} = 2100 lb T;
F_{BD} = F_{CD} = 1250 lb C; F_{BE} = F_{CE} = 1250 lb C;
F_{DE} = 1500 lb T.

6.39 F_{AB} = 840 N C; F_{AC} = 110.6 N C; F_{AD} = 394 N C;
F_{AE} = 0; F_{BC} = 160.0 N T; F_{BE} = 200 N T; F_{CD} = 225 N T;
F_{CE} = 233 N C; F_{DE} = 120.0 N T.

6.40 F_{AB} = F_{AE} = F_{BC} = 0; F_{AC} = 995 N T; F_{AD} = 1181 N C;
F_{BE} = 600 N T; F_{CD} = 375 V T; F_{CE} = 700 N C;
F_{DE} = 360 N T.

6.43 F_{CD} = 9.00 kN C; F_{DF} = 12.00 kN T.

6.44 F_{FG} = 5.00 kN T; F_{FH} = 20.0 kN T.

6.45 F_{CE} = 8000 lb T; F_{DE} = 2600 lb T; F_{DF} = 9000 lb C.

6.46 F_{EG} = 7500 lb T; F_{FG} = 3900 lb C; F_{FH} = 6000 lb C.

6.49 F_{AD} = 13.50 kN C; F_{CD} = 0; F_{CE} = 56.1 kN T.

6.50 F_{DG} = 75.0 kN C; F_{FG} = 56.1 kN T; F_{FH} = 69.7 kN T.

6.51 F_{AB} = 8.20 kips T; F_{AG} = 4.50 kips T; F_{FG} 11.60 kips C.

6.52 F_{AE} = 17.46 kips T; F_{EF} = 11.60 kips C; F_{FJ} = 18.45 kips C.

6.53 F_{CD} = 20.0 kN C; F_{DF} = 52.0 kN C.

6.54 F_{CE} = 36.0 kN T; F_{EF} = 15.00 kN C.

6.55 F_{FG} = 5.23 kN C; F_{EG} = 0.1476 kN T; F_{EH} = 5.08 kN T.

6.56 F_{KM} = 5.02 kN T; F_{LM} = 1.963 kN C; F_{LN} = 3.95 kN C.

6.59 F_{DE} = 25.0 kips T; F_{DF} = 13.00 kips C.

6.60 F_{EG} = 16.00 kips T; F_{EF} = 6.40 kips C.

6.63 F_{DG} = 3.75 kN T; F_{FI} = 3.75 kN C.

6.64 F_{GJ} = 11.25 kN T; F_{TK} = 11.25 kN C.

6.65 F_{BG} = 5.48 kips C; F_{DG} = 1.825 kips T.

6.66 F_{CF} = 3.65 kips T; F_{CH} = 7.30 kips T.

6.67 (a) CJ. (b) 1.026 kN T.

6.68 (a) IO. (b) 2.05 kN T.

6.69 (a) improperly constrained. (b) completely constrained,
determinate. (c) completely constrained, indeterminate.

6.70 (a) completely constrained, determine. (b) partially
constrained. (c) improperly constrained.

6.71 (a) completely constrained, determinate. (b) completely
constrained, indeterminate. (c) improperly constrained.

6.72 (a) partially constrained. (b) completely constrained,
determinate. (c) completely constrained, indeterminate.

6.75 F_{BD} = 780 lb T; C_x = 720 lb ←, C_y = 140.0 lb ↓.

6.76 F_{BD} = 255 N C; C_x = 120.0 N →, C_y = 625 N ↑.

6.77 A_x = 480 N →, A_y = 120.0 N ↑; B_x = 480 N ←,
B_y = 320 N ↓; C_x = 120.0 N ↓; D = 320 N ↑.

6.79 A_x = 25.0 kips ←, A_y = 20.0 kips ↑; B_x = 25.0 kips,
B_y = 10.00 kips ↓; C_x = 50.0 kips →, C_y = 10.00 kips ↓.

6.81 A = 375 N; B_x = 375 N ←, B_y = 150.0 N ↑;
C = 50.0 N ↑; D = 200 N ↓.

6.82 A = 150.0 N →; B = 0; C_x = 150.0 N ←, C_y = 100.0 N ↑;
D = 100.0 N ↓.

6.83 (a) A_x = 300 N ←, A_y = 660 N ↑; E_x = 300 N →,
E_y = 90.0 N ↑. (b) A_x = 300 N ←, A_y = 150.0 N ↑;
E_x = 300 N →, E_y = 600 N ↑.

6.84 (a) A_x = 450 N ←, A_y = 525 N ↑; E_x = 450 N →,
E_y = 225 N ↑; (b) A_x = 450 N ←, A_y = 150.0 N ↑;
E_x = 450 N →, E_y = 600 N ↑.

6.87 (a) A = 65.0 lb ⬈ 22.6°; C = 120.0 lb →; G = 60.0 lb ←;
I = 25.0 lb ↑. (b) A = 65.0 lb ⬈ 22.6°; C = 60.0 lb →;
G = 0; I = 25.0 lb ↑.

6.88 (a) A = 65.0 lb ⬈ 22.6°; C = 120.0 lb →; G = 60.0 lb ←;
I = 25.0 lb ↑.
(b) A = 65.0 lb ⬈ 22.6°; C = 100.0 lb →; G = 80.0 lb ←;
I = 25.0 lb ↑.

6.89 (a) A_x = 80.0 lb ←, A_y = 40.0 lb ↑; B_x = 80.0 lb →, B_y =
60.0 lb ↑. (b) A_x = 0, A_y = 40.0 lb ↑; B_x = 0, B_y = 60.0 lb ↑.

6.91 (a) E_x = 2.00 kips ←, E_y = 2.25 kips ↑.
(b) C_x = 4.00 kips ←, C_y = 5.75 kips ↑.

6.92 (a) E_x = 3.00 kips ←, E_y = 1.500 kips ↑.
(b) C_x = 3.00 kips ←, C_y = 6.50 kips ↑.

6.93 A_x = 150.0 N ←, A_y = 250 N ↑; E_x = 150.0 N →,
E_y = 450 N ↑.

6.94 B_x = 700 N ←, B_y = 200 N ↓; E_x = 700 N →,
E_y = 500 N ↑.

6.95 (a) A = 982 lb ↑; B = 935 lb ↑; C = 733 lb ↑.
(b) ΔB = +291 lb; ΔC = −72.7 lb.

6.96 (a) 572 lb. (b) A = 1070 lb ↑; B = 709 lb ↑; C = 870 lb ↑.

6.99 A_x = 13.00 kN ←, A_y = 4.00 kN ↓; B_x = 36.0 kN →,
B_y = 6.00 kN ↑; E_x = 23.0 kN ←, E_y = 2.00 kN ↓.

6.100 $\mathbf{A}_x = 2025$ N $\leftarrow$, $\mathbf{A}_y = 1800$ N $\downarrow$; $\mathbf{B}_x = 4050$ N $\rightarrow$, $\mathbf{B}_y = 1200$ N $\uparrow$; $\mathbf{E}_x = 2025$ N $\leftarrow$, $\mathbf{E}_y = 600$ N $\uparrow$.

6.101 $\mathbf{A}_x = 1110$ lb $\leftarrow$, $\mathbf{A}_y = 600$ lb $\uparrow$; $\mathbf{B}_x = 1110$ lb $\leftarrow$, $\mathbf{B}_y = 800$ lb $\downarrow$; $\mathbf{D}_x = 2220$ lb $\rightarrow$, $\mathbf{D}_y = 200$ lb $\uparrow$.

6.102 $\mathbf{A}_x = 660$ lb $\leftarrow$, $\mathbf{A}_y = 240$ lb $\uparrow$; $\mathbf{B}_x = 660$ lb $\leftarrow$, $\mathbf{B}_y = 320$ lb $\downarrow$; $\mathbf{D}_x = 1320$ lb $\rightarrow$, $\mathbf{D}_y = 80.0$ lb $\uparrow$.

6.103 $\mathbf{C}_x = 21.7$ lb $\rightarrow$, $\mathbf{C}_y = 37.5$ lb $\downarrow$; $\mathbf{D}_x = 21.7$ lb $\leftarrow$, $\mathbf{D}_y = 62.5$ lb $\uparrow$.

6.104 $\mathbf{C}_x = 78.0$ lb $\leftarrow$, $\mathbf{C}_j = 28.0$ lb $\uparrow$; $\mathbf{F}_x = 78.0$ lb $\leftarrow$, $\mathbf{F}_y = 12.00$ lb $\uparrow$.

6.107 $\mathbf{F}_x = 300$ lb $\leftarrow$, $\mathbf{F}_y = 1200$ lb $\uparrow$; $\mathbf{F}_{AE} = 1000$ lb C; $\mathbf{F}_{BD} = 500$ lb T.

6.108 $\mathbf{A} = 327$ lb $\rightarrow$; $\mathbf{B} = 827$ lb $\leftarrow$; $\mathbf{D} = 621$ lb $\uparrow$; $\mathbf{E} = 246$ lb $\uparrow$.

6.109 (a) $\mathbf{A}_x = 200$ kN $\rightarrow$, $\mathbf{A}_y = 122.0$ kN $\uparrow$. (b) $\mathbf{B}_x = 200$ kN $\leftarrow$, $\mathbf{B}_y = 10.00$ kN $\downarrow$.

6.110 (a) $\mathbf{A}_x = 205$ kN $\rightarrow$, $\mathbf{A}_y = 134.5$ kN $\uparrow$. (b) $\mathbf{B}_x = 205$ kN $\leftarrow$, $\mathbf{B}_y = 5.50$ kN $\uparrow$.

6.112 $\mathbf{F}_{AF} = P/4$ C; $\mathbf{F}_{BG} = \mathbf{F}_{DG} = P/\sqrt{2}$ C; $\mathbf{F}_{EH} = P/4$ T.

6.113 $\mathbf{F}_{AG} = \sqrt{2}P/6$ C; $\mathbf{F}_{BF} = 2\sqrt{2}P/3$ C; $\mathbf{F}_{DI} = \sqrt{2}P/3$ C; $\mathbf{F}_{EH} = \sqrt{2}P/6$ T.

6.115 $\mathbf{F}_{AF} = \mathbf{M}_0/4a$ C; $\mathbf{F}_{BG} = \mathbf{F}_{DG} = \mathbf{M}_0/\sqrt{2}a$ T; $\mathbf{F}_{EH} = 3\mathbf{M}_0/4a$ C.

6.116 $\mathbf{F}_{AF} = \mathbf{M}_0/6a$ T; $\mathbf{F}_{BG} = \sqrt{2}\mathbf{M}_0/6a$ T; $\mathbf{F}_{DG} = \sqrt{2}\mathbf{M}_0/3a$ T; $\mathbf{F}_{EH} = \mathbf{M}_0/6a$ C.

6.117 $\mathbf{E} = P/5 \downarrow$; $\mathbf{F} = 8P/5 \uparrow$; $\mathbf{G} = 4P/5 \downarrow$; $\mathbf{H} = 2P/5 \uparrow$.

6.118 $\mathbf{A} = P/15 \uparrow$; $\mathbf{D} = 2P/15 \uparrow$; $\mathbf{E} = 8P/15 \uparrow$; $\mathbf{H} = 4P/15 \uparrow$.

6.121 (a) $\mathbf{A} = 2.06P \measuredangle 14.04°$; $\mathbf{B} = 2.06 \searrow 14.04°$; frame is rigid. (b) Frame is not rigid. (c) $\mathbf{A} = 1.25P \searrow 36.9°$; $\mathbf{B} = 1.031P \measuredangle 14.04°$; frame is rigid.

6.122 (a) 2860 N $\downarrow$. (b) 2700 N $\nearrow$ 68.5°.

6.123 (a) 746 N $\downarrow$. (b) 565 N $\searrow$ 61.3°.

6.126 (a) $(\mathbf{F}_{BD})_y = 96.0$ lb $\downarrow$. (b) $\mathbf{F}_{BD} = 100.0$ lb $\measuredangle 73.7°$.

6.127 (a) $(\mathbf{F}_{BD})_y = 240$ lb $\downarrow$. (b) $\mathbf{F}_{BD} = 250$ lb $\measuredangle 73.7°$.

6.128 (a) $\mathbf{P} = 109.8$ N $\rightarrow$. (b) 126.8 N T. (c) 139.8 N $\searrow$ 38.3°.

6.129 (a) 160.8 N $\cdot$ m $\uparrow$. (b) 155.9 N $\cdot$ m $\uparrow$.

6.130 (a) 117.8 N $\cdot$ m $\uparrow$. (b) 47.9 N $\cdot$ m $\uparrow$.

6.131 (a) 21.0 kN $\leftarrow$. (b) 52.5 kN $\leftarrow$.

6.132 (a) 1143 N $\cdot$ m $\downarrow$. (b) 457 N $\cdot$ m $\downarrow$.

6.133 832 lb $\cdot$ in. $\uparrow$.

6.134 360 lb $\cdot$ in. $\uparrow$.

6.135 18.43 N $\cdot$ m $\downarrow$.

6.136 208 N $\cdot$ m $\downarrow$.

6.139 $\mathbf{F}_{AE} = 800$ N T; $\mathbf{F}_{DG} = 100.0$ N C.

6.140 $\mathbf{P} = 120.0$ N $\downarrow$; $\mathbf{Q} = 110.0$ N $\leftarrow$.

6.141 $\mathbf{D} = 30.0$ kN $\leftarrow$; $\mathbf{F} = 37.5$ kN $\searrow$ 36.9°.

6.142 $\mathbf{D} = 150.0$ kN; $\mathbf{F} = 96.4$ kN $\searrow$ 13.50°.

6.144 $\mathbf{F} = 3290$ lb $\searrow$ 15.12°; $\mathbf{D} = 4450$ lb $\leftarrow$.

6.145 8.45 kN.

6.147 (a) 475 lb. (b) 528 lb $\searrow$ 63.3°.

6.148 44.8 kN.

6.149 (a) 312 lb. (b) 135.0 lb $\cdot$ in. $\downarrow$.

6.150 140.0 N.

6.152 21.3 lb $\searrow$.

6.153 (a) 9.29 kN $\searrow$ 44.4°. (b) 8.04 kN $\searrow$ 34.4°.

6.155 (a) 2.86 kips C. (b) 9.43 kips C.

6.156 (a) 4.91 kips C. (b) 10.69 kips C.

6.159 (a) 27.0 mm. (b) 40.0 N $\cdot$ m $\downarrow$.

6.160 (a) $(90.0$ N $\cdot$ m$)\mathbf{i}$. (b) $\mathbf{A} = 0$; $\mathbf{M}_A = -(48.0$ N $\cdot$ m$)\mathbf{i}$; $\mathbf{B} = 0$; $\mathbf{M}_B = -(72.0$ N $\cdot$ m$)\mathbf{i}$.

6.163 $\mathbf{E}_x = 100.0$ kN $\rightarrow$, $\mathbf{E}_y = 154.9$ kN $\uparrow$; $\mathbf{F}_x = 26.5$ kN $\rightarrow$, $\mathbf{F}_y = 118.1$ kN $\downarrow$; $\mathbf{H}_x = 126.5$ kN $\leftarrow$, $\mathbf{H}_y = 36.8$ kN $\downarrow$.

6.164 $\mathbf{F}_{AB} = \mathbf{F}_{BD} = 0$; $\mathbf{F}_{AC} = 675$ N T; $\mathbf{F}_{AD} = 1125$ N C; $\mathbf{F}_{CD} = 900$ N T; $\mathbf{F}_{CE} = 2025$ N T; $\mathbf{F}_{CF} = 2250$ N C; $\mathbf{F}_{DF} = 675$ N C; $\mathbf{F}_{EF} = 1800$ N T.

6.165 $\mathbf{F}_{AB} = 6.24$ kN C; $\mathbf{F}_{AC} = 2.76$ kN T; $\mathbf{F}_{BC} = 2.50$ kN C; $\mathbf{F}_{BD} = 4.16$ kN C; $\mathbf{F}_{CD} = 1.867$ kN T; $\mathbf{F}_{CE} = 2.88$ kN T; $\mathbf{F}_D = 3.75$ kN C; $\mathbf{F}_{DF} = 0$; $\mathbf{F}_{EF} = 1.200$ kN C.

6.166 $\mathbf{F}_{DF} = 10.48$ kips C; $\mathbf{F}_{DG} = 3.35$ kips C; $\mathbf{F}_{EG} = 13.02$ kips T.

6.168 (a) 80.0 lb T. (b) 72.1 lb $\nearrow$ 16.10°.

6.170 $\mathbf{D}_x = 13.60$ kN $\rightarrow$, $\mathbf{D}_y = 7.50$ kN $\uparrow$; $\mathbf{E}_x = 13.60$ kN $\leftarrow$, $\mathbf{E}_y = 2.70$ kN $\downarrow$.

6.172 (a) 301 lb $\searrow$ 48.4°. (b) 375 lb T.

6.173 764 N $\leftarrow$.

6.175 25.0 lb $\downarrow$.

6.C1 (a) $\theta = 30°$: $W = 472$ lb, $A_{AB} = 1.500$ in.^{2}, $A_{AC} = A_{CE} = 1.299$ in.^{2}, $A_{BC} = A_{BE} = 0.500$ in.^{2}, $A_{BD} = 1.732$ in.^{2}. (b) $\theta_{opt} = 56.8°$: $W = 312$ lb, $A_{AB} = 0.896$ in.^{2}, $A_{AC} = A_{CE} = 0.491$ in.^{2}, $A_{BC} = 0.500$ in.^{2}, $A_{BE} = 0.299$ in.^{2}, $A_{BD} = 0.655$ in.^{2}.

6.C2 (a) Fox $x = 9.75$ m, $F_{BH} = 3.19$ kN T. (b) For $x = 3.75$ m, $F_{BH} = 1.313$ kN C. (c) Fox $x = 6$ m, $F_{GH} = 3.04$ kN T.

6.C3 $\theta = 30°$: $\mathbf{M} = 5860$ lb $\cdot$ ft $\uparrow$; $\mathbf{A} = 670$ lb $\measuredangle 75.5°$. (a) $M_{max} = 8680$ lb $\cdot$ ft when $\theta = 65.9°$. (b) $A_{max} = 1436$ lb when $\theta = 68.5°$.

6.C4 $\theta = 30°$: $\mathbf{M}_A = 1.669$ N $\cdot$ m $\downarrow$, $F = 11.79$ N, $\theta = 80°$; $\mathbf{M}_A = 3.21$ N $\cdot$ m $\uparrow$, $F = 11.98$ N.

6.C5 $d = 0.40$ in.: 634 lb C; $d = 0.55$ in.: 286 lb C; $d = 0.473$ in.: $F_{AB} = 500$ lb C.

6.C6 $\theta = 20°$: $M = 31.8$ N $\cdot$ m; $\theta = 75°$: $M = 12.75$ N $\cdot$ m; $\theta = 60.0°$: $M_{min} = 12.00$ N $\cdot$ m.

CHAPTER 7

7.1 $\mathbf{F} = 720$ lb $\rightarrow$; $V = 140.0$ lb $\uparrow$; $\mathbf{M} = 1120$ lb $\cdot$ in. $\uparrow$ (On JC).

7.2 $\mathbf{F} = 1106$ lb $\nearrow$ 20.6°; $V = 386$ lb $\searrow$ 69.4°; $\mathbf{M} = 1650$ lb $\cdot$ ft $\downarrow$ (On JD).

7.3 $\mathbf{F} = 125.0$ N $\measuredangle 67.4°$; $V = 300$ N $\searrow$ 22.6°; $\mathbf{M} = 156.0$ N $\cdot$ m $\downarrow$ (On BJ).

7.4 $\mathbf{F} = 2330$ N $\measuredangle 67.4°$; $V = 720$ N $\searrow$ 22.6°; $\mathbf{M} = 374$ N $\cdot$ m $\downarrow$ (On BJ).

7.7 $\mathbf{F} = 12.50$ lb $\measuredangle 30.0°$; $V = 21.7$ lb $\searrow$ 60.0°; $\mathbf{M} = 75.0$ lb $\cdot$ in. $\downarrow$ (On BJ).

7.8 $\mathbf{F} = 108.3$ lb $\measuredangle 60.0°$; $V = 62.5$ $\searrow$ 30.0°; $\mathbf{M} = 100.5$ lb $\cdot$ in. $\uparrow$ (On DK).

7.9 $\mathbf{F} = 103.9$ N $\searrow$ 60.0°; $V = 60.0$ N $\measuredangle 30.0°$; $\mathbf{M} = 18.71$ N $\cdot$ m $\downarrow$ (On AJ).

7.10 $\mathbf{F} = 60.0$ N $\nearrow$ 30.0°; $V = 103.9$ $\searrow$ 60.0°; $\mathbf{M} = 10.80$ N $\cdot$ m $\uparrow$ (On BK).

7.11 $\mathbf{F} = 194.6$ N $\searrow$ 60.0°; $V = 257$ N $\measuredangle 30.0°$; $\mathbf{M} = 24.7$ N $\cdot$ m $\downarrow$ (On AJ).

7.12 45.2 N $\cdot$ m for $\theta = 82.9°$.

7.15 $\mathbf{F} = 250$ N $\searrow$ 36.9°; $V = 120.0$ N $\measuredangle 53.1$; $\mathbf{M} = 120.0$ N $\cdot$ m $\uparrow$ (On BJ).

7.16 $\mathbf{F} = 560$ N $\leftarrow$; $V = 90.0$ N $\downarrow$; $\mathbf{M} = 72.0$ N $\cdot$ m $\downarrow$ (On AK).

7.17 150.0 lb $\cdot$ in. at D.

7.18 105.0 lb $\cdot$ in. at E.

7.19 (a) $\mathbf{F} = 500$ N $\leftarrow$; $V = 500$ N $\uparrow$; $\mathbf{M} = 300$ N $\cdot$ m $\downarrow$ (On AJ). (b) $\mathbf{F} = 970$ N $\uparrow$; $V = 171.0$ N $\leftarrow$; $\mathbf{M} = 446$ N $\cdot$ m $\downarrow$ (On AK).

7.20 (a) $\mathbf{F} = 500$ N $\leftarrow$; $V = 500$ N $\uparrow$; $\mathbf{M} = 300$ N $\cdot$ m $\downarrow$ (On AJ). (b) $\mathbf{F} = 933$ N $\uparrow$; $V = 250$ N $\leftarrow$; $\mathbf{M} = 375$ N $\cdot$ m $\downarrow$ (On AK).

7.23 0.0557 Wr $\uparrow$ (On AJ).

7.24 0.289 Wr $\downarrow$ (On BJ).

7.25 0.1009 Wr for $\theta = 57.3°$.

7.26 $0.357\ Wr$ for $\theta = 49.3°$.

7.29 (b) $|V|_{max} = wL$; $|M|_{max} = wL^2/2$.

7.30 (b) $|V|_{max} = wL/2$; $|M|_{max} = w_0L^2/6$.

7.31 (b) $|V|_{max} = 2P/3$; $|M|_{max} = PL/9$.

7.32 (b) $|V|_{max} = P$; $|M|_{max} = PL/2$.

7.35 (b) $|V|_{max} = 35.0$ kN; $|M|_{max} = 12.50$ kN $\cdot$ m.

7.36 (b) $|V|_{max} = 50.5$ kN; $|M|_{max} = 39.8$ kN $\cdot$ m.

7.39 (b) $|V|_{max} = 64.0$ kN; $|M|_{max} = 92.0$ kN $\cdot$ m.

7.40 (b) $|V|_{max} = 30.0$ kN; $|M|_{max} = 72.0$ kN $\cdot$ m.

7.41 (b) $|V|_{max} = 18.00$ kips; $|M|_{max} = 48.5$ kip $\cdot$ ft.

7.42 (b) $|V|_{max} = 15.30$ kips; $|M|_{max} = 46.8$ kip $\cdot$ ft.

7.45 (b) $|V|_{max} = 1.800$ kN; $|M|_{max} = 0.225$ kN $\cdot$ m.

7.46 (b) $|V|_{max} = 2.00$ kN; $|M|_{max} = 0.500$ kN $\cdot$ m.

7.47 (a) $M \geq 0$ everywhere.
(b) $|V|_{max} = 4.50$ kips; $|M|_{max} = 13.50$ kip $\cdot$ ft.

7.48 (a) $M \leq 0$ everywhere.
(b) $|V|_{max} = 4.50$ kips; $|M|_{max} = 13.50$ kip $\cdot$ ft.

7.49 $|V|_{max} = 180.0$ N; $|M|_{max} = 36.0$ N $\cdot$ m.

7.50 $|V|_{max} = 800$ N; $|M|_{max} = 180.0$ N $\cdot$ m.

7.51 $|V|_{max} = 90.0$ lb; $|M|_{max} = 1400$ lb $\cdot$ in.

7.52 $|V|_{max} = 165.0$ lb; $|M|_{max} = 1625$ lb $\cdot$ in.

7.55 (a) $54.5°$. (b) 675 N $\cdot$ m.

7.56 (a) 1.236. (b) $0.1180\ wa^2$.

7.57 (a) 0.311 m. (b) 193.0 N $\cdot$ m.

7.58 (a) 0.840 m. (b) 1.680 N $\cdot$ m.

7.59 $0.207\ L$.

7.62 (a) $0.414\ wL$; $0.0858\ wL^2$. (b) $0.250\ wL$; $0.250\ wL^2$.

7.69 (b) $|V|_{max} = 6.40$ kN; $|M|_{max} = 4.00$ kN $\cdot$ m.

7.70 (b) $|V|_{max} = 9.00$ kN; $|M|_{max} = 14.00$ kN $\cdot$ m.

7.77 (b) 75.0 kN $\cdot$ m, 4.00m from A.

7.78 (b) 1.378 kN $\cdot$ m, 1.050m from A.

7.79 (b) 40.5 kN $\cdot$ m, 1.800m from A.

7.80 (b) 60.5 kN $\cdot$ m, 2.20m from A.

7.81 (a) 18.00 kip $\cdot$ ft, 3.00 ft from A.
(b) 34.1 kip $\cdot$ ft, 2.25 ft from A.

7.82 (a) 12.00 kip $\cdot$ ft at C. (b) 6.25 kip $\cdot$ ft, 2.50 ft from A.

7.86 (a) $V = (w_0/6L)(L^2 - 3x^2)$; $M = (w_0/6L)(L^2x - x^3)$.
(b) $0.0642\ w_0\ L^2 A \measuredangle = 0.577L$.

7.87 (a) $V = (w_0/3L)(2x^2 - 3Lx + L^2)$; $M = (w_0/8L)(4x^3 - 9Lx^2 + 6L^2 x - L^3)$.
(b) $w_0/L^2/72$, at $x = L/2$.

7.89 (a) $\mathbf{P} = 4.00$ kN $\downarrow$; $\mathbf{Q} = 6.00$ kN $\downarrow$. (b) $M_C = -900$ N $\cdot$ m.

7.90 (a) $\mathbf{P} = 2.50$ kN $\downarrow$; $\mathbf{Q} = 7.50$ kN $\downarrow$. (b) $M_C = -900$ N $\cdot$ m.

7.91 (a) $\mathbf{P} = 1.350$ kips $\downarrow$; $\mathbf{Q} = 0.450$ kips $\downarrow$. (b) $V_{max} = 2.70$ kips at A; $M_{max} = 6.345$ kip $\cdot$ ft, 5.40 ft from A.

7.92 (a) $\mathbf{P} = 0.540$ kips $\downarrow$; $\mathbf{Q} = 1.860$ kips $\downarrow$.
(b) $V_{max} = 3.14$ kips at B; $M_{max} = 7.00$ kip $\cdot$ ft, 6.88 ft from A.

7.93 (a) $\mathbf{E}_x = 8.00$ kN $\rightarrow$; $\mathbf{E}_y = 5.00$ kN $\uparrow$. (b) 9.43 kN.

7.94 2.00 m.

7.95 (a) 838 lb $\measuredangle$ $17.35°$. (b) 971 lb $\measuredangle$ $34.5°$.

7.96 (a) 2670 lb $\measuredangle$ $2.10°$. (b) 2810 lb $\measuredangle$ 18.65.

7.97 (a) $d_B = 1.733$ m; $d_D = 4.20$ m. (b) 21.5 kN $\measuredangle$ $3.81°$.

7.98 (a) 2.80 m. (b) $\mathbf{A} = 32.0$ kN $\measuredangle$ $38.7°$; $\mathbf{E} = 25.0$ kN $\rightarrow$.

7.101 196.2 N.

7.102 157.0 N.

7.103 (a) 240 lb. (b) 9.00 ft.

7.104 $a = 7.50$ ft; $b = 17.50$ ft.

7.107 (a) 2770 N. (b) 75.14 m.

7.109 (a) $66,900$ kips. (b) 4353 ft.

7.110 3.75 ft.

7.111 (a) $56,400$ kips. (b) 4284 ft.

7.112 (a) 6.75 m. (b) $T_{AB} = 615$ N; $T_{BC} = 600$ N.

7.114 (a) $\sqrt{3L\Delta/8}$. (b) 12.25 ft.

7.115 $h = 27.6$ mm; $\theta_A = 25.5°$; $\theta_C = 27.6°$.

7.116 (a) 4.05 m. (b) 6.41 m. (c) $A_x = 5890$ N $\leftarrow$, $A_y = 5300$ N $\uparrow$.

7.117 (a) $58,900$ kips, (b) $29.2°$.

7.118 (a) 16.00 ft to the left of B. (b) 2000 lb.

7.125 $Y = h[1 - \cos(\pi x/L)]$; $T_{min} = w_0L^2/h\pi^2$;
$T_{max} = (w_0L/\pi)\sqrt{(L^2/h^2\pi^2)} + 1$

7.127 (a) 9.89 m. (b) 60.3 N.

7.128 (a) 495 ft. (b) 1125 lb.

7.129 (a) 35.6 m. (b) 49.2 kg.

7.130 199.5 ft.

7.133 (a) 5.89 m. (b) 10.89 N $\rightarrow$.

7.134 10.05 ft

7.135 (a) 4.22 ft. (b) $80.3°$.

7.136 (a) 30.2 m. (b) 56.6 kg.

7.139 31.8 N.

7.140 29.8 N.

7.143 (a) $a = 79.0$ ft; $b = 60.0$ ft. (b) 103.9 ft.

7.144 (a) $a = 65.8$ ft; $b = 50.0$ ft. (b) 86.6 ft.

7.145 119.1 N $\rightarrow$.

7.146 177.6 N $\rightarrow$.

7.147 3.50 ft.

7.148 5.71 ft.

7.151 0.394 m and 10.97 m

7.152 0.1408.

7.153 (a) 0.338. (b) $56.5°$; $0.755\ wL$.

7.154 $\mathbf{F} = 625$ N $\downarrow$; $\mathbf{V} = 120.0$ N $\leftarrow$; $\mathbf{M} = 27.0$ N $\cdot$ m γ (on CJ).

7.156 $\mathbf{F} = 23.6$ lb $\measuredangle$ $76.0°$; $V = 29.1$ lb $\measuredangle$ $14.04°$;
$\mathbf{M} = 540$ lb $\cdot$ in. $\downarrow$ (on BJ).

7.157 $\mathbf{F} = 200$ N $\measuredangle$ $36.9°$; $\mathbf{V} = 120.0$ N $\measuredangle$ $53.1°$; $\mathbf{M} = 120$ N $\cdot$ m γ (on BJ).

7.158 (a) 40.0 kips. (b) 40.0 kip $\cdot$ ft.

7.161 (b) 12.00 kip $\cdot$ ft, 6.00 ft from A.

7.163 (a) 2.28 m. (b) $\mathbf{D}_x = 13.67$ kN $\rightarrow$; $\mathbf{D}_y = 7.80$ kN $\uparrow$.
(c) 15.94 kN.

7.164 (a) 138.1 m. (b) 602 N.

7.165 (a) 56.3 ft. (b) 2.36 lb/ft.

7.C1 (a) $M_D = +39.8$ kN $\cdot$ m. (b) $M_D = +14.00$ kip $\cdot$ ft.
(c) $M_D = +1800$ lb $\cdot$ in.

7.C3 $a = 1.923$ m; $M_{max} = 37.0$ kN $\cdot$ m at 4.64 from A.

7.C4 (b) $M_{max} = 5.42$ kip $\cdot$ ft when $x = 8.5$ ft and 11.5 ft.

7.C8 $c/L = 0.300$; $h/L = 0.5225$; $s_{AB}/L = 1.532$; $T_0/wL = 0.300$;
$T_{max}/wL = 0.823$.

CHAPTER 8

8.1 Equilibrium; $\mathbf{F} = 172.6$ N $\searrow$.

8.2 Block moves; $\mathbf{F} = 279$ N $\nwarrow$.

8.3 Block moves; $\mathbf{F} = 31.0$ lb. $\searrow$.

8.4 Equilibrium; $\mathbf{F} = 23.5$ lb $\searrow$.

8.5 (a) 74.8 lb. (b) 59.7 lb. (c) 6.76 lb.

8.6 (a) 170.5 N. (b) $14.04°$.

8.8 (a) 403 N. (b) 229 N.

8.10 143.0 N $\leq P \leq 483$ N.

8.11 $31.0°$.

8.12 $53.5°$.

8.13 (a) 353 N $\leftarrow$. (b) 196.2 N $\leftarrow$.

8.14 (a) 275 N $\leftarrow$. (b) 196.2 N $\leftarrow$.

8.17 (a) 36.0 lb $\rightarrow$. (b) 30.0 lb $\rightarrow$. (c) 12.86 lb $\rightarrow$.

8.18 (a) 36.0 lb $\rightarrow$. (b) 40.0 in.

8.19 8.34 lb.

8.20 7.50 lb.

8.21 151.5 N · m.

8.22 1.473 kN.

8.23 $6.35 \leq L/a \leq 10.81$.

8.25 0.208.

8.27 664 N ↓.

8.29 (a) Plate in equilibrium. (b) Plate moves downward.

8.30 10.00 lb < P < 36.7 lb.

8.32 0.860.

8.34 0.0533.

8.35 (a) 1.333. (b) 1.192. (c) 0.839.

8.36 (b) 2.69 lb.

8.37 0.225.

8.39 $168.4 \text{ N} \leq P \leq 308 \text{ N}$.

8.40 $9.38 \text{ N} \cdot \text{m} \leq M \leq 15.01 \text{ N} \cdot \text{m}$

8.41 135.0 lb.

8.43 (a) System slides; P = 62.8 N. (b) System rotates about B; P = 73.2 N.

8.44 35.8°.

8.45 20.5°.

8.46 1.225 W.

8.47 $46.4° \leq \theta \leq 52.4°$ and $67.6° \leq \theta \leq 79.4°$.

8.48 (a) 620 N ←. (b) $\mathbf{B}_x = 1390$ N ←; $\mathbf{B}_y = 1050$ N ↓.

8.49 (a) 234 N →. (b) $\mathbf{B}_x = 1824$ N ←; $\mathbf{B}_y = 1050$ N ↓.

8.52 313 lb →.

8.53 297 lb →.

8.54 9.86 kN ←.

8.55 9.13 N ←.

8.56 (a) 28.1°. (b) 728 N ∡ 14.04°.

8.57 (a) 62.7 lb. (b) 62.7 lb.

8.59 67.4 N.

8.60 1.400 lb.

8.62 (a) 197.0 lb →. (b) Base will not move.

8.63 (a) 280 lb ←. (b) Base moves.

8.64 (b) 283 N ←.

8.65 0.442.

8.66 0.1103.

8.67 0.1013.

8.71 1068 N · m

8.72 153.1 lb · in.

8.73 41.4 lb · in.

8.75 4.18 N · m.

8.77 (a) 0.238. (b) 218 N ↓.

8.78 4.70 kips.

8.79 450 N.

8.80 412 N.

8.81 344 N.

8.82 376 N.

8.84 $T_{AB} = 77.5$ lb; $T_{CD} = 72.5$ lb. $T_{EF} = 67.8$ lb.

8.86 (a) 4.80 kN. (b) 1.375°.

8.88 22.0 lb ←.

8.89 1.948 lb ↓.

8.90 18.01 lb ←.

8.92 0.1670.

8.93 3.75 lb.

8.98 10.87 lb.

8.99 0.0600 in.

8.100 154.4 N.

8.101 300 mm.

8.102 (a) 1.288 kN. (b) 1.058 kN.

8.103 $73.0 \text{ lb} \leq P \leq 1233 \text{ lb}$.

8.104 (a) 0.329. (b) 2.67 turns.

8.105 (a) 22.8 kg. (b) 291 N.

8.106 (a) 109.7 kg. (b) 828 N.

8.109 44.9 N · m ↖.

8.110 (a) $T_A = 8.40$ lb; $T_B = 19.60$ lb. (b) 0.270.

8.111 (a) $T_A = 11.13$ lb; $T_B = 20.9$ lb. (b) 91.3 lb · in. ↓.

8.112 35.1 N · m.

8.113 (a) 27.0 N · m. (b) 675 N.

8.114 (a) 39.0 N · m. (b) 844 N.

8.117 4.49 in.

8.118 (a) 11.66 kg. (b) 38.6 kg. (c) 34.4 kg.

8.119 (a) 9.46 kg. (b) 167.2 kg. (c) 121.0 kg.

8.120 (a) 10.39 lb. (b) 58.5 lb.

8.121 (a) 28.9 lb. (b) 28.9 lb.

8.124 5.97 N.

8.125 9.56 N.

8.126 0.350.

8.128 (a) 30.3 lb · in. ↖. (b) 3.78 lb ↓.

8.129 (a) 17.23 lb · in. ↓. (b) 2.15 lb ↑.

8.133 (a) 51.0 N · m. (b) 875 N.

8.134 Block moves; $\mathbf{F} = 103.5$ N ↖.

8.136 (a) 0.300 Wr. (b) 0.349 Wr.

8.137 (a) 136.4°. (b) 0.928 W.

8.139 0.750.

8.140 $-46.8 \text{ N} \leq P \leq 34.3 \text{ N}$.

8.141 (a) $\mathbf{P} = 56.6$ lb ←. (b) $\mathbf{B}_x = 82.6$ lb ←; $\mathbf{B}_y = 96.0$ lb ↓.

8.143 169.7 lb · in.

8.144 0.226.

8.C1 x = 500 mm: 63.3 N; P_{max} = 67.8 N at x = 355 mm.

8.C2 W_B = 10 lb: θ = 46.4°; W_B = 70 lb: θ = 21.3°.

8.C3 μ_A = 0.25: M = 0.0603 N · m.

8.C4 θ = 30°: $1.336 \text{ N} \cdot \text{m} \leq M_A \leq 2.23 \text{ N} \cdot \text{m}$.

8.C5 θ = 60°: **P** = 16.40 lb ↓; R = 5.14 lb.

8.C6 θ = 20°: 10.39 N · m.

8.C7 θ = 20°: 30.3 lb; 13.25 lb.

8.C8 (a) $x_0 = 0.600L$; $x_m = 0.604L$; $\theta_1 = 5.06°$. (b) $\theta_2 = 55.4°$.

CHAPTER 9

9.1 $a^3(h_1 + 3h_2)/12$.

9.2 $3a^3b/10$.

9.3 $ha^3/5$.

9.4 $4a^3b/21$.

9.6 $ab^3/6$.

9.8 $4ab^3/13$.

9.9 $ab^3/28$.

9.10 $(ab^3/3)/(3n + 1)$.

9.11 $0.1056\, ab^3$.

9.12 $a^3b/20$.

9.15 $3ab^3/35$; $b\sqrt{9/35}$.

9.16 $\pi ab^3/8$; $b/2$.

9.17 $3a^3b/35$; $a\sqrt{9/35}$.

9.18 $\pi a^3b/8$; $a/2$.

9.21 $43a^4/48$; 0.773a.

9.22 $4ab(a^2 + 4b^2)/3$; $\sqrt{(a^2 + 4b^2)/3}$.

9.23 $64\, a^4/15$; 1.265 a.

9.25 (a) $\pi(R_2^4 - R_1^4)/4$. (b) $I_x = I_y = \pi(R_2^4 - R_1^4)/8$.

9.26 (b) -10.56%; -2.99%; $\underline{-0.1248\%}$.

9.28 $bh\,(12h^2 + b^2)/48$; $\sqrt{(12h^2 + b^2)/24}$.

9.31 390×10^3 mm⁴; 21.9 mm.

9.32 46.0 in⁴; 1.599 in.

9.33 64.3×10^3 mm⁴; 8.87 mm.

9.34 46.5 in⁴; 1.607 in.

9.37 $\bar{I}_x = 150.0$ in⁴; $\bar{I}_y = 300$ in⁴.

9.39 $A = 4000 \text{ mm}^2$; $\bar{I} = 500 \times 10^3 \text{ mm}^4$.

9.40 $46.2 \times 10^6 \text{ mm}^4$.

9.41 $\bar{I}_x = 1.874 \times 10^6 \text{ mm}^4$; $\bar{I}_y = 5.82 \times 10^6 \text{ mm}^4$.

9.42 $\bar{I}_x = 479 \times 10^3 \text{ mm}^4$; $\bar{I}_y = 149.7 \times 10^3 \text{ mm}^4$.

9.43 $\bar{I}_x = 191.3 \text{ in}^4$; $\bar{I}_y = 75.2 \text{ in}^4$.

9.44 $\bar{I}_x = 18.13 \text{ in}^4$; $\bar{I}_y = 4.51 \text{ in}^4$.

9.47 (a) $11.57 \times 10^6 \text{ mm}^4$. (b) $7.81 \times 10^6 \text{ mm}^4$.

9.48 (a) $3.13 \times 10^6 \text{ mm}^4$. (b) $2.41 \times 10^6 \text{ mm}^4$.

9.49 $\bar{I}_x = 186.7 \times 10^6 \text{ mm}^4$; $\bar{k}_x = 118.6 \text{ mm}$; $\bar{I}_y = 167.7 \times 10^6 \text{ mm}^4$; $\bar{k}_y = 112.4 \text{ mm}$.

9.50 $\bar{I}_x = 44.5 \text{ in}^4$; $\bar{k}_x = 2.16 \text{ in.}$; $\bar{I}_y = 27.7 \text{ in}^4$; $\bar{k}_y = 1.709 \text{ in.}$

9.51 $\bar{I}_x = 254 \text{ in}^4$; $\bar{k}_x = 4.00 \text{ in.}$; $\bar{I}_y = 102.1 \text{ in}^4$; $\bar{k}_y = 2.54 \text{ in.}$

9.52 $\bar{I}_x = 260 \times 10^6 \text{ mm}^4$; $\bar{k}_x = 144.6 \text{ mm}$; $\bar{I}_y = 17.53 \text{ mm}^4$; $\bar{k}_y = 37.6 \text{ mm}$.

9.54 $\bar{I}_x = 745 \times 10^6 \text{ mm}^4$; $\bar{I}_y = 91.3 \times 10^6 \text{ mm}^4$.

9.55 $\bar{I}_x = 3.55 \times 10^6 \text{ mm}^4$; $\bar{I}_y = 49.8 \times 10^6 \text{ mm}^4$.

9.57 $h/2$.

9.58 $(a + 3b) h/(2a + 4b)$.

9.59 $3\pi b/16$.

9.60 $4h/7$.

9.63 $5a/8$.

9.64 80.0 mm.

9.67 $a^4/2$.

9.68 $b^2 h^2/8$.

9.69 $a^2 b^2/16$.

9.71 $-1.760 \times 10^6 \text{ mm}^4$.

9.72 $2.40 \times 10^6 \text{ mm}^4$.

9.74 -0.380 in^4.

9.75 $471 \times 10^3 \text{ mm}^4$.

9.76 -9010 in^4.

9.78 $1.165 \times 10^6 \text{ mm}^4$.

9.79 (a) $\bar{I}_{x'} = 0.482a^4$; $\bar{I}_{y'} = 1.482a^4$; $\bar{I}_{x'y'} = -0.589a^4$. (b) $\bar{I}_{x'} = 1.120a^4$; $\bar{I}_{y'} = 0.843a^4$; $\bar{I}_{x'y'} = 0.760a^4$.

9.80 $\bar{I}_{x'} = 2.12 \times 10^6 \text{ mm}^4$; $\bar{I}_{y'} = 8.28 \times 10^6 \text{ mm}^4$; $\bar{I}_{x'y'} = -0.532 \times 10^6 \text{ mm}^4$.

9.81 $\bar{I}_{x'} = 1033 \text{ in}^4$; $\bar{I}_{y'} = 2020 \text{ in}^4$; $\bar{I}_{x'y'} = -873 \text{ in}^4$.

9.83 $\bar{I}_{x'} = 0.236 \text{ in}^4$; $\bar{I}_{y'} = 1.244 \text{ in}^4$; $\bar{I}_{x'y'} = 0.1132 \text{ in}^4$.

9.85 $20.2°$; $1.754a^4$; $0.209a^4$.

9.86 $25.1°$; $\bar{I}_{max} = 8.32 \times 10^6 \text{ mm}^4$; $\bar{I}_{min} = 2.08 \times 10^6 \text{ mm}^4$.

9.87 $29.7°$; 2530 in^4; 524 in^4.

9.89 $-23.7°$ and $66.3°$; 1.257 in^4; 0.224 in^4.

9.91 (a) $\bar{I}_{x'} = 0.482a^4$; $\bar{I}_{y'} = 1.482a^4$; $\bar{I}_{x'y'} = -0.589a^4$. (b) $\bar{I}_{x'} = 1.120a^4$; $\bar{I}_{y'} = 0.843a^4$; $0.760a^4$.

9.92 $\bar{I}_{x'} = 2.12 \times 10^6 \text{ mm}^4$; $\bar{I}_{y'} = 8.28 \times 10^6 \text{ mm}^4$; $\bar{I}_{x'y'} = -0.532 \times 10^6 \text{ mm}^4$.

9.93 $\bar{I}_{x'} = 1033 \text{ in}^4$; $\bar{I}_{y'} = 2020 \text{ in}^4$; $\bar{I}_{x'y'} = -873 \text{ in}^4$.

9.95 $\bar{I}_{x'} = 0.236 \text{ in}^4$; $\bar{I}_{y'} = 1.244 \text{ in}^4$; $\bar{I}_{x'y'} = 0.1132 \text{ in}^4$.

9.97 $20.2°$; $1.754a^4$; $0.209a^4$.

9.98 $25.1°$ counterclockwise at C; $I_{max} = 8.32 \times 10^6 \text{ mm}^4$; $\bar{I}_{min} = 2.08 \times 10^6 \text{ mm}^4$.

9.99 $-33.4°$; $22.1 \times 10^3 \text{ in}^4$; 2490 in^4.

9.100 $29.7°$; 2530 in^4; 524 in^4.

9.103 (a) -1.146 in^4. (b) $29.1°$ clockwise. (c) 3.39 in^4.

9.104 $23.8°$ clockwise; $0.524 \times 10^6 \text{ mm}^4$; $0.0917 \times 10^6 \text{ mm}^4$.

9.105 $19.54°$ counterclockwise; $4.34 \times 10^6 \text{ mm}^4$; $0.647 \times 10^6 \text{ mm}^4$.

9.106 (a) $25.3°$. (b) 1459 in^4; 40.5 in^4.

9.107 (a) $88.0 \times 10^6 \text{ mm}^4$. (b) $96.3 \times 10^6 \text{ mm}^4$; $39.7 \times 10^6 \text{ mm}^4$.

9.111 (a) $\bar{I}_{AA'} = \bar{I}_{BB'} = ma^2/24$. (b) $ma^2/12$.

9.112 (a) $5mb^2/4$. (b) $5m (a^2 + b^2)/4$.

9.113 (a) $0.0699 \, ma^2$. (b) $0.320 \, ma^2$.

9.114 (a) $25 \, mr_2^2/64$. (b) $0.1522 \, mr_2^2$.

9.117 (a) $ma^2/3$. (b) $3ma^2/2$.

9.118 (a) $7ma^2/6$. (b) $ma^2/2$.

9.119 $m(3a^2 + 4L^2)/12$.

9.120 $1.329 \, mh^2$.

9.121 (a) $0.241 \, mh^2$. (b) $m(3a^2 + 0.1204 \, h^2)$.

9.122 $m(b^2 + 3h^2)/5$.

9.124 $m(a^2 + 3h^2)/6$.

9.126 $I_x = I_y = ma^2/4$; $I_z = ma^2/2$.

9.127 $1.160 \times 10^{-6} \text{ lb} \cdot \text{ft} \cdot \text{s}^2$; 0.341 in.

9.128 $837 \times 10^{-9} \text{ kg} \cdot \text{m}^2$; 6.92 mm.

9.130 $ma^2/2$; $a/\sqrt{2}$.

9.131 (a) 2.30 in. (b) $20.6 \times 10^{-3} \text{ lb} \cdot \text{ft} \cdot \text{s}^2$; 2.27 in.

9.132 (a) $\pi p l^2 [6a^2 t(5a^2/3l^2 + 2a/l + 1) + d^2 l/4]$. (b) 0.1851.

9.133 (a) 27.5 mm to the right of A. (b) 32.0 mm.

9.135 $I_x = 0.877 \text{ kg} \cdot \text{m}^2$; $I_y = 1.982 \text{ kg} \cdot \text{m}^2$; $I_z = 1.652 \text{ kg} \cdot \text{m}^2$.

9.136 $I_x = 175.5 \times 10^{-3} \text{ kg} \cdot \text{m}^2$; $I_y = 309 \times 10^{-3} \text{ kg} \cdot \text{m}^2$; $I_z = 154.4 \times 10^{-3} \text{ kg} \cdot \text{m}^2$.

9.138 $I_x = 745 \times 10^{-6} \text{ lb} \cdot \text{ft} \cdot \text{s}^2$; $I_y = 896 \times 10^{-6} \text{ lb} \cdot \text{ft} \cdot \text{s}^2$; $I_z = 304 \text{ lb} \cdot \text{ft} \cdot \text{s}^2$.

9.139 $I_x = 344 \times 10^{-6} \text{ lb} \cdot \text{ft} \cdot \text{s}^2$; $I_y = 132.1 \times 10^{-6} \text{ lb} \cdot \text{ft} \cdot \text{s}^2$; $I_z = 453 \times 10^{-6} \text{ lb} \cdot \text{ft} \cdot \text{s}^2$.

9.141 (a) $13.99 \times 10^{-3} \text{ kg} \cdot \text{m}^2$. (b) $20.6 \times 10^{-3} \text{ kg} \cdot \text{m}^2$. (c) $14.30 \times 10^{-3} \text{ kg} \cdot \text{m}^2$.

9.142 $I_x = 28.3 \times 10^{-3} \text{ kg} \cdot \text{m}^2$; $I_y = 183.8 \times 10^{-3} \text{ kg} \cdot \text{m}^2$; $k_x = 42.9 \text{ mm}$; $k_y = 109.3 \text{ mm}$.

9.143 $0.1785 \text{ lb} \cdot \text{ft} \cdot \text{s}^2$.

9.145 (a) $26.4 \times 10^{-3} \text{ kg} \cdot \text{m}^2$. (b) $31.2 \times 10^{-3} \text{ kg} \cdot \text{m}^2$. (c) $8.58 \times 10^{-3} \text{ kg} \cdot \text{m}^2$.

9.147 $I_x = 0.0392 \text{ lb} \cdot \text{ft} \cdot \text{s}^2$; $I_y = 0.0363 \text{ lb} \cdot \text{ft} \cdot \text{s}^2$; $I_z = 0.0304 \text{ lb} \cdot \text{ft} \cdot \text{s}^2$.

9.148 $I_x = 0.323 \text{ kg} \cdot \text{m}^2$; $I_y = I_z = 0.419 \text{ kg} \cdot \text{m}^2$.

9.149 $I_{xy} = 2.50 \times 10^{-3} \text{ kg} \cdot \text{m}^2$; $I_{yz} = 4.06 \times 10^{-3} \text{ kg} \cdot \text{m}^2$; $I_{zx} = 8.81 \times 10^{-3} \text{ kg} \cdot \text{m}^2$.

9.150 $I_{xy} = 286 \times 10^{-6} \text{ kg} \cdot \text{m}^2$; $I_{yz} = I_{zx} = 0$.

9.151 $I_{xy} = -1.726 \times 10^{-3} \text{ lb} \cdot \text{ft} \cdot \text{s}^2$; $I_{yz} = 0.507 \times 10^{-3} \text{ lb} \cdot \text{ft} \cdot \text{s}^2$; $I_{zx} = -2.12 \times 10^{-3} \text{ lb} \cdot \text{ft} \cdot \text{s}^2$.

9.152 $I_{xy} = -538 \times 10^{-6} \text{ lb} \cdot \text{ft} \cdot \text{s}^2$; $I_{yz} = -171.4 \times 10^{-6} \text{ lb} \cdot \text{ft} \cdot \text{s}^2$; $I_{zx} = 1120 \times 10^{-6} \text{ lb} \cdot \text{ft} \cdot \text{s}^2$.

9.155 $I_{xy} = -8.04 \times 10^{-3} \text{ kg} \cdot \text{m}^2$; $I_{yz} = 12.90 \times 10^{-3} \text{ kg} \cdot \text{m}^2$; $I_{zx} = 94.0 \times 10^{-3} \text{ kg} \cdot \text{m}^2$.

9.156 $I_{xy} = 0$; $I_{yz} = 48.3 \times 10^{-6} \text{ kg} \cdot \text{m}^2$; $I_{zx} = -4.43 \times 10^{-3} \text{ kg} \cdot \text{m}^2$.

9.157 $I_{xy} = 47.9 \times 10^{-6} \text{ kg} \cdot \text{m}^2$; $I_{yz} = 102.1 \times 10^{-6} \text{ kg} \cdot \text{m}^2$; $I_{zx} = 64.1 \times 10^{-6} \text{ kg} \cdot \text{m}^2$.

9.158 $I_{xy} = -m' R_1^3/2$; $I_{yz} = m' R_1^3/2$; $I_{zx} = -m' R_2^3/2$.

9.159 $I_{xy} = wa^3 (1 - 5\pi)/g$; $I_{yz} = -11\pi \, wa^3/g$; $I_{zx} = 4wa^3 (1 + 2\pi)/g$.

9.160 $I_{xy} = -11wa^3/g$; $I_{yz} = wa^3(\pi + 6)/2g$; $I_{zx} = -wa^3/4g$.

9.162 (a) $mac/20$. (b) $I_{xy} = mab/20$; $I_{yz} = mbc/20$.

9.165 $18.17 \times 10^{-3} \text{ kg} \cdot \text{m}^2$.

9.166 $11.81 \times 10^{-3} \text{ kg} \cdot \text{m}^2$.

9.167 $5Wa^2/18g$.

9.168 $4.41 \, rta^4/g$.

9.169 $281 \times 10^{-3} \text{ kg} \cdot \text{m}^2$.

9.170 $0.354 \text{ kg} \cdot \text{m}^2$.

9.173 (a) $1/\sqrt{3}$. (b) $\sqrt{7/12}$.

9.174 (a) $b/a = 2$; $c/a = 2$. (b) $b/a = 1$; $c/a = 0.5$.

9.175 (a) 2. (b) $\sqrt{2/3}$.

9.179 (a) $K_1 = 0.363ma^2$; $K_2 = 1.583ma^2$; $K_3 = 1.720ma^2$. (b) $(\theta_x)_1 = (\theta_z)_1 = 49.7°$, $(\theta_y)_1 = 113.7°$; $(\theta_x)_2 = 45.0°$, $(\theta_y)_2 = 90.0°$, $(\theta_z)_2 = 135.0°$; $(\theta_x)_3 = (\theta_z)_3 = 73.5°$, $(\theta_y)_3 = 23.7°$.

9.180 (a) $K_1 = 14.30 \times 10^{-3}$ kg · m²; $K_2 = 13.96 \times 10^{-3}$ kg · m²; $K_3 = 20.6 \times 10^{-3}$ kg · m².
(b) $(\theta_x)_1 = (\theta_y)_1 = 90.0°$, $(\theta_z)_1 = 0$; $(\theta_x)_2 = 3.42°$, $(\theta_y)_2 = 86.6°$, $(\theta_z)_2 = 90.0°$; $(\theta_x)_3 = 93.4°$, $(\theta_y)_3 = 3.43°$, $(\theta_z)_3 = 90.0°$.

9.182 (a) $K_1 = 0.1639Wa^2/g$; $K_2 = 1.054Wa^2/g$; $K_3 = 1.115Wa^2/g$.
(b) $(\theta_x)_1 = 36.7°$, $(\theta_y)_1 = 71.6°$, $(\theta_z)_1 = 59.5°$; $(\theta_x)_2 = 74.9°$, $(\theta_y)_2 = 54.5°$, $(\theta_z)_2 = 140.5°$; $(\theta_x)_3 = 57.5°$, $(\theta_y)_3 = 138.8°$, $(\theta_z)_3 = 112.4°$.

9.183 (a) $K_1 = 2.26\gamma ta^4/g$; $K_2 = 17.27\gamma ta^4/g$; $K_3 = 19.08\gamma ta^4/g$.
(b) $(\theta_x)_1 = 85.0°$, $(\theta_y)_1 = 36.8°$, $(\theta_z)_1 = 53.7°$; $(\theta_x)_2 = 81.7°$, $(\theta_y)_2 = 54.7°$; $(\theta_z)_2 = 143.4°$; $(\theta_x)_3 = 9.70°$, $(\theta_y)_3 = 99.0°$, $(\theta_z)_3 = 86.3°$.

9.185 $I_x = a^4/8$, $I_y = 3a^4/2$.
9.186 $a^3b/6$; $a/\sqrt{3}$.
9.188 $I_x = 48.9 \times 10^3$ mm⁴, $I_y = 8.35 \times 10^3$ mm⁴.
9.189 (a) 80.9×10^6 mm⁴. (b) 57.4×10^6 mm⁴.
9.191 -2.81 in⁴.
9.193 (a) $5ma^2/18$. (b) $3.61ma^2$.
9.195 $I_x = 26.0 \times 10^{-3}$ kg · m²; $I_y = 38.2 \times 10^{-3}$ kg · m²; $I_z = 17.55 \times 10^{-3}$ kg · m².
9.196 $I_x = 38.1 \times 10^{-3}$ kg · m²; $k_x = 110.7$ mm.
9.C1 $\theta = 20°$; $I_{x'} = 14.20$ in⁴, $I_{y'} = 3.15$ in⁴, $I_{x'y'} = -3.93$ in⁴.
9.C3 (a) $\bar{I}_{x'} = 371 \times 10^3$ mm⁴, $\bar{I}_{y'} = 64.3 \times 10^3$ mm⁴; $\bar{k}_{x'} = 21.3$ mm, $\bar{k}_{y'} = 8.87$ mm. (b) $\bar{I}_{x'} = 40.4$ in⁴, $\bar{I}_{y'} = 46.5$ in⁴, $\bar{k}_{x'} = 1.499$ in., $\bar{k}_{y'} = 1.607$ in. (c) $\bar{k}_x = 2.53$ in., $\bar{k}_y = 1.583$ in. (d) $\bar{k}_x = 1.904$ in., $\bar{k}_y = 0.950$ in.
9.C5 (a) 5.99×10^{-3} kg · m². (b) 77.4×10^{-3} kg · m².
9.C6 (a) 74.0×10^{-6} lb · ft · s². (b) 645×10^{-6} lb · ft · s². (c) 208×10^{-6} lb · ft · s².

CHAPTER 10

10.1 270 N ↑.
10.2 60.0 lb ↓.
10.3 32.4 N · m ↙.
10.4 600 lb · in. ↙.
10.5 500 N ↑.
10.6 750 N ↑.
10.9 $Q = 3 P \tan \theta$.
10.10 $Q = P [(l/a)] \cos^3 \theta - 1]$.
10.12 $Q = 2 P \sin \theta/\cos (\theta/2)$.
10.14 $Q = (3P/2) \tan \theta$.
10.15 $M = Pl/2 \tan \theta$.
10.16 $M = Pl(\sin \theta + \cos \theta)$.
10.17 $M = \frac{1}{2}Wl \tan \alpha \sin \theta$.
10.18 $M = PR \csc^2 \theta$.
10.19 85.2 lb · ft ↙.
10.20 22.8 lb ⤢ 70.0°.
10.23 39.2°.
10.26 19.81° and 51.9°.
10.27 36.4°.
10.28 67.1°.
10.29 40.2°.
10.31 15.60 in.
10.32 13.20 in.
10.34 57.2°.
10.35 38.7°.
10.36 60.4°.
10.37 22.6°.

10.38 51.1°.
10.39 59.0°.
10.40 78.7°, 324°, 379°.
10.43 12.03 kN ↘.
10.44 20.4°.
10.45 2370 lb ↖.
10.46 2550 lb ↖.
10.48 300 N · m, 81.8 N · m.
10.49 $\eta = 1/(1 + \mu \cot \alpha)$.
10.50 $\eta = \tan \theta/\tan (\theta + \phi_s)$.
10.52 37.6 N, 31.6 N.
10.53 7.75 kN ↑.
10.54 $H = 1.361$ kN ↑; $M_H = 550$ N · m ↙.
10.57 0.833 in. ↓.
10.58 0.625 in. →.
10.69 $\theta = -45.0°$, unstable; $\theta = 135.0°$, stable.
10.70 $\theta = -63.4°$, unstable; $\theta = 116.6°$, stable.
10.71 (a) 0, unstable. (b) 137.8°, stable.
10.72 $\theta = 0$ and $\theta = 180.0°$, unstable; $\theta = 75.5°$ and $\theta = 284°$, stable.
10.73 59.0°, stable.
10.74 78.7°, stable; 324°, unstable; 379°, stable.
10.77 357 mm.
10.78 252 mm.
10.80 9.39° and 90.0°, stable; 34.2°, unstable.
10.81 17.11°, stable; 72.9°, unstable.
10.83 49.1°.
10.86 16.88 m.
10.87 54.8°.
10.88 37.4°.
10.89 $P < kl/2$.
10.91 $k > 6.94$ lb/in.
10.92 15.00 in.
10.93 $P < 2kL/9$.
10.94 $P < kL/18$.
10.96 $P < 160.0$ N.
10.98 $P < 764$ N.
10.100 (a) $P < 10.00$ lb. (b) $P < 20.0$ lb.
10.101 120.0 lb →.
10.102 1200 lb · in. ↙.
10.103 (a) 60.0 N C, 8.00 mm ↓. (b) 300 N C, 40.0 mm ↓.
10.105 $M = 7Pa \cos \theta$.
10.107 19.40°.
10.108 7.13 in.
10.110 $P < k (l - a)^2/2l$.
10.112 (a) 22.0°. (b) 30.6°.
10.C1 $\theta = 60°$: 2.42 in.; $\theta = 120°$: 1.732 in.; $(M/P)_{max} = 2.25$ in. at $\theta = 73.7°$.
10.C2 $\theta = 60°$: 171.1 N C. For $32.5° \le \theta \le 134.3°$, $|F| \le 400$ N.
10.C3 $\theta = 60°$; 296 N T. For $\theta \le 125.7°$, $|F| \le 400$ N.
10.C4 (b) $\theta = 60°$, *datum at C:* $V = -294$ in · lb. (c) 34.2°, stable; 90°, unstable; 145.8°, stable.
10.C5 (b) $\theta = 50°$, *datum at E:* $V = 100.5$ J. $dV/d\theta = 22.9$ J. (c) $\theta = 0$, unstable; 30.4°.
10.C6 (b) $\theta = 60°$, *datum at B:* 30.0 J. (c) $\theta = 0$, unstable; 41.4°, stable.
10.C7 (b) $\theta = 60°$, *datum at $\theta = 0$:* -37.0 J. (c) 52.2°, stable.

Centroids of Common Shapes of Areas and Lines

Shape		$\bar{x}$	$\bar{y}$	Area
Triangular area			$\dfrac{h}{3}$	$\dfrac{bh}{2}$
Quarter-circular area		$\dfrac{4r}{3\pi}$	$\dfrac{4r}{3\pi}$	$\dfrac{\pi r^2}{4}$
Semicircular area		0	$\dfrac{4r}{3\pi}$	$\dfrac{\pi r^2}{2}$
Semiparabolic area		$\dfrac{3a}{8}$	$\dfrac{3h}{5}$	$\dfrac{2ah}{3}$
Parabolic area		0	$\dfrac{3h}{5}$	$\dfrac{4ah}{3}$
Parabolic spandrel		$\dfrac{3a}{4}$	$\dfrac{3h}{10}$	$\dfrac{ah}{3}$
Circular sector		$\dfrac{2r\sin\alpha}{3\alpha}$	0	αr^2
Quarter-circular arc		$\dfrac{2r}{\pi}$	$\dfrac{2r}{\pi}$	$\dfrac{\pi r}{2}$
Semicircular arc		0	$\dfrac{2r}{\pi}$	πr
Arc of circle		$\dfrac{r\sin\alpha}{\alpha}$	0	$2\alpha r$

Moments of Inertia of Common Geometric Shapes

Rectangle

$$\bar{I}_{x'} = \tfrac{1}{12}bh^3$$
$$\bar{I}_{y'} = \tfrac{1}{12}b^3h$$
$$I_x = \tfrac{1}{3}bh^3$$
$$I_y = \tfrac{1}{3}b^3h$$
$$J_C = \tfrac{1}{12}bh(b^2 + h^2)$$

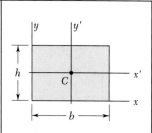

Triangle

$$\bar{I}_{x'} = \tfrac{1}{36}bh^3$$
$$I_x = \tfrac{1}{12}bh^3$$

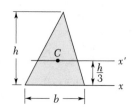

Circle

$$\bar{I}_x = \bar{I}_y = \tfrac{1}{4}\pi r^4$$
$$J_O = \tfrac{1}{2}\pi r^4$$

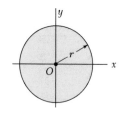

Semicircle

$$I_x = I_y = \tfrac{1}{8}\pi r^4$$
$$J_O = \tfrac{1}{4}\pi r^4$$

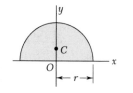

Quarter circle

$$I_x = I_y = \tfrac{1}{16}\pi r^4$$
$$J_O = \tfrac{1}{8}\pi r^4$$

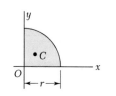

Ellipse

$$\bar{I}_x = \tfrac{1}{4}\pi ab^3$$
$$\bar{I}_y = \tfrac{1}{4}\pi a^3b$$
$$J_O = \tfrac{1}{4}\pi ab(a^2 + b^2)$$

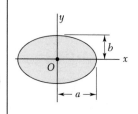

Mass Moments of Inertia of Common Geometric Shapes

Slender rod

$$I_y = I_z = \tfrac{1}{12}mL^2$$

Thin rectangular plate

$$I_x = \tfrac{1}{12}m(b^2 + c^2)$$
$$I_y = \tfrac{1}{12}mc^2$$
$$I_z = \tfrac{1}{12}mb^2$$

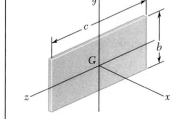

Rectangular prism

$$I_x = \tfrac{1}{12}m(b^2 + c^2)$$
$$I_y = \tfrac{1}{12}m(c^2 + a^2)$$
$$I_z = \tfrac{1}{12}m(a^2 + b^2)$$

Thin disk

$$I_x = \tfrac{1}{2}mr^2$$
$$I_y = I_z = \tfrac{1}{4}mr^2$$

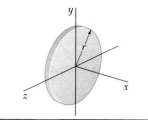

Circular cylinder

$$I_x = \tfrac{1}{2}ma^2$$
$$I_y = I_z = \tfrac{1}{12}m(3a^2 + L^2)$$

Circular cone

$$I_x = \tfrac{3}{10}ma^2$$
$$I_y = I_z = \tfrac{3}{5}m(\tfrac{1}{4}a^2 + h^2)$$

Sphere

$$I_x = I_y = I_z = \tfrac{2}{5}ma^2$$

Course **Intro to Engineering Analysis**

urse Number **ENGR-1100**

Rensselaer Polytech Inst

ENGINEERING

http://create.mcgraw-hill.com

ISBN-10: 1121566189   ISBN-13: 9781121566187

Contents

Credits

Systems of Linear Equations
and Matrices

1.1 ▶ Systems of Linear Equations

As the introductory example illustrates, many naturally occurring processes are modeled using more than one equation and can require many equations in many variables. For another example, models of the economy contain thousands of equations and thousands of variables. To develop this idea, consider the set of equations

$$\begin{cases} 2x - y = 2 \\ x + 2y = 6 \end{cases}$$

which is a system of two equations in the common variables x and y. A *solution* to this system consists of values for x and y that simultaneously satisfy each equation. In this example we proceed by solving the first equation for y, so that

$$y = 2x - 2$$

To find the solution, substitute $y = 2x - 2$ into the second equation to obtain

$$x + 2(2x - 2) = 6 \quad \text{and solving for } x \text{ gives} \quad x = 2$$

Substituting $x = 2$ back into the first equation yields $2(2) - y = 2$, so that $y = 2$. Therefore the unique solution to the system is $x = 2, y = 2$. Since both of these equations represent straight lines, a solution exists provided that the lines intersect. These lines intersect at the unique point $(2, 2)$, as shown in Fig. 1(a). A system of equations is **consistent** if there is at least one solution to the system. If there are no solutions, the system is **inconsistent**. In the case of systems of two linear equations with two variables, there are three possibilities:

1. The two lines have different slopes and hence intersect at a unique point, as shown in Fig. 1(a).

2. The two lines are identical (one equation is a nonzero multiple of the other), so there are infinitely many solutions, as shown in Fig. 1(b).

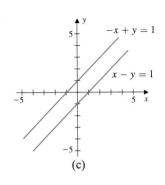

Figure 1

3. The two lines are parallel (have the same slope) and do not intersect, so the system is inconsistent, as shown in Fig. 1(c).

When we are dealing with many variables, the standard method of representing linear equations is to affix subscripts to coefficients and variables. A **linear equation** in the n variables $x_1, x_2, \ldots, x_n$ is an equation of the form

$$a_1 x_1 + a_2 x_2 + \cdots + a_n x_n = b$$

To represent a system of m linear equations in n variables, two subscripts are used for each coefficient. The first subscript indicates the equation number while the second specifies the term of the equation.

DEFINITION 1

System of Linear Equations   A **system of m linear equations in n variables,** or a **linear system**, is a collection of equations of the form

$$\begin{cases} a_{11}x_1 + a_{12}x_2 + \cdots + a_{1n}x_n = b_1 \\ a_{21}x_1 + a_{22}x_2 + \cdots + a_{2n}x_n = b_2 \\ a_{31}x_1 + a_{32}x_2 + \cdots + a_{3n}x_n = b_3 \\ \quad\vdots \qquad\quad \vdots \qquad\quad \vdots \qquad \vdots \qquad \vdots \\ a_{m1}x_1 + a_{m2}x_2 + \cdots + a_{mn}x_n = b_m \end{cases}$$

This is also referred to as an $m \times n$ linear system.

For example, the collection of equations

$$\begin{cases} -2x_1 + 3x_2 + x_3 - x_4 = -2 \\ x_1 \qquad\quad + x_3 - 4x_4 = 1 \\ 3x_1 - x_2 \qquad\quad - x_4 = 3 \end{cases}$$

is a linear system of three equations in four variables, or a 3×4 linear system.

A **solution** to a linear system with n variables is an ordered sequence $(s_1, s_2, \ldots, s_n)$ such that each equation is satisfied for $x_1 = s_1, x_2 = s_2, \ldots, x_n = s_n$. The **general solution** or **solution set** is the set of all possible solutions.

The Elimination Method

The elimination method, also called *Gaussian elimination*, is an algorithm used to solve linear systems. To describe this algorithm, we first introduce the *triangular form* of a linear system.

An $m \times n$ linear system is in **triangular form** provided that the coefficients $a_{ij} = 0$ whenever $i > j$. In this case we refer to the linear system as a **triangular system**. Two examples of triangular systems are

$$\begin{cases} x_1 - 2x_2 + x_3 = -1 \\ \quad\quad x_2 - 3x_3 = 5 \\ \quad\quad\quad\quad x_3 = 2 \end{cases} \quad \text{and} \quad \begin{cases} x_1 + x_2 - x_3 - x_4 = 2 \\ \quad\quad x_2 - x_3 - 2x_4 = 1 \\ \quad\quad\quad\quad 2x_3 - x_4 = 3 \end{cases}$$

When a linear system is in triangular form, then the solution set can be obtained using a technique called **back substitution**. To illustrate this technique, consider the linear system given by

$$\begin{cases} x_1 - 2x_2 + x_3 = -1 \\ \quad\quad x_2 - 3x_3 = 5 \\ \quad\quad\quad\quad x_3 = 2 \end{cases}$$

From the last equation we see that $x_3 = 2$. Substituting this into the second equation, we obtain $x_2 - 3(2) = 5$, so $x_2 = 11$. Finally, using these values in the first equation, we have $x_1 - 2(11) + 2 = -1$, so $x_1 = 19$. The solution is also written as $(19, 11, 2)$.

DEFINITION 2   **Equivalent Linear Systems**   Two linear systems are **equivalent** if they have the same solutions

For example, the system

$$\begin{cases} x_1 - 2x_2 + x_3 = -1 \\ 2x_1 - 3x_2 - x_3 = 3 \\ x_1 - 2x_2 + 2x_3 = 1 \end{cases}$$

has the unique solution $x_1 = 19$, $x_2 = 11$, and $x_3 = 2$, so the linear systems

$$\begin{cases} x_1 - 2x_2 + x_3 = -1 \\ \quad\quad x_2 - 3x_3 = 5 \\ \quad\quad\quad\quad x_3 = 2 \end{cases} \quad \text{and} \quad \begin{cases} x_1 - 2x_2 + x_3 = -1 \\ 2x_1 - 3x_2 - x_3 = 3 \\ x_1 - 2x_2 + 2x_3 = 1 \end{cases}$$

are equivalent.

The next theorem gives three operations that transform a linear system into an equivalent system, and together they can be used to convert any linear system to an equivalent system in triangular form.

THEOREM 1   Let

$$\begin{cases} a_{11}x_1 + a_{12}x_2 + \cdots + a_{1n}x_n = b_1 \\ a_{21}x_1 + a_{22}x_2 + \cdots + a_{2n}x_n = b_2 \\ a_{31}x_1 + a_{32}x_2 + \cdots + a_{3n}x_n = b_3 \\ \quad\vdots \qquad \vdots \qquad \vdots \qquad \vdots \qquad \vdots \\ a_{m1}x_1 + a_{m2}x_2 + \cdots + a_{mn}x_n = b_m \end{cases}$$

be a linear system. Performing any one of the following operations on the linear system produces an equivalent linear system.

1. Interchanging any two equations.
2. Multiplying any equation by a nonzero constant.
3. Adding a multiple of one equation to another.

Proof   Interchanging any two equations does not change the solution of the linear system and therefore yields an equivalent system. If equation i is multiplied by a constant $c \neq 0$, then equation i of the new system is

$$ca_{i1}x_1 + ca_{i2}x_2 + \cdots + ca_{in}x_n = cb_i$$

Let $(s_1, s_2, \ldots, s_n)$ be a solution to the original system. Since

$$a_{i1}s_1 + a_{i2}s_2 + \cdots + a_{in}s_n = b_i, \qquad \text{then} \qquad ca_{i1}s_1 + ca_{i2}s_2 + \cdots + ca_{in}s_n = cb_i$$

Hence $(s_1, s_2, \ldots, s_n)$ is a solution of the new linear system. Consequently, the systems are equivalent.

For part (3) of the theorem, consider the new system obtained by adding c times equation i to equation j of the original system. Thus, equation j of the new system becomes

$$(ca_{i1} + a_{j1})x_1 + (ca_{i2} + a_{j2})x_2 + \cdots + (ca_{in} + a_{jn})x_n = cb_i + b_j$$

or equivalently,

$$c(a_{i1}x_1 + a_{i2}x_2 + \cdots + a_{in}x_n) + (a_{j1}x_1 + a_{j2}x_2 + \cdots + a_{jn}x_n) = cb_i + b_j$$

Now let $(s_1, s_2, \ldots, s_n)$ be a solution for the original system. Then

$$a_{i1}s_1 + a_{i2}s_2 + \cdots + a_{in}s_n = b_i \qquad \text{and} \qquad a_{j1}s_1 + a_{j2}s_2 + \cdots + a_{jn}s_n = b_j$$

Therefore,

$$c(a_{i1}s_1 + a_{i2}s_2 + \cdots + a_{in}s_n) + (a_{j1}s_1 + a_{j2}s_2 + \cdots + a_{jn}s_n) = cb_i + b_j$$

so that $(s_1, s_2, \ldots, s_n)$ is a solution of the modified system and the systems are equivalent.

EXAMPLE 1   Use the elimination method to solve the linear system.

$$\begin{cases} x + y = 1 \\ -x + y = 1 \end{cases}$$

Solution   Adding the first equation to the second gives the equivalent system

$$\begin{cases} x + y = 1 \\ 2y = 2 \end{cases}$$

From the second equation, we have $y = 1$. Using back substitution gives $x = 0$. The graphs of both systems are shown in Fig. 2. Notice that the solution is the same in both, but that adding the first equation to the second rotates the line $-x + y = 1$ about the point of intersection.

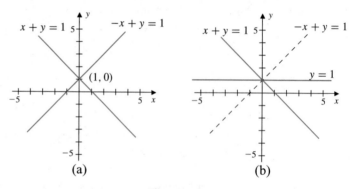

Figure 2

Converting a linear system to triangular form often requires many steps. Moreover, the operations used to convert one linear system to another are not unique and may not be apparent on inspection. To articulate this process, the notation, for example,

$$(-2) \cdot E_1 + E_3 \longrightarrow E_3$$

will mean *add* -2 *times equation 1 to equation 3, and replace equation 3 with the result*. The notation $E_i \leftrightarrow E_j$ will be used to indicate that equation i and equation j are interchanged.

EXAMPLE 2   Solve the linear system.

$$\begin{cases} x + y + z = 4 \\ -x - y + z = -2 \\ 2x - y + 2z = 2 \end{cases}$$

Solution   To convert the system to an equivalent triangular system, we first eliminate the variable x in the second and third equations to obtain

$$\begin{cases} x + y + z = 4 \\ -x - y + z = -2 \\ 2x - y + 2z = 2 \end{cases} \qquad \begin{array}{c} E_1 + E_2 \to E_2 \\ -2E_1 + E_3 \to E_3 \end{array} \longrightarrow \begin{cases} x + y + z = 4 \\ 2z = 2 \\ -3y = -6 \end{cases}$$

Interchanging the second and third equations gives the triangular linear system

$$\begin{cases} x + y + z = 4 \\ 2z = 2 \\ -3y = -6 \end{cases} \qquad E_2 \leftrightarrow E_3 \longrightarrow \begin{cases} x + y + z = 4 \\ -3y = -6 \\ 2z = 2 \end{cases}$$

Using back substitution, we have $z = 1$, $y = 2$, and $x = 4 - y - z = 1$. Therefore, the system is consistent with the unique solution $(1, 2, 1)$.

Recall from solid geometry that the graph of an equation of the form $ax + by + cz = d$ is a plane in three-dimensional space. Hence, the unique solution to the linear system of Example 2 is the point of intersection of three planes, as shown in Fig. 3(a). For another perspective on this, shown in Fig. 3(b) are the lines of the pairwise intersections of the three planes. These lines intersect at a point that is the solution to the 3×3 linear system.

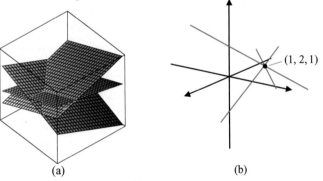

(a) (b)

Figure 3

Similar to the 2×2 case, the geometry of Euclidean space helps us better understand the possibilities for the general solution of a linear system of three equations in three variables. In particular, the linear system can have a unique solution if the three planes all intersect at a point, as illustrated by Example 2. Alternatively, a 3×3 system can have infinitely many solutions if

1. The three planes are all the same.

2. The three planes intersect in a line (like the pages of a book).

3. Two of the planes are the same with a third plane intersecting them in a line.

For example, the linear system given by

$$\begin{cases} -y + z = 0 \\ y = 0 \\ z = 0 \end{cases}$$

represents three planes whose intersection is the x axis. That is, $z = 0$ is the xy plane, $y = 0$ is the xz plane, and $y = z$ is the plane that cuts through the x axis at a $45°$ angle.

Finally, there are two cases in which a 3×3 linear system has no solutions. First, the linear system has no solutions if at least one of the planes is parallel to, but not the same as, the others. Certainly, when all three planes are parallel, the system has no solutions, as illustrated by the linear system

$$\begin{cases} z &= 0 \\ z &= 1 \\ z &= 2 \end{cases}$$

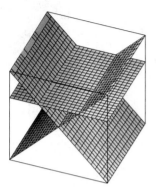

Figure 4

Also, a 3×3 linear system has no solutions, if the lines of the pairwise intersections of the planes are parallel, but not the same, as shown in Fig. 4.

From the previous discussion we see that a 3×3 linear system, like a 2×2 linear system, has no solutions, has a unique solution, or has infinitely many solutions. We will see in Sec. 1.4 that this is the case for linear systems of any size.

In Example 3 we consider a linear system with four variables. Of course the geometric reasoning above cannot be applied to the new situation directly, but provides the motivation for understanding the many possibilities for the solutions to linear systems with several variables.

EXAMPLE 3   Solve the linear system.

$$\begin{cases} 4x_1 - 8x_2 - 3x_3 + 2x_4 = 13 \\ 3x_1 - 4x_2 - x_3 - 3x_4 = 5 \\ 2x_1 - 4x_2 - 2x_3 + 2x_4 = 6 \end{cases}$$

Solution   Since every term of the third equation can be divided evenly by 2, we multiply the third equation by $\frac{1}{2}$. After we do so, the coefficient of x_1 is 1. We then interchange the first and third equations, obtaining

$$\begin{cases} 4x_1 - 8x_2 - 3x_3 + 2x_4 = 13 \\ 3x_1 - 4x_2 - x_3 - 3x_4 = 5 \\ 2x_1 - 4x_2 - 2x_3 + 2x_4 = 6 \end{cases} \quad \tfrac{1}{2}E_3 \to E_3 \quad \longrightarrow \quad \begin{cases} 4x_1 - 8x_2 - 3x_3 + 2x_4 = 13 \\ 3x_1 - 4x_2 - x_3 - 3x_4 = 5 \\ x_1 - 2x_2 - x_3 + x_4 = 3 \end{cases}$$

$$E_1 \leftrightarrow E_3 \quad \longrightarrow \quad \begin{cases} x_1 - 2x_2 - x_3 + x_4 = 3 \\ 3x_1 - 4x_2 - x_3 - 3x_4 = 5 \\ 4x_1 - 8x_2 - 3x_3 + 2x_4 = 13 \end{cases}$$

Next using the operations $-3E_1 + E_2 \to E_2$ and $-4E_1 + E_3 \to E_3$, we obtain the linear system

$$\begin{cases} x_1 - 2x_2 - x_3 + x_4 = 3 \\ 2x_2 + 2x_3 - 6x_4 = -4 \\ x_3 - 2x_4 = 1 \end{cases}$$

which is an equivalent system in triangular form. Using back substitution, the general solution is

$$x_3 = 2x_4 + 1 \qquad x_2 = x_4 - 3 \qquad x_1 = 3x_4 - 2$$

with x_4 free to assume any real number. It is common in this case to replace x_4 with the parameter t. The general solution can now be written as

$$S = \{(3t - 2, t - 3, 2t + 1, t) \mid t \in \mathbb{R}\}$$

and is called a *one-parameter family* of solutions. The reader can check that $x_1 = 3t - 2, x_2 = t - 3, x_3 = 2t + 1$, and $x_4 = t$ is a solution for any t by substituting these values in the original equations. A particular solution can be obtained by letting t be a specific value. For example, if $t = 0$, then a particular solution is $(-2, -3, 1, 0)$.

In Example 3, the variable x_4 can assume any real number, giving infinitely many solutions for the linear system. In this case we call x_4 a **free variable**. When a linear system has infinitely many solutions, there can be more than one free variable. In this case, the solution set is an r-parameter family of solutions where r is equal to the number of free variables.

EXAMPLE 4   Solve the linear system.

$$\begin{cases} x_1 - x_2 - 2x_3 - 2x_4 - 2x_5 = 3 \\ 3x_1 - 2x_2 - 2x_3 - 2x_4 - 2x_5 = -1 \\ -3x_1 + 2x_2 + x_3 + x_4 - x_5 = -1 \end{cases}$$

Solution   After performing the operations $E_3 + E_2 \to E_3$ followed by $E_2 - 3E_1 \to E_2$, we have the equivalent system

$$\begin{cases} x_1 - x_2 - 2x_3 - 2x_4 - 2x_5 = 3 \\ x_2 + 4x_3 + 4x_4 + 4x_5 = -10 \\ - x_3 - x_4 - 3x_5 = -2 \end{cases}$$

The variables x_4 and x_5 are both free variables, so to write the solution, let $x_4 = s$ and $x_5 = t$. From the third equation, we have

$$x_3 = 2 - x_4 - 3x_5 = 2 - s - 3t$$

Substitution into the second equation gives

$$\begin{aligned} x_2 &= -10 - 4x_3 - 4x_4 - 4x_5 \\ &= -10 - 4(2 - s - 3t) - 4s - 4t \\ &= -18 + 8t \end{aligned}$$

Finally, substitution into the first equation gives

$$x_1 = 3 + x_2 + 2x_3 + 2x_4 + 2x_5$$
$$= 3 + (-18 + 8t) + 2(2 - s - 3t) + 2s + 2t$$
$$= -11 + 4t$$

The *two-parameter* solution set is therefore given by

$$S = \{(-11 + 4t, -18 + 8t, 2 - s - 3t, s, t) \mid s, t \in \mathbb{R}\}$$

Particular solutions for $s = t = 0$ and $s = 0, t = 1$ are $(-11, -18, 2, 0, 0)$ and $(-7, -10, -1, 0, 1)$, respectively.

EXAMPLE 5   Solve the linear system.

$$\begin{cases} x_1 - x_2 + 2x_3 = 5 \\ 2x_1 + x_2 \quad\quad = 2 \\ x_1 + 8x_2 - x_3 = 3 \\ -x_1 - 5x_2 - 12x_3 = 4 \end{cases}$$

Solution   To convert the linear system to an equivalent triangular system, we will eliminate the first terms in equations 2 through 4, and then the second terms in equations 3 and 4, and then finally the third term in the fourth equation. This is accomplished by using the following operations.

$$\begin{cases} x_1 - x_2 + 2x_3 = 5 \\ 2x_1 + x_2 \quad\quad = 2 \\ x_1 + 8x_2 - x_3 = 3 \\ -x_1 - 5x_2 - 12x_3 = 4 \end{cases} \quad \begin{matrix} -2E_1 + E_2 \rightarrow E_2 \\ -E_1 + E_3 \rightarrow E_3 \\ E_1 + E_4 \rightarrow E_4 \end{matrix} \rightarrow \begin{cases} x_1 - x_2 + 2x_3 = 5 \\ 3x_2 - 4x_3 = -8 \\ 9x_2 - 3x_3 = -2 \\ -6x_2 - 10x_3 = 9 \end{cases}$$

$$\begin{matrix} -3E_2 + E_3 \rightarrow E_3 \\ 2E_2 + E_4 \rightarrow E_4 \end{matrix} \rightarrow \begin{cases} x_1 - x_2 + 2x_3 = 5 \\ 3x_2 - 4x_3 = -8 \\ 9x_3 = 22 \\ -18x_3 = -7 \end{cases}$$

$$2E_3 + E_4 \rightarrow E_4 \quad \rightarrow \begin{cases} x_1 - x_2 + 2x_3 = 5 \\ 3x_2 - 4x_3 = -8 \\ 9x_3 = 22 \\ 0 = -37 \end{cases}$$

The last equation of the final system is an impossibility, so the original linear system is inconsistent and has no solution.

In the previous examples the algorithm for converting a linear system to triangular form is based on using a *leading variable* in an equation to eliminate the same variable in each equation below it. This process can always be used to convert any linear system to triangular form.

EXAMPLE 6 Find the equation of the parabola that passes through the points $(-1, 1)$, $(2, -2)$, and $(3, 1)$. Find the vertex of the parabola.

Solution The general form of a parabola is given by $y = ax^2 + bx + c$. Conditions on a, b, and c are imposed by substituting the given points into this equation. This gives

$$
\begin{aligned}
1 &= a(-1)^2 + b(-1) + c = a - b + c \\
-2 &= a(2)^2 + b(2) + c = 4a + 2b + c \\
1 &= a(3)^2 + b(3) + c = 9a + 3b + c
\end{aligned}
$$

From these conditions we obtain the linear system

$$
\begin{cases}
a - b + c = 1 \\
4a + 2b + c = -2 \\
9a + 3b + c = 1
\end{cases}
$$

First, with a as the leading variable, we use row operations to eliminate a from equations 2 and 3. In particular, we have

$$
\begin{cases}
a - b + c = 1 \\
4a + 2b + c = -2 \\
9a + 3b + c = 1
\end{cases}
\quad
\begin{aligned}
-4E_1 + E_2 &\to E_2 \\
-9E_1 + E_3 &\to E_3
\end{aligned}
\quad \to \quad
\begin{cases}
a - b + c = 1 \\
6b - 3c = -6 \\
12b - 8c = -8
\end{cases}
$$

Next, with b as the leading variable we, eliminate b from equation 3, so that

$$
\begin{cases}
a - b + c = 1 \\
6b - 3c = -6 \\
12b - 8c = -8
\end{cases}
\quad
-2E_2 + E_3 \to E_3
\quad \to \quad
\begin{cases}
a - b + c = 1 \\
6b - 3c = -6 \\
- 2c = 4
\end{cases}
$$

Now, using back substitution on the last system gives $c = -2$, $b = -2$, and $a = 1$. Thus, the parabola we seek is

$$
y = x^2 - 2x - 2
$$

Completing the square gives the parabola in standard form

$$
y = (x - 1)^2 - 3
$$

with vertex $(1, -3)$, as shown in Fig. 5.

Figure 5

Fact Summary

1. A $m \times n$ linear system has a unique solution, infinitely many solutions, or no solutions.
2. Interchanging any two equations in a linear system does not alter the set of solutions.
3. Multiplying any equation in a linear system by a nonzero constant does not alter the set of solutions.

> **4.** Replacing an equation in a linear system with the sum of the equation and a scalar multiple of another equation does not alter the set of solutions.
>
> **5.** Every linear system can be reduced to an equivalent triangular linear system.

Exercise Set 1.1

1. Consider the linear system

$$\begin{cases} x_1 - x_2 - 2x_3 = 3 \\ -x_1 + 2x_2 + 3x_3 = 1 \\ 2x_1 - 2x_2 - 2x_3 = -2 \end{cases}$$

Perform the operations $E_1 + E_2 \to E_2$ and $-2E_1 + E_3 \to E_3$, and write the new equivalent system. Solve the linear system.

2. Consider the linear system

$$\begin{cases} 2x_1 - 2x_2 - x_3 = -3 \\ x_1 - 3x_2 + x_3 = -2 \\ x_1 - 2x_2 = 2 \end{cases}$$

Perform the operations $E_1 \leftrightarrow E_2$, $-2E_1 + E_2 \to E_2$, $-E_1 + E_3 \to E_3$, $E_2 \leftrightarrow E_3$, and $-4E_2 + E_3 \to E_3$, and write the new equivalent system. Solve the linear system.

3. Consider the linear system

$$\begin{cases} x_1 + 3x_4 = 2 \\ x_1 + x_2 + 4x_4 = 3 \\ 2x_1 + x_3 + 8x_4 = 3 \\ x_1 + x_2 + x_3 + 6x_4 = 2 \end{cases}$$

Perform the operations $-E_1 + E_2 \to E_2$, $-2E_1 + E_3 \to E_3$, $-E_1 + E_4 \to E_4$, $-E_2 + E_4 \to E_4$, and $-E_3 + E_4 \to E_4$, and write the new equivalent system. Solve the linear system.

4. Consider the linear system

$$\begin{cases} x_1 + x_3 = -2 \\ x_1 + x_2 + 4x_3 = -1 \\ 2x_1 + 2x_3 + x_4 = -1 \end{cases}$$

Perform the operations $-E_1 + E_2 \to E_2$ and $-2E_1 + E_3 \to E_3$, and write the new equivalent system. Solve the linear system.
In Exercises 5–18, solve the linear system using the elimination method.

5. $\begin{cases} 2x + 3y = -2 \\ -2x = 0 \end{cases}$

6. $\begin{cases} x + 3y = -1 \\ -y = -1 \end{cases}$

7. $\begin{cases} 4x = 4 \\ -3x + 2y = -3 \end{cases}$

8. $\begin{cases} 2x + 3y = -1 \\ x - y = 0 \end{cases}$

9. $\begin{cases} 3x - 2y = 4 \\ x - \frac{2}{3}y = \frac{4}{3} \end{cases}$

10. $\begin{cases} 3x - 5y = 1 \\ -x + \frac{5}{3}y = -\frac{1}{3} \end{cases}$

11. $\begin{cases} -3x - 2y + 2z = -2 \\ -x - 3y + z = -3 \\ x - 2y + z = -2 \end{cases}$

12. $\begin{cases} x + 3y + z = 2 \\ -2x + 2y - 4z = -1 \\ -y + 3z = 1 \end{cases}$

13. $\begin{cases} -2x - 2y + 2z = 1 \\ \quad x \qquad + 5z = -1 \\ \quad 3x + 2y + 3z = -2 \end{cases}$

14. $\begin{cases} -x + y + 4z = -1 \\ \quad 3x - y + 2z = 2 \\ \quad 2x - 2y - 8z = 2 \end{cases}$

15. $\begin{cases} 3x_1 + 4x_2 + 3x_3 = 0 \\ 3x_1 - 4x_2 + 3x_3 = 4 \end{cases}$

16. $\begin{cases} -2x_1 + x_2 \qquad = 2 \\ \quad 3x_1 - x_2 + 2x_3 = 1 \end{cases}$

17. $\begin{cases} \quad x_1 - 2x_2 - 2x_3 - x_4 = -3 \\ -2x_1 + x_2 + x_3 - 2x_4 = -3 \end{cases}$

18. $\begin{cases} 2x_1 + 2x_2 - x_3 \qquad = 1 \\ \qquad - x_2 \quad + 3x_4 = 2 \end{cases}$

In Exercises 19–22, solve for x, y, and z in terms of a, b, and c.

19. $\begin{cases} -2x + y = a \\ -3x + 2y = b \end{cases}$

20. $\begin{cases} 2x + 3y = a \\ \quad x + y = b \end{cases}$

21. $\begin{cases} 3x + y + 3z = a \\ -x - \qquad z = b \\ -x + 2y \qquad = c \end{cases}$

22. $\begin{cases} -3x + 2y + z = a \\ \quad x - y - z = b \\ \quad x - y - 2z = c \end{cases}$

In Exercises 23–28, give restrictions on a, b, and c such that the linear system is consistent.

23. $\begin{cases} \quad x - 2y = a \\ -2x + 4y = 2 \end{cases}$

24. $\begin{cases} -x + 3y = a \\ \quad 2x - 6y = 3 \end{cases}$

25. $\begin{cases} \quad x - 2y = a \\ -x + 2y = b \end{cases}$

26. $\begin{cases} \quad 6x - 3y = a \\ -2x + y = b \end{cases}$

27. $\begin{cases} \quad x - 2y + 4z = a \\ \quad 2x + y - z = b \\ \quad 3x - y + 3z = c \end{cases}$

28. $\begin{cases} \quad x - y + 2z = a \\ \quad 2x + 4y - 3z = b \\ \quad 4x + 2y + z = c \end{cases}$

In Exercises 29–32, determine the value of a that makes the system inconsistent.

29. $\begin{cases} \quad x + y = -2 \\ 2x + ay = 3 \end{cases}$

30. $\begin{cases} 2x - y = 4 \\ ax + 3y = 2 \end{cases}$

31. $\begin{cases} \quad x - y = 2 \\ 3x - 3y = a \end{cases}$

32. $\begin{cases} 2x - y = a \\ 6x - 3y = a \end{cases}$

In Exercises 33–36, find an equation in the form $y = ax^2 + bx + c$ for the parabola that passes through the three points. Find the vertex of the parabola.

33. $(0, 0.25)$, $(1, -1.75)$, $(-1, 4.25)$

34. $(0, 2)$, $(-3, -1)$, $(0.5, 0.75)$

35. $(-0.5, -3.25)$, $(1, 2)$, $(2.3, 2.91)$

36. $(0, -2875)$, $(1, -5675)$, $(3, 5525)$

37. Find the point where the three lines $-x + y = 1$, $-6x + 5y = 3$, and $12x + 5y = 39$ intersect. Sketch the lines.

38. Find the point where the four lines $2x + y = 0$, $x + y = -1$, $3x + y = 1$, and $4x + y = 2$ intersect. Sketch the lines.

39. Give an example of a 2×2 linear system that
  a. Has a unique solution
  b. Has infinitely many solutions
  c. Is inconsistent

40. Verify that if $ad - bc \neq 0$, then the system of equations
$$\begin{cases} ax + by = x_1 \\ cx + dy = x_2 \end{cases}$$
has a unique solution.

41. Consider the system

$$\begin{cases} x_1 - x_2 + 3x_3 - x_4 = 1 \\ x_2 - x_3 + 2x_4 = 2 \end{cases}$$

a. Describe the solution set where the variables x_3 and x_4 are free.

b. Describe the solution set where the variables x_2 and x_4 are free.

42. Consider the system

$$\begin{cases} x_1 - x_2 + x_3 - x_4 + x_5 = 1 \\ x_2 - x_4 - x_5 = -1 \\ x_3 - 2x_4 + 3x_5 = 2 \end{cases}$$

a. Describe the solution set where the variables x_4 and x_5 are free.

b. Describe the solution set where the variables x_3 and x_5 are free.

43. Determine the values of k such that the linear system

$$\begin{cases} 9x + ky = 9 \\ kx + y = -3 \end{cases}$$

has

a. No solutions

b. Infinitely many solutions

c. A unique solution

44. Determine the values of k such that the linear system

$$\begin{cases} kx + y + z = 0 \\ x + ky + z = 0 \\ x + y + kz = 0 \end{cases}$$

has

a. A unique solution

b. A one-parameter family of solutions

c. A two-parameter family of solutions